Daniel Bershader
1959

ELEMENTS of STATISTICAL MECHANICS

KARL LARK-HOROVITZ

Consulting Editor

ELEMENTS of STATISTICAL MECHANICS

D. ter HAAR

Lecturer in Theoretical Physics
in St. Salvator's College
St. Andrews University, Scotland

RINEHART & COMPANY, INC. NEW YORK

Library of Congress Catalog Card Number: 54–5402

TO MY WIFE

PREFACE

It is usual for an author to explain in a preface the reasons for writing the particular book which he is presenting to the public, to state who are the readers whom he has in mind for the book, to sketch the history of the writing of the book, and, last but not least, to express his thanks to all people who have been of assistance during the completion of the book.

The reason for writing another textbook on statistical mechanics was the feeling that there should be a textbook which combined in not too large a volume an outline of the main elements of statistical mechanics, starting from the Maxwell distribution and ending with quantum mechanical grand ensembles, with an account of a number of successful applications of these elements. Almost all existing textbooks stress only one or the other of these two aspects. It is hoped that readers will point out to me in how far my own attempt has been successful, and I should at this point like to express the hope that reviewers will let me have the benefit of their detailed criticism.

The book is meant to be a textbook and is thus primarily intended for students. I have had in mind graduate students. This means that it should be used as a text for graduate lectures in the United States or for postgraduate lectures in the United Kingdom. It will probably be too advanced as a textbook for honors courses in British universities, although parts of it might be used as such and have been used as such by me. It is hoped that the book can also be used as a research tool and that it is possible to see from the applications how the theory might be applied to other subjects. For that reason I have tried to give as complete a bibliography as was feasible in the framework of a textbook. As the manuscript of the book was essentially completed at the beginning of 1952, references to papers published in 1951 or 1952 will not be complete.

A first rough outline of the book was sketched during the last war-winter in Leiden. A number of students were deprived of the regular lecture courses because Leiden University was closed by the occupying authorities, and the outline of the present book served as a substitute for the regular statistical mechanics course. The manuscript then rested until I wrote the first draft of Parts A and B at Purdue University during 1947–1948. There was another interval until 1950, when I came to St. Andrews, where the manuscript in its present form was started and finished.

It is a pleasant task to thank the many physicists who have given me their advice on parts of the manuscript. My thanks are especially due to Professors F. J. Belinfante, H. M. James, K. Lark-Horovitz, H. Margenau, R. E. Peierls, and F. E. Simon, who have helped me with their criticism and advice. If the approach is sometimes not very clear and if my English has sometimes a distinct foreign flavor, it cannot be blamed on Professor F. Y. Poynton, who has tried to make Parts A and B as far as possible easy reading for students, or on Professors E. S. Akeley and J. F. Allen, who have tried to weed out of the text all barbarisms. I should like to express to them my warmest gratitude. Finally I should like to express my great indebtedness to Professor H. A. Kramers. Anybody who is familiar with his lectures on statistical mechanics will immediately see how much this book owes to him. It is far from a platitude to say that it would never have been written but for Professor Kramers. Not only did he give me an outline of the contents of Parts A and B; in discussions and in lectures he has taught me the fundamental ideas of the subject. I can therefore with some justification claim that the method of treatment in Parts A and B goes straight back to Boltzmann, via Kramers and Ehrenfest. Large parts of the book are, indeed, nearly wholly based on a series of lectures given by Professor Kramers in Leiden during 1944–1945.

In conclusion, I should like to express my thanks to Professor K. Lark-Horovitz and Miss A. Scudder for their help in editing the manuscript.

D.t.H.

Department of Natural Philosophy,
St. Andrews
January, 1954

CONTENTS

ELEMENTS of STATISTICAL MECHANICS

INTRODUCTION

Statistical mechanics or thermostatistics, to use a phrase coined by Kramers, is a subject which can be fruitfully studied only if a great number of other subjects in physics are well understood. It has thus been assumed that the reader is well acquainted with classical mechanics, quantum theory, thermodynamics, nuclear physics, and calculus. As an indication of the standard assumed we give the following, rather arbitrary, list of textbooks.

GENERAL THEORETICAL PHYSICS:

J. C. Slater and N. H. Frank, *Introduction to Theoretical Physics*, New York 1933.

G. Joos, *Theoretical Physics*, New York 1944.

F. K. Richtmyer and E. H. Kennard, *Introduction to Modern Physics*, New York 1947.

A. Sommerfeld, *Lectures on Theoretical Physics* (6 vols.), New York 1949.

CLASSICAL MECHANICS:

E. T. Whittaker, *Analytical Dynamics*, Cambridge 1937.

H. Goldstein, *Classical Mechanics*, Cambridge, Mass. 1950.

QUANTUM THEORY:

E. C. Kemble, *Fundamental Principles of Quantum Mechanics*, New York 1937.

H. A. Kramers, *Hand- u. Jahrb. d. Chem. Phys.*, Vol. I, Leipzig 1938.

L. I. Schiff, *Quantum Mechanics*, New York 1949.

D. Bohm, *Quantum Theory*, New York 1951.

THERMODYNAMICS:

E. A. Guggenheim, *Thermodynamics*, New York 1950.

M. W. Zemansky, *Heat and Thermodynamics*, New York 1951.

NUCLEAR PHYSICS:

E. Fermi, *Nuclear Physics*, Chicago 1949.

J. M. Blatt and V. F. Weisskopf, *Theoretical Nuclear Physics*, New York 1952.

MATHEMATICAL PHYSICS:

E. T. Whittaker and G. N. Watson, *Modern Analysis*, Cambridge 1927.

H. and B. S. Jeffreys, *Mathematical Physics*, Cambridge 1946.

Many subjects which belong to statistical mechanics have not been treated in the present book; hence to the following textbooks we refer the reader for those subjects and for a different presentation of the subjects which are treated.

J. W. Gibbs, *Elementary Principles in Statistical Mechanics*, New Haven 1902.

R. H. Fowler, *Statistical Mechanics*, Cambridge 1936.

R. C. Tolman, *Statistical Mechanics*, Oxford 1938.

R. H. Fowler and E. A. Guggenheim, *Statistical Thermodynamics*, Cambridge 1939.

J. E. and M. G. Mayer, *Statistical Mechanics*, New York 1940.

E. Schrödinger, *Statistical Thermodynamics*, Cambridge 1948.

G. S. Rushbrooke, *Introduction to Statistical Mechanics*, Oxford 1949.

We further refer to the monographs and papers mentioned at the end of each chapter.

This book consists of four parts. The first part deals with the elementary approach of statistical mechanics, while in Part B ensemble theory is developed. Together, these two parts form the theoretical backbone of the book. In Part C it is shown how the theory can be applied. The list of applications is far from complete. Among the subjects which are not discussed one will find the theory of liquids, astrophysical applications, chemical reactions, solutions, ionic problems. The last part of the book contains in several appendices a discussion of a number of subjects which should not really be omitted from a textbook but which, on the other hand, are too advanced for most students. Use is also made of sections printed in small type to indicate arguments which can be omitted on first reading and which are slightly more advanced or complicated than the rest of the text. It was originally intended to include a discussion of the so-called intermediate statistics in an appendix. However, as one can show (see, e.g., D. ter Haar, Physica, **18**, 199, 1952) that all results particular to the intermediate statistics are spurious, it was felt that it would serve no useful purpose to include this discussion.

The decimal system is used to number the equations. The number before the decimal point refers to the chapter (or if preceded by an A, to the Appendix) and the first decimal number to the section. Equations in the Mathematical Appendix have MA and the section number in front of the decimal point. Figures are numbered consecutively throughout the book.

It is hoped that our notation conforms to normal usage. As far as the chief thermodynamic functions are concerned, our notation is the same as the one used, e.g., by Fowler with two exceptions, namely, we use U (instead of E) for the internal energy and g (instead of μ) for the partial (thermal) potential. Since the natural logarithm is nowadays usually denoted by ln we have followed this modern trend.

PART A

STATISTICS OF INDEPENDENT PARTICLES

CHAPTER I

THE MAXWELL DISTRIBUTION

§1. **The Maxwell Distribution.** Clausius, Maxwell, and Boltzmann developed in the nineteenth century the kinetic theory of gases. In this theory it was shown how phenomenological concepts such as temperature and entropy could be interpreted in terms of the interplay of the particles which were the constituent parts of the systems under consideration. In 1901 J. W. Gibbs coined the name "statistical mechanics" for that branch of physics which dealt statistically with systems consisting of large numbers of particles. In present-day statistical mechanics one is concerned with calculating the macroscopic or phenomenological behavior of systems which are too complicated to permit an exact calculation of their microscopic behavior, partly because of the "well-nigh unsurmountable mathematical difficulties" which confront us when we try to solve the relevant equations and partly because of the incomplete experimental data which can be provided. As Kramers put it, statistical mechanics deals with the atomistic interpretation of the thermal properties of matter and radiation, and he suggested the name "thermostatistics" instead of statistical mechanics.†

We shall confine ourselves for the present to the case of a monatomic gas enclosed in a vessel of volume V. We shall assume that there are no external forces acting on the gas apart from the forces which the walls of the vessel will exert on the gas and which in fact will keep the gas inside the vessel. In order to describe the system we introduce Cartesian coordinates x, y, and z and we shall denote the x-, y-, and z-components of the velocity by u, v, and w. Once the positions and velocities of all the atoms are given, the microscopic behavior of the system is completely determined, provided the interatomic forces and the forces between the walls and the atoms are known. If there are N atoms in the system, we need $6N$ quantities, x_i, y_i, z_i, u_i, v_i, w_i ($i = 1$ to N) or combinations of these coordinates and velocities, to determine the microscopic behavior. However, if we are

† H. A. Kramers, Nuovo cimento, **6,** Suppl., 158, 1949.

interested only in the macroscopic behavior of the system, there will be only a few combinations of the $6N$ quantities which will interest us. We mentioned a moment ago that the exact knowledge of all $6N$ coordinates and velocities is anyhow outside the experimental possibilities while the computation of their values from the equations of motion is outside our mathematical powers. We can, however, use the fact that there are many particles in the system and apply statistical methods. As we shall see later on (Chapters V to VII), the fact that N is large makes the fluctuations negligible.

We shall assume for the moment that if we choose one cm^3, the number of atoms in that cm^3 will be independent of the position of the cm^3 in the gas. In making this assumption, we neglect first of all the influence of the wall and, secondly, possible fluctuations. We shall return to both of these points later on (see pp. 34 and 111). If we denote this number of atoms per cm^3 by n, we have

$$n = \frac{N}{V}. \tag{1.101}$$

Let us denote by

$$f(u,v,w)dudvdw$$

the number of atoms per cm^3 the velocity components of which lie in the specified intervals $(u,u + du)$, $(v,v + dv)$, and $(w,w + dw)$. The function $f(u,v,w)$ will be called the *distribution function*. It determines the fraction of atoms with velocities within given intervals. This fraction is obtained by dividing $f(u,v,w)dudvdw$ by n.

We shall call the Cartesian three-dimensional space in which we can plot the x-, y-, and z-components of the velocities *velocity space*, and the point (u,v,w) in velocity space will be called the *representative point* of an atom with velocity components u, v, and w.

From the definition of $f(u,v,w)$ it follows that it satisfies the equation of *normalization*

$$\int_{-\infty}^{+\infty} du \int_{-\infty}^{+\infty} dv \int_{-\infty}^{+\infty} dw f(u,v,w) = n. \tag{1.102}$$

In the present chapter we shall assume that $f(u,v,w)$ not only is independent of x, y, and z, but also does not depend explicitly on the time t.

Let A be a quantity which is a function of the velocity components of an atom, but which does not explicitly depend on either x, y, and z or t. As an example we may give the kinetic energy of an atom. We can now ask for the *average value*, $\bar{A}$, of $A(u,v,w)$ where the average is taken over all the atoms of the gas and where the average value is equivalent to the arithmetic mean, i.e., defined by the equation

$$\bar{A} = \frac{1}{n}\iiint_{-\infty}^{+\infty} dudvdwA(u,v,w)f(u,v,w). \tag{1.103}$$

Neither A nor f depends on x, y, z, or t. $\bar{A}$ will therefore also be independent of x, y, z, and t.

In the following sections of this chapter it will be proved that the distribution function of a gas in equilibrium at an absolute temperature T will be given by the equation

$$f(u,v,w) = n\left(\frac{m}{2\pi kT}\right)^{3/2} e^{-\frac{m(u^2+v^2+w^2)}{2kT}}, \tag{1.104}$$

where m is the mass of one atom and k is Boltzmann's constant.† The distribution given by equation (1.104) is called the *Maxwell distribution* and was first introduced by Maxwell in 1859. It can easily be shown that the $f(u,v,w)$ given by equation (1.104) satisfies equation (1.102). Equations (1.103) and (1.104) can now be used to calculate average values.

Denoting by c the absolute value of the velocity of an atom,

$$c^2 = u^2 + v^2 + w^2, \tag{1.105}$$

and by $\mathcal{T}\ (= \frac{1}{2}mc^2)$ the kinetic energy of an atom, we have‡

$$\overline{c^2} = \frac{3kT}{m}, \tag{1.106}$$

$$\bar{c} = \sqrt{\frac{8kT}{\pi m}}, \tag{1.107}$$

$$\bar{u} = \bar{v} = \bar{w} = 0, \tag{1.108}$$

$$\overline{u^2} = \overline{v^2} = \overline{w^2} = \tfrac{1}{3}\overline{c^2} = \frac{kT}{m}, \tag{1.109}$$

$$\overline{\mathcal{T}} = \tfrac{1}{2}m\overline{c^2} = \tfrac{3}{2}kT. \tag{1.110}$$

There are three points in connection with equations (1.106) to (1.110) worth noting.

---

† Boltzmann never deduced the value of k; this was first done by Planck in connection with his radiation law (1900). Smekal (Enzyklopädie der mathematischen Wissenschaften, Vol. V, Pt. 28, Leipzig-Berlin 1926) and Meissner (Science, **113**, 78, 1951) suggest calling k the Boltzmann-Planck constant. We refer to Appendix VII for a list of constants and their values.

‡ The definite integrals which occur in the evaluation of these average values can be found in §1 of the Mathematical Appendix.

a) Firstly, comparing equations (1.106) and (1.107) we see that there exists a difference between the mean absolute velocity $\bar{c}$ and the root-mean-square velocity $\sqrt{\overline{c^2}}$,

$$\sqrt{\overline{c^2}} = \sqrt{\frac{3\pi}{8}}\,\bar{c} = 1.085\bar{c}. \tag{1.111}$$

b) Secondly, equation (1.110) shows that the mean kinetic energy is independent of the mass of the atoms. Thus we get the same result for any gas, provided the temperature is the same. We can therefore use equation (1.110) as a definition of the temperature of a gas.

c) Lastly, from equation (1.109) it follows that the average kinetic energy pertaining to the x-, y-, or z-direction is the same and is equal to one third of the average total kinetic energy. We shall return to this point later on.

§2. The Perfect Gas Law. In this section, we shall assume that there is no interaction between the atoms of the gas which we are considering. The case where the atoms exert forces on each other will be briefly considered in the next section, but a more detailed discussion will be given later in Chapter VIII.

If we may assume that the distribution function is given by equation (1.104), we can calculate the pressure of the gas in terms of n and T. Two derivations of the formula for the pressure will be given. The first derivation is due to Clausius and the second one to Lorentz.

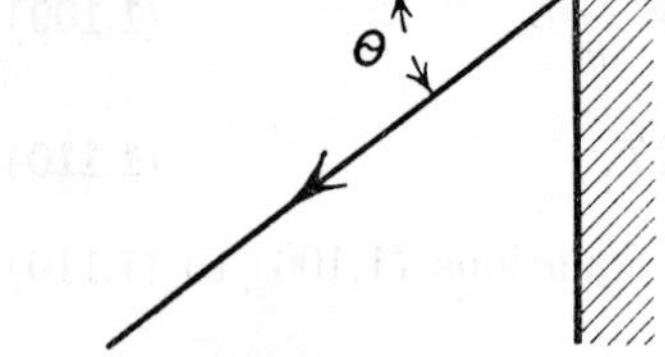

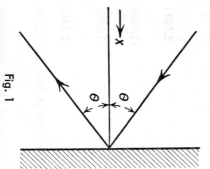

Fig. 1

In order to derive the formula in the way it was done by Clausius, we must remember that according to Newton's second law force is equivalent to rate of change of momentum. The pressure of the gas is defined either as the force exerted by the gas on 1 cm^2 of the wall, or as the total transfer of momentum per sec from the gas to 1 cm^2 of the wall. The Cartesian axes will be chosen in such a way that the negative x-axis falls along the normal to the wall (see Fig. 1). We neglect all effects which arise from the fact that there might exist a potential energy between the wall and the gas atoms which is different from zero at a distance from the wall; these effects will be briefly discussed in §4 of Chapter II. Finally we assume that the gas atoms will be perfectly reflected by the wall.

In the case of a perfect reflection, only the velocity component perpendicular to the wall will change during the collision of a gas atom with the wall. This component will change its sign, but the other components will remain unchanged. If an atom with velocity **c**† strikes the wall at an angle θ, the momentum transferred during the collision will be given by the expression

$$2mc\cos\theta = 2mu. \tag{1.201}$$

In order to calculate the total transfer of momentum, we must next determine the number of collisions per sec on 1 cm^2. For a given velocity **c** this number is zero if u is negative. If u is positive, the number of collisions is given by the total number of atoms contained in a cylinder with a base of 1 cm^2 and a slant height c, parallel to **c**. The volume of this cylinder is $c\cos\theta$. If the number of atoms per cm^3 with given velocity **c** is $n(\mathbf{c})$, the number of collisions N_{coll} per sec on 1 cm^2 will be given by the equation

$$N_{\text{coll}}(\mathbf{c}) = n(\mathbf{c})c\cos\theta = n(\mathbf{c})u. \tag{1.202}$$

The total momentum transferred to 1 cm^2 of the wall per sec by atoms of given velocity **c** is found by combining equations (1.201) and (1.202) and is equal to

$$2mn(\mathbf{c})u^2. \tag{1.203}$$

The function $n(\mathbf{c})$ will be the distribution function $f(u,v,w)$ which is assumed to be given by equation (1.104). Averaging expression (1.203) over the distribution function under the condition $u \geqslant 0$, we obtain for the pressure p

$$p = 2m\int_0^{+\infty} du \int_{-\infty}^{+\infty} dv \int_{-\infty}^{+\infty} dwf(u,v,w)u^2,$$

$$p = nkT. \tag{1.204}$$

Equation (1.204) is called the *perfect gas law* or Boyle–Gay-Lussac's law.

Introducing the absolute gas constant R by the equation

$$R = k\mathfrak{A}, \tag{1.205}$$

where $\mathfrak{A}$ is Avogadro's number, i.e., the number of atoms in one mole, and introducing the molar volume V_m, we can write equation (1.204) in the form

$$pV_m = RT. \tag{1.206}$$

Clausius' derivation of the perfect gas law involves certain assumptions

† We shall now and henceforth denote by **c** the velocity vector, i.e., the vector with x-, y-, and z-components equal to u, v, and w.

about the reflection of the atoms from the wall. These assumptions are unnecessary if the pressure is defined in a slightly different manner. Consider for this purpose a surface of unit area somewhere in the gas. The pressure can now be defined as the total momentum in the direction of the normal to the surface transported per sec through this surface in the direction of the positive normal.† Momentum transported in the opposite direction should be counted with a negative sign.

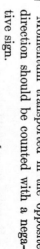

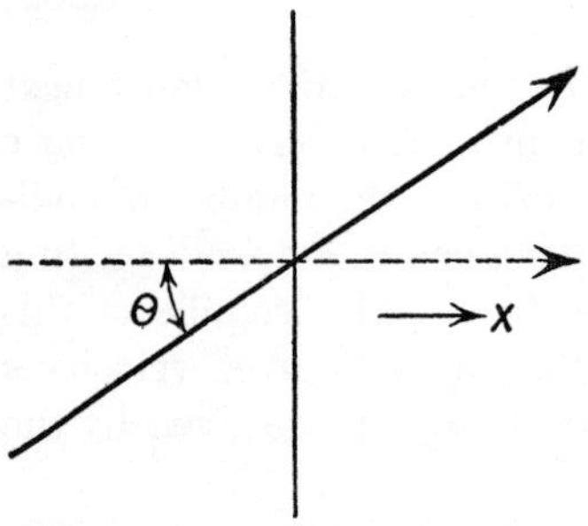

Fig. 2

The above definition of the pressure is due to Lorentz, whose derivation of the perfect gas law proceeds as follows. Let the positive x-axis be in the direction of the positive normal to the surface considered (see Fig. 2). An atom which crosses the chosen surface in the direction of the positive normal with a velocity **c** will transport in the $+x$-direction an amount of momentum in the $+x$-direction equal to the x-component of its own momentum ($=mu$). The total number of atoms crossing the unit area per sec is again given by expression (1.202). In this way, the total momentum transported by atoms with a velocity **c**, the x-component of which is positive, will be given by the expression

$$n(\mathbf{c})u\,mu. \qquad (u > 0). \tag{1.207}$$

The total momentum in $+x$-direction transported by atoms with velocities, the x-component of which is negative, is also given by expression (1.207). The momentum is negative, but it is transported from the positive to the negative x-axis and should thus be subtracted from the total momentum transported through the surface.

The total pressure is thus obtained by averaging expression (1.207) over *all* possible **c**-values, or

$$p = \overline{mn(\mathbf{c})u^2} = m \iiint_{-\infty}^{+\infty} dudvdwf(u,v,w)u^2, \tag{1.208}$$

which leads again to equation (1.204).

† Strictly speaking, one must still prove that the pressure defined in this way is identically equal to the force per cm^2 on the wall, since this force is the pressure which is measured. The proof follows if one considers a cylinder with cross section of 1 cm^2 and axis parallel to the normal to the wall, starting from the wall and extending into the gas. From the requirement that the gas inside this cylinder is in equilibrium, the equivalence of the two pressures follows.

§3. Van der Waals' Law. Up to now we have assumed that the atoms (or molecules) of the gas are not exerting forces on each other. This is, of course, a very rough idealization of the true state of affairs. In Chapter VIII we shall discuss in detail the case of nonideal gases. In the present section we shall merely indicate qualitatively how the perfect gas law has to be modified when the particles in the gas exert forces on each other. We shall assume that these forces can be derived from a potential energy curve such as, e.g., that shown by Figure 3. Two atoms will attract each other at large distances apart, but will repel each other when the distance apart becomes small. This latter effect means that the atoms take up a certain volume.

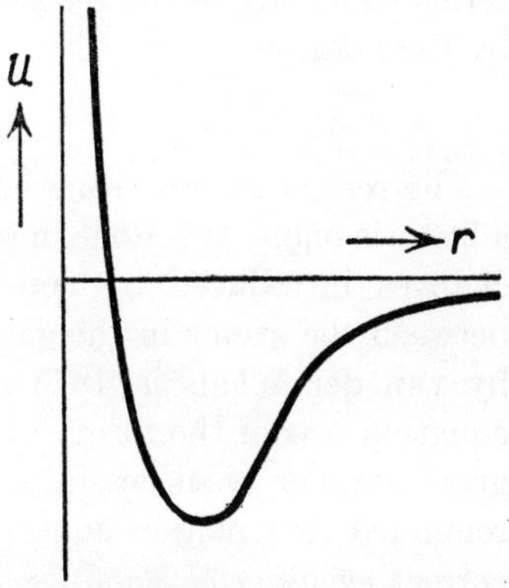

U: potential energy
r: distance apart of the two atoms

Fig. 3

Various equations for the potential energy $U(r)$ have been suggested. Lennard-Jones† has proposed an equation of the form

$$U(r) = \frac{A}{r^n} - \frac{B}{r^m}, \quad (n > m, A > 0, B > 0) \qquad \textbf{(1.301)}$$

where A, B, n, and m should be determined from experimental data. Morse,‡ on the other hand, has used a potential energy function given by the equation

$$U(r) = D[e^{-2a(r-r_1)} - e^{-a(r-r_1)}]. \qquad (D > 0, a > 0). \qquad \textbf{(1.302)}$$

(A more detailed discussion of the merits of various forms of the potential energy function and of ways of determining this function will be given in Appendix V.)

The repulsive forces between the atoms will produce a smaller free volume for the gas. In equation (1.206) the factor V_m has thus to be replaced by a factor which is slightly smaller, say, $V_m - b$. If repulsive forces decrease the factor V_m, attractive forces should increase it, and we have to introduce a further correction and replace V_m by $V_m - b + a$, where we have now separated the effects of the attractive and the repulsive forces. The relation between pressure and volume now becomes

$$p(V_m - b + a) = RT. \qquad \textbf{(1.303)}$$

As long as the temperature or the density of the gas is not too high, b and a

† J. E. Jones, Proc. Roy. Soc. (London), **A106**, 463, 1924.
‡ P. M. Morse, Phys. Rev., **34**, 57, 1929.

will be only very small corrections to V_m, and it is possible to rewrite equation (1.303) as

$$\left(p + \frac{a'}{V_m^{\,2}}\right)(V_m - b) = RT, \tag{1.304}$$

where the left-hand sides of equations (1.303) and (1.304) differ only by terms which are of the second order in a/V_m or b/V_m, provided a' is given by the relation

$$a' = aRT. \tag{1.305}$$

The reason for rewriting equation (1.303) in the form (1.304) is purely a historic one. It is done in order to show that to a first approximation the changes introduced by considering the attractive and repulsive forces between the atoms in the gas will lead to the famous equation introduced by van der Waals in 1873 and hence called *van der Waals' law*. This equation was of the form (1.304). Its importance lies mainly in the very great number of successful empirical applications, but the reader may be reminded that neither equation (1.303) nor equation (1.304) gives us the correct *equation of state*, as the relation between p, V_m, and T is called. We shall discuss the derivation of the equation of state from the known interatomic forces in detail in Chapter VIII. We only wish to remark at this point that the equation of state is usually written in a form giving pV_m/RT as a power series in descending powers of V_m,

$$pV_m = RT\left(1 + \frac{B}{V_m} + \frac{C}{V_m^{\,2}} + \cdots\right), \tag{1.306}$$

where B, C, $\cdots$, which are functions of T, are called the *virial coefficients*, B being called the second virial coefficient, C the third virial coefficient, and so on.

The word "virial" used in this connection arises from the function

$$\mathcal{V} = \sum_i (x_i X_i + y_i Y_i + z_i Z_i) \tag{1.307}$$

introduced into kinetic theory by Clausius and called by him the virial. In equation (1.307) x_i, y_i, and z_i are the coordinates of the ith atom, and X_i, Y_i, and Z_i, the components of the total force (hence the name "virial") acting on the ith atom. The summation is extended over all atoms in the gas.

Clausius established an important theorem relating $\mathcal{V}$ to the pressure as follows. From Newton's second law we have

$$m_i \frac{d^2 x_i}{dt^2} = X_i,$$

and hence

$$\mathcal{V} = \sum_i m_i \left(x_i \cdot \frac{d^2 x_i}{dt^2} \right).$$

Taking the time average (denoted by a bar across) of the virial, one gets

$$\overline{\mathcal{V}} = \frac{1}{\tau}\int_0^\tau \mathcal{V}dt = \frac{1}{\tau}\int_0^\tau \sum_i m_i \left(\mathbf{x}_i \cdot \frac{d^2\mathbf{x}_i}{dt^2} \right) dt,$$

$$= -\frac{1}{\tau}\int_0^\tau \sum_i m_i \left(\frac{d\mathbf{x}_i}{dt} \right)^2 dt + \frac{1}{\tau}\left[\sum_i m_i \left(\mathbf{x}_i \cdot \frac{d\mathbf{x}_i}{dt} \right) \right]_0^\tau . \quad (1.308)$$

Since both $\mathbf{x}_i$ and $d\mathbf{x}_i/dt$ will always be finite, equation (1.308) can be reduced to the following form by making the integrated term arbitrarily small through increasing τ,

$$\overline{\mathcal{V}} = -2N\overline{\mathcal{T}}, \quad (1.309)$$

where N is the number of atoms in the gas and $\overline{\mathcal{T}}$ the average kinetic energy per atom.†

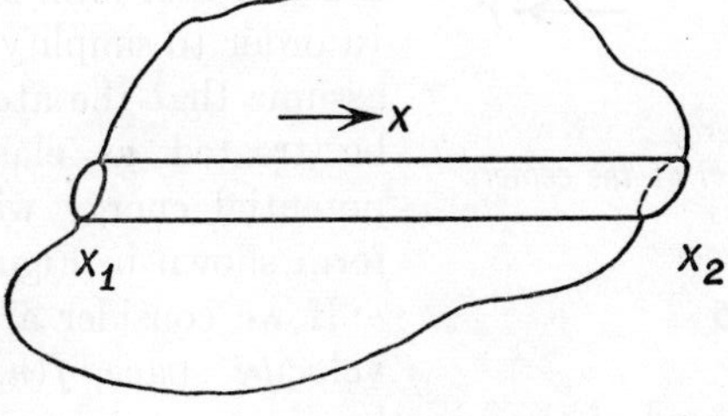

Fig. 4

We can obtain another equation for $\overline{\mathcal{V}}$ by dividing the virial into two parts, one part $\mathcal{W}$ due to the intermolecular forces and one part due to the pressure on the walls of the vessel (or the forces exerted by the wall on the gas)

$$\overline{\mathcal{V}} = \overline{\mathcal{W}} + \sum_{x,S_x} (x_1 - x_2) S_x p, \quad (1.310)$$

where S_x is the projection of the surface element on the y, z-plane (compare Fig. 4) and p the pressure of the gas. From equation (1.310) it follows that

$$\overline{\mathcal{V}} = \overline{\mathcal{W}} - 3Vp, \quad (1.311)$$

where V is the volume occupied by the gas.

† It should be noted that the bar across the $\mathcal{T}$ indicates an average both over time and over the system of the gas atoms.

Combining equations (1.309) and (1.311) and using equation (1.110) for the average value of the kinetic energy per atom, we obtain the equation

$$pV = NkT + \tfrac{1}{3}\overline{\mathfrak{W}}. \qquad \textbf{(1.312)}$$

If we compare equations (1.306) and (1.312), it is clear why B, C, $\cdots$ are called virial coefficients.

§4. **Collisions.** In the present section we wish to consider the influence of collisions between the atoms on the velocity distribution. If we maintained the assumptions of §2 that the atoms do not exert forces upon one another, there would be no collisions. We must therefore make some kind of assumption about the nature of the interatomic forces, or of the interatomic potential energy. It will be shown later (Chap. VIII) that the actual form of the interaction determines the second, third, $\cdots$ virial coefficient, but that the first term is not affected by it. In order to simplify the discussion, we assume that the atoms in the gas may be treated as elastic spheres. The potential energy will then be of the form shown in Figure 5.

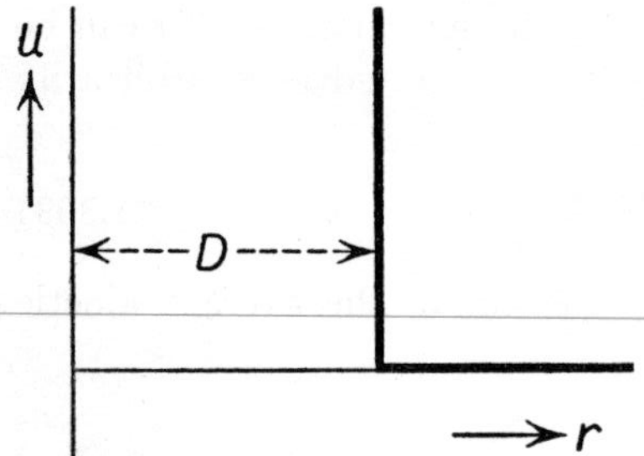

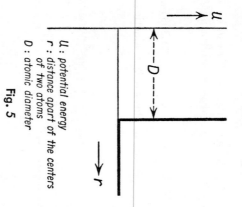

U : *potential energy*
r : *distance apart of the centers of two atoms*
D : *atomic diameter*

Fig. 5

If we consider a volume $dudvdw$ in velocity space, $f(u,v,w)dudvdw$ atoms will exist in each cm^3 of the gas the representative points of which can be found in this volume of velocity space, where $f(u,v,w)$ is again the distribution function. If there are collisions in the gas, there will be atoms which will leave the volume $dudvdw$† and there will be atoms which will enter the volume $dudvdw$. If the number of atoms per cm^3 which are leaving $dudvdw$ per sec is denoted by A and the number of atoms per cm^3 which are entering $dudvdw$ by B, the following equation is valid for the change of f per unit time,

$$\frac{\partial f}{\partial t} dudvdw = -A + B, \qquad \textbf{(1.401)}$$

where the partial derivative indicates that we are interested at the moment only in the change of f due to collisions.

† In order to avoid cumbersome sentences we shall use the expression "atoms leaving the volume $dudvdw$" when we want to say "atoms the representative points of which are leaving the volume $dudvdw$."

In order to calculate A and B we have to consider in detail collisions between two atoms (see Figs. 6 and 7). We denote by $\mathbf{c}_1$ and $\mathbf{c}_2$ the velocities of the two atoms before the collision and by $\mathbf{c}_1'$ and $\mathbf{c}_2'$ the velocities

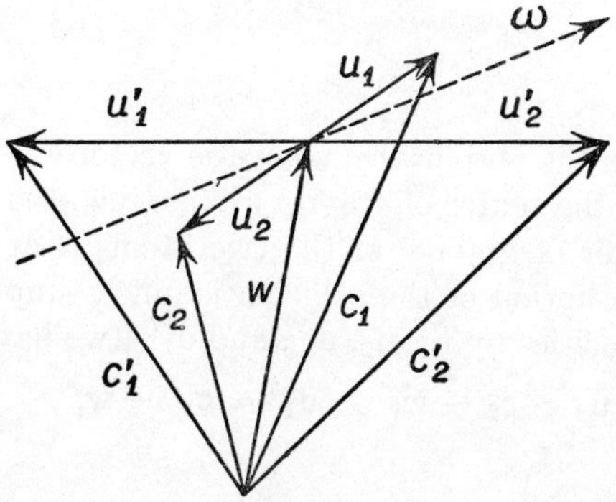

Fig. 6

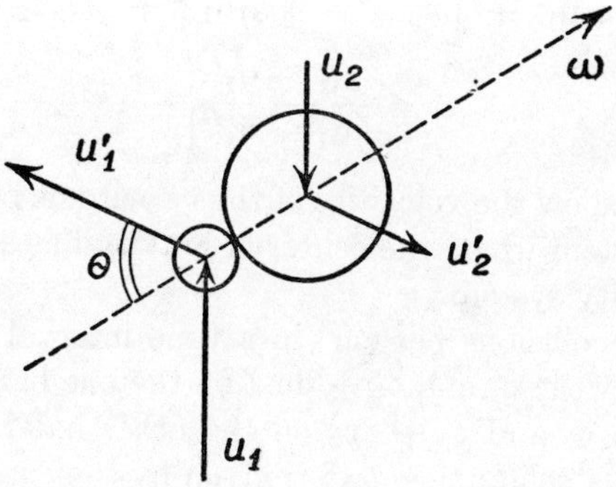

Fig. 7

after the collision. The velocity of the center of gravity will be denoted by $\mathbf{w}$ and is given by the equation

$$(m_1 + m_2)\mathbf{w} = m_1\mathbf{c}_1 + m_2\mathbf{c}_2. \qquad \mathbf{(1.402)}$$

The velocities $\mathbf{c}_1'$ and $\mathbf{c}_2'$ are not completely determined by $\mathbf{c}_1$ and $\mathbf{c}_2$ since there are only four equations from which the six components have to be determined. These four equations are

$$\tfrac{1}{2}m_1c_1^2 + \tfrac{1}{2}m_2c_2^2 = \tfrac{1}{2}m_1c_1'^2 + \tfrac{1}{2}m_2c_2'^2 \quad \text{(conservation of energy)} \qquad \mathbf{(1.403)}$$

and

$$m_1\mathbf{c}_1 + m_2\mathbf{c}_2 = m_1\mathbf{c}_1' + m_2\mathbf{c}_2'. \quad \text{(conservation of momentum)} \qquad \mathbf{(1.404)}$$

However, if we give the direction of the *line of centers*, i.e., the line connecting the center of atom 1 with the center of atom 2, $\mathbf{c}_1'$ and $\mathbf{c}_2'$ are completely determined. Denoting by $\boldsymbol{\omega}$ a unit vector in the direction of the line of centers, we have (compare Figs. 6 and 7)

$$\boldsymbol{\omega} = \frac{\mathbf{c}_1 - \mathbf{c}_1'}{|\mathbf{c}_1 - \mathbf{c}_1'|}, \tag{1.405}$$

where $|\mathbf{c}|$ denotes the absolute value of the vector $\mathbf{c}$.

If we introduce the center of gravity system, i.e., the coordinate system in which the center of gravity of the two atoms is at rest ($\mathbf{w} = 0$), the mathematical description of the collision is much simpler. Denoting the corresponding velocities by $\mathbf{u}_1$, $\mathbf{u}_2$, $\mathbf{u}_1'$, and $\mathbf{u}_2'$,† we have

$$\mathbf{u}_1 = \mathbf{c}_1 - \mathbf{w}, \qquad \mathbf{u}_2 = \mathbf{c}_2 - \mathbf{w}, \qquad \mathbf{u}_1' = \mathbf{c}_1' - \mathbf{w}, \qquad \mathbf{u}_2' = \mathbf{c}_2' - \mathbf{w}, \tag{1.406}$$

$$m_1\mathbf{u}_1 + m_2\mathbf{u}_2 = m_1\mathbf{u}_1' + m_2\mathbf{u}_2' = 0, \tag{1.407}$$

$$\tfrac{1}{2}m_1\mathbf{u}_1^2 + \tfrac{1}{2}m_2\mathbf{u}_2^2 = \tfrac{1}{2}m_1\mathbf{u}_1'^2 + \tfrac{1}{2}m_2\mathbf{u}_2'^2. \tag{1.408}$$

$$\boldsymbol{\omega} = \frac{\mathbf{u}_1 - \mathbf{u}_1'}{|\mathbf{u}_1 - \mathbf{u}_1'|}. \tag{1.409}$$

Figures 6 and 7 show the velocities of the two atoms before and after the collision in the system where the center of gravity has a velocity $\mathbf{w}$ and in the center of gravity system.

The number of collisions per cm^3 in a time interval dt between atoms with velocities between $\mathbf{c}_1$ and $\mathbf{c}_1 + d\mathbf{c}_1$‡ on the one hand and atoms with velocities between $\mathbf{c}_2$ and $\mathbf{c}_2 + d\mathbf{c}_2$ on the other hand, while the line of centers lies within a solid angle $d\boldsymbol{\omega}$,§ is given by the expression

$$a_{12\to 1'2'}f(u_1,v_1,w_1)f(u_2,v_2,w_2)\,du_1dv_1dw_1du_2dv_2dw_2d\boldsymbol{\omega}dt. \tag{1.410}$$

In the case of our spherical atoms $a_{12\to 1'2'}$ can easily be calculated. It follows from the consideration that expression (1.410) is equal to the number per cm^3 of atoms with velocities between $\mathbf{c}_1$ and $\mathbf{c}_1 + d\mathbf{c}_1$, which is $f(u_1,v_1,w_1)du_1dv_1dw_1$, multiplied by the number of atoms with velocities between $\mathbf{c}_2$ and $\mathbf{c}_2 + d\mathbf{c}_2$ which collide with one atom in an inter-

† The reader should note the difference between $\mathbf{u}$ (velocity in the center of gravity system) and u (x-component of $\mathbf{c}$) or between $\mathbf{w}$ and w.

‡ We shall use this shorthand notation to indicate velocities with an x-component between u and $u + du$, a y-component between v and $v + dv$, and a z-component between w and $w + dw$.

§ We shall denote an element of solid angle by $d\boldsymbol{\omega}$. If $\boldsymbol{\omega}$ is characterized by two angles ϑ and φ, ϑ being the angle between the $+z$-axis and $\boldsymbol{\omega}$, and φ being the angle between the $+x$-axis and the projection of $\boldsymbol{\omega}$ on the x,y-plane, $d\boldsymbol{\omega}$ will be equal to $\sin\vartheta\, d\vartheta\, d\varphi$.

val dt in such a way that the line of centers has the direction $\boldsymbol{\omega}$ within a margin $d\boldsymbol{\omega}$. If $\mathbf{c}_{\mathrm{rel}}$ is the relative velocity of atom 2 with respect to atom 1 ($\mathbf{c}_{\mathrm{rel}} = \mathbf{c}_2 - \mathbf{c}_1$) and if we denote its absolute value by c_{rel}, it can be seen from Figure 8 that the number of atoms which collide with one atom is equal to the number of atoms which is contained in a cylinder with base $D^2 d\boldsymbol{\omega}$ (D = diameter of an atom; compare Fig. 5†) and slant height $c_{\mathrm{rel}}dt$. Since the number of atoms per cm^3 with velocities between $\mathbf{c}_2$ and $\mathbf{c}_2 + \mathbf{dc}_2$ is equal to $f(u_2,v_2,w_2)du_2dv_2dw_2$, we find for $a_{12\to1'2'}$

$$\left.\begin{aligned} a_{12\to1'2'} &= D^2 c_{\mathrm{rel}} \cos\theta, && \cos\theta > 0, \\ a_{12\to1'2'} &= 0, && \cos\theta \leqslant 0, \end{aligned}\right\} \quad \textbf{(1.411)}$$

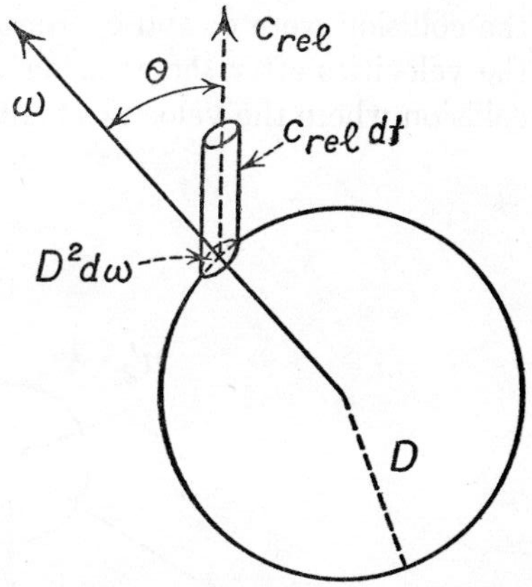

Fig. 8

where θ is the angle between $\boldsymbol{\omega}$ and $\mathbf{c}_{\mathrm{rel}}$.

If the atoms do not behave like rigid spheres, $a_{12\to1'2'}$ will be much more complicated, but will still only depend on θ and c_{rel}.

The number of atoms A leaving the volume $du_1dv_1dw_1$ in velocity space per unit time will now be obtained by integrating expression (1.410) over all possible values of u_2,v_2,w_2 and over all allowed values of $\boldsymbol{\omega}$, and dividing by dt,

$$A = f(u_1,v_1,w_1)du_1dv_1dw_1 \int f(u_2,v_2,w_2)du_2dv_2dw_2 \int a_{12\to1'2'}d\boldsymbol{\omega}. \quad \textbf{(1.412)}$$

We must remark here that in deriving equation (1.412) we have tacitly assumed, as did Clausius in 1858, that there is no correlation whatever between velocities and positions of different atoms. More specifically, whereas $[f(u_2,v_2,w_2)du_2dv_2dw_2] \cdot dV$ is the number of atoms with velocities between $\mathbf{c}_2$ and $\mathbf{c}_2 + \mathbf{dc}_2$ that will be found in a volume element dV selected at random, it does not follow that we may use the same expression for the particular volume element (the volume of the cylinder which we just considered) since this is not selected at random. We must introduce as a basic assumption that we may still use the same expression. This assumption is called the *Stosszahlansatz*. The implications of this assumption will be discussed more fully in Appendix I. We may mention at this point that it is often called the assumption of *molecular chaos*. However, with Boltzmann and the Ehrenfests we shall distinguish between these two

† If the radii of the two atoms are unequal, D will be equal to $r_1 + r_2$.

assumptions (see p. 353) and therefore use the German expression for the assumption introduced at this point.

We must now calculate the number of collisions which will bring back atoms into the volume $du_1dv_1dw_1$. These are collisions where the velocity of one of the two colliding atoms lies between $\mathbf{c}_1$ and $\mathbf{c}_1 + \mathbf{dc}_1$ *after* the collision. We have just considered a collision where the velocities before the collision were $\mathbf{c}_1$ and $\mathbf{c}_2$, the line of centers was determined by $\boldsymbol{\omega}$, and the velocities after the collision were $\mathbf{c}_1'$ and $\mathbf{c}_2'$. Let us now consider a collision where the velocities before the collision were $\mathbf{c}_1'$ and $\mathbf{c}_2'$ and after

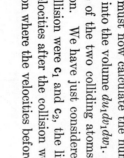

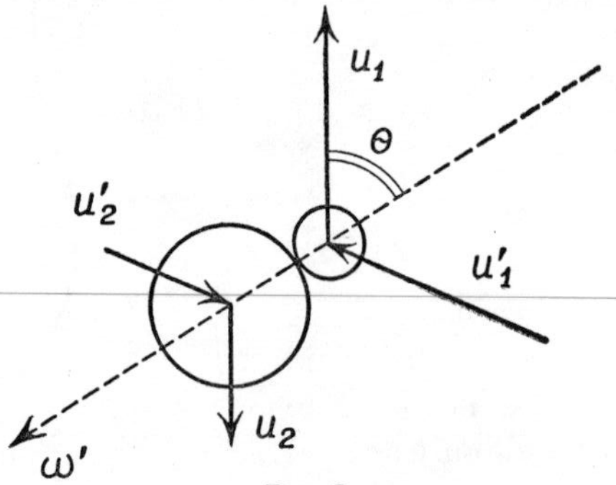

Fig. 9

the collision $\mathbf{c}_1$ and $\mathbf{c}_2$. From equation (1.405) it then follows that the new line of centers ($\boldsymbol{\omega}'$) is determined by $-\boldsymbol{\omega}$ instead of $\boldsymbol{\omega}$ (see Fig. 9, where this inverse collision is pictured in the center of gravity system). This second collision will be called the *inverse* collision corresponding to the original collision pictured in Figure 7. It can easily be verified that there is a one-to-one correspondence between original and inverse collisions. This is a consequence of the fact that $\mathbf{c}_1$, $\mathbf{c}_2$, and $\boldsymbol{\omega}$ determine $\mathbf{c}_1'$, $\mathbf{c}_2'$, and $\boldsymbol{\omega}'(= -\boldsymbol{\omega})$.

The total number of inverse collisions per cm^3 per sec where the velocities before the collision lie between $\mathbf{c}_1'$ and $\mathbf{c}_1' + \mathbf{dc}_1'$, and $\mathbf{c}_2'$ and $\mathbf{c}_2' + \mathbf{dc}_2'$ while $\boldsymbol{\omega}'$ lies within a solid angle $d\boldsymbol{\omega}'$ is given by (compare expression [1.410])

$$a_{1'2'\to 12} f(u_1',v_1',w_1')du_1'dv_1'dw_1'f(u_2',v_2',w_2')du_2'dv_2'dw_2'd\boldsymbol{\omega}'. \quad \textbf{(1.413)}$$

In order to get B we must integrate expression (1.413) over all allowed values of $\mathbf{c}_1'$, $\mathbf{c}_2'$, and $\boldsymbol{\omega}'$. Only those values of $\mathbf{c}_1'$, $\mathbf{c}_2'$, and $\boldsymbol{\omega}'$ are allowed where one of the velocities after the collision lies between $\mathbf{c}_1$ and $\mathbf{c}_1 + \mathbf{dc}_1$. If we indicate this restriction by priming the integral sign, we have

$$B = \int' du_1'dv_1'dw_1'du_2'dv_2'dw_2'f(u_1',v_1',w_1')f(u_2',v_2',w_2')\int a_{1'2'\to 12}d\boldsymbol{\omega}'. \quad \textbf{(1.414)}$$

It is possible to simplify the expression for B, since $\mathbf{c}_1'$, $\mathbf{c}_2'$, and $\boldsymbol{\omega}'$ are completely determined by $\mathbf{c}_1$, $\mathbf{c}_2$, and $\boldsymbol{\omega}$ by equations (1.403) to (1.405) and the equation $\boldsymbol{\omega}' = -\boldsymbol{\omega}$ which is a consequence of equation (1.405). If we change variables, using u_1,v_1,w_1,u_2,v_2,w_2, and $\boldsymbol{\omega}$ instead of the primed quantities we can write equation (1.414) in the form

$$B = du_1dv_1dw_1 \int du_2dv_2dw_2 J f(u_1',v_1',w_1')f(u_2',v_2',w_2') \int a_{1'2'\to 12}d\boldsymbol{\omega}. \tag{1.415}$$

The arguments of the distribution functions in equation (1.415) are functions of the unprimed quantities through equations (1.403) to (1.405) and J is the Jacobian of the transformation

$$J = \frac{\partial(u_1',v_1',w_1',u_2',v_2',w_2',\boldsymbol{\omega}')}{\partial(u_1,v_1,w_1,u_2,v_2,w_2,\boldsymbol{\omega})} = \begin{vmatrix} \dfrac{\partial u_1'}{\partial u_1} & \dfrac{\partial v_1'}{\partial u_1} & \dfrac{\partial w_1'}{\partial u_1} & \cdots & \dfrac{\partial w_2'}{\partial u_1} \\ \cdots & \cdots & \cdots & \cdots & \cdots \\ \cdots & \cdots & \cdots & \cdots & \cdots \\ \cdots & \cdots & \cdots & \cdots & \cdots \\ \dfrac{\partial u_1'}{\partial w_2} & \cdots & \cdots & \cdots & \dfrac{\partial w_2'}{\partial w_2} \end{vmatrix} \cdot \frac{\partial \boldsymbol{\omega}'}{\partial \boldsymbol{\omega}}. \tag{1.416}$$

It can be proved that J is always equal to one.†

We shall prove it in the case of an elastic collision between two particles with masses m_1 and m_2. We choose the $+x$-axis parallel to $\boldsymbol{\omega}$. Since the collision is elastic, we have from equations (1.403) to (1.405)

$$\left.\begin{aligned} &v_1 = v_1', \qquad w_1 = w_1'; \qquad v_2 = v_2', \qquad w_2 = w_2'; \\ &u_1' = \frac{(m_1 - m_2)u_1 + 2m_2u_2}{m_1 + m_2}, \qquad u_2' = \frac{(m_2 - m_1)u_2 + 2m_1u_1}{m_1 + m_2}. \end{aligned}\right\} \tag{1.417}$$

Equations (1.417) are most easily obtained by remembering that in the center of gravity system, the y- and z-components of the velocities are unchanged while the x-component only changes sign. The Jacobian now reduces to

$$J = \begin{vmatrix} \dfrac{\partial u_1'}{\partial u_1} & \dfrac{\partial u_2'}{\partial u_1} \\ \dfrac{\partial u_1'}{\partial u_2} & \dfrac{\partial u_2'}{\partial u_2} \end{vmatrix} \cdot \frac{\partial \boldsymbol{\omega}'}{\partial \boldsymbol{\omega}} = -\frac{\partial \boldsymbol{\omega}'}{\partial \boldsymbol{\omega}} = 1. \tag{1.418}$$

Since $a_{12\to 1'2'}$ or $a_{1'2'\to 12}$ depends only on c_{rel} and θ, neither of which changes by going over to the inverse collision, $a_{12\to 1'2'} = a_{1'2'\to 12}$, and we get from equations (1.401), (1.412), and (1.415), dropping the subscripts

† This is a consequence of Liouville's theorem. See p. 102.

of the a's, putting $J = 1$, and dividing by $du_1dv_1dw_1$,

$$\frac{\partial f_1}{\partial t} = -\int (f_1f_2 - f_1'f_2')\,a\,du_2dv_2dw_2d\omega. \tag{1.419}$$

In equation (1.419) we used the abbreviated notation

$$f_i = f(u_i,v_i,w_i), \qquad f_i' = f(u_i',v_i',w_i'). \tag{1.420}$$

If the distribution function is given by equation (1.104), we have

$$f_1f_2 = f_1'f_2', \tag{1.421}$$

due to the conservation of energy (equation [1.403]). Thus for a Maxwell distribution we find

$$\frac{\partial f}{\partial t} = 0. \tag{1.422}$$

This means that the Maxwell distribution is an equilibrium distribution, and that once it has been established, collisions will not alter it.

The distribution function can be slightly generalized,

$$\hat{f} = Ke^{-\frac{mc^2}{2kT} - (\boldsymbol{\alpha}\cdot\mathbf{c})}, \tag{1.423}$$

where K is a normalizing constant and $\boldsymbol{\alpha}$ a given constant vector. The distribution $\hat{f}$ corresponds to a case where the system as a whole is moving with a constant velocity, as we shall prove later in this section. Due to the conservation of momentum (equation [1.404]) $\hat{f}$ is a stationary distribution,

$$\hat{f}_1\hat{f}_2 = \hat{f}_1'\hat{f}_2' \qquad \text{or} \qquad \frac{\partial \hat{f}_1}{\partial t} = 0. \tag{1.424}$$

One might ask whether there may be other equilibrium distributions besides those given by equations (1.104) and (1.423). This cannot be the case so long as we are interested in a system of independent particles in the absence of external forces. To prove this we need only say that in order that $\partial f/\partial t = 0$, the following relation must hold:†

$$\ln f_1 + \ln f_2 = \text{the same before and after the collision.} \tag{1.425}$$

If $\psi(u,v,w)$ is a function of the velocity components of an atom such that $\psi(u_1,v_1,w_1) + \psi(u_2,v_2,w_2)$ remains unchanged by a collision, $\ln f = \psi$ will be a solution of equation (1.425). If there are several such functions, $\psi_1, \psi_2, \psi_3, \cdots$, the general solution of equation (1.425) will be

$$\ln f = c_0 + c_1\psi_1 + c_2\psi_2 + c_3\psi_3 + \cdots. \tag{1.426}$$

We know four ψ's having this property, the energy and the three components of the momentum. The conservation laws for energy and

† For a different proof compare, e.g., J. E. and M. G. Mayer, Statistical Mechanics, New York 1940, p. 12.

momentum, together with the direction of the line of centers, completely determine the six velocity components after the collision, once the six velocity components before the collision are given. Hence it follows that there will be only these four ψ's. From equation (1.426) it then follows that

$$\ln f = c_0 + c_1 \cdot \tfrac{1}{2}m(u^2 + v^2 + w^2) + c_2 \cdot mu + c_3 \cdot mv + c_4 \cdot mw,$$

or

$$f = Ke^{-a(\mathbf{c}-\mathbf{c}_0)^2}. \qquad \textbf{(1.427)}$$

In equation (1.427) K is again a normalization constant (which, by the way, is different from the K in equation [1.423]). That the distribution (1.427) corresponds to a system moving as a whole with a velocity $\mathbf{c}_0$ follows easily. If we perform a transformation to a coordinate system moving with velocity $\mathbf{c}_0$ with respect to our original system of reference, the distribution function will be given by the equation

$$f' = Ke^{-ac^2}, \qquad \textbf{(1.428)}$$

which is the Maxwell distribution of a system at rest.

The movement of the system can also be shown by calculating the average velocity $\bar{\mathbf{c}}$ of the atoms in the system. It is then found that

$$\bar{\mathbf{c}} = \mathbf{c}_0, \qquad \textbf{(1.429)}$$

which again leads to the conclusion that the system corresponding to the distribution function (1.427) is moving as a whole with a velocity $\mathbf{c}_0$.

In order to prove that the distribution (1.427) (or [1.428]) is really the Maxwell distribution, we have only to show that

$$a = \frac{m}{2kT}. \qquad \textbf{(1.430)}$$

This can be done in two different ways, depending on the way the temperature is introduced. If the temperature is introduced through equation (1.110) for the average value of the kinetic energy† or through the equation of state for a perfect gas (1.204), equation (1.430) follows immediately, since from equation (1.428) it can be seen that

$$\overline{\mathbf{c}^2} = \frac{3}{2a} \qquad \textbf{(1.431)}$$

once K has been determined by means of equation (1.102).

A different method of proving equation (1.430) will be met in §6, where the temperature appears as the thermodynamical temperature, i.e., as an integrating factor. The proof in §6 is not complete and is only implicit in the discussion, but a complete proof will be given in Chapter IV (p. 80).

We have now proved that the generalized Maxwell distribution is the only possible equilibrium distribution in the case of a gas which is not in an external field of force. In the next section it will be shown that the equi-

† In the case of the moving distribution, we should write: the average value of the *thermal* kinetic energy which is the average value of $\frac{1}{2}m(\mathbf{c} - \mathbf{c}_0)^2$.

librium is a stable one and that every other distribution will tend to go over into the Maxwell distribution.

We may make one remark here about equation (1.421) which is a sufficient (and as will be shown in the next section also a necessary) condition for equilibrium. Equation (1.421) means that in unit time there are as many inverse collisions as original ones. This is but one example of the far more general *principle of detailed balancing* which will be discussed in §9 of Appendix I.

§5. The *H*-Theorem. Boltzmann introduced in 1872 the function

$$H = \overline{\ln f} = \int f \ln f du dv dw. \tag{1.501}$$

In equation (1.501) f is any distribution function $f(u,v,w)$, not necessarily that given by equation (1.104) or (1.423). Since the integration is over the whole of velocity space, H will be a function of time only. For its derivative we find†

$$\frac{dH}{dt} = \int \frac{\partial f}{\partial t} (\ln f + 1) d\mathbf{c}. \tag{1.502}$$

If we use equation (1.419) for $\partial f/\partial t$, equation (1.502) becomes

$$\frac{dH}{dt} = \int (f'f_1' - ff_1)(\ln f + 1) a d\mathbf{c} d\mathbf{c}_1 d\boldsymbol{\omega}. \tag{1.503a}$$

We have seen that H is dependent on the time only. The expression on the right-hand side of equation (1.503a) will thus not change if $\mathbf{c}$ and $\mathbf{c}_1$ are interchanged. The result of this interchange is

$$\frac{dH}{dt} = \int (f'f_1' - ff_1)(\ln f_1 + 1) a d\mathbf{c} d\mathbf{c}_1 d\boldsymbol{\omega}. \tag{1.503b}$$

In deriving equation (1.503b) use has been made of the fact that $a_{12\to1'2'}$ depends only on c_{rel} and θ and therefore does not change when $\mathbf{c}$ and $\mathbf{c}_1$ are interchanged. We can also interchange primed and unprimed variables in equations (1.503a) and (1.503b). This leads to the two equations (where a' stands for $a_{1'2'\to12}$)

$$\frac{dH}{dt} = \int (ff_1 - f'f_1')(\ln f' + 1) a' d\mathbf{c}' d\mathbf{c}_1' d\boldsymbol{\omega}', \tag{1.503c}$$

$$\frac{dH}{dt} = \int (ff_1 - f'f_1')(\ln f_1' + 1) a' d\mathbf{c}' d\mathbf{c}_1' d\boldsymbol{\omega}'. \tag{1.503d}$$

† We use the abbreviation dc for $dudvdw$. It must be noted that dc is not a vector but a symbolical notation for a volume element in velocity space. It should not be confused with the small vector $\mathbf{dc}$.

Now, $\mathbf{c}'$, $\mathbf{c}_1'$, and $\boldsymbol{\omega}'$ are functions of $\mathbf{c}$, $\mathbf{c}_1$, and $\boldsymbol{\omega}$ and it is possible to perform a transformation from the primed to the unprimed variables. Using the results of the preceding section and performing the transformation, we get

$$\frac{dH}{dt} = \int (ff_1 - f'f_1')(\ln f' + 1)a d\mathbf{c} d\mathbf{c}_1 d\boldsymbol{\omega}, \tag{1.503e}$$

$$\frac{dH}{dt} = \int (ff_1 - f'f_1')(\ln f_1' + 1)a d\mathbf{c} d\mathbf{c}_1 d\boldsymbol{\omega}. \tag{1.503f}$$

Equations (1.503a), (1.503b), (1.503e), and (1.503f) are four equivalent equations for dH/dt. Adding these four equations and dividing by four, we get for dH/dt

$$\frac{dH}{dt} = -\frac{1}{4}\int (f'f_1' - ff_1) \ln \frac{f'f_1'}{ff_1} a d\mathbf{c} d\mathbf{c}_1 d\boldsymbol{\omega}. \tag{1.504}$$

Since a is a positive quantity and since $(p - q) \ln (p/q)$ is positive except when $p = q$, in which case it is zero, it follows from equation (1.504) that

$$\frac{dH}{dt} \leqslant 0. \tag{1.505}$$

The equality in equation (1.505) is valid only if for *every* two velocities $\mathbf{c}$ and $\mathbf{c}_1$ we have $ff_1 = f'f_1'$. Equation (1.505), which expresses that H can never increase, is known as Boltzmann's *H-theorem*.†

It can be seen from equation (1.505) that H will decrease as long as the distribution function does not satisfy equation (1.421). If a distribution differs appreciably from the equilibrium distribution, the return to equilibrium is usually very rapid.‡ The relaxation time, i.e., the time necessary to return to equilibrium, in the case of a gas under normal conditions ($T = 300°$ K, $p = 1$ atm) is, e.g., of the order of 10^{-9} sec.

It is worth while to show that we arrive at the generalized Maxwell distribution (1.423) if we start from the requirement that it is that distribution which makes H a minimum, that is, when we take as the equilibrium condition

$$H = \text{a minimum}, \tag{1.506}$$

under the restricting conditions that the total number of atoms N in the gas, the total energy E of the gas and its total momentum $\mathbf{P}$ are given. One can then use the method of *Lagrangian multipliers* (see §4 of the

† In Appendix I the implications of the H-theorem and its connection with the Stosszahlansatz will be discussed.

‡ The return to equilibrium and other irreversible processes will be discussed in Appendix II.

Mathematical Appendix) to prove that the generalized Maxwell distribution follows from equation (1.506).

If $f(u,v,w)$ is an equilibrium distribution, *any* small change δf (which itself will be a function of u, v, and w) will have to satisfy the following conditions:

$$\delta H = \int \delta f(\ln f + 1)d\mathbf{c} = 0, \quad \text{(equilibrium condition)} \tag{1.507a}$$

$$\delta E = \int \delta f(\tfrac{1}{2}mc^2)d\mathbf{c} = 0, \quad \text{(conservation of energy)} \tag{1.507b}$$

$$\delta \mathbf{P} = \int \delta f(m\mathbf{c})d\mathbf{c} = 0, \quad \text{(conservation of momentum)} \tag{1.507c}$$

$$\delta N = V \int \delta f d\mathbf{c} = 0, \quad \text{(conservation of the number of particles)} \tag{1.507d}$$

where V is the volume of the gas.

Equations (1.507) express that for any δf which satisfies equations (1.507b, c, d) the distribution function f must be such that equation (1.507a) is satisfied. However, we can remove the restrictions on δf and assume that it is any arbitrary change, if we add the four equations after multiplying each by an (arbitrary) constant (see the last section of the Mathematical Appendix).

Taking

$$\nu\, \delta H + \mu\, \delta E + (\boldsymbol{\lambda} \cdot \delta \mathbf{P}) + \frac{\nu - 1}{V}\, \delta N,$$

which must be zero according to equations (1.507), we get the equation

$$\int \delta f[\ln f + \mu \cdot \tfrac{1}{2}mc^2 + (\boldsymbol{\lambda} \cdot m\mathbf{c}) + \nu]d\mathbf{c} = 0, \tag{1.508}$$

and now δf is an arbitrary change of f. Equation (1.508) can be satisfied only if

$$\ln f = -\mu \cdot \tfrac{1}{2}mc^2 - (\boldsymbol{\lambda} \cdot m\mathbf{c}) - \nu, \tag{1.509}$$

or

$$f = e^{-\nu} e^{-\frac{1}{2}\mu mc^2 - m(\boldsymbol{\lambda} \cdot \mathbf{c})}, \tag{1.510}$$

which is the same as expression (1.423) with a slightly different notation. The quantity μ must be determined from the total energy E of the system, $\boldsymbol{\lambda}$ from the total momentum $\mathbf{P}$ of the system, while ν will be determined from the normalizing condition (1.102). In the special case of a gas at rest ($\boldsymbol{\lambda} = 0$) we get for ν the equation

$$e^{-\nu} = \left(\frac{\mu m}{2\pi}\right)^{3/2} n. \tag{1.511}$$

§6. The Connection between *H* and Entropy. In Chapter IV we shall discuss in more detail the relations between statistical mechanics and classical thermodynamics. In the special case of a gaseous system consisting of noninteracting atoms, the connection between Boltzmann's H-function and the thermodynamical quantity called the entropy will be given in this section.

From equations (1.509) and (1.511) we get for the case of a gas at rest

$$\ln f = \ln n + \tfrac{3}{2}\ln \mu - \tfrac{1}{2}\mu m c^2 + \text{constant}. \tag{1.601}$$

Introducing the volume v of 1 g of gas,

$$v = \frac{1}{nm}, \tag{1.602}$$

we can write equation (1.601) in the form

$$\ln f = -\ln v + \tfrac{3}{2}\ln \mu - \tfrac{1}{2}\mu m c^2 + \text{constant}. \tag{1.603}$$

It follows now from the definition of H (equation [1.501]) that

$$\frac{H}{n} = -\ln v + \tfrac{3}{2}\ln \mu - \tfrac{1}{2}\mu m \overline{c^2} + \text{constant},$$

or, after evaluating $\overline{c^2}$,

$$\frac{H}{n} = -\ln v + \tfrac{3}{2}\ln \mu + \text{constant}. \tag{1.604}$$

If we are dealing with a perfect gas, μ will be equal to $1/kT$ (compare equation [1.430]) and we have from equation (1.604)

$$\frac{H}{n} = -\ln v - \tfrac{3}{2}\ln T + \text{constant}. \tag{1.605}$$

If the entropy and the internal energy per unit mass are denoted by s and u, the second law of thermodynamics gives us the following relation between the changes in s, u and the work done by the pressure,

$$ds = \frac{đq}{T} = \frac{du + p\,dv}{T}, \tag{1.606}$$

where $đq$ is the heat increase per unit mass.†

---

† In this section, quantities referring to the whole system will be denoted by capital letters (S, V, U, Q, etc.); quantities referring to unit mass, by small type (s, v, u, q, etc.); and quantities referring to one mole by the subscript m (S_m, V_m, U_m, Q_m, etc.). If M is the molecular weight of the gas, we have $S_m = Ms$, $V_m = Mv$, etc. Quantities referring to unit volume will be indicated by a subscript v (S_v, etc.).

The symbols $đ$ or $\eth$ will indicate that we are not dealing with a total differential or variation.

The perfect gas law can be written in the form

$$pv = \frac{R}{M}T, \tag{1.607}$$

where M is the molecular weight of the gas. Since the internal energy of a perfect gas consists of the kinetic energy only, we have

$$du = c_v dT = \frac{3}{2}\frac{R}{M}dT, \tag{1.608}$$

where c_v is the specific heat (per unit mass) at constant volume.

From equations (1.606), (1.607), and (1.608) it follows that

$$ds = c_v \frac{dT}{T} + \frac{R}{M}\frac{dv}{v}, \tag{1.609}$$

or

$$s = \frac{R}{M}\left(\tfrac{3}{2}\ln T + \ln v\right) + \text{constant}. \tag{1.610}$$

Using equation (1.206) we get for the entropy per unit volume

$$S_v = \frac{Mn}{\mathfrak{A}} s = nk\left(\tfrac{3}{2}\ln T + \ln v\right) + \text{constant}. \tag{1.611}$$

Comparing equations (1.605) and (1.611) we see that there exists the following relation between H and the entropy per unit volume,

$$S_v = -kH. \tag{1.612}$$

The fact that H can never increase thus corresponds to the well-known statement of the second law of thermodynamics that the entropy will never decrease.

It may be remarked here that although in thermodynamics the entropy is, strictly speaking, defined only in the case of equilibrium, H is also defined for nonequilibrium situations and one can use equation (1.612) as a definition of the entropy in such nonequilibrium situations.

§7. Connection between H and Probability. Although a more detailed discussion of the connection between statistical mechanics and probability will be given in Chapter IV, we shall give here a preliminary discussion adapted to the case of a perfect gas.

We shall divide the velocity space into a number of cells Z_k, each cell being a volume element *dudvdw*, and we shall distribute the representative points of N particles in such a way that the a priori probability for a point falling into a cell Z_k will be proportional to Z_k.† If N_1 points fall in Z_1,

† The importance and implications of this assumption of a priori probability will be discussed in §8 of Appendix I.

N_2 in $Z_2, \cdots$, we speak of this particular distribution as an N_i-distribution and we define the probability $W(N_1,\cdots,N_k,\cdots)$ or $W(N_i)$ as the fraction of all possible arrangements where this specially considered distribution is realized. For this quantity W we find

$$W(N_1,N_2,\cdots,N_i,\cdots) = CN!\prod_i \frac{Z_i^{N_i}}{N_i!}, \tag{1.701}$$

where C is a normalization constant.

In order to derive equation (1.701) we have to remember that the number of possible ways of choosing A objects out of B is given by the binomial coefficient

$$\binom{B}{A} = \frac{B!}{A!(B-A)!}. \tag{1.702}$$

In our case we have to choose first N_1 objects out of N, then N_2 objects out of $N - N_1$, N_3 out of $N - N_1 - N_2$, and so on, and for the total number of possible ways we thus get

$$\binom{N}{N_1}\binom{N-N_1}{N_2}\binom{N-N_1-N_2}{N_3}\cdots = \frac{N!}{N_1!(N-N_1)!}\cdot\frac{(N-N_1)!}{N_2!(N-N_1-N_2)!}\cdots = \frac{N!}{N_1!N_2!\cdots}. \tag{1.703}$$

Multiplying this *multinomial* coefficient with the a priori probability then gives us expression (1.701).

The name "multinomial coefficient" arises from the fact that these coefficients appear in the multinomial expansion

$$(a_1 + a_2 + \cdots)^N = \sum \frac{N!}{N_1!N_2!\cdots} a_1^{N_1}a_2^{N_2}a_3^{N_3}\cdots \tag{1.704}$$

where the summation extends over all nonnegative values of N_i in such a way that their sum is equal to N.

We must now seek that distribution which makes $W(N_i)$ maximum under the restricting conditions that

$$\sum N_i = N \tag{1.705}$$

and

$$\sum N_i\epsilon_i = E, \tag{1.706}$$

where ϵ_i is the energy of an atom in cell Z_i. Conditions (1.705) and (1.706) fix the total number of particles in the gas and the total energy of the system.

In order to find the distribution for which we are looking, we shall require $\ln W$ to be maximum instead of W. Now we have from equation (1.701)

$$\ln W = \ln N! + \sum_i [N_i \ln Z_i - \ln N_i!] + \text{constant}. \tag{1.707}$$

If we may assume that all of the N_i are large compared with unity, we can use for the factorials the Stirling formula,†

$$x! \approx x^x e^{-x}. \tag{1.708}$$

Combining equations (1.707) and (1.708) and observing condition (1.705), we obtain

$$\ln W = -\sum_i N_i \ln \frac{N_i}{NZ_i} + \text{constant}. \tag{1.709}$$

Looking for the maximum of $\ln W$ under the conditions (1.705) and (1.706), we can again use Lagrange's method of undetermined multipliers. For a variation δN_i of the N_i we have

$$\delta \ln W = 0 = -\sum_i \delta N_i \left[\ln \frac{N_i}{NZ_i} + 1 \right], \tag{1.710a}$$

$$\delta N = 0 = \sum_i \delta N_i, \tag{1.710b}$$

$$\delta E = 0 = \sum_i \delta N_i \epsilon_i. \tag{1.710c}$$

Multiplying these equations by 1, $\nu + 1$ and $-\mu$ respectively and adding them, we obtain

$$\sum_i \delta N_i \left[-\ln \frac{N_i}{NZ_i} + \nu - \mu\epsilon_i \right] = 0. \tag{1.711}$$

Since in equation (1.711) the δN_i can be taken to be arbitrary, it follows that

$$\ln \frac{N_i}{NZ_i} = \nu - \mu\epsilon_i$$

or

$$N_i = NZ_i e^{\nu - \mu\epsilon_i}. \tag{1.712}$$

The quantities ν and μ can be determined from conditions (1.705) and (1.706).

We can now apply these formulae to the case of a perfect gas. The cells Z_i are then volumes in velocity space, or

$$Z_i = du dv dw. \tag{1.713}$$

As N is the total number of particles, N_i is the total number of particles with velocities between **c** and **c** + **dc**. Thus

$$\frac{N_i}{N} = \frac{1}{n} f(u,v,w) du dv dw, \tag{1.714}$$

n = N/V
f = # of atoms/cc per unit velocity

† For a derivation of the Stirling formula see §3 of the Mathematical Appendix. The fact that the use of the Stirling formula yields averages instead of most probable values is discussed in Appendix IV. (See footnote on p. 409.)

$H = f \ln f$

$W = N_i \ln N_i$

ϵ_i of the atoms are given by

$$\epsilon_i = \tfrac{1}{2}mc^2. \tag{1.715}$$

o over into integrals without further change, equation y the Maxwell distribution (1.104). (1.709), (1.713), and (1.714) we then get

$$\text{n } W = -\int f \ln f du dv dw + \text{constant}. \tag{1.716}$$

tions (1.501) and (1.716), we see that, apart from an n W and $-H$ are the same. The tendency for a decrease r an increase of entropy corresponds thus to a tendency robability for the most probable distribution.† ions (1.612), (1.501), and (1.716) and omitting for the additive constants to which we shall return later, we

$$-kH = S_v = k \ln W, \tag{1.717}$$

iown relation between entropy and probability.

BIBLIOGRAPHICAL NOTES

:es dealing with the material of this chapter are
/orlesungen über Gastheorie, 2 vols., Leipzig 1896–1898.
renfest, Enzyklopädie der mathematischen Wissenschaften, Leipzig-Berlin 1911.
J. Nabl, Enzyklopädie der mathematischen Wissenschaften, Vol. V, Pt. 8, Leipzig-Berlin 1905.

§1. The Maxwell distribution was introduced by Maxwell in 1859:

4. J. C. Maxwell, Phil. Mag., **19**, 19, 1860. (This paper was read before the British Association in Aberdeen on September 21, 1859.)

In the paper, Maxwell derives his distribution from the following assumptions:

a) The distribution function depends only on the absolute magnitude of the velocity.
b) The probability that the x-component of the velocity lies within a certain interval is independent of the value of the y- or z-component.

From these two assumptions the Maxwell distribution follows in a straightforward manner. The derivation which is given in §4, and which does not depend on the above assumptions, was given by Maxwell in 1867:

5. J. C. Maxwell, Trans. Roy. Soc. (London), **157**, 49, 1867 (= Phil. Mag., **35**, 129, 185, 1868).

See also

6. L. Boltzmann, Wien. Ber.,‡ **58**, 517, 1868.

† Or better, for the average distribution. Compare the footnote on p. 24.

‡ Wien. Ber. = Sitzungsberichte der kaiserlichen Akademie der Wissenschaften in Wien, Klasse IIa.

Experimental verifications of the Maxwell distribution were, e.g., obtained by Ornstein and van Wijk, who studied the shape of spectral lines, and by Stern and collaborators and by Kofsky and Levinstein, who used the molecular beam method:

7. L. S. Ornstein and W. R. v. Wijk, Z. Physik, **78**, 734, 1932.
8. I. Estermann, O. C. Simpson, and O. Stern, Phys. Rev., **71**, 238, 1947.
9. I. L. Kofsky and H. Levinstein, Phys. Rev., **74**, 500, 1948.

Equations (1.106) to (1.111) can be found in Maxwell's papers (refs. 4 and 5).

§2. The perfect gas law as a formula describing experimental data is due to the combined efforts of many scientists, such as Boyle, Mariotte, Gay-Lussac. In Russian literature (e.g., L. Landau and E. Lifshitz, Statistical Physics, Oxford 1938, p. 70; A. I. Khinchin, Statistical Mechanics, New York 1949, p. 121) the perfect gas law is often called Clapeyron's law, probably because Clapeyron was the first to write the law in the form $pV = RT$:

10. E. Clapeyron, J. d'école polytech., **14**, 153, 1834.

Clapeyron, however, explicitly mentions Mariotte and Gay-Lussac as the ones who discovered and stated the gas law.

The idea that the pressure of a gas is due to the movement of its constituent particles is very old. Both Maxwell (reference 5) and Clausius (Ann. Physik, **115**, 2, 1862) give long lists of early papers discussing this idea. Herapath, e.g., showed that the pressure was inversely proportional to the volume and independent of the form of the vessel:

11. J. Herapath, Ann. Philos., **1**, 273, 340, 401, 1821.

Joule was the first to show that the pressure is proportional to the square of the velocity:

12. J. P. Joule, Mem. and Proc. Manchester Lit. & Phil. Soc., **9**, 107, 1851 (= Phil. Mag., **14**, 211, 1857).

By assuming that all the atoms had the same speed c and that one sixth of all the atoms were flying in the $+x$-direction, one sixth in the $-x$-direction, and so on, Krönig derived the equation $pV = \frac{1}{3}nmc^2$, and from this equation deduced that mc^2 should be proportional to T:

13. A. Krönig, Ann. Physik, **99**, 315, 1856.

Krönig can probably be considered to be the father of kinetic gas theory. In the introduction to his paper he writes: "... die Bahn jedes Gasatoms muss deshalb eine so unregelmässige seyn, dass sie sich der Berechnung entzieht. Nach den Gesetzen der Wahrscheinlichkeitsrechnung wird man jedoch statt dieser vollkommenen Unregelmässigkeit eine vollkommene Regelmässigkeit annehmen dürfen."

Clausius derives the perfect gas law under slightly less stringent assumptions:

14. R. Clausius, Ann. Physik, **100**, 353, 1857 (= Phil. Mag., **14**, 108, 1857).

In this paper, Clausius actually gives a definition of a perfect gas. There are three conditions which the gas must fulfill:

a) Its own volume must be small as compared to the total volume of the system.
b) The period during which two atoms are actually colliding must be small compared to the period between two collisions (or, the molecular dimensions must be small as compared to the mean free path).
c) There may only be a weak interaction between the atoms.

More precisely and in more modern language we can say: A perfect gas is a gas where the total potential energy of the system at any time is negligibly small compared to the total kinetic energy of the system.

In all the papers mentioned thus far, the perfect gas law is derived by considering the transfer of momentum from the gas to the wall. In describing pressure and tensions in liquids, Maxwell (ref. 5) uses the idea of transfer of momentum through an imaginary unit area. The use of this definition in deriving the gas law is usually attributed to Lorentz.†

§3. The idea that the volume taken up by the atoms would change the gas law is very old. Bernoulli derived in 1738 that b should simply be equal to the volume ω of the atoms:

15. D. Bernoulli, Hydrodynamica, Argentorati, 1738, Chap. X.

Van der Waals showed, however, that as long as $b \ll V$, $b = 4\omega$:

16. J. D. v. d. Waals, Over de Continuïteit van den Gas- en Vloeistoftoestand, Thesis, Leiden 1873.

For an account of van der Waals' thesis see

17. J. C. Maxwell, Nature, **10**, 477, 1874.

For extensive bibliographies about the van der Waals' law, see ref. 3 and

18. H. Kamerlingh Onnes and W. H. Keesom, Enzyklopädie der mathematischen Wissenschaften, Vol. V, Pt. 10, Leipzig-Berlin 1912 (= Comm. Leiden Suppl. 23).
19. J. R. Partington, Physical Chemistry, Vol. I, London 1949, §VIIC.

The term "virial coefficient" was first introduced by Onnes:

20. H. Kamerlingh Onnes, Proc. Kon. Ned. Akad. Wet., Amsterdam, **4**, 125, 1902 (= Comm. Leiden 71).

The use of the virial for calculating the pressure of a gas and the term "virial" are, however, due to Clausius:

21. R. Clausius, Ann. Physik, **141**, 124, 1870 (= Phil. Mag., **40**, 122, 1870).

§4. The derivation of the Maxwell distribution by considering collisions between elastic spheres was given by Maxwell (ref. 5) and Boltzmann (ref. 6). See also ref. 1.

The Stosszahlansatz was implied in many early calculations. For instance, Clausius used it in his calculations of the mean free path in the form: number of collisions per atom = (volume swept through by the atom) × (number of atoms per cm^3):

22. R. Clausius, Ann. Physik, **105**, 239, 1858.

For a detailed discussion and bibliography we refer to App. I.

§5. The function H and the H-theorem are both due to Boltzmann:

23. L. Boltzmann, Wien. Ber., **66**, 275, 1872.

In this paper Boltzmann still uses the letter E (entropy) for H.

§§6 and 7. The considerations of these two sections can, for instance, be found in Boltzmann's papers (see also ref. 1).

† See, for instance, his paper in Collected Papers, Vol. VI, The Hague, 1938, p. 143.

CHAPTER II

THE MAXWELL-BOLTZMANN DISTRIBUTION

§1. The Barometer Formula. In the previous chapter we limited ourselves to the case of a perfect gas which was not under the influence of any external field of force. In the present chapter we wish to extend the theory to the case where external fields of force are present. We shall in addition no longer confine ourselves to monatomic gases, but we shall restrict ourselves to conservative systems where the force on each atom (or molecule) can be derived from a potential energy.

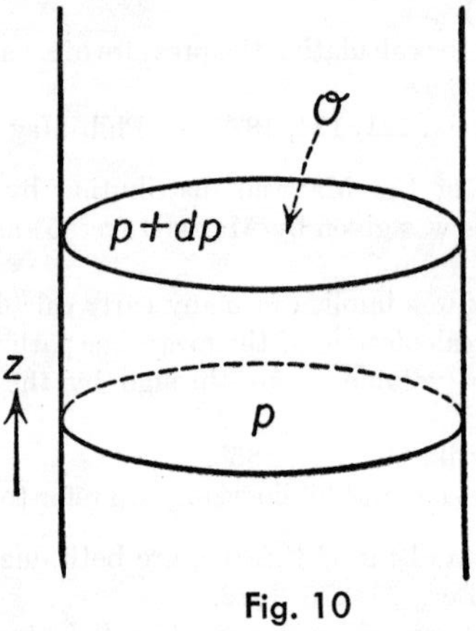

Fig. 10

Before discussing the general case in detail we shall first discuss in a rough, phenomenological way the case of a perfect gas under the influence of a homogeneous gravitational field.

The equation of motion of a disc of gas of cross section O and thickness dz at a height z (see Fig. 10) can be written in the form

$$(p + dp)O = pO - g\rho O dz, \qquad \textbf{(2.101)}$$

where g is the gravitational acceleration and ρ the density of the gas.

Using the perfect gas law (1.204) in the form

$$p = \frac{\rho}{m} kT, \tag{2.102}$$

where m is the mass of one atom, we find from equation (2.101)

$$\rho = \rho_0 e^{-\frac{mgz}{kT}}. \tag{2.103}$$

Equation (2.103) is known as the *barometer formula.*

We can interpret this formula in the following way. Let us introduce a generalized distribution function $f(x,y,z;u,v,w)$. This function is defined in such a way that $f(x,y,z;u,v,w)dxdydzdudvdw$ is the number of atoms with positions between $\mathbf{r}$ and $\mathbf{r} + \mathbf{dr}$† and velocities between $\mathbf{c}$ and $\mathbf{c} + \mathbf{dc}$.

The density $\rho(x,y,z)$ can be obtained from $f(x,y,z;u,v,w)$ by integration over the whole of velocity space:

$$\rho(x,y,z) = m \iiint_{-\infty}^{+\infty} f(x,y,z;u,v,w)dudvdw. \tag{2.104}$$

We shall see in the next section that in the equilibrium state there exists a Maxwell distribution of velocities at every point in (coordinate) space. In that case $f(x,y,z;u,v,w)$ contains a factor

$$e^{-\frac{mc^2}{2kT}}, \tag{2.105}$$

and, combining the results of equations (2.103), (2.104), and (2.105), we may expect that the distribution function has the form

$$f(x,y,z;u,v,w) = Ce^{-\frac{mc^2}{2kT}-\frac{mgz}{kT}}, \tag{2.106}$$

where C is a normalizing constant.

Expression (2.106) can be written in the form

$$f(x,y,z;u,v,w) = Ce^{-\frac{\epsilon}{kT}}, \tag{2.107}$$

where ϵ is the total energy of one atom in the gravitational field

$$\epsilon = \mathcal{T} + U = \tfrac{1}{2}mc^2 + mgz, \tag{2.108}$$

if $\mathcal{T}$ and U are the kinetic and potential energy of one atom.

Equation (2.107) comprises both equation (2.106) of which the barometer formula is a consequence and the Maxwell distribution (1.204), since

† The vectors $\mathbf{r}$ and $\mathbf{r} + \mathbf{dr}$ have the components x, y, z and $x + dx$, $y + dy$, $z + dz$. A volume element $dxdydz$ will often symbolically be denoted by $d\boldsymbol{r}$ (not to be confused with $\mathbf{dr}$).

in the latter case $U = 0$. We shall see later on that equation (2.107) is an instance of the general formula of the Maxwell-Boltzmann distribution.

§2. The μ-space. We arrived at the distribution function (2.106) or (2.107) by a rather heuristic procedure. We shall have to justify our results by more rigorous methods. However, before doing this we first wish to generalize equation (2.107). For this purpose we shall introduce generalized coordinates and momenta, as is done in theoretical classical mechanics.†

Consider a particle with s degrees of freedom. Its condition will be completely determined by the values of a set of s suitably chosen quantities $q_i (i = 1, 2, \cdots, s)$ and the values of their time derivatives $\dot{q}_i$. The q_i are called *generalized coordinates* and their time derivatives *generalized velocities*.

Let us consider a few examples. One atom will have 3 degrees of freedom, if we may disregard its internal degrees of freedom, i.e., if we may forget that an atom consists of a complicated nucleus with accompanying electrons.‡ In this case we can use for the q's the Cartesian coordinates x, y, and z and for the generalized velocities the linear velocities u, v, and w.

A more complicated case is the so-called dumbbell molecule, i.e., a diatomic molecule where the two atoms are a fixed distance, d, apart. The number of degrees of freedom is here 5. It is possible to use x_1, y_1, z_1, x_2, y_2, and z_2 as the coordinates with the restriction

$$(x_1 - x_2)^2 + (y_1 - y_2)^2 + (z_1 - z_2)^2 = d^2. \qquad \textbf{(2.201)}$$

However, it is much more convenient to introduce as q's the three coordinates of the center of gravity X, Y, and Z and two angles θ and φ, defining the direction of the axis of the molecule. The generalized velocities are then $\dot{X}$, $\dot{Y}$, $\dot{Z}$, $\dot{\theta}$, and $\dot{\varphi}$. We may draw attention to the fact that, as one can see from this example, generalized coordinates have not necessarily the dimensions of a length.

The total energy of a particle consists of two parts: the kinetic energy $\mathcal{T}$ and the potential energy U. It can be shown that the kinetic energy $\mathcal{T}$ is a quadratic function of the $\dot{q}_i$, where the coefficients in the quadratic expression may still depend on the q_i:

$$\mathcal{T} = \mathcal{T}(q_i, \dot{q}_i) = \sum_{k,l=1}^{s} a_{kl}(q_i)\dot{q}_k\dot{q}_l. \qquad \textbf{(2.202)}$$

† For an account of classical mechanics we refer to the textbooks mentioned in the introduction, but we shall briefly summarize those results which we shall need in the present discussion.

‡ The reason why we may treat an atom as a point particle will be discussed in the next chapter (p. 62). A similar case of apparent neglect of degrees of freedom occurs in the discussion of a diatomic molecule where we neglect the relative movement of the two atoms in the direction of the axis of the molecule.

As far as the potential energy is concerned, we shall restrict ourselves to cases where U depends only on the q_i:

$$U = U(q_i). \tag{2.203}$$

The total energy ϵ is given by the equation

$$\epsilon = \epsilon(q_i,\dot{q}_i) = \mathcal{T}(q_i,\dot{q}_i) + U(q_i). \tag{2.204}$$

It is more convenient to introduce instead of the generalized velocities $\dot{q}_i$ a new set of variables, the *generalized momenta*, p_i, which are defined by the equations

$$p_i = \frac{\partial \mathcal{T}}{\partial \dot{q}_i} = \sum_j a_{ij}\dot{q}_j, \tag{2.205}$$

where we have used equation (2.202) for $\mathcal{T}$. If q_k is a Cartesian coordinate, p_k will be the linear momentum (=mass times velocity). Transforming from the $\dot{q}_i$ to the p_i we have, instead of equation (2.204),

$$\mathcal{H}(p_i,q_i) = \mathcal{T}(p_i,q_i) + U(q_i), \tag{2.206}$$

where $\mathcal{T}$ is now a quadratic function of the p_i. In equation (2.206) the total energy is denoted by $\mathcal{H}$. If the energy is expressed in terms of the p_i and the q_i it is called the *Hamiltonian* of the system, hence the notation $\mathcal{H}$. The $2s$ coordinates $p_1, p_2, \cdots, p_s, q_1, q_2, \cdots, q_s$ are called *canonical* coordinates. In theoretical mechanics it is shown that, expressed in the canonical coordinates, the equations of motion take on the canonical or Hamiltonian form, or,

$$\dot{q}_i = \frac{\partial \mathcal{H}}{\partial p_i}, \qquad \dot{p}_i = -\frac{\partial \mathcal{H}}{\partial q_i}. \tag{2.207}$$

The s p_i and s q_i together form the *phase* of the molecule. Once they are given at one time, they follow at any other time from the equations of motion. The behavior of the molecule can be pictured by an orbit in the $2s$-dimensional space which is determined by the $2s$ coordinates $p_1, \cdots, p_s, q_1, \cdots, q_s$. This space is called the *phase space* of the molecule or, with the Ehrenfests, μ-space where μ stands for the first letter of molecule. We shall discuss later (p. 33) the reason why μ-space is preferred to a $2s$-dimensional space where the $2s$ coordinates are the generalized coordinates and generalized velocities.

A volume element in μ-space will be denoted by $d\omega$,

$$d\omega = \prod_{i=1}^{s} dp_i dq_i. \tag{2.208}$$

If $f(p_i,q_i)d\omega$ is the number of molecules the p_i and q_i of which lie in the intervals $(p_i,p_i + dp_i)$ and $(q_i,q_i + dq_i)$, then in the case of equilibrium the distribution function $f(p_i,q_i)$ will be given by

$$f(p_i,q_i) = Ce^{-\frac{\mathcal{H}(p_i,q_i)}{kT}}, \tag{2.209}$$

where C is again a normalizing constant. This form of the distribution function was introduced by Boltzmann in 1871. In 1868 Boltzmann generalized the distribution function to include a potential energy, and in 1871 he extended it further to include the case of polyatomic molecules. The distribution of equation (2.209) is called the *Maxwell-Boltzmann distribution*.

The average value $\overline{G}$ of a function $G(p_i,q_i)$ of the p_i and q_i is now defined as

$$\overline{G} = \frac{\int G(p_i,q_i)f(p_i,q_i)d\omega}{\int f(p_i,q_i)d\omega}, \tag{2.210}$$

where the integrations extend over the whole of μ-space.

We can apply formula (2.210) to calculate the average value of the kinetic energy. Since $\mathcal{T}$ is a homogeneous, quadratic polynomial in the p_i, we have from Euler's theorem on homogeneous functions

$$\mathcal{T} = \frac{1}{2}\sum_i \frac{\partial \mathcal{T}}{\partial p_i} p_i. \tag{2.211}$$

For the average value of $\mathcal{T}$ we then find

$$\overline{\mathcal{T}} = s \cdot \tfrac{1}{2}kT. \tag{2.212}$$

The result of equation (2.212) is obtained as follows. If the expression (2.211) for $\mathcal{T}$ is substituted into equation (2.210) there will result s integrals of the type

$$\frac{1}{2}\int \frac{\partial \mathcal{T}}{\partial p_k} p_k e^{-\frac{\mathcal{H}}{kT}} dp_k d\omega', \tag{2.213}$$

where $d\omega'$ stands for the product of all the dp_i and dq_i except dp_k. Integrating by parts will give us

$$\tfrac{1}{2}kT \int f(p_i,q_i)d\omega, \tag{2.214}$$

since the integrated parts will be zero. Equation (2.212) then follows immediately.

Expression (2.212) means that for every degree of freedom there is a contribution $\frac{1}{2}kT$ to the average kinetic energy, and this is called the *equipartition* of the kinetic energy. We met an example of this equipartition in §1 of the previous chapter when we considered a monatomic gas and found that the average kinetic energy pertaining to either the x-, or the y-, or the z-direction was the same and equal to $\frac{1}{2}kT$. Another case would be the dumbbell molecule where the number of degrees of freedom is 5 and where we find for the average kinetic energy $\frac{5}{2}kT$.

§3. The *H*-theorem; *H* and Probability. In order to prove that the distribution function given by equation (2.209) is the equilibrium distribution function for a system of independent particles, Boltzmann considered a function H

$$H = \overline{\ln f} = \int f \ln f d\omega, \tag{2.301}$$

where the integration extends over the whole of μ-space. As long as the distribution function f is not given by equation (2.209), dH/dt will be negative, provided a slightly modified Stosszahlansatz is valid. Furthermore, dH/dt will only be zero, if f is given by formula (2.209). This is a consequence of the fact that during any collision the total energy will be conserved. Although we shall not give a proof of these properties of H, it is along the same lines as that given in §5 of Chapter I, but much more complicated. An essential point in the proof is that the integration in expression (2.301) is over μ-space and not over a $q_i, \dot{q}_i$-space.

The function H is again equal to the negative of the entropy (apart from a multiplying constant and a possible additive constant). We shall return to this point at the end of §7. It is also possible to relate H to the probability in phase space. The argument is the same as in §7 of Chapter I, if we replace the cells Z_i by volumes in μ-space,

$$Z_i \to d\omega, \tag{2.302}$$

replace the N_i by the total number of particles with p_k and q_k in the intervals $(p_k, p_k + dp_k)$ and $(q_k, q_k + dq_k)$,

$$N_i \to f(p_k, q_k) d\omega, \tag{2.303}$$

and replace the ϵ_i by the total energy of a molecule,

$$\epsilon_i \to \mathcal{H}(p_k, q_k). \tag{2.304}$$

§4. Applications of the Maxwell-Boltzmann Formula. In many cases, the potential energy may contain a term which depends only on the position of the center of gravity of the molecule. This will, for instance, be the case if we are considering a system in a gravitational field, or inside a vessel the walls of which exert forces which can be derived from a potential energy such as shown in Figure 11. In such cases, we can take as three of the q_i (say q_1, q_2, and q_3) the x-, y-, and z-coordinates of the center of gravity. Integrating the distribution function over all the other q_i and over all the p_i, we get the density of the gas as a function of the position in space

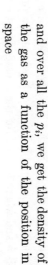

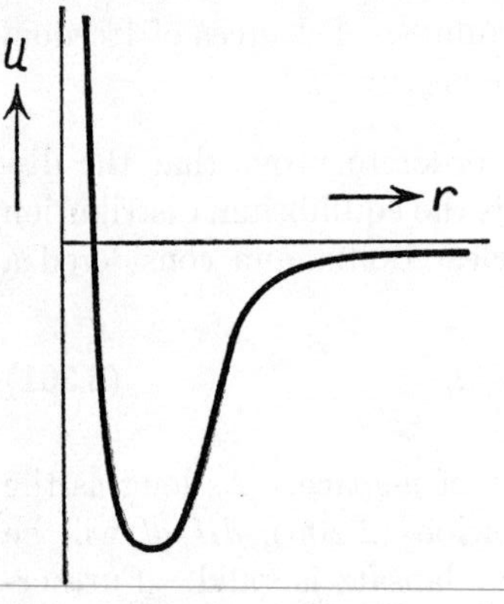

U: potential energy
r: distance from the wall

Fig. 11

$$\rho(x,y,z) = C\int dp_1 \cdots dp_s dq_4 \cdots dq_s e^{-\frac{\mathcal{H}}{kT}}, \quad (2.401)$$

or

$$\rho(x,y,z) = C' e^{-\frac{U(x,y,z)}{kT}}, \quad (2.402)$$

where we have put

$$\mathcal{H} = \mathcal{T}(p_i;q_4,\cdots,q_s) + U(q_1,q_2,q_3) + U'(q_4,\cdots,q_s). \quad (2.403)$$

In writing down equation (2.403) we have assumed that the potential energy can be split into two parts, one depending on the coordinates of the center of gravity only and one not depending on those coordinates. It can be shown that the kinetic energy does not depend on the x-, y-, or z-coordinate of the center of gravity.

One instance of formula (2.402) is the barometer formula (2.103). In general we see that the density will be highest at places where the potential energy is lowest. In the case where the forces exerted by a wall are derived from the potential energy of Figure 11, adsorption on the wall will take place.

Let us now consider the case where the potential energy is a quadratic function of the q_i,

$$U = \tfrac{1}{2} \sum_{k,l=1}^{s} b_{kl} q_k q_l. \quad (2.404)$$

By a suitable choice of linear combinations of the q_i we can reduce this expression to a sum of t squares where $t \leqslant s$,

$$U = \tfrac{1}{2} \sum_{k=1}^{t} b_k q_k'^2, \quad (2.405)$$

where the q_i' are the linear combinations just mentioned, which we use as new coordinates.

One finds the average value of the potential energy in much the same way as was used on page 32 to calculate the average value of the kinetic energy. We have therefore

$$\overline{U} = t \cdot \tfrac{1}{2}kT. \tag{2.406}$$

The average value of the total energy is now obtained by combining equations (2.212) and (2.406):

$$\bar{\epsilon} = \overline{\mathcal{T}} + \overline{U} = (s + t) \cdot \tfrac{1}{2}kT. \tag{2.407}$$

Equation (2.407) expresses a more general equipartition of energy, namely, each degree of freedom contributing to the kinetic energy and each degree of freedom contributing a quadratic term to the potential energy will give rise to a term $\frac{1}{2}kT$ in the average total energy.

The specific heat per mole C_v will now be given by the equation

$$C_v = \mathfrak{N} \frac{\partial \bar{\epsilon}}{\partial T} = \tfrac{1}{2}(s + t)R. \tag{2.408}$$

As an example we can calculate the average energy of an isotropic three-dimensional harmonic oscillator. The energy is given by the equation

$$\epsilon = \frac{p_x{}^2 + p_y{}^2 + p_z{}^2}{2m} + \tfrac{1}{2}\alpha(x^2 + y^2 + z^2), \tag{2.409}$$

and its average value is given by the equation

$$\bar{\epsilon} = 3kT, \tag{2.410}$$

leading to a specific heat of $3R$ per mole.

We now encounter a famous problem, the solution of which cannot be given in the classical framework which we are considering at this moment. We shall discuss the solution in the next chapter when we consider quantum mechanical statistics. Suppose that we want to determine the specific heat of a gas made up of dumbbell molecules, for example, HCl. If we treat the molecules as real dumbbells, that is, molecules with a fixed distance between the H and the Cl atom, we have $s = 5, t = 0$ and the specific heat per mole will be $\frac{5}{2}R$, which is observed experimentally, at any rate, at not too high temperatures.

The idea of a completely fixed distance apart of the two atoms is an abstraction, since there is always the possibility of vibration along the axis of the molecule. We should thus use $s = 6$ and $t = 1$, and we should expect a specific heat of $\frac{7}{2}R$ which is not found experimentally.

A similar problem arises in the case of nonlinear polyatomic molecules. If all the distances in the molecule are completely fixed, it will behave as a solid body and since it then would have three rotational and three translational degrees of freedom we should expect a specific heat per mole equal to $3R(s = 6,\ t = 0)$ which has been found experimentally. However, if there are N atoms in the molecule, and if we take into account all possible vibrations, we find $3N$ degrees of freedom of which $3N - 6$ contribute to the potential energy. Only the translational and rotational degrees of freedom do not make a contribution to the potential energy. If all $3N - 6$ terms in the potential energy are quadratic, we should expect a specific heat per mole of $3(N - 1)R$ which is not found experimentally. The situation becomes even more complicated and leads to even larger specific heats if we take the degrees of freedom belonging to the electronic and nuclear movements into account.

We must warn our readers here that in the discussion of the paradox of the specific heats we have presented the situation as being simpler than it really is. The reader can, however, easily verify the real state of affairs, once the discussion of the next chapter is understood. It is then also possible to see for what temperatures our present considerations will hold.

Finally let us consider the case where the dumbbell molecule possesses a magnetic (or electric) dipole moment, and let us calculate the average moment in a homogeneous field. For the sake of simplicity we shall choose as our q_i the 3 coordinates of the center of gravity X, Y, Z, the angle θ between the magnetic moment $\boldsymbol{\mu}$, and the magnetic field $\mathfrak{H}$ and the angle φ between the projection of $\boldsymbol{\mu}$ on a plane perpendicular to $\mathfrak{H}$ and a fixed axis in this plane. The corresponding momenta will be denoted by p_X, p_Y, p_Z, p_θ, and p_φ. If the absolute values of the permanent magnetic moment and of the homogeneous magnetic field are denoted by μ and H, the potential energy will be given by the expression

$$U = -\mu H \cos\theta. \tag{2.411}$$

For the average magnetic moment in the direction of the field we get

$$\frac{\bar{\mu}}{\mu} = \frac{\int \cos\theta\, e^{-\frac{\mathcal{T}+U}{kT}}\, d\omega}{\int e^{-\frac{\mathcal{T}+U}{kT}}\, d\omega} = \mathfrak{L}\left(\frac{\mu H}{kT}\right), \tag{2.412}$$

where $\mathfrak{L}(x)$ is the Langevin function:

$$\mathfrak{L}(x) = \coth x - x. \tag{2.413}$$

The behavior of $\mathfrak{L}(x)$ is illustrated in Figure 12.

In order to derive equation (2.412) we have to remember that the kinetic energy $\mathcal{T}$ expressed in p_X, p_Y, p_Z, p_θ, and p_φ is

$$\mathcal{T} = \frac{p_X^2 + p_Y^2 + p_Z^2}{2M} + \frac{p_\theta^2}{2A} + \frac{p_\varphi^2}{2A\sin^2\theta}, \tag{2.414}$$

where M is the total mass of the molecule and where A is the moment of inertia of the molecule with respect to an axis through the center of gravity, perpendicular to the axis of the molecule.

Integration over p_φ produces, apart from constants which cancel in numerator and denominator, a factor sin θ. In this way, we have finally to evaluate the expression

$$\int_0^\pi \cos\theta e^{\frac{\mu H}{kT}\cos\theta} \sin\theta d\theta \Big/ \int_0^\pi e^{\frac{\mu H}{kT}\cos\theta} \sin\theta d\theta, \qquad (2.415)$$

which leads to equation (2.412).

Equation (2.412) was derived by Langevin in 1905, and Debye derived in 1912 a similar formula for a system of electric dipoles. From Figure 12

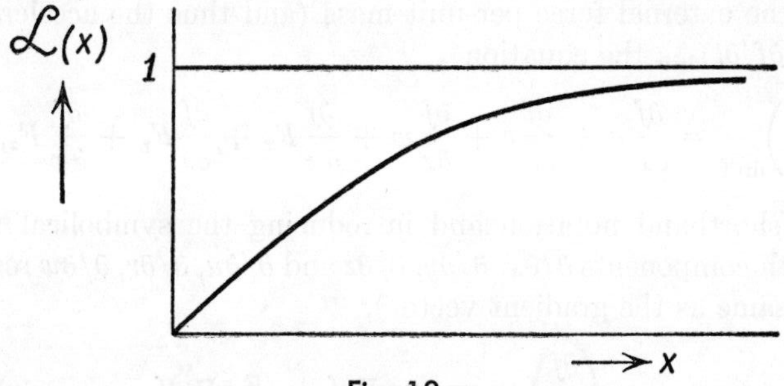

Fig. 12

we see that $\bar{\mu}$ approaches μ for low temperatures (or large fields); i.e., saturation sets in at low temperatures, while at higher temperatures thermal agitation produces a smaller mean dipole moment.

§5. **Boltzmann's Integrodifferential Equation.** In §3 of the present chapter and in §5 of Chapter I we saw that collisions will change the distribution function in such a way as to decrease the value of H. Although in those two cases we were not interested in the actual change of the distribution function itself, nevertheless, it is sometimes important to follow the change of f, for example, if we wish to know how soon equilibrium will be reached.

In order to find the general equation which must be satisfied by the distribution function, we must consider not only the change of this distribution function by collisions, but also the change owing to the continuous motion of the particles. We shall only consider, for the sake of simplicity, the case of systems consisting of atoms and the distribution function will then be a function of the coordinates x, y, and z and of the velocity components u, v, and w.

We shall consider the atoms which have coordinates between $\mathbf{r}$ and $\mathbf{r} + \mathbf{dr}$ and velocities between $\mathbf{c}$ and $\mathbf{c} + \mathbf{dc}$. Let N_1 and N_2 be respectively the number of such atoms at t and $t + dt$. We have for N_1 the equation†

$$N_1 = f(\mathbf{r},\mathbf{c},t)d\mathbf{r}d\mathbf{c}. \tag{2.501}$$

At $t + dt$ other atoms will have representative points in the volume element $d\mathbf{r}d\mathbf{c}$ which we are considering, and we can write

$$\frac{\partial f}{\partial t} = \left(\frac{\partial f}{\partial t}\right)_{\text{drift}} + \left(\frac{\partial f}{\partial t}\right)_{\text{coll}}, \tag{2.502}$$

expressing the fact that the distribution may not be stationary due to the circumstance that there may not be a balance between (a) the number of atoms which have left the volume element due to their motion and (b) the net increase of the number of atoms due to collisions.

If $\mathbf{F}$ is the external force per unit mass (and thus the acceleration) we have for $(\partial f/\partial t)_{\text{drift}}$ the equation

$$-\left(\frac{\partial f}{\partial t}\right)_{\text{drift}} = \frac{\partial f}{\partial x}u + \frac{\partial f}{\partial y}v + \frac{\partial f}{\partial z}w + \frac{\partial f}{\partial u}F_x + \frac{\partial f}{\partial v}F_y + \frac{\partial f}{\partial w}F_z, \tag{2.503}$$

or, using shorthand notation and introducing the symbolical vectors ∇ and ∇_c with components $\partial/\partial x$, $\partial/\partial y$, $\partial/\partial z$ and $\partial/\partial u$, $\partial/\partial v$, $\partial/\partial w$ respectively (∇ is the same as the gradient vector),

$$-\left(\frac{\partial f}{\partial t}\right)_{\text{drift}} = (\mathbf{c}\cdot\nabla)f + (\mathbf{F}\cdot\nabla_c)f. \tag{2.504}$$

From equations (2.502) and (2.504) we get

$$\frac{\partial f}{\partial t} + (\mathbf{c}\cdot\nabla)f + (\mathbf{F}\cdot\nabla_c)f - \left(\frac{\partial f}{\partial t}\right)_{\text{coll}} = 0, \tag{2.505}$$

or, using equations (1.401) and (1.419),

$$\frac{\partial f}{\partial t} + (\mathbf{c}\cdot\nabla)f + (\mathbf{F}\cdot\nabla_c)f = A - B, \tag{2.506}$$

when A and B have a slightly different meaning from that on page 10, or

$$\frac{\partial f}{\partial t} + (\mathbf{c}\cdot\nabla)f + (\mathbf{F}\cdot\nabla_c)f + \int (ff_1 - f'f_1')a\,d\mathbf{c}_1\,d\boldsymbol{\omega} = 0. \tag{2.507}$$

Equation (2.507) is known as *Boltzmann's transport equation* or, more simply, as *Boltzmann's equation*.‡

If there are no external forces, the Maxwell distribution will be an (equilibrium) solution of equation (2.507). Since f does not depend on

† We use the abbreviated expression $f(\mathbf{r},\mathbf{c},t)$ for $f(x,y,z;u,v,w;t)$.
‡ For applications, see Chaps. X and XI.

x, y, or z, $\nabla f = 0$, also $\mathbf{F} = 0$ and $(\partial f/\partial t)_{\text{coll}} = 0$, as we saw in §4 of Chapter I, and thus $\partial f/\partial t = 0$.

If the external forces can be derived from a potential energy function $U(x,y,z)$, the Maxwell-Boltzmann distribution (2.107) will be a solution. We have

$$\mathbf{F} = -\frac{1}{m}\nabla U, \tag{2.508}$$

$$\nabla f = -\frac{1}{kT} f \nabla U, \tag{2.509}$$

$$\nabla_c f = -\frac{1}{kT} f \nabla_c \mathcal{T} = -\frac{m\mathbf{c}}{kT} f, \tag{2.510}$$

and

$$f f_1 = f' f_1', \tag{2.511}$$

because of the conservation of energy.

From equations (2.507) to (2.511) it then follows again that $\partial f/\partial t = 0$.

Equation (2.507) can, for instance, be used to estimate the time necessary to re-establish equilibrium. Its most important applications have, however, been in the discussion of steady nonequilibrium states by means of which in the years 1916 and 1917 Chapman and Enskog, working independently and using powerful approximation methods, derived theoretical expressions for the viscosity coefficient, thermal conductivity, and other kinetic properties of gases. A detailed discussion of their methods lies outside the scope of this book, but in Chapters X and XI we shall use equation (2.506) to derive expressions for the electrical and thermal conductivity and for the Hall constant of metals and semiconductors.

§6. External Parameters. In §4 we met a case where the energy of a molecule depended not only on the p_i and q_i, but also on the magnitude of the magnetic (or electric) field. In general, it is possible for the energy of a molecule to depend on a number of *external parameters*, a_i. Examples of such parameters are the volume of a gas, the electric field strength, and so on. We have then

$$\epsilon = \epsilon(p_1, \cdots, p_s, q_1, \cdots, q_s; a_1, a_2, \cdots). \tag{2.601}$$

Let us first consider the case where a is the "volume" of a one-dimensional gas (see Fig. 13). If $U(q)$ is the potential energy of the molecule, then $-\partial U/\partial q$ will be the force exerted by the wall on the molecule. Apart from q, U will also depend on the "volume" l of the one-dimensional vessel: $U = U(q,l)$. Let us now displace the wall a distance δl. If we displace the molecule at the same time a distance δq equal to δl, there will be no change in potential energy, or

$$\delta U = 0 = \frac{\partial U}{\partial q}\,\delta q + \frac{\partial U}{\partial l}\,\delta l, \qquad \text{if } \delta q = \delta l, \tag{2.602}$$

or

$$\frac{\partial U}{\partial l} = -\frac{\partial U}{\partial q}\,. \tag{2.603}$$

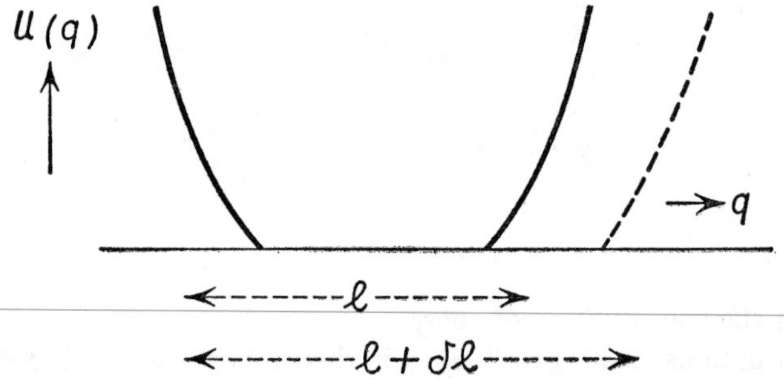

Fig. 13

Since $-\partial U/\partial q$ is the force exerted by the "volume" on the molecule, $-\partial U/\partial l$ will be the force exerted by the molecule "on the volume." In general we can introduce quantities A_i defined by the equation

$$A_i = -\frac{\partial \epsilon}{\partial a_i}\,. \tag{2.604}$$

These A_i can be called the *generalized forces* (per molecule) exerted by the system tending to increase the parameters. If N is the total number of particles in the system, the total force exerted by the system tending to increase the parameter a_i will be equal to $N\bar{A}_i$.

In the case considered in §4, the parameter was the magnetic field and the generalized force was there $-\partial\epsilon/\partial H = \mu \cos\theta$, that is, the magnetic moment in the direction of the magnetic field.

§7. The Phase Integral; Connection with Classical Thermodynamics. We introduce the quantity

$$Z_\mu = e^{-\frac{F}{kT}} = A\int e^{-\frac{\epsilon}{kT}}\,d\omega, \tag{2.701}$$

where the suffix μ indicates that the integration is over the whole of μ-space. The quantity Z_μ is called the *phase integral* or *partition function* of one molecule. Both Z_μ and F, the physical meaning of which we shall see in a moment, are functions of the temperature and of the external parameters.

The constant A enters in order that Z_μ may be made a dimensionless quantity.

We can write equation (2.701) in the form

$$\frac{1}{A} = \int e^{\frac{F-\epsilon}{kT}}\, d\omega. \tag{2.702}$$

If we vary the temperature and the external parameters, we get from equation (2.702)

$$\delta \frac{1}{A} = 0 = \int \delta \frac{F}{kT} e^{\frac{F-\epsilon}{kT}}\, d\omega - \int \epsilon \delta \frac{1}{kT} e^{\frac{F-\epsilon}{kT}}\, d\omega - \int \frac{\delta\epsilon}{kT} e^{\frac{F-\epsilon}{kT}}\, d\omega. \tag{2.703}$$

Since

$$\delta\epsilon = \sum_i \frac{\partial \epsilon}{\partial a_i}\, \delta a_i = -\sum_i A_i \delta a_i, \tag{2.704}$$

equations (2.703) lead to

$$\delta \frac{F}{T} = \bar{\epsilon}\delta \frac{1}{T} - \frac{1}{T} \sum_i \bar{A}_i \delta a_i, \tag{2.705}$$

where we now have used equations (2.701), (2.702), and (2.210), the last for the definition of the average values.

The second law of thermodynamics states that

$$\delta S = \frac{\delta Q}{T} = \frac{\delta U + \delta W}{T}, \tag{2.706}$$

where W is the work done by the system and where the other quantities have the same meaning as in equation (1.606).

If we apply equations (2.706) to the average per molecule, we have

$$U = \bar{\epsilon} \quad \text{and} \quad \delta W = \sum_i \bar{A}_i \delta a_i. \tag{2.707}$$

Combining equations (2.706) and (2.707), we see that the right-hand side of equation (2.705) can be written in the form

$$\bar{\epsilon}\delta \frac{1}{T} - \frac{1}{T} \sum_i \bar{A}_i \delta a_i = \delta \left(\frac{U}{T} - S \right). \tag{2.708}$$

From this it follows that F satisfies the equation

$$F = U - TS \tag{2.709}$$

and thus corresponds to the free energy per molecule, apart from a possible additive constant.

In the case where the volume V is the only external parameter, equations

(2.705) and (2.706) can be written in the form (compare equation [1.606])

$$\delta S = \frac{1}{T}\,\delta\bar{\epsilon} + \frac{p}{NT}\,\delta V \qquad \textbf{(2.710)}$$

and

$$\delta\,\frac{F}{T} = \bar{\epsilon}\delta\,\frac{1}{T} - \frac{p}{NT}\,\delta V, \qquad \textbf{(2.711)}$$

where all the quantities refer to one molecule except the pressure (hence the factor N).

The temperature and the external parameters determine the *thermodynamic state* of the system. Once they are given, one can calculate the phase integral Z_μ and thus the free energy F.† All thermodynamic quantities can then be derived from Z_μ or F. Since $F = -kT \log Z_\mu$ we shall give only the equations involving F. From equation (2.705) we see that we have

$$\bar{\epsilon} = \frac{\partial \frac{F}{T}}{\partial \frac{1}{T}} = -T^2\,\frac{\partial \frac{F}{T}}{\partial T}, \qquad \textbf{(2.712)}$$

$$\bar{A}_i = -T\,\frac{\partial \frac{F}{T}}{\partial a_i} \qquad \textbf{(2.713)}$$

and from equation (2.712) we get for the specific heat per molecule c_v

$$c_v = \frac{\partial\bar{\epsilon}}{\partial T} = -\frac{\partial}{\partial T}\,T^2\,\frac{\partial \frac{F}{T}}{\partial T} = -2T\,\frac{\partial \frac{F}{T}}{\partial T} - T^2\,\frac{\partial^2 \frac{F}{T}}{\partial T^2}. \qquad \textbf{(2.714)}$$

If one of the a_i is the volume, we get for the pressure p the equation

$$p = -NT\,\frac{\partial \frac{F}{T}}{\partial V}. \qquad \textbf{(2.715)}$$

Equation (2.715) can be used to obtain the equation of state. If the entropy is known as a function of the volume, the equation of state can also be obtained from the equation

$$p = NT\,\frac{\partial S}{\partial V}, \qquad \textbf{(2.716)}$$

which follows from equation (2.710).

† The discussion in the present section is rather condensed and we refer for a fuller discussion to §4 of Chap. IV.

At this moment it is not yet possible to give reasons for a particular choice of the constant A in equation (2.701). In most applications, for instance, equations (2.712) to (2.715), only derivatives of F/T enter and the value of the constant is immaterial. It enters only if we wish to determine the absolute value of F (or S). We shall only mention the value of A here and leave to later discussion the reasons for this particular choice of A (see pp. 59 and 143). We shall take

$$A = \frac{e}{N} h^{-s}, \tag{2.717}$$

where h is Planck's constant, s the number of degrees of freedom, e the base of the natural logarithms, and N the number of molecules in the system. It can easily be verified that Z_μ is now dimensionless. In the next section we shall thus use for Z_μ the expression

$$Z_\mu = \frac{e}{N} \int e^{-\frac{\epsilon}{kT}} \frac{d\omega}{h^s}. \tag{2.718}$$

From the definition of the distribution function it follows that $\int f d\omega$, integrated over the whole of μ-space, should be equal to N. It follows then from equation (2.718) that

$$f = \frac{e}{h^s} e^{\frac{F-\epsilon}{kT}}, \tag{2.719}$$

and for Boltzmann's H-function we get

$$H = \int f \ln f d\omega = \frac{F - \bar{\epsilon}}{kT} + \text{constant} = -\frac{S}{k} + \text{constant}, \tag{2.720}$$

showing once more that kH, apart from an additive constant, is equal to $-S$.

§8. Applications: The Monatomic Perfect Gas. We now wish to apply the formulae of the previous section to the case of a monatomic perfect gas. The energy of one atom is given by the equation

$$\epsilon = \frac{p_x^2 + p_y^2 + p_z^2}{2m} + F(x,y,z), \tag{2.801}$$

where the potential energy function F is such that the gas stays inside the vessel V. This can be realized if F is given by the equations

$$\left.\begin{aligned} F(x,y,z) &= 0 \quad \text{inside } V; \\ F(x,y,z) &= \infty \text{ outside } V. \end{aligned}\right\} \tag{2.802}$$

Introducing expression (2.801) into expression (2.718) for Z_μ, we get, after integrating over $x,y,z,p_x,p_y,$ and p_z,

$$Z_\mu = \frac{e}{N} V \left(\frac{2\pi mkT}{h^2}\right)^{3/2}, \tag{2.803}$$

while from equations (2.712) and (2.714) we get, respectively,

$$\bar{\epsilon} = \tfrac{3}{2}kT, \tag{2.804}$$

and the specific heat

$$c_v = \tfrac{3}{2}k. \tag{2.805}$$

If we apply equation (2.715), we obtain the pressure in its usual form of the perfect gas law,

$$p = \frac{NkT}{V}, \tag{2.806}$$

while equation (2.803) gives us the free energy per atom

$$F = kT\,[\ln N - 1 - \ln V - \tfrac{3}{2}\ln(2\pi mkT) + 3\ln h]. \tag{2.807}$$

Introducing a constant $\mathfrak{C}$ by means of the equation†

$$\mathfrak{C} = \ln k \left(\frac{2\pi m_H k}{h^2}\right)^{3/2}, \tag{2.808}$$

where m_H is the molecular weight unit, we get for the free energy per atom

$$F = kT\,(\ln p - \tfrac{5}{2}\ln T - \mathfrak{C} - \tfrac{3}{2}\ln M - 1), \tag{2.809}$$

where we have used the perfect gas law and where M is the molecular weight of the gas.

From equations (2.804) and (2.809) we find for the entropy per atom

$$S = \frac{\bar{\epsilon} - F}{T} = k[\tfrac{5}{2}\ln T - \ln p + \mathfrak{C} + \tfrac{3}{2}\ln M + \tfrac{5}{2}]. \tag{2.810}$$

This equation is called the Sackur-Tetrode equation (see the discussion in Appendix III).

BIBLIOGRAPHICAL NOTES

General references for this chapter are

1. L. Boltzmann, Vorlesungen über Gastheorie, Leipzig 1896–1898.
2. S. Chapman and T. G. Cowling, The Mathematical Theory of Non-Uniform Gases, Cambridge 1939.
3. J. W. Gibbs, Elementary Principles in Statistical Mechanics (Vol. II of his Collected Works), New Haven 1948.

§1. A rather crude attempt to derive the barometer formula can be found in Krönig's paper on kinetic theory:

† The importance of this constant and its relation to the so-called chemical constants will be discussed in §2 of Appendix III

4. A. Krönig, Ann. Physik, **99,** 315, 1856.

The exact barometer formula was first given by Boltzmann:

5. L. Boltzmann, Wien. Ber., **78,** 7, 1879.

§2. The term "μ-space" was introduced by the Ehrenfests:

6. P. and T. Ehrenfest, Enzyklopädie der mathematischen Wissenschaften, Vol. IV, Pt. 32, Leipzig-Berlin 1911, p. 36.

The Maxwell-Boltzmann distribution was derived by Boltzmann in 1871:

7. L. Boltzmann, Wien. Ber., **58,** 517, 1868.
8. L. Boltzmann, Wien. Ber., **63,** 397, 1871.

In ref. 7 Boltzmann gives the distribution in the case of an external field of force, while in ref. 8 he also takes into account the internal degrees of freedom of a molecule. The name "Maxwell-Boltzmann distribution" was suggested by G. H. Bryan in a paper read before the British Association at Oxford in 1894.

The equipartition of kinetic energy over the different degrees of freedom was proved by Boltzmann:

9. L. Boltzmann, Wien. Ber., **63,** 712, 1871.

Compare also:

10. R. C. Tolman, Phys. Rev., **11,** 261, 1918.

§3. The generalized H-theorem is also due to Boltzmann:

11. L. Boltzmann, Wien. Ber., **72,** 427, 1875.

§4. Formula (2.412) was first derived by Langevin for the case of molecules possessing magnetic dipole moments:

12. P. Langevin, J. phys., **4,** 678, 1905.
13. P. Langevin, Ann. chim. et phys., **5,** 70, 1905.

The case of electric dipoles was studied by Debye, see, e.g.,

14. P. Debye, Physik Z., **13,** 97, 1912.

§5. The transport equation is due to Boltzmann:

15. L. Boltzmann, Wien. Ber., **74,** 503, 1876.

Probably the most important papers on the solution of the equation are those by Chapman and Enskog†:

16. S. Chapman, Trans. Roy. Soc. (London), **A216,** 279, 1916.
17. S. Chapman, Trans. Roy. Soc. (London), **A217,** 115, 1917.
18. D. Enskog, Dissertation, Uppsala 1917.

For a thorough discussion of the whole subject, we refer to ref. 2.

§6. The introduction of external parameters into the statistical discussion was made by Gibbs, ref. 3, p. 4.

§7. The phase integral and its relation to the free energy were introduced and used by Gibbs, ref. 3, Chaps. IV *et seq.*

Darwin and Fowler first introduced the term "partition function":

19. C. G. Darwin and R. H. Fowler, Phil. Mag., **44,** 450, 1922.

Tolman uses in his textbook the term "sum over states" (which is certainly *not* meant as a translation of Zustandssumme, as Partington suggests (Physical Chemistry, London 1949, p. 305).

† Born (Nuovo cimento, **6,** Suppl., 296, 1949) has drawn attention to the fact that Hilbert had developed methods similar to those of Chapman and Enskog for solving the Boltzmann equation. His results were given in a series of lectures at Göttingen and only a short account of them was published in 1912 (Math. Ann., **72,** 562, 1912).

CHAPTER III

QUANTUM STATISTICS

§1. The One-dimensional Harmonic Oscillator in the Old Quantum Theory. In the first two chapters we have used classical mechanics, but we know that in many instances classical mechanics is inadequate to describe the physical behavior of systems and that only a quantum mechanical treatment can give the correct results. In the same way, therefore, we must build statistical mechanics on a quantum mechanical basis and afterward show that the classical formulae which we derived in the previous chapters are limiting instances of the quantum mechanical formulae. We must remark here that in the present chapter we shall derive formulae for systems of particles which in principle are still distinguishable. The important question of indistinguishable particles, which led incidentally to the Pauli principle, will be discussed in the next chapter. In the first section of this chapter we shall use the old quantum theory or model theory which was so instrumental in paving the way to Schrödinger's wave mechanics and Heisenberg's matrix mechanics. This manner of introducing quantum statistics is appropriate, since Planck's introduction of h into the statistical picture is closely related to the old quantum theory.

Let us consider a one-dimensional harmonic oscillator which is defined by a quadratic potential energy function $U(q)$,

$$U(q) = \tfrac{1}{2}\alpha q^2, \tag{3.101}$$

where α is a constant and q the coordinate describing the position of the oscillator. If the mass of the oscillator is m, its frequency ν will be related to α by the equation

$$\nu = \frac{1}{2\pi}\sqrt{\frac{\alpha}{m}}. \tag{3.102}$$

Its total energy can then be written in the form

$$\epsilon(p,q) = \frac{p^2}{2m} + \frac{m}{2}(2\pi\nu)^2 q^2. \tag{3.103}$$

In this case, μ-space has only two dimensions. We can draw curves of constant energy in this phase plane. These curves will be ellipses, a few of which are drawn in Figure 14. As long as the oscillator is not disturbed from outside, it will move in such a way that its representative point will stay on one ellipse.

The area of the ellipse is given by the equation

$$I = \oint p\,dq, \tag{3.104}$$ †

where the integration extends over one period of the oscillator.

Since p and q are given by the equations

$$q = q_0 \sin 2\pi\nu t, \qquad p = m\dot{q} = 2\pi\nu m q_0 \cos 2\pi\nu t, \tag{3.105}$$

we find for I

$$I = \int_0^{1/\nu} p\dot{q}\,dt = 2\pi^2 m\nu q_0{}^2 = \frac{\epsilon}{\nu}. \tag{3.106}$$

Although in classical mechanics any ellipse in the phase plane could represent a state of the oscillator, this will no longer be true in quantum mechanics. In order to find out how to select the possible energy levels

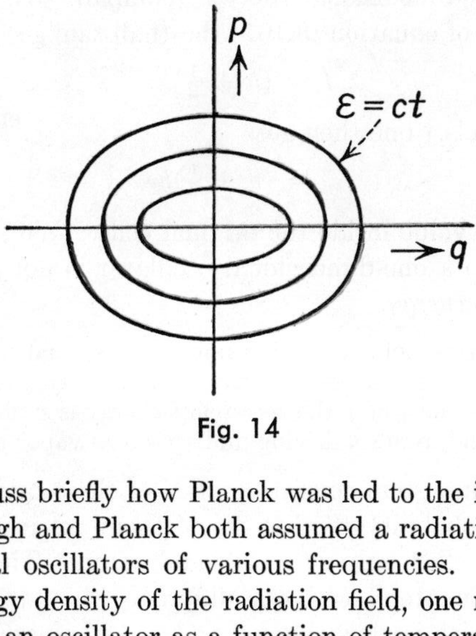

Fig. 14

we shall first discuss briefly how Planck was led to the introduction of his constant. Rayleigh and Planck both assumed a radiation field to consist of one-dimensional oscillators of various frequencies. Then in order to calculate the energy density of the radiation field, one must calculate the average energy of an oscillator as a function of temperature. To do this Planck divided the phase plane into sections of area h and allotted to each cell a certain representative energy. His original idea was then to take the limit for $h \rightarrow 0$, but it turned out, much to his surprise, that the radia-

† This integral is sometimes called *phase integral*. Since we have already used this term in a different connection, we shall not use it for I, to avoid confusion.

tion density corresponded to that found experimentally, if h were not put equal to zero, but to $6.6 \cdot 10^{-27}$ erg sec. A few years later in 1915, Sommerfeld and Wilson suggested that this division of the phase plane into cells of area h was the correct way to arrive at the possible values which the energy of a one-dimensional system could assume. In fact, Sommerfeld's quantization rule is

$$I = nh, \tag{3.107}$$

where n is a nonnegative integer.

If one uses the quantization rule (3.107), the energy corresponding to the nth cell is determined by equation (3.106) and given by

$$\epsilon_n = nh\nu, \qquad n = 0, 1, 2, \cdots. \tag{3.108}$$

In this way we have allotted to each energy level a cell of area h in μ-space. The energy corresponding to a cell is that corresponding to the inner boundary (ellipse) of the cell, if we call ϵ_n the $n + 1$st level, n indicating not the actual number of the level, but the value of the corresponding *quantum number*.

In order to get a better agreement with the experimental evidence regarding the three-dimensional rotator (compare §3), Sommerfeld later introduced instead of equation (3.107) the (halbzahlige) quantization rule,

$$I = (n + \tfrac{1}{2})h. \tag{3.109}$$

For the energy levels,† one then gets

$$\epsilon_n = (n + \tfrac{1}{2})h\nu, \tag{3.110}$$

corresponding to a value inside the original cells. We see that the lowest energy available to a one-dimensional oscillator is not zero, but $\frac{1}{2}h\nu$, the so-called *zero-point energy*.

That such a zero-point energy is not just a special way of choosing the energy scale, but a physical reality, can, for example, be seen in the case of liquid helium where the zero-point energy is sufficiently great to prevent the liquid from solidifying under its own vapor pressure.

Let us consider a system consisting of N of these oscillators, and let us write down the probability W that N_1 of them are in cell 1 (or have an energy ϵ_1), N_2 in cell 2 (energy $= \epsilon_2$), and so on. The procedure is the same as in §7 of Chapter I with the difference that we now have a well-defined cell size which is always equal to h. As before, then,

$$W = C\frac{N!}{\prod_i N_i!}, \tag{3.111}$$

† These energy levels are actually the same as those following from the Schrödinger equation.

where we have used the fact that all the Z_i are equal. Otherwise expression (3.111) is the same as expression (1.701).

Also, by the reasoning of Chapter I, §7, we find the number N_i of oscillators with energy ϵ_i to be

$$N_i = e^{\nu - \mu\epsilon_i}, \tag{3.112}$$

since we have again the constraining conditions of constant total energy and constant total number of particles,

$$\sum_i N_i = N, \quad \sum_i N_i\epsilon_i = E. \tag{3.113}$$

The quantities ν and μ can be calculated by substituting expression (3.112) into equations (3.113).

The physical meaning of ν and μ will be discussed in the next chapter, but as we must employ μ immediately we will assume the value for it,

$$\mu = \frac{1}{kT}. \tag{3.114}$$

Instead of a phase integral we now introduce as the partition function a sum

$$Z_\mu^{(\mathrm{qu})} = \frac{e}{N}\sum_i e^{-\mu\epsilon_i} = \frac{e}{N}\sum_{n=0}^{\infty} e^{-\mu nh\nu}[\cdot\, e^{-\frac{1}{2}\mu h\nu}], \tag{3.115}$$

where the factor between square brackets occurs if we use equation (3.110) for the energy levels, and does not occur if we use equation (3.108). We introduce again a function F by the equation

$$e^{-\frac{F}{kT}} = Z. \tag{3.116}$$

It is possible to prove that F is the free energy of the oscillator and that the average energy follows from F by equation (2.712). These properties of F will be proved in the next chapter.

For the average energy $\bar{\epsilon}$ we get

$$\bar{\epsilon} = \frac{\partial \dfrac{F}{T}}{\partial \dfrac{1}{T}} = \frac{h\nu}{e^{\frac{h\nu}{kT}} - 1}[+\tfrac{1}{2}h\nu]. \tag{3.117}$$

Formula (3.117) can be simplified both at high temperatures ($h\nu/kT \ll 1$) and at low temperatures ($h\nu/kT \gg 1$) as follows,

$$h\nu \ll kT: \qquad \bar{\epsilon} = kT - \tfrac{1}{2}h\nu[+\tfrac{1}{2}h\nu] + \text{series in } \frac{h\nu}{kT} \tag{3.118}$$

$$h\nu \gg kT: \qquad \bar{\epsilon} = [\tfrac{1}{2}h\nu] + h\nu \cdot e^{-\frac{h\nu}{kT}} + \cdots. \tag{3.119}$$

Figure 15 shows the behavior of $\bar{\epsilon}$ as a function of temperature. From the considerations of the previous chapter we might have expected $\bar{\epsilon} = kT$ (equation [2.407] with $s = t = 1$). We see that this behavior is realized at high temperatures. This is an example of the *correspondence principle* (Bohr 1920) which states that in the limit of large quantum numbers, the results obtained from quantum mechanics will be the same as those obtained from classical mechanics. Or we can put it in another way. Quantum mechanics will go over into classical mechanics in the limit $h \to 0$. The identity of these two statements can be shown in the case of the oscillator from equation (3.110) where the condition $h \to 0$ would entail $n \to \infty$ for a given energy. Equation (3.118) also shows that for $h \to 0$, $\bar{\epsilon} \to kT$.

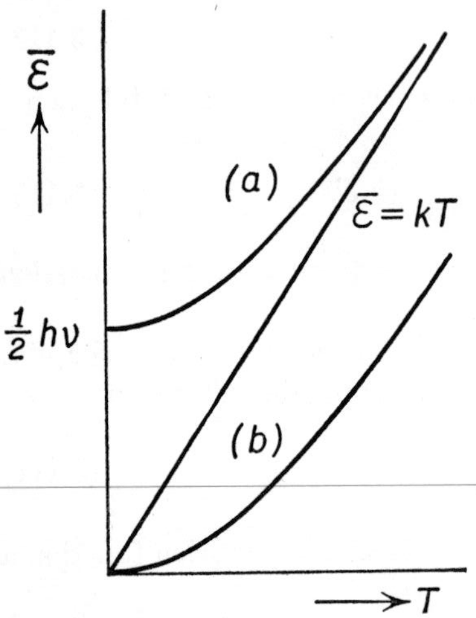

Fig. 15. The average energy of a one-dimensional harmonic oscillator: (a) with zero-point energy; (b) without zero-point energy.

§2. Planck's Radiation Law. We shall assume with Planck and Rayleigh that the radiation field in a volume V can be considered as consisting of one-dimensional oscillators of frequencies $\nu_1, \nu_2, \cdots$. If the first oscillator is in the state corresponding to quantum number n_1, the second one in that corresponding to n_2, and so on, the total energy of the system will be given by the equation

$$E = \sum_i \epsilon_i = \sum_i n_i h\nu_i, \qquad \textbf{(3.201)}$$

in which it will be noticed that we have omitted the zero-point energies. The reason why this leads to a correct result is that one really should discuss the radiation field in terms of light quanta (compare the discussion in Chapter IV, §1).

The zero-point energies would have given rise to an infinite zero-point energy of the electromagnetic radiation field. This infinite "self-energy" can, however, be disposed of in a manner which is slightly more satisfactory than the ways in which other self-energies such as that of the electron have been pushed aside in recent developments of quantum electrodynamics. For a discussion of the radiation field self-energy we may refer to H. A. Kramers, Hand- u. Jahrbuch d. Chem. Phys., Vol. I, Leipzig 1938, §87; G. Wentzel, Quantum Theory of Fields, New York 1949, p. 73; Phys. Rev., **74,** 1070, 1948.

From equation (3.117) we have for the average energy of the ith oscillator

$$\bar{\epsilon}_i = \frac{h\nu_i}{e^{\frac{h\nu_i}{kT}} - 1}. \tag{3.202}$$

We must draw attention to one important difference between equations (3.117) and (3.202). Equation (3.117) gives us the average energy when the average is taken over a large number of identical oscillators, that is, we get a system average. In the present case, however, we have only one oscillator with a frequency ν_i and expression (3.202) must be considered to give an average over a large period rather than over a large number, that is, we have a time average. That we may use the time average and the system average interchangeably follows from the general equivalence of these two kinds of average. This equivalence will be discussed in Part B (p. 126) and in more detail in Appendix I, §5.

If the frequencies are lying very densely, the sum in equation (3.201) is virtually an integral. In order to evaluate this sum (or integral) we must know the number of frequencies $D(\nu)d\nu$ between ν and $\nu + d\nu$. This can be done in the following way.

In order to simplify the considerations we assume that the volume V is a cube of edge length l. It can be proved that this simplification does not

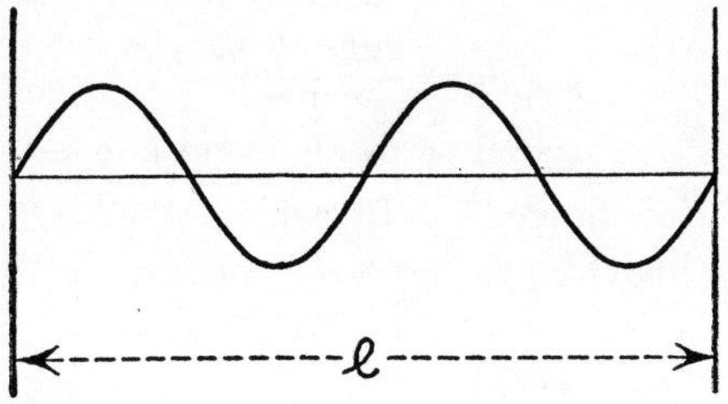

Fig. 16

affect the final result for $D(\nu)$. Since we are dealing with standing waves, the wavelength λ of the waves in the cube must be such that the amplitude at the walls is zero (Fig. 16). In the one-dimensional case this leads to the equation

$$l = \frac{n\lambda}{2} = \frac{nc}{2\nu}, \tag{3.203}$$

where for the velocity of light c we have used the relation $c = \nu\lambda$, while in the three-dimensional case we have three such relations. If α, β, and γ are the direction cosines of the normal to the plane of constant phase with respect to the edges of the cube, we have

$$\frac{2\nu l \cos \alpha}{c} = n_1, \qquad \frac{2\nu l \cos \beta}{c} = n_2, \qquad \frac{2\nu l \cos \gamma}{c} = n_3, \tag{3.204}$$

where n_1, n_2, and n_3 are positive integers.

From equations (3.204) it follows that

$$n_1^2 + n_2^2 + n_3^2 = \frac{4\nu^2 l^2}{c^2}. \tag{3.205}$$

If we wish to know how many frequencies there are between ν and $\nu + d\nu$, we have to calculate the number of lattice points with integer coordinates in a spherical shell of radius $2\nu l/c$ and thickness $2ld\nu/c$. In this way we get for $D(\nu)$ the equation

$$D(\nu)d\nu = 2 \cdot \frac{1}{8} \cdot \frac{4\pi \cdot 4\nu^2 l^2 \cdot 2ld\nu}{c^3} = \frac{8\pi\nu^2 V}{c^3}\, d\nu. \tag{3.206}$$

The factor 2 in the second member of equation (3.206) arises from the fact that the transverse light waves have two polarization degrees of freedom. The factor $\frac{1}{8}$ arises, since we can only use that part of the spherical shell for which n_1, n_2, and n_3 are all positive.

The energy density per cm^3 due to oscillators with frequencies between ν and $\nu + d\nu$ can now be obtained from equations (3.201), (3.202), and (3.206), thus,

$$\rho(\nu)d\nu = \frac{8\pi h}{c^3} \frac{\nu^3 d\nu}{e^{\frac{h\nu}{kT}} - 1}. \tag{3.207}$$

Equation (3.207) was derived by Planck in 1900 and is called *Planck's radiation law*. For high frequencies ($h\nu \gg kT$) it goes over into *Wien's law*,

$$\rho(\nu) = \frac{8\pi h}{c^3} \nu^3 e^{-\frac{h\nu}{kT}}, \tag{3.208}$$

while for low frequencies ($h\nu \ll kT$) it becomes *Rayleigh's law*,

$$\rho(\nu) = \frac{8\pi kT}{c^3} \nu^2, \tag{3.209}$$

the same result which Planck achieved by letting $h \to 0$. Since by letting h go to zero he could obviously not obtain Wien's law for high frequencies, Planck was obliged to let h remain finite.

For the total energy density per cm^3 we get

$$\rho = \int_0^\infty \rho(\nu)d\nu = \frac{8\pi h}{c^3} \int_0^\infty \frac{\nu^3 d\nu}{e^{\frac{h\nu}{kT}} - 1},$$

or

$$\rho = aT^4, \tag{3.210}$$

where a is given by the equation

$$a = \frac{8\pi^5 k^4}{15h^3c^3} = 7.56 \cdot 10^{-15} \text{ erg degree}^{-4} \text{ cm}^{-3}. \tag{3.211}$$

In the calculations leading to equation (3.210) we must evaluate the integral

$$\int_0^\infty \frac{x^3dx}{e^x - 1} = \int_0^\infty e^{-x}x^3(1 + e^{-x} + e^{-2x} + \cdots)dx$$

$$= \sum_{n=1}^{\infty} \int_0^\infty e^{-nx}x^3dx = 6\zeta(4) = \frac{\pi^4}{15},$$

where $\zeta(s) = \sum_{n=1}^{\infty} n^{-s} =$ Riemann's ζ-function.

Equation (3.210) is called the *Stefan-Boltzmann law*, which states that the total energy density in a radiation field in temperature equilibrium is proportional to the fourth power of the temperature.

Let us consider briefly the case where we have an equilibrium between atoms and a radiation field. From the known quantum mechanical transition probabilities we can then again derive the radiation law (3.207). We assume that there is only one kind of atom present which can be in stationary states with energies ϵ_k. According to Bohr's postulate (1913) the transition from a state k to a state l will be accompanied by the absorption or emission of a light quantum of frequency ν_{kl},

$$\nu_{kl} = \left| \frac{\epsilon_k - \epsilon_l}{h} \right|, \tag{3.212}$$

where emission takes place when $\epsilon_k > \epsilon_l$, and absorption when $\epsilon_k < \epsilon_l$. If N_k denotes the number of atoms in the kth state, the number of atoms $N_{k\to l}$ making a transition from k to l per sec will be given by the equation

$$N_{k\to l} = N_kA_{kl} + N_kB_{kl}\rho(\nu_{kl}), \tag{3.213}$$

where we have assumed that $\epsilon_k > \epsilon_l$. The first term on the right-hand side of equation (3.213) corresponds to spontaneous transitions and will be proportional to N_k, the factor of N_k being denoted by A_{kl}. The second term corresponds to the induced emissions (or negative absorptions) and will be proportional both to N_k and to the density of the radiation field at the frequency concerned, the factor here being denoted by B_{kl}.

The number of atoms $N_{l\to k}$ making the transition $l \to k$ per sec is given by the equation

$$N_{l\to k} = N_l B_{lk}\rho(\nu_{kl}), \tag{3.214}$$

since in this case no spontaneous transition can take place.

The coefficients A_{kl} and B_{kl} were introduced by Einstein in 1917 and are called the *Einstein transition probabilities.* In the quantum theory of radiation it is proved that†

$$B_{lk} = B_{kl}, \tag{3.215}$$

and

$$A_{kl} = \frac{8\pi h\nu_{kl}^3}{c^3} B_{kl}. \tag{3.216}$$

We should perhaps mention here that the A_{kl} and B_{kl} are atomic quantities which do *not* depend on the temperature.

The principle of detailed balancing (see §9 of Appendix I) states that in equilibrium $N_{k\to l}$ will be equal to $N_{l\to k}$, thus leading to the equation

$$N_k[A_{kl} + B_{kl}\rho(\nu_{kl})] = N_l B_{lk}\rho(\nu_{kl}). \tag{3.217}$$

Since N_k and N_l will satisfy equation (3.112) we have

$$N_k : N_l = e^{-\frac{\epsilon_k}{kT}} : e^{-\frac{\epsilon_l}{kT}}, \tag{3.218}$$

and combining equations (3.215) to (3.218) we can calculate the equilibrium density in the radiation field for which we will again obtain expression (3.207).

§3. The Two- and Three-dimensional Harmonic Oscillators. A two-dimensional harmonic oscillator is defined by its Hamiltonian

$$\epsilon = \frac{1}{2m}(p_1^2 + p_2^2) + \frac{m}{2}(2\pi\nu_1)^2 q_1^2 + \frac{m}{2}(2\pi\nu_2)^2 q_2^2, \tag{3.301}$$

and the energy levels of the stationary states, which follow from the Schrödinger equation,‡ are given by

$$\epsilon_{n_1 n_2} = (n_1 + \tfrac{1}{2})h\nu_1 + (n_2 + \tfrac{1}{2})h\nu_2. \tag{3.302}$$

For the partition function we have, generalizing equation (3.115),

$$Z = \frac{e}{N}\sum_{n_1, n_2} e^{-\frac{\epsilon_{n_1 n_2}}{kT}}, \tag{3.303}$$

† See, e.g., H. A. Kramers, Hand- u. Jahrbuch d. Chem. Phys., Vol. I, Leipzig 1938, §82.

‡ For a discussion of quantum mechanics and its main results we refer to the textbooks mentioned in the Introduction.

which leads to the expression

$$Z = \frac{e}{N} e^{-\frac{h(\nu_1+\nu_2)}{2kT}} \left[1 - e^{-\frac{h\nu_1}{kT}}\right]^{-1} \cdot \left[1 - e^{-\frac{h\nu_2}{kT}}\right]^{-1}. \qquad (3.304)$$

For a three-dimensional oscillator the corresponding equations will be

$$\epsilon = \frac{1}{2m}(p_1^2 + p_2^2 + p_3^2) + 2\pi^2 m[\nu_1^2 q_1^2 + \nu_2^2 q_2^2 + \nu_3^2 q_3^2], \qquad (3.305)$$

$$\epsilon_{n_1 n_2 n_3} = (n_1 + \tfrac{1}{2})h\nu_1 + (n_2 + \tfrac{1}{2})h\nu_2 + (n_3 + \tfrac{1}{2})h\nu_3, \qquad (3.306)$$

$$Z = \frac{e}{N} \sum_{n_1,n_2,n_3} e^{-\frac{\epsilon_{n_1n_2n_3}}{kT}}, \qquad (3.307)$$

or

$$Z = \frac{e}{N} e^{-\frac{h(\nu_1+\nu_2+\nu_3)}{2kT}} \left[1 - e^{-\frac{h\nu_1}{kT}}\right]^{-1} \left[1 - e^{-\frac{h\nu_2}{kT}}\right]^{-1} \left[1 - e^{-\frac{h\nu_3}{kT}}\right]^{-1}. \qquad (3.308)$$

These formulae become interesting only if we consider isotropic oscillators. For the two-dimensional case, equations (3.302) to (3.304) become

$$\epsilon_n = (n + 1)h\nu, \qquad (\nu_1 = \nu_2 = \nu), \qquad (3.309)$$

$$Z = \frac{e}{N} \sum_n (n + 1) e^{-\frac{\epsilon_n}{kT}}, \qquad (3.310)$$

or

$$Z = \frac{e}{N} e^{-\frac{h\nu}{kT}} \left[1 - e^{-\frac{h\nu}{kT}}\right]^{-2}. \qquad (3.311)$$

Equation (3.310) follows from the fact that there are $n + 1$ different ways of writing n as the sum of two nonnegative integers n_1 and n_2. Equation (3.311) follows either from equation (3.304) by putting $\nu_1 = \nu_2$ or directly from equation (3.310) by observing that

$$\sum_n n e^{-nx} = -\frac{d}{dx}[\sum_n e^{-nx}]. \qquad (3.312)$$

In the three-dimensional case, we get

$$\epsilon_n = (n + \tfrac{3}{2})h\nu, \qquad (\nu_1 = \nu_2 = \nu_3 = \nu), \qquad (3.313)$$

$$Z = \frac{e}{N} \sum_n \tfrac{1}{2}(n + 1)(n + 2) e^{-\frac{\epsilon_n}{kT}}, \qquad (3.314)$$

or

$$Z = \frac{e}{N} e^{-\frac{3h\nu}{2kT}} \left[1 - e^{-\frac{h\nu}{kT}}\right]^{-3}. \qquad (3.315)$$

As in the two-dimensional case, equation (3.314) follows from the fact that the number of different ways of writing n as the sum of three non-negative integers is $\frac{1}{2}(n + 1)(n + 2)$. Equation (3.315) then follows either from equation (3.308) or from equation (3.314) by using equations similar to (3.312).

The easiest way to compute the number of ways of writing n as a sum of three nonnegative integers is by thinking of it as a division of n dots by 2 strokes (Fig. 17). Since there are $(n + 2)!$ different ways of

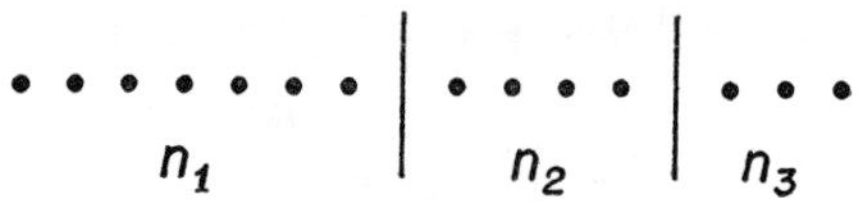

Fig. 17

arranging these n dots and 2 strokes, and since a rearrangement of the dots or of the strokes does not interest us, the total number of different divisions will be equal to $(n + 2)!/n!2! = \frac{1}{2}(n + 1)(n + 2)$.

As long as the oscillators are anisotropic the situation is practically the same as in the case of the one-dimensional oscillator. For instance in the three-dimensional case, μ-space has six dimensions and each energy level corresponds to one cell with a (six-dimensional) volume h^3. We could think of obtaining these cells (and their corresponding energy levels) by applying the Sommerfeld rules for each of the three independent oscillations.

However, as soon as we are dealing with the isotropic case, the situation becomes different. In the three-dimensional case an energy level ϵ_n does not correspond to one cell but to $\frac{1}{2}(n + 1)(n + 2)$ cells. The Schrödinger equation in this case allows $\frac{1}{2}(n + 1)(n + 2)$ linearly independent solutions for the same energy level, and the energy level is said to be g-fold *degenerate* with $g = \frac{1}{2}(n + 1)(n + 2)$.

§4. The Partition Function; Transition to Classical Statistics. The Schrödinger equation of a particle will give us the energy levels of the stationary states ϵ_n and their degree of degeneracy g_n where n stands for all the quantum numbers which determine the energy level. We can introduce a partition function Z by the equation

$$Z_\mu^{(\mathrm{qu})} = \frac{e}{N} \sum_n g_n e^{-\frac{\epsilon_n}{kT}}, \tag{3.401}$$

where N is again the total number of particles in the system. We see that expression (3.401) comprises all expressions which we have met up to now in this chapter for Z (equations [3.115], [3.303], [3.307], [3.310], and [3.314]).

Each level corresponds to a volume $g_n h^s$ in μ-space where s is the number of degrees of freedom of the particle. If we accept that the a priori probability of finding the representative point inside a specified volume of μ-space is proportional to this volume (compare the considerations on pp. 22, 33, and 379), we see that nondegenerate energy levels all have equal a priori probabilities of being realized, but that the a priori probability of a degenerate level is weighted with a factor g_n. For this reason the degree of degeneracy g_n is often called the (*statistical*) *weight* of the level ϵ_n.

Let us now return to the partition function. As we shall prove in the next chapter, the free energy F per particle is related to Z by equation (3.116), or

$$e^{-\frac{F}{kT}} = Z, \tag{3.402}$$

and all thermodynamical quantities can be derived from F or Z in the same way as was done in §7 of Chapter II.

In §4 of Chapter II we saw that often some degrees of freedom did not contribute to the average energy or the specific heat. In order to see how this can happen, let us consider the case of the anisotropic two-dimensional harmonic oscillator, and let us assume that ν_1 is much smaller than ν_2.

The partition function in this case is given by equation (3.304) and for the average energy we get (compare equation [3.117])

$$\bar{\epsilon} = kT^2 \frac{\partial \ln Z}{\partial T}, \tag{3.403}$$

or

$$\bar{\epsilon} = \tfrac{1}{2}h(\nu_1 + \nu_2) + \frac{h\nu_1}{e^{\frac{h\nu_1}{kT}} - 1} + \frac{h\nu_2}{e^{\frac{h\nu_2}{kT}} - 1}. \tag{3.404}$$

Let us now consider three temperature regions around T_1, T_2, and T_3 where

$$kT_1 \ll h\nu_1 \ll kT_2 \ll h\nu_2 \ll kT_3. \tag{3.405}$$

For $\bar{\epsilon}$ we get, in these three regions,

$$T \sim T_1: \quad \bar{\epsilon} = \tfrac{1}{2}h(\nu_1 + \nu_2) + h\nu_1 e^{-\frac{h\nu_1}{kT}} + \cdots, \tag{3.406}$$

$$T \sim T_2: \quad \bar{\epsilon} = \tfrac{1}{2}h\nu_2 + kT + h\nu_2 e^{-\frac{h\nu_2}{kT}} + \frac{(h\nu_1)^2}{12kT} + \cdots, \tag{3.407}$$

$$T \sim T_3: \quad \bar{\epsilon} = 2kT + \frac{h(\nu_1 + \nu_2)}{12kT} + \cdots. \tag{3.408}$$

The specific heat follows from the equation

$$c_v = \frac{\partial \bar{\varepsilon}}{\partial T}, \tag{3.409}$$

or

$$T \sim T_1: \quad c_v = k\left[\left(\frac{h\nu_1}{kT}\right)^2 e^{-\frac{h\nu_1}{kT}} + \cdots\right], \tag{3.410}$$

$$T \sim T_2: \quad c_v = k\left[1 - \frac{1}{12}\left(\frac{h\nu_1}{kT}\right)^2 + \left(\frac{h\nu_2}{kT}\right)^2 e^{-\frac{h\nu_2}{kT}} + \cdots\right], \tag{3.411}$$

$$T \sim T_3: \quad c_v = k\left[2 - \frac{1}{12}\left(\frac{h\nu_2}{kT}\right)^2 + \cdots\right]. \tag{3.412}$$

Figure 18 shows the behavior of c_v as a function of the temperature. From this figure we see the following:

a) If the temperature is sufficiently high, the specific heat will reach its classical value $2k$ (compare equation [2.408] with $s = t = 2$).

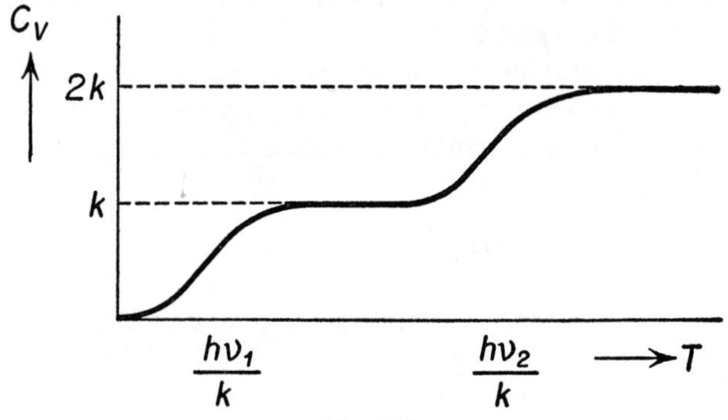

Fig. 18

b) At temperatures which are large compared to $h\nu_1/k$, but small compared to $h\nu_2/k$, the specific heat is only k. It is as if one degree of freedom were frozen.

c) Finally, at very low temperatures the specific heat is practically equal to zero.

That the classical behavior follows at sufficiently high temperatures is again an instance of the correspondence principle. Indeed, from equation (3.408) it follows that if $kT \gg h\nu_2$, then both $\bar{n}_1$ and $\bar{n}_2$ are large compared to 1, while if $h\nu_2 \gg kT \gg h\nu_1$, then although $\bar{n}_1$ is large as compared to unity, $\bar{n}_2$ is small and only the first degree of freedom will give the classical contribution k.

The problem with which we are thus left is to explain why at low temperatures the specific heat is so much smaller than its classical value. This can best be done by considering the transition from the quantum mechanical formulae to the classical ones.

We can start with the partition function

$$Z = \frac{e}{N} \sum_n g_n e^{-\frac{\epsilon_n}{kT}}. \tag{3.413}$$

The sum in equation (3.413) must be replaced by an integral over μ-space if we wish to go over to the classical case. Since each nondegenerate energy level corresponds to a volume h^s in μ-space, we should expect

$$\sum_n g_n \rightarrow \int \frac{d\omega}{h^s}. \tag{3.414}$$

We do not have to worry about degeneracy. A degenerate level corresponds to a volume $g \cdot h^s$ so that g disappears in the final result. We see that by making the transition in this way we get, indeed, the classical formula (2.718) for the partition function.

According to the old quantum statistics one can justify the transition (3.414) rather easily as long as one is dealing with multiply periodic systems. One introduces the phase integrals

$$J_k = \oint p_k dq_k,$$

where the p_k and q_k are the generalized momenta and coordinates and where the integration is extended over one complete period. It is possible to perform a canonical transformation from the p_k and q_k to the J_k and their conjugate coordinates w_k.† The w_k measure the phase during the periodical motion and change by 1 over one period. Because the transformation is canonical, we have

$$\prod_k dp_k\, dq_k = \prod_k dJ_k\, dw_k.$$

The volume Ω of phase space corresponding to J_k values between $J_{k'}$ and $J_{k''}$ and w_k between $w_{k'}$ and $w_{k'} + 1$ is given by the equation

$$\Omega = \prod_k (J_{k''} - J_{k'}).$$

If we are in the region of high quantum numbers, we have $J_{k''} = n_{k''}h$, $J_{k'} = n_{k'}h$ according to the Sommerfeld rules. The volume is thus equal to

$$\Omega = h^s \prod_k (n_{k''} - n_{k'}).$$

† See J. M. Burgers, Het Atoommodel van Rutherford-Bohr, Thesis, Leiden 1918.

The number of stationary states in the volume under consideration is clearly

$$\prod_k (n_{k''} - n_{k'}).$$

We see thus that each stationary state corresponds to a volume h^s in μ-space. We do not wish to discuss here the importance of the theorem of the invariance of the statistical weights, but refer the reader to the literature.

The situation becomes more complicated when we consider modern quantum theory. In many textbooks on statistical mechanics one finds the statement that the transition (3.414) is connected with the Heisenberg relations, which are then written in the form

$$\Delta p \cdot \Delta q \geqslant h.$$

It can readily be seen that this statement can reveal only part of the true state of affairs, since the Heisenberg relations in their most rigorous form read

$$\Delta p \cdot \Delta q \geqslant \frac{h}{4\pi}.$$

One is thus led to ask why the conversion factor should be h^s and not, for instance, $(h/4\pi)^s$.

It seems to us, however, that one can justify the factor h^s in the following way. In classical mechanics the phase of the particle is given by the representative point in μ-space. One can consider this point in μ-space to be the combination of a point in coordinate- or q-space and a point in momentum- or p-space. In quantum mechanics, however, one must consider a probability density both in q- and in p-space. These two probability densities are not independent. The density in q-space is determined by the wave function ψ, and is in fact $|\psi|^2$. If one transforms the wave function from a coordinate representation to a momentum representation,† one obtains the probability amplitude in p-space, A. The probability density in p-space is then given by $|A|^2$.

From the transformation theory it follows that A and ψ are Fourier transforms of one another, if we consider q and p/h as the variables. (The h enters here through the commutation expressions of which the Heisenberg relations are also a consequence.) Since ψ must be normalized to represent the actual state of a particle,

$$\int |\psi|^2 dq = 1,$$

it follows from the theory of Fourier transforms‡ that

$$\int |A|^2 dp = h^s.$$

† For a more thorough discussion of the details of this transformation and proofs of the subsequent statements we refer to W. Heisenberg, Die physikalischen Prinzipien der Quantentheorie, Leipzig 1930.

‡ The functions ψ and A are functions of $q_1, \cdots, q_s$ and $p_1, \cdots, p_s$, respectively. We write abbreviatedly only one p or q. Also dq and dp are abbreviated notations for volume elements in q- and p-space.

The total volume in phase space corresponding to one stationary state is now obtained by multiplying the probability density in q-space with the probability density in p-space and integrating over the whole of μ-space. The result is then h^s. We shall return to this problem in Appendix III.†

The next question is, Under what conditions is the approximation of the sum in equation (3.413) by an integral a good one? The condition for this is that the successive terms in the sum do not differ appreciably or, in other words, that

$$\epsilon_n - \epsilon_{n-1} \ll kT. \tag{3.415}$$

Condition (3.415) will certainly be realized in the limit where $h \to 0$, since ϵ_n and ϵ_{n-1} are the representative energies of neighboring cells in μ-space and will become the energies of neighboring representative points after $h \to 0$.

We also see that the higher the temperature the greater the chance that condition (3.415) will be satisfied. In general, then, we may expect that the higher the temperature the closer the approach to the classical formulae.

If, however, condition (3.415) is not fulfilled, we are not allowed to substitute an integral for the sum. Let us assume for the sake of simplicity that $\epsilon_0 = 0$ (no zero-point energy) and that all levels are non-degenerate. The partition function can then be written in the form

$$Z = \frac{e}{N}\left[1 + e^{-\frac{\epsilon_1}{kT}} + e^{-\frac{\epsilon_2}{kT}} + \cdots\right]. \tag{3.416}$$

Since the terms in equation (3.416) are decreasing, we get to a first approximation and, assuming that $\epsilon_1 \gg kT$, $\epsilon_2 - \epsilon_1 \gg kT, \cdots,$

$$Z \approx \frac{e}{N}\left[1 + e^{-\frac{\epsilon_1}{kT}}\right], \tag{3.417}$$

and for the average energy and specific heat we get from equations (3.403), (3.409), and (3.417)

$$\bar{\epsilon} \approx \epsilon_1 e^{-\frac{\epsilon_1}{kT}}, \tag{3.418}$$

and

$$c_v \approx \frac{\epsilon_1{}^2}{kT^2} e^{-\frac{\epsilon_1}{kT}}. \tag{3.419}$$

Since according to our assumptions $\epsilon_1 \gg kT$, both $\bar{\epsilon}$ and c_v will be very small. We may therefore make the general statement that *a degree of*

† Similar considerations are to be found in P. A. M. Dirac, The Principles of Quantum Mechanics, Oxford 1935, §37.

freedom for which $\epsilon_1 - \epsilon_0 \gg kT$ *will not make any appreciable contribution to the specific heat.*† This explains why the specific heat of diatomic gases is $\frac{5}{2}k$ per molecule. The energies corresponding to vibrations along the axis of the molecule are of the order of magnitude of electron volts, that is, they correspond to temperatures of the order of 10,000°K. The degree of freedom which such vibrations represent is thus completely frozen and will not contribute a term k to the specific heat.

§5. **The Rigid Rotator; the Hydrogen Molecule.** Let us consider a dumbbell molecule. At room temperatures the electronic degrees of freedom and the degree of freedom corresponding to a vibration along the axis of the molecule are frozen and the molecule may be regarded as a *rigid rotator*, that is, a particle which has two rotational degrees of freedom around its center of gravity. The three degrees of freedom relating to the movement of the center of gravity may be treated classically and will contribute $\frac{3}{2}kT$ to the average energy and $\frac{3}{2}k$ to the specific heat.

The energy levels of a point particle in a cubical box of edge length a are given by the equation (compare equation [4.501])

$$\epsilon = \epsilon_0(k^2 + l^2 + m^2) \quad \text{where} \quad \epsilon_0 = \frac{h^2}{8ma^2}. \tag{3.501}$$

Since $\epsilon_0/k \approx 10^{-15}$°K, if $m = 10^{-23}$ g, $a = 1$ cm, we see that we are always in the classical region.

If we consider for the moment only the rotational part of the energy, we have (compare equation [2.414]),

$$\epsilon = \frac{p_\theta^{\,2}}{2A} + \frac{p_\varphi^{\,2}}{2A\sin^2\theta}, \tag{3.502}$$

where A is the moment of inertia of the molecule with respect to an axis through the center of gravity, perpendicular to the axis of the molecule, and where θ and ϕ are two angles determining the direction of the axis of the molecule. For θ we can take the angle between the axis of the molecule and the z-axis and for ϕ the angle between the x-axis and the projection of the molecular axis on the x,y-plane. If m_1 and m_2 are the masses of the two atoms out of which the molecule is built up and if r_0 is their equilibrium distance apart, we have for A

$$A = \frac{m_1 m_2}{m_1 + m_2}\, r_0^{\,2}. \tag{3.503}$$

† The statement in this form presupposes that the total energy of the particle is built up *additively* from the energies corresponding to the different degrees of freedom. That this situation is often realized follows from a consideration of the Schrödinger equation in the case where the classical energy is built up in this way.

From the Schrödinger equation it follows that the energy levels of the rotator and their weights are given by the equations

$$\epsilon_j = \frac{\hbar^2}{2A} j(j+1), \qquad g_j = 2j+1, \qquad j = 0, 1, 2, \cdots, \qquad \textbf{(3.504)}$$

where $\hbar$ is Dirac's constant, $2\pi\hbar = h$, and where j is the rotational quantum number.

In order to determine the temperature above which classical behavior may be expected, we consider the "rotational" temperature $\Theta = \hbar^2/2Ak$ (see equation [3.415]). Expressing both m_1 and m_2 in units of proton mass and r_0 in Ångströms, we find

$$\Theta = 23 \frac{m_1 + m_2}{m_1 m_2 r_0^2} \,{}^\circ\mathrm{K}. \qquad \textbf{(3.505)}$$

Above room temperatures the classical formulae will probably be all right, but at lower temperatures the quantum mechanical formulae must be used.

The partition function is in this case

$$Z = \frac{e}{N} \sum_{j=0}^{\infty} (2j+1) e^{-\frac{\Theta}{T} j(j+1)}. \qquad \textbf{(3.506)}$$

At high temperatures ($T \gg \Theta$) the sum can be replaced by an integral,

$$Z \approx \frac{e}{N} \int_0^\infty (2x+1) e^{-\frac{\Theta}{T} x(x+1)}\, dx = \frac{e}{N} \frac{T}{\Theta}, \qquad \textbf{(3.507)}$$

and at low temperatures ($T \ll \Theta$) we get a power series,

$$Z = \frac{e}{N} \left[1 + 3e^{-2\frac{\Theta}{T}} + 5e^{-6\frac{\Theta}{T}} + \cdots \right]. \qquad \textbf{(3.508)}$$

For the average rotational energy we get from equations (3.507) and (3.508)

$$\text{if } T \gg \Theta, \qquad \bar{\epsilon} \approx kT, \qquad \textbf{(3.509)}$$

$$\text{and if } T \ll \Theta, \qquad \bar{\epsilon} \approx k\Theta \left[6e^{-2\frac{\Theta}{T}} - 18e^{-4\frac{\Theta}{T}} + \cdots \right]. \qquad \textbf{(3.510)}$$

Finally, for the rotational specific heat we get

$$\text{if } T \gg \Theta, \qquad c_v \approx k; \qquad \textbf{(3.511)}$$

$$\text{and if } T \ll \Theta, \qquad c_v = k \left(\frac{\Theta}{T} \right)^2 \left[12e^{-2\frac{\Theta}{T}} - 72e^{-4\frac{\Theta}{T}} + \cdots \right]. \qquad \textbf{(3.512)}$$

Formulae (3.509) and (3.511) correspond to the classical expressions, since there is no potential energy and there are two degrees of freedom.

As an example of such a rigid rotator we can name the hydrogen molecule. In Figure 19 we have drawn both the theoretical behavior of the rotational specific heat (*a*) and the experimental specific heat of molecular hydrogen as determined by Eucken (*b*). The difference between the calculated and observed curves cannot be due to the fact that we have neglected the vibrational and electronic energies. Firstly, these energies are far too large to have an effect at temperatures where the difference occurs and, secondly, if they were important, the observed curve should lie higher than the calculated one and not lower.

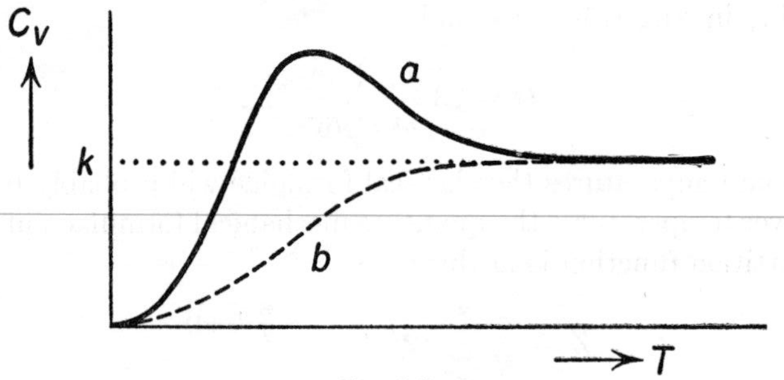

Fig. 19

However, we have neglected two other factors. First of all, we have neglected the fact that both hydrogen nuclei have spin $\frac{1}{2}$.† Secondly, we have neglected the fact that the hydrogen molecule is built up out of two identical atoms.

Since both atoms have spin $\frac{1}{2}$, the total spin S of the molecule can either be 0 (antiparallel spins) or 1 (parallel spins). The weight of a state with spin S is $2S + 1$ corresponding to the $2S + 1$ possibilities of orientation of the total spin.‡ The state with $S = 0$, which is called the *para* state, has thus a weight $g_S{}^p = 1$, while the *ortho* state with $S = 1$ has a weight $g_S{}^o = 3$.

These spin weight factors have no effect on the average energy if the two atoms are not identical. If they are not identical, the partition function is multiplied by a constant factor $(2s_1 + 1)(2s_2 + 1)(=4 = g_S{}^p + g_S{}^o$ in our case), where s_1 and s_2 are the spins of the two atoms in the molecule. However, when the two atoms are identical, the Pauli principle intervenes. This principle states that the final total wave function of the molecule should be antisymmetrical in the two atoms. The vibrational and elec-

† The value of the spin is always expressed in units of $\hbar$.

‡ More precisely, there are $2S + 1$ linearly independent spin functions corresponding to the same total spin S.

tronic parts of the wave function are symmetrical in the ground state, which is the only state of the electronic and vibrational parts which has to be considered. The spin function corresponding to para states is antisymmetrical while the spin functions corresponding to ortho states are symmetrical. The rotational wave functions are symmetrical or antisymmetrical according as j is even or odd. Since the total wave function has to be antisymmetrical we see that we have the following combinations:

$$\left.\begin{array}{lll} j = 0, 2, 4, \cdots, & S = 0, & g_S{}^p = 1, \\ j = 1, 3, 5, \cdots, & S = 1, & g_S{}^o = 3, \end{array}\right\} \tag{3.513}$$

and the partition function is not given by equation (3.506) but by the equation

$$Z = Z_p + 3Z_o, \tag{3.514}$$

where

$$Z_p = \frac{e}{N} \sum_{j=\text{even}} (2j+1) e^{-\frac{\Theta}{T} j(j+1)} \tag{3.515}$$

and

$$Z_o = \frac{e}{N} \sum_{j=\text{odd}} (2j+1) e^{-\frac{\Theta}{T} j(j+1)} . \tag{3.516}$$

Using expression (3.514) for the partition function one can again calculate the specific heat, but once more the calculated curve does not agree with the experimental one.

The final solution to this problem was given by Dennison in 1927. In order to understand it we must first calculate the ratio, r, of the total number of ortho- to the total number of para-hydrogen molecules at room temperature. To do this we use formula (3.112) for the number of particles in a given energy level, and, remembering that that expression has to be multiplied by the degree of degeneracy, we get

$$r = \frac{N_{\text{ortho}}}{N_{\text{para}}} = \frac{\sum_{j=\text{odd}} 3(2j+1) e^{-\frac{\Theta}{T} j(j+1)}}{\sum_{j=\text{even}} (2j+1) e^{-\frac{\Theta}{T} j(j+1)}} . \tag{3.517}$$

We see immediately that r approaches zero as $T \to 0$ and that at high temperatures ($T \gg \Theta$) r has the value 3. As soon as T is well above Θ the sums can be replaced by integrals and are the same apart from the spin degeneracy factor. At room temperature, then, since this is well above Θ, there will be three times as many ortho-hydrogen as para-hydrogen molecules present in the gas. If now the temperature is lowered, one should expect the ratio to decrease in the appropriate manner according to equation (3.517). However, one runs into the following difficulty. Since the transition from ortho- to para-hydrogen involves the changing of sign of the spin of one of the atoms, the transition probability will be small and one cannot expect equilibrium with regard to the ortho-para ratio to have been attained in a short period. Indeed, the periods concerned are of the order of years, even at relatively high temperatures such as room temperature. If one therefore performs a measurement of the specific heat of hydrogen at low temperatures, one is dealing with a mixture of ortho- and para-hydrogen in the ratio of 3 to 1, and one should expect for the specific heat

$$c_v = 3c_{vo} + c_{vp}, \tag{3.518}$$

where c_{vo} and c_{vp} are the specific heats calculated from the ortho- and para-partition functions (3.516) and (3.515). The specific heat curve calculated in this way agrees well with the observed specific heat curve.

Further evidence that Dennison's explanation is the correct one can be obtained by performing experiments with ortho-para mixtures where r has a value different from 3. One can speed up the ortho-para conversion by passing the hydrogen over activated charcoal. By doing this at various temperatures and afterward removing the catalyst one can fix r at any value between 0 and 3. The specific heat will then follow a curve obtained by mixing c_{vo} and c_{vp} with appropriate weights. If one measures c_v in such a way that r has at every temperature the value corresponding to equation (3.517), it will follow the curve calculated from the expression for the partition function given in equation (3.514).

Analogous considerations apply to the case of heavy hydrogen D_2. In the case of HD there are no complications, since the two constituent atoms are different and the specific heat can be calculated from expression (3.506) for the partition function.

BIBLIOGRAPHICAL NOTES

General references for this chapter are

1. P. Jordan, Statistische Mechanik auf Quantentheoretischer Grundlage, Braunschweig 1933.
2. M. Planck, Theorie der Wärme, Leipzig 1930; Theory of Heat, London 1932.

§1. The story of the introduction of h is beautifully told by Planck himself in

3. M. Planck, Naturwiss., **31,** 153, 1943.

For an account of the old quantum theory we may refer to

4. A. Sommerfeld, Atombau und Spektrallinien, Vol. I, Braunschweig 1919.

The Sommerfeld quantization rules were independently proposed by Sommerfeld and Wilson:

5. A. Sommerfeld, Münchener Ber., **1915,** 425, 459; **1916,** 131

6. W. Wilson, Phil. Mag., **29,** 795, 1915.

The "halbzahlige" quantization was introduced in 1920:

7. A. Sommerfeld, Ann. Physik, **63,** 221, 1920.

The correspondence principle was first clearly stated by Bohr in 1920:

8. N. Bohr, Z. Physik, **2,** 423, 1920.

A discussion of the reasons why and when the Sommerfeld rules are exactly correct is usually given by the W-K-B method:

9. G. Wentzel, Z. Physik, **38,** 518, 1926.
10. H. A. Kramers, Z. Physik, **39,** 828, 1926.
11. L. Brillouin, C. R., **183,** 24, 1926.

See also

12. A. Zwaan, Intensitäten im Ca-Funkenspektrum, Thesis, Utrecht 1929.

For a general account of this method see, for instance,

13. E. C. Kemble, The Fundamental Principles of Quantum Mechanics, New York 1937, §21.

The mathematical method had previously been introduced by Jeffreys:

14. H. Jeffreys, Proc. London Math. Soc., **23,** 428, 1923.

§2. See ref. 3. Planck's law and Rayleigh's law were both derived in 1900:

15. M. Planck, Verhandl. deut. physik. Ges., **2,** 202, 237, 1900.
16. Lord Rayleigh, Phil. Mag., **49,** 539, 1900.
17. J. H. Jeans, Phil. Mag., **10,** 91, 1905.

Wien's law is older and was stated in 1896:

18. W. Wien, Ann. Physik, **58,** 662, 1896.

Stefan-Boltzmann's law was first deduced from experiments in **1879** by Stefan and deduced theoretically by Boltzmann in 1884:

19. J. Stefan, Wien. Ber., **79,** 391, 1879.
20. L. Boltzmann, Ann. Physik, **22,** 31, 291, 616, 1884.

The derivation of Planck's radiation law from atomic considerations can be found in the paper in which Einstein introduced his transition probabilities:

21. A. Einstein, Physik. Z., **18,** 121, 1917.

§§3 and 4. See refs. 1 and 2.

§5. An approximate formula which can be used to evaluate the partition function of the three-dimensional rigid rotator was given by Mulholland:

22. H. P. Mulholland, Proc. Cambridge Phil. Soc., **24,** 280, 1928.

For an account of the history of the hydrogen rotational specific heat see

23. A. Farkas, Orthohydrogen, Parahydrogen and Heavy Hydrogen, Cambridge 1935.

The specific heat of normal hydrogen was measured by Eucken:

24. A. Eucken, Sitz. ber. preuss. Akad. Wiss., **1912,** 41.

The specific heat curves of mixtures of ortho- and para-hydrogen were measured by Eucken and Hiller and by Clusius and Hiller:

25. A. Eucken and K. Hiller, Z. physik. Chem., **B4,** 142, 1929.
26. K. Clusius and K. Hiller, Z. physik. Chem., **B4,** 158, 1929.

The theoretical explanation of the specific heat curve of normal hydrogen was given by Dennison in

27. D. M. Dennison, Proc. Roy. Soc. (London), **A115,** 483, 1927.

CHAPTER IV

BOSE-EINSTEIN AND FERMI-DIRAC STATISTICS

§1. Deviations from Boltzmann Statistics. In §2 of the previous chapter we discussed the radiation field and derived Planck's radiation law (3.207) for the energy density $\rho(\nu)$ in the radiation field. It was mentioned at that time that Planck had been obliged to introduce his quantum of action h, different from zero, since formula (3.207) with finite h agreed with the observational evidence.

Let us examine for a moment the basic assumptions used in deriving equation (3.207). It was assumed that the radiation field was built up out of one-dimensional harmonic oscillators which all possessed different frequencies. A given situation was completely described by giving the quantum numbers n_i of the stationary states in which the various oscillators were. When we wished to obtain the expression for the total energy of the system in temperature equilibrium we remarked that it can be shown that the time average of the energy of one oscillator is equal to the system average of the energy of a system of many identical oscillators. In calculating this last average one uses the assumption of equal a priori probability for different (nondegenerate) stationary states (p. 57). In other words, in order to derive Planck's radiation law—which agrees well with experimental data—we must assume that any sequence $n_1, n_2, \cdots, n_i, \cdots$ of the quantum numbers of the oscillators has the same probability. However, we know that a modern picture of the radiation field must take into account the fact that light is quantized, that is, that it occurs as light quanta. This means that the situation which we just described by the sequence $n_1, n_2, \cdots, n_i, \cdots$ in reality corresponds to a radiation field in which there are n_1 quanta with energy $h\nu_1$, n_2 quanta with energy $h\nu_2$, and so on. Instead of having one oscillator corresponding to a given frequency ν_i we have n_i quanta with energy $h\nu_i$. If we wished to calculate the energy density of the field without having recourse to our previous considerations, our first task would be to find the a priori probability to find n_1 quanta of energy $h\nu_1$, n_2 quanta of energy $h\nu_2$, and so on. This probability

$W(n_1,n_2,\cdots,n_i,\cdots)$† of distributing $n_1 + n_2 + \cdots$ particles over the possible energy levels $h\nu_1$, $h\nu_2$, $\cdots$ was calculated in §1 of Chapter III (equation [3.111]). We found there

$$W(n_i) = A\prod_i \frac{1}{n_i!}, \tag{4.101}$$

where A is a normalizing constant which we shall leave undetermined for the time being. In §2 of the present chapter we shall make some particular choice for A and then we shall also give the reasons for our choice.

A moment ago, however, we saw that in order to obtain the radiation law which agrees with experiments we must assign the value of 1 to $W(n_i)$ irrespective of the values of the n_i, or

$$W(n_i) = 1. \tag{4.102}$$

We see here a departure from the formulae which were used in the preceding chapters. If we try to use formula (4.101) for the a priori probability, we end up with a formula for the radiation density which is in disagreement with the observational evidence. This is often expressed in the following way. Light quanta do not obey Boltzmann statistics, but they obey *Bose-Einstein statistics.* Formula (4.102) for the a priori probability was introduced by Bose in 1924 for the case of light quanta and applied by Einstein in the same year to the case of an ideal gas.

It must be remarked here that the term "Bose-Einstein *statistics*" (or Boltzmann *statistics* or Fermi-Dirac *statistics*) could imply that different statistical methods are used. This is not the case. It would thus be less confusing to talk about Boltzmann *formulae,* Bose-Einstein *formulae,* or Fermi-Dirac *formulae.* However, the other nomenclature has been and is used so extensively that we shall also continue to use it, the more readily since there seems to be no danger of serious misunderstandings.

There exists a second kind of statistics which differs from the classical or Boltzmann statistics which we discussed in the preceding chapters. These statistics were introduced by Fermi and extensively discussed by Dirac in 1926. They are called the *Fermi-Dirac statistics* and are characterized by the following values of $W(n_i)$:

$$\left.\begin{aligned} W(n_i) &= 1, \quad \text{if all the } n_i \text{ are } \leqslant 1; \\ W(n_i) &= 0, \quad \text{if there is at least one } n_i > 1. \end{aligned}\right\} \tag{4.103}$$

We shall discuss presently the connection between this choice of $W(n_i)$ and Pauli's exclusion principle.

In the last section of the present chapter we shall discuss briefly a few cases where the Bose-Einstein and Fermi-Dirac statistics are applied and

† We shall mostly use the abbreviated notation $W(n_i)$ for $W(n_1,n_2,\cdots,n_i,\cdots)$.

why one can no longer apply the classical statistics in these cases. We may mention here only that the Bose-Einstein statistics have been mainly applied to a discussion of the behavior of helium at low temperatures and to the case of light quanta. The Fermi-Dirac statistics are mainly used for a description of the behavior of conduction electrons in metals.

In the present chapter we shall treat the two "new" statistics, as the Bose-Einstein and Fermi-Dirac statistics are sometimes called, in a way analogous to that used for the Boltzmann statistics in the preceding chapters. The Bose-Einstein and Fermi-Dirac statistics are also often called the "quantum" statistics. The reason for this name we shall see in later sections of this chapter. The name is rather misleading, since one can quite often get a good approximation to the behavior of a system by applying Boltzmann formulae to systems where the energy levels have been computed by quantum mechanical methods, as we did in Chapter III, for instance. We shall also see later on that, indeed, in the classical limit where $h \to 0$, the "quantum" statistics go over into the Boltzmann statistics.

§2. The Probability Aspect of Statistics. We shall use here a formulation which is slightly different from the one used in Chapter I, since we wish to apply quantum mechanics from the start.

Let us assume that we are dealing with a system consisting of N identical independent particles. The Hamiltonian of the system will be the sum of the Hamiltonians of the particles

$$\mathcal{H}_{\text{syst}} = \sum_i \mathcal{H}_i(p_k{}^{(i)}, q_k{}^{(i)}). \tag{4.201}$$

In equation (4.201) k runs from 1 to s where s is the number of degrees of freedom of one particle. The $\mathcal{H}_i$ differ only in the indices enumerating the particles, but are otherwise identical.

The time-independent Schrödinger equation for the system will be

$$\mathcal{H}_{\text{syst}}\Psi = E\Psi, \tag{4.202}$$

where E and Ψ are respectively the total energy of the system and its wave function. Since the Hamiltonian is a sum, equation (4.202) can be solved by the method of the separation of coordinates and we have

$$\Psi = \prod_i \psi_i, \tag{4.203}$$

$$E = \sum_i \epsilon_i, \tag{4.204}$$

$$\mathcal{H}_i\psi_i = \epsilon_i\psi_i. \tag{4.205}$$

The ϵ_i are the energy levels corresponding to the Schrödinger equation of one particle (4.205) and the ψ_i are the corresponding wave functions.

A stationary state of the system can be described by giving the number of particles in each stationary state corresponding to the one-particle Schrödinger equation. If there are n_1 particles in the first stationary state, n_2 particles in the second stationary state, and so on, we have from equation (4.203)

$$\Psi = \psi_1(1)\psi_1(2)\cdots\psi_1(n_1)\psi_2(n_1+1)\psi_2(n_1+2)\cdots\psi_2(n_1+n_2)\psi_3(\cdots)\cdots, \tag{4.206}$$

where $\psi_i(m)$ stands for $\psi_i(q_k{}^{(m)})$.

Since the particles are supposed to be identical, a situation which differs from the one considered in the last paragraph only by a permutation of particles will have the same properties as the original one. If $k_1, k_2, \cdots, k_i, \cdots, k_N$ is a permutation of the numbers $1, 2, \cdots, i, \cdots, N$, such a situation is described by a wave function $P\Psi$ (where P indicates that $P\Psi$ is obtained from Ψ by a permutation of the arguments) given by the equation

$$P\Psi = \psi_1(k_1)\psi_1(k_2)\cdots\psi_1(k_{n_1})\psi_2(k_{n_1+1})\cdots\psi_2(k_{n_1+n_2})\psi_3(k_{\cdots})\cdots. \tag{4.207}$$

In classical mechanics it was regarded as permissible to imagine labels attached to each of the N particles, even though they are identical. In that way each of them could be followed along its orbit and localized at every moment. This possibility of distinguishing between the various (identical) particles would entail that Ψ and $P\Psi$ describe two different stationary states of the system. We shall call such a stationary state a *microsituation*. Both Ψ and $P\Psi$, though they correspond to different microsituations, describe the same *macrosituation* which is characterized by the numbers $n_1, n_2, n_3, \cdots$. The a priori probability or *weight* of this macrosituation $W(n_i)$ will be given, so long as we are only considering the classical case, by the number of permutations of $1, 2, \cdots, N$ which give n_1 numbers in group 1, n_2 numbers in group 2, and so on. We computed this weight in §1 of Chapter III and found

$$W(n_i) = N!\prod_i \frac{1}{n_i!}. \tag{4.208}$$

In many cases we can still assume that the particles are localizable even though we are applying quantum mechanics. This will, for instance, be the case when we are dealing with crystals and we can then use expression (4.208) for $W(n_i)$. However, if we are dealing with a gas and applying quantum mechanics, the atoms will no longer be localizable in the sense that we can label them and keep track of each separate atom. We then get $N!$ different microsituations which differ only in a permutation of the N particles. These microsituations not only correspond to the same macrosituation; there is no way of distinguishing between them. If the weight of the various macrosituations were to be taken as given by equation (4.208), we should be counting each distinguishable macrosituation $N!$ times. In order to avoid this we have to divide expression (4.208) by $N!$ so that we obtain the correct weight of each n_i-distribution. The weights which we obtain in this way will be called the Boltzmann weights and are thus given by the equation

$$W_{\mathrm{Bo}}(n_i) = \prod_i \frac{1}{n_i!}. \qquad (4.209)$$

We have followed mainly Rushbrooke's arguments† in going from equation (4.208) to equation (4.209). He points out that the labeling in the case of a crystal occurs because we can label the lattice sites. Even though the atoms in the crystal can and do change places, we can describe the situation by giving the quantum state of the atom on a well-defined position in space.

Rushbrooke states that the transition from (4.208) to (4.209) in the case of a gas is *not* a quantum mechanical effect. I would beg to differ here. So long as we are dealing with classical systems, the $N!$ microsituations are in fact different and can be distinguished from one another. In quantum mechanical systems, however, we can no longer distinguish them. This is certainly due to the fact that we cannot follow the atoms so closely along their orbits that we can, for instance, know which atom is which after a collision. This again is a consequence of Heisenberg's famous relations. That this impossibility of following the individual particles along their orbits has a physical meaning follows, for instance, from a discussion of experiments where α-particles are scattered by α-particles.‡ Another case in which the indistinguishability plays an important part is the helium atom where the two orbital electrons are identical and indistinguishable leading to the *exchange integral* which in fact gives to some extent the "period of exchange."§ I agree, of course, with Rushbrooke that in deriving equation (4.209) only part of the complete quantum mechanical argument has been used. The exclusion principle has not been used and should have been used in a complete quantum mechanical treatment. (Compare also Kramers' remarks [*loc. cit.*] on the interpretation of the exchange integral.)

We shall have many opportunities to discuss the consequences and importance of the omission of the factor $N!$.

In the discussion leading from equation (4.208) to equation (4.209) we have on purpose forgotten complications such as the Pauli principle. However, it is known that the physical phenomena as they are observed in experiments can be explained if only such situations occur in nature where

† G. S. Rushbrooke, Introduction to Statistical Mechanics, Oxford 1949, Chap. III, §1.

‡ Compare J. R. Oppenheimer, Phys. Rev., **32**, 361, 1928; N. F. Mott, Proc. Roy. Soc. (London), **A125**, 222, 1929; **A126**, 259, 1930.

§ Compare, e.g., H. A. Kramers, Hand- u. Jahrb. d. Chem. Phys., Vol. I, Leipzig 1938, p. 349.

the wave function is either completely symmetrical or completely antisymmetrical in all the arguments corresponding to identical particles.

If the wave function is symmetrical in all its arguments, the only possible wave function (or *accessible* state, as Fowler calls it) $\Psi_{\text{B.E.}}$ will be given by the equation

$$\Psi_{\text{B.E.}} = C\sum_P P\Psi, \qquad (4.210)$$

where C is a normalization constant and where the summation is extended over all $N!$ possible permutations of the arguments.

We see that there corresponds to every n_i-distribution only *one* wave function. The weight of the distribution will thus be independent of the distribution and we have

$$W_{\text{B.E.}}(n_i) = 1. \qquad (4.211)$$

Since equation (4.211) is the same as equation (4.102), we see the reason for the index B.E.

In the case of the antisymmetrical wave function the only possibility is given by

$$\Psi_{\text{F.D.}} = C\sum_P \epsilon_P P\Psi, \qquad (4.212)$$

where ϵ_P is $+1$ or -1 according as the permutation is even or odd. Expression (4.212) is often called a *Slater determinant,* since it was used extensively by Slater† in the form of a determinant,‡

$$\Psi_{\text{F.D.}} = C\begin{vmatrix} \psi_{l_1}(1) & \psi_{l_1}(2) & \cdots & \psi_{l_1}(N) \\ \psi_{l_2}(1) & \psi_{l_2}(2) & \cdots & \psi_{l_2}(N) \\ \vdots & \vdots & \ddots & \vdots \\ \psi_{l_N}(1) & \psi_{l_N}(2) & \cdots & \psi_{l_N}(N) \end{vmatrix} \qquad (4.213)$$

From equation (4.213) it is seen immediately that as soon as one n_i is larger than 1, $\Psi_{\text{F.D.}} = 0$. In the Fermi-Dirac case no two particles can be in the same state. This corresponds to the Pauli principle which was first stated for electrons.

For the weight of an n_i-distribution we now have

$$\left.\begin{aligned} W_{\text{F.D.}}(n_i) &= 1, \qquad \sum_i n_i^2 = N; \\ W_{\text{F.D.}}(n_i) &= 0, \qquad \sum_i n_i^2 > N, \end{aligned}\right\} \qquad (4.214)$$

which is the same as equations (4.103).

† J. C. Slater, Phys. Rev., **34**, 1293, 1929.

‡ Instead of numbering the rows n_1 times 1, n_2 times 2, and so on, as in equation (4.206), we have numbered them $l_1, l_2, \cdots, l_N$.

In the remainder of this chapter we shall mainly consider cases where the energy levels are lying so densely that we can practically speak of a continuous energy spectrum. In that case we can bundle the energy levels into groups. The number of levels in the jth group will be denoted by Z_j. The number of particles with energies in that interval will be denoted by N_j. Since the energy levels are supposed to lie very densely, it will be possible to ascribe to each group a rather well-defined energy value E_j. We shall assume that we are dealing with cases where without losing the accuracy with which E_j is defined we can choose Z_j so large that N_j is also a large number.

For the total energy and total number of particles we have the equations

$$\sum_j N_j E_j = E \tag{4.215}$$

and

$$\sum_j N_j = N. \tag{4.216}$$

We now wish to calculate the probability $W(N_1, N_2, \cdots, N_i, \cdots)$ $(= W[N_i])$ that there are N_1 particles in group Z_1, N_2 particles in group Z_2, and so on. Figure 20 depicts one possible distribution.

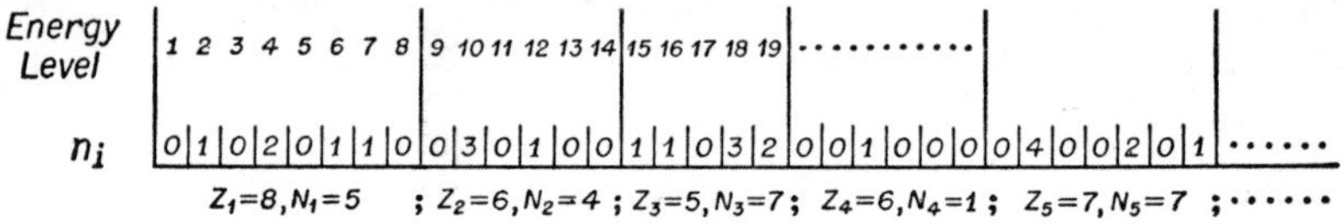

Fig. 20

The $W(N_i)$ are related to the $W(n_i)$ by the equation

$$W(N_i) = \sum_{N_i = Ct} W(n_i), \tag{4.217}$$

where the summation extends over all possible n_i-distributions corresponding to a given N_i-distribution.

We have three different cases corresponding to formulae (4.209), (4.211), and (4.214) for $W(n_i)$. First of all we shall consider the Boltzmann case. Let us consider the group (or cell) Z_i and let the number of particles in the first level be n_1, in the second level n_2, $\cdots$, in the last level n_{Z_i}. If we keep the other n_i constant, the contribution from this group will be

$$\sum_{n_1+n_2+\cdots+n_{Z_i}=N_i} \frac{1}{n_1!n_2!\cdots n_{Z_i}!} = \frac{1}{N_i!}\sum \frac{N_i!}{n_1!n_2!\cdots n_{Z_i}!} = \frac{Z_i^{N_i}}{N_i!}, \tag{4.218}$$

where we have used equation (1.704) for the polynomial equation.

For the $W_{\text{Bo}}(N_i)$ we get thus

$$W_{\text{Bo}}(N_i) = \sum W_{\text{Bo}}(n_i) = \prod_j \frac{Z_j^{N_j}}{N_j!}. \tag{4.219}$$

Apart from a constant factor, expression (4.219) is identical with the expression from probability calculus for the probability that N points are distributed among cells Z_j in such a way that there are N_j points in cell Z_j. We met the same expression on page 23 when we discussed the distribution of representative points over volumes in velocity space.

Since $W_{\text{B.E.}}(n_i)$ does not depend on the values of the n_i, we obtain $W_{\text{B.E.}}(N_i)$ if we evaluate the number of different ways by which N_j particles can be distributed over Z_j levels. This number of ways is equal to $(N_j + Z_j - 1)!/N_j!\,(Z_j - 1)!$ and we get thus for $W_{\text{B.E.}}(N_i)$

$$W_{\text{B.E.}}(N_i) = \sum W_{\text{B.E.}}(n_i) = \prod_j \frac{(N_j + Z_j - 1)!}{N_j!(Z_j - 1)!}. \tag{4.220}$$

The expression for the number of ways by which N_j particles can be distributed among Z_j levels can be obtained by a generalization of the argument given in small type on page 56. We now have to write N_j as a sum of Z_j nonnegative integers. That means that we have to divide N_j dots by $Z_j - 1$ strokes. We then get immediately the final result.

If we wish to calculate $W_{\text{F.D.}}(N_i)$ we have to evaluate the number of ways by which N_j particles can be distributed over Z_j levels without having more than one particle in any level. This number is simply the binomial coefficient $\binom{Z_j}{N_j}$. We thus get for $W_{\text{F.D.}}(N_i)$

$$W_{\text{F.D.}}(N_i) = \sum W_{\text{F.D.}}(n_i) = \prod_j \frac{Z_j!}{(Z_j - N_j)!N_j!}. \tag{4.221}$$

If $N_j \ll Z_j$ we can write equations (4.220) and (4.221) in the following form:

$$W_{\text{B.E.}}(N_i) = \prod_j \frac{(N_j + Z_j - 1)(N_j + Z_j - 2)\cdots(Z_j + 1)Z_j}{N_j!}$$

$$\approx \prod_j \frac{Z_j^{N_j}}{N_j!} = W_{\text{Bo}}(N_i)$$

and

$$W_{\text{F.D.}}(N_i) = \prod_j \frac{Z_j(Z_j - 1)\cdots(Z_j - N_j + 2)(Z_j - N_j + 1)}{N_j!}$$

$$\approx \prod_j \frac{Z_j^{N_j}}{N_j!} = W_{\text{Bo}}(N_i).$$

We see that in the limit where $N_j \ll Z_j$ the Bose-Einstein and the Fermi-Dirac formulae go over into the Boltzmann formulae. This can be understood as follows. If $N_j \ll Z_j$, most levels will be empty and practically all n_i will be equal to 0 or 1, which means that $W_{\text{Bo}}(n_i) \simeq W_{\text{B.E.}}(n_i) \simeq W_{\text{F.D.}}(n_i) = 1$.

We should like to draw attention to the following property of the probabilities given by equations (4.219) to (4.221). Consider two completely separated systems composed of the same kind of particles. The total number of particles in the two systems may be $N^{(1)}$ and $N^{(2)}$ with distributions $N_i^{(1)}$ and $N_i^{(2)}$. Let $W^{(1)}$ be the probability of the $N_i^{(1)}$-distribution and $W^{(2)}$ that of the $N_i^{(2)}$-distribution. The total probability W that we have distributions $N_i^{(1)}$ in the first and $N_i^{(2)}$ in the second system will be given by the expression $W = W^{(1)} \cdot W^{(2)}$ so long as we use one of the expressions (4.219) to (4.221). However, if we should use expression (4.208) for $W(n_i)$ and a corresponding expression for $W(N_i)$, this multiplication property of the $W(N_i)$ would no longer hold. Since the multiplication property of the $W(N_i)$ ensures that the entropy, which, as we shall see presently, is given by the equation $S = k \ln W$, will have the necessary *additive* property, the multiplication property is most desirable.

Both the fact that the choice of equation (4.209) for $W_{\text{Bo}}(n_i)$ has as a consequence that $W_{\text{Bo}}(N_i)$ is the limiting value of both $W_{\text{B.E.}}(N_i)$ and $W_{\text{F.D.}}(N_i)$, and the multiplication property of our $W_{\text{Bo}}(N_i)$ are strong arguments in favor of the omission of the $N!$. This omission corresponds to the introduction of the factor e/N in the expression for the partition function (pp. 43 and 49; e/N enters here as the Nth power root of $1/N!$ for large values of N) as we shall see later on.

§3. The Elementary Method of Statistics. The elementary method of statistics consists of determining the values of N_i for which $W(N_i)$ is a maximum for a given total number of particles and total energy. It is then assumed that this N_i-distribution, for which $W(N_i)$ is maximum, will be realized in an actual physical system in equilibrium. The implications of this assumption will be discussed in Appendix I.

As soon as this N_i-distribution has been determined, the thermodynamical quantities can be calculated. In particular we shall show that the entropy is given by the equation

$$S = k \ln W_{\text{max}}. \tag{4.301}$$

Before we start to determine W_{max}, we must remind ourselves that the energy levels ϵ_i and hence the representative energy values E_i may depend on external parameters,

$$\epsilon_i = \epsilon_i(a_1, a_2, \cdots) \tag{4.302}$$

and

$$E_i = E_i(a_1,a_2, \cdots). \tag{4.303}$$

Following the discussion in §6 of Chapter II we introduce the force A_{km} exerted by one particle in the kth stationary state on the external parameter a_m. The total force† A_m exerted by the system on the parameter a_m will be given by the equation

$$A_m = -\sum_k n_k \frac{\partial \epsilon_k}{\partial a_m} = -\sum_j N_j \frac{\partial E_j}{\partial a_m}. \tag{4.304}$$

We shall now determine the N_i-distribution for which W is maximum, or rather for which $\ln W$ is maximum. We shall assume that all Z_i, N_i, and $Z_i - N_i$ (in the Fermi-Dirac case) are large compared to one so that we can use Stirling's formula for the factorial. We then have

$$\ln W_{\text{Bo}} = \sum_j N_j \left[\ln \frac{Z_j}{N_j} + 1\right], \tag{4.305}$$

$$\ln W_{\text{B.E.}} = \sum_j \left[(N_j + Z_j) \ln \left(\frac{Z_j}{N_j} + 1\right) - Z_j \ln \frac{Z_j}{N_j}\right], \tag{4.306}$$

$$\ln W_{\text{F.D.}} = \sum_j \left[(N_j - Z_j) \ln \left(\frac{Z_j}{N_j} - 1\right) + Z_j \ln \frac{Z_j}{N_j}\right]. \tag{4.307}$$

Since the total energy E and the total number of particles N are fixed, the conditions for a maximum of $\ln W$ are that for any variation δN_j of the N_j we have

$$\delta \ln W = 0, \qquad \delta N = 0, \qquad \text{and} \qquad \delta E = 0. \tag{4.308}$$

From equations (4.305) to (4.307) we have for $\delta \ln W$

$$\delta \ln W_{\text{Bo}} = \sum_j \ln \frac{Z_j}{N_j} \delta N_j, \tag{4.309}$$

$$\delta \ln W_{\text{B.E.}} = \sum_j \ln \left(\frac{Z_j}{N_j} + 1\right) \delta N_j, \tag{4.310}$$

$$\delta \ln W_{\text{F.D.}} = \sum_j \ln \left(\frac{Z_j}{N_j} - 1\right) \delta N_j. \tag{4.311}$$

In order not to have every equation three times, we shall write instead of equations (4.309) to (4.311) in general

$$\delta \ln W = \sum_j F_j \delta N_j. \tag{4.312}$$

† It must be remarked here that while the A_m on p. 40 were the forces per molecule, the A_m introduced here are the total forces exerted by the system.

Using equations (4.215), (4.216), and (4.312), equations (4.308) can be written in the form

$$\delta \ln W = \sum_j F_j \delta N_j = 0, \tag{4.313}$$

$$\delta N = \sum_j \delta N_j = 0, \tag{4.314}$$

$$\delta E = \sum_j E_j \delta N_j = 0. \tag{4.315}$$

Using Lagrange's method of undetermined multipliers, we have that for any arbitrary choice of δN_j

$$\delta \ln W + \nu \delta N - \mu \delta E = 0. \tag{4.316}$$

Hence it follows that

$$F_j = -\nu + \mu E_j. \tag{4.317}$$

Since the F_j are functions of the N_j only, the N_j are determined by equation (4.317) as functions of ν, μ, and the a_i (through the E_j). If we wish to do so, we can express ν and μ in terms of N and E, using equations (4.215) and (4.216).

From equations (4.309) to (4.312) and equation (4.317), we get for the N_i-distributions which make $W(N_i)$ a maximum the following expressions

$$\text{Boltzmann:} \qquad N_j = Z_j e^{\nu} e^{-\mu E_j}, \tag{4.318}$$

$$\text{Bose-Einstein:} \qquad N_j = \frac{Z_j}{e^{-\nu+\mu E_j} - 1}, \tag{4.319}$$

$$\text{Fermi-Dirac:} \qquad N_j = \frac{Z_j}{e^{-\nu+\mu E_j} + 1}. \tag{4.320}$$

Equation (4.318) gives us once more the Maxwell-Boltzmann distribution. Equation (4.319) reminds us of equation (3.202), but with the difference that we have to put $\nu = 0$ in order to get equation (3.202). This corresponds to the fact that for light quanta we have to use Bose-Einstein statistics but without any restrictions as to the total number of particles.

From equations (4.318) to (4.320) we see that the Bose-Einstein and Fermi-Dirac formulae will go over into the Boltzmann formulae if

$$e^{-\nu+\mu E_j} \gg 1. \tag{4.321}$$

This is, however, equivalent to the condition $N_j/Z_j \ll 1$ as can immediately be seen from equation (4.318). One way of satisfying condition (4.321) is by choosing ν to be large and negative.

From equations (4.318) and (4.320) we see that any value of ν will correspond to an N_i-distribution in the case of Boltzmann or Fermi-Dirac statistics. In the case of Bose-Einstein statistics, however, we see that ν

is restricted to such values that

$$e^{\nu} < e^{\mu\epsilon_0}, \tag{4.322}$$

where ϵ_0 is the lowest energy level of a particle in the system. We shall return to the importance and consequences of restriction (4.322) in Chapter IX.

§4. **Connection with Classical Thermodynamics.** We shall discuss in this section the connection between our probability arguments and classical thermodynamics. The discussion will develop along much the same lines as the discussion in §6 of Chapter I or §7 of Chapter II.

For this purpose we compare two states of the system for which ν, μ, and the external parameters a_i have slightly different values, the differences being denoted by $\delta\nu$, $\delta\mu$, and δa_i. In both cases we shall assume that we are dealing with the equilibrium N_i-distribution corresponding to a maximum of $\ln W$. In the remainder of the chapter N_i will denote the values of an equilibrium N_i-distribution, and W (or $W_{\max}$) the maximum value of W.

From equations (4.312) and (4.317) we have

$$\delta \ln W_{\max} = -\nu\sum_j \delta N_j + \mu \sum_j E_j \delta N_j. \tag{4.401}$$

Denoting by δA the work done by the system on the external parameters when these parameters change from a_i to $a_i + \delta a_i$, and using equations (4.304) and (4.303), we have

$$\delta A = \sum_i A_i \delta a_i = -\sum_j\sum_i N_j \frac{\partial E_j}{\partial a_i}\delta a_i = -\sum_j N_j \delta E_j. \tag{4.402}$$

From equations (4.216) and (4.215) we have also

$$\delta N = \sum_j \delta N_j, \tag{4.403}$$

$$\delta E = \sum_j E_j \delta N_j + \sum_j N_j \delta E_j = \sum_j E_j \delta N_j - \delta A. \tag{4.404}$$

We define now a quantity δQ by the equation

$$\delta Q = \sum_j E_j \delta N_j. \tag{4.405}$$

From equations (4.404) and (4.405) it follows that

$$\delta Q = \delta E + \delta A, \tag{4.406}$$

or δQ is the heat added to the system, that is, the increase of energy not accounted for by macroscopically measurable work (compare the definition of δA).

Combining equations (4.401) and (4.403) to (4.406), we have

$$\delta \ln W_{\max} = -\nu\delta N + \mu\delta Q = -\nu\delta N + \mu(\delta E + \delta A). \qquad \mathbf{(4.407)}$$

In connection with equation (4.317) we mentioned that F_j and thus $\ln W_{\max}$ were functions of ν, μ, and the a_i. We also mentioned that in principle it is possible to express ν and μ in terms of N and E. In equation (4.407) we have, indeed, used N, E, and the a_i as independent variables, since the resulting expression for $\delta \ln W_{\max}$ is much simpler.

Let us consider for a moment two states of the system for which $\delta N = 0$. In that case we see that μ is an integrating factor of δQ. From classical thermodynamics we then know that μ has to be proportional to the reciprocal of the absolute temperature T and that $\mu\delta Q$ must be proportional to the variation of the entropy S, and we have

$$\mu = \frac{1}{kT}, \qquad \mathbf{(4.408)}$$

$$S = k \ln W_{\max}. \qquad \mathbf{(4.409)}$$

The constant k occurring in equations (4.408) and (4.409) is again Boltzmann's constant. This can be proved, for instance, by comparing the equation of state following from equation (4.407) with the perfect gas law (see §5, equation [4.513]).

The complete proof that k is really Boltzmann's constant is slightly more complicated. It involves the consideration of a system consisting of the system under consideration combined with a "gas thermometer." One then first proves that μ is the same for the two systems (compare the discussion on p. 122) and, secondly, one assumes that the gas in the "thermometer" is so diluted that it can be treated as a perfect gas. We refer to the literature for a more extensive discussion.†

From equations (4.407) and (4.409) we see that the entropy is not only a function of the a_i and μ (or T), but also of ν. We know from classical thermodynamics that the entropy is an extensive or additive quantity, that is, that for two systems (1) and (2) which are independent the total entropy will be equal to $S^{(1)} + S^{(2)}$. This property follows from equation (4.409), since the $W_{\max}$ are multiplicative (compare the discussion at the end of §2).

Let us now consider the physical meaning of ν. For the free energy F ($= E - ST$) of the system we have from equations (4.407) to (4.409)

$$\delta F = \delta(E - ST) = -S\delta T + \frac{\nu}{\mu}\,\delta N - \delta A. \qquad \mathbf{(4.410)}$$

† See, e.g., R. C. Tolman, The Principles of Statistical Mechanics, Oxford 1938, p. 85.

We thus get

$$\frac{\nu}{\mu} = \left(\frac{\partial F}{\partial N}\right)_{T, a_i} = g, \tag{4.411}$$

where g is the free energy per particle, or the thermal potential per particle. For ν we thus have

$$\nu = \mu g = \frac{g}{kT} \cdot \tag{4.412}$$

That g can be interpreted as the partial thermal potential follows easily when we consider a system where the volume V is one of the external parameters. We shall assume for the sake of simplicity that it is actually the only one, so that $\delta A = p\delta V$.

Introducing the thermal potential† G by the equation

$$G = F + pV = E - ST + pV, \tag{4.413}$$

we have for its variation

$$\delta G = \delta F + p\delta V + V\delta p = -S\delta T + \frac{\nu}{\mu}\,\delta N + V\delta p, \tag{4.414}$$

whence

$$g = \left(\frac{\partial G}{\partial N}\right)_{T,p} \cdot \tag{4.415}$$

Before we apply our formulae to the case of a perfect gas, we wish to introduce a new thermodynamical quantity, called by Kramers the q-potential. This q-potential is dimensionless and is defined by the equation

$$q = \ln W_{\max} + \nu N - \mu E = \frac{ST + gN - E}{kT} \cdot \tag{4.416}$$

Using equation (4.407) we get for its variation

$$\delta q = N\delta\nu - E\delta\mu + \mu\delta A. \tag{4.417}$$

We see that in this case ν, μ, and the a_i are the natural choice of independent variables. From equations (4.417) and (4.402) we get the equations

$$N = \frac{\partial q}{\partial \nu}, \tag{4.418}$$

$$E = -\frac{\partial q}{\partial \mu}, \tag{4.419}$$

† The thermal potential is also sometimes called the chemical potential or the thermodynamic potential.

and

$$A_i = \frac{1}{\mu} \frac{\partial q}{\partial a_i}. \tag{4.420}$$

If we are dealing with a homogeneous system of which the volume is one of the external parameters, we have

$$gN = G = E - ST + pV, \tag{4.421}$$

and hence from equation (4.416),

$$q = \frac{pV}{kT}. \tag{4.422}$$

§5. **The Perfect Boltzmann Gas.** We shall consider in the present and in the subsequent sections the case of a perfect gas. In order to simplify the expression for the energy levels we assume that the gas is enclosed in a cube of edge length L and of volume V $(= L^3)$.

If m is the mass of one particle, the energy levels are given by the equation

$$\epsilon = \frac{\epsilon_0}{3}(k_1{}^2 + k_2{}^2 + k_3{}^2), \qquad \epsilon_0 = \frac{3h^2}{8mL^2}, \tag{4.501}$$

where k_1, k_2, and k_3, which are positive integers, are the quantum numbers corresponding to the three translational degrees of freedom. The quantity ϵ_0 is the lowest energy level corresponding to $k_1 = k_2 = k_3 = 1$.

Each stationary state corresponds to a point in the three-dimensional k_1,k_2,k_3-space which is situated in the positive octant. Introducing k by the equation

$$k^2 = k_1{}^2 + k_2{}^2 + k_3{}^2, \tag{4.502}$$

we find for the number of energy levels dZ with k between k and $k + dk$ the expression

$$dZ = \tfrac{1}{8} \cdot 4\pi k^2 dk. \tag{4.503}$$

Using equations (4.501) and (4.502), this expression for dZ can be written in the form

$$dZ = 2\pi \left(\frac{2m}{h^2}\right)^{3/2} V\sqrt{\epsilon}d\epsilon. \tag{4.504†}$$

If we consider a Boltzmann gas, we have from equations (4.305) and (4.318)

$$\ln W_{\text{Bo}} = \sum_j N_j(-\nu + \mu E_j + 1) = -(\nu - 1)N + \mu E, \tag{4.505}$$

† It has to be remarked that equation (4.504) remains valid even if the volume V is not a cube. See, e.g., R. Courant and D. Hilbert, Methoden der Mathematischen Physik, Vol. I, Berlin 1931, p. 373.

where we have dropped the index "max" on the W and where the N_i are once more the equilibrium values.

For the q-potential we get

$$q_{\text{Bo}} = \ln W + \nu N - \mu E = N = \sum_j N_j, \tag{4.506}$$

or

$$q_{\text{Bo}} = e^{\nu} \sum_j Z_j e^{-\mu E_j} = e^{\nu} Z(\mu), \tag{4.507}$$

where $Z(\mu)$ is the *partition function* which is a function of the μ (and of the external parameters),

$$Z(\mu) = \sum_j Z_j e^{-\mu E_j}. \tag{4.508}$$

For the groups of energy levels Z_j we can take in the case of a gas energy intervals dZ, and then all sums will go over into integrals.

Using expression (4.504) for dZ, we get for the partition function

$$Z = 2\pi \left(\frac{2m}{h^2}\right)^{3/2} V \int_0^{\infty} \epsilon^{1/2} e^{-\mu\epsilon} d\epsilon = \left(\frac{2\pi m}{\mu h^2}\right)^{3/2} V, \tag{4.509}$$

and for the q-potential

$$q_{\text{Bo}} = \left(\frac{2\pi m}{\mu h^2}\right)^{3/2} V e^{\nu}. \tag{4.510}$$

From equation (4.418) we get

$$N = \frac{\partial q_{\text{Bo}}}{\partial \nu} = q_{\text{Bo}}, \tag{4.511}$$

which is the same as equation (4.506).

If we assume that V is the only external parameter so that $\delta A = p\delta V$, we have from equation (4.420) (see also equation [4.422]),

$$\mu p = \frac{\partial q_{\text{Bo}}}{\partial V} = \frac{q_{\text{Bo}}}{V} = \frac{N}{V}, \tag{4.512}$$

or

$$pV = \frac{N}{\mu} = NkT, \tag{4.513}$$

which is once more the perfect gas law.

The energy E of the system follows from equation (4.419)

$$E = -\frac{\partial q_{\text{Bo}}}{\partial \mu} = \frac{3}{2}\frac{q_{\text{Bo}}}{\mu} = \frac{3}{2}NkT, \tag{4.514}$$

corresponding to the equipartition of the kinetic energy, giving a contribution $\frac{1}{2}kT$ for each degree of freedom.

The partial thermal potential divided by kT, ν, is given by

$$\nu = \ln \frac{q_{\text{Bo}}}{Z} = \ln p - \frac{5}{2} \ln T - \mathfrak{C} - \frac{3}{2} \ln M, \tag{4.515}$$

where M is the molecular weight of the gas and $\mathfrak{C}$ the constant given by equation (2.808).

Finally we get for the entropy from equation (4.416), using equations (4.511) and (4.514),

$$S = kq_{\text{Bo}} - k\nu N + \frac{E}{T} = Nk\left(\frac{5}{2} - \nu\right), \tag{4.516}$$

which is the same as equation (2.810), as can be checked by substituting for ν expression (4.515).

§6. The Perfect Bose-Einstein Gas. In this and the next section we shall discuss the perfect Bose-Einstein and Fermi-Dirac gases. We shall then also be in a position to see what differences between the various statistics occur. First of all, however, we shall investigate under what circumstances we can safely apply Boltzmann statistics.

Since all energy values are positive and since $\mu\epsilon_0$ is practically always very small compared to one (compare the discussion on p. 62), the condition for the applicability of Boltzmann statistics (equation [4.322]) reduces to the condition

$$e^{-\nu} \gg 1. \tag{4.601}$$

The total number of particles will now be given to a fair approximation by the same equation for the three statistics,

$$N = \sum_j N_j \approx \sum_j Z_j e^{\nu - \mu E_j},$$

or

$$N \cong e^{\nu} \left(\frac{2\pi mkT}{h^2}\right)^{3/2} V, \tag{4.602}$$

where we have used equations (4.318) to (4.320), (4.601), (4.508), and (4.509).

We thus get for $e^{-\nu}$ approximately

$$e^{-\nu} \cong \left(\frac{2\pi mk}{h^2}\right)^{3/2} T^{3/2} \left(\frac{N}{V}\right)^{-1}. \tag{4.603}$$

From equations (4.603) and (4.601) we see first of all that in the limit $h \to 0$, Boltzmann statistics may be applied. We can thus understand why Boltzmann statistics are often called the classical statistics.

Secondly we see that in the limit of high temperatures or low densities condition (4.601) is satisfied and Boltzmann statistics can be applied.

We should like to write equation (4.603) in a slightly different form. The average energy per particle—which is in the present case the same as the average kinetic energy—is in the classical limit equal to $\frac{3}{2}kT$ (compare equation [4.514]). It follows from the usual quantum mechanical arguments that the De Broglie wavelength λ_{DBr} of the particle will be given by the equation

$$\lambda_{\mathrm{DBr}} = \frac{h}{p} = \frac{h}{\sqrt{2m\epsilon}} = \left(\frac{h^2}{3mkT}\right)^{1/2}, \tag{4.604}$$

where p is the momentum of the particle.

Combining equations (4.603) and (4.604), we have

$$e^{\nu} \cong \left(\frac{3}{2\pi}\right)^{3/2} \lambda_{\mathrm{DBr}}{}^{3} \frac{N}{V}. \tag{4.605}$$

We see from equation (4.605) that condition (4.601) is equivalent to the condition that the De Broglie wavelength of the particles is small compared to the average distance apart in the gas.

It need hardly be mentioned that equations (4.603) and (4.605) are only valid in the case where $e^{\nu} \ll 1$. They actually represent the first terms of series expansions.

Let us now return to a perfect Bose-Einstein gas. From equations (4.306) and (4.319) we have

$$\ln W_{\mathrm{B.E.}} = \sum_j N_j(-\nu + \mu E_j) - \sum_j Z_j \ln (1 - e^{\nu - \mu E_j}). \tag{4.606}$$

The q-potential follows from equation (4.416) and is given by the equation

$$q_{\mathrm{B.E.}} = -\sum_j Z_j \ln (1 - e^{\nu - \mu E_j}). \tag{4.607}$$

In most cases we can use an integral instead of the sum (compare the remarks on p. 61), and then we can apply equation (4.504) and get

$$q_{\mathrm{B.E.}} = -2\pi \left(\frac{2m}{h^2}\right)^{3/2} V \int_0^{\infty} \sqrt{\epsilon} \ln (1 - e^{\nu - \mu\epsilon}) d\epsilon, \tag{4.608}$$

or

$$q_{\mathrm{B.E.}} = \left(\frac{2\pi m}{\mu h^2}\right)^{3/2} V g(\nu), \tag{4.609}$$

where

$$g(\nu) = \sum_{n=1}^{\infty} \frac{e^{n\nu}}{n^{5/2}}. \tag{4.610}$$

We have for $g(\nu)$, so long as $e^\nu \leqslant 1$,

$$g(\nu) = \frac{-2}{\sqrt{\pi}} \int_0^\infty \sqrt{x} \ln (1 - e^{\nu - x}) dx$$

$$= \frac{2}{\sqrt{\pi}} \sum_{n=1}^{\infty} \frac{1}{n} \int_0^\infty \sqrt{x} e^{n\nu - nx} dx,$$

whence equation (4.610) follows.

For the total number of particles we have from equation (4.418)

$$N = \frac{\partial q_{\text{B.E.}}}{\partial \nu} = \left(\frac{2\pi m}{\mu h^2}\right)^{3/2} V g'(\nu) = q_{\text{B.E.}} \frac{g'(\nu)}{g(\nu)}, \tag{4.611}$$

where

$$g'(\nu) = \frac{dg(\nu)}{d\nu} = \sum_{n=1}^{\infty} \frac{e^{n\nu}}{n^{3/2}}. \tag{4.612}$$

The pressure and total energy are given by the equations

$$p = \frac{q_{\text{B.E.}}}{\mu V}, \tag{4.613}$$

$$E = -\frac{\partial q_{\text{B.E.}}}{\partial \mu} = \frac{3}{2} \frac{q_{\text{B.E.}}}{\mu}. \tag{4.614}$$

We see that from equations (4.613) and (4.614) it follows that

$$p = \frac{2}{3} \frac{E}{V}. \tag{4.615}$$

This equation could have been derived much more easily. From equation (4.501) we see that the energy of a particle is proportional to $V^{-2/3}$. As $-\partial\epsilon/\partial V$ is the pressure exerted by one particle, it follows that this partial pressure is equal to $\frac{2}{3}\epsilon/V$ and equation (4.615) follows immediately. It also follows from this derivation that this equation must hold irrespective of the kind of statistics. Indeed, from equations (4.513) and (4.514) it follows in the Boltzmann case, and it will also be found to hold in the Fermi-Dirac case.

From equations (4.611) and (4.613) we get

$$pV = NkT \frac{g(\nu)}{g'(\nu)}. \tag{4.616}$$

Since in the Bose-Einstein case equation (4.322) will always be satisfied, we can always expand in powers of e^ν. If we expand $g(\nu)/g'(\nu)$ in powers of e^ν we get from equation (4.616)

$$pV = NkT\left[1 - \frac{e^\nu}{2^{5/2}} + \cdots\right]. \tag{4.617}$$

We observe here deviations from the perfect gas law. These deviations tend to zero when ν goes to $-\infty$.

Introducing a quantity α by the equation

$$\alpha = \left(\frac{h^2}{2\pi mkT}\right)^{3/2}\frac{N}{V}, \tag{4.618}$$

we get from equation (4.611) the following series expansion for e^ν,

$$e^\nu = \alpha\left[1 - \frac{\alpha}{2^{3/2}} + \cdots\right], \tag{4.619}$$

and we see that, indeed, equation (4.603) follows in the limit $\alpha \to 0$.

From equations (4.617) and (4.619), we then get for the equation of state

$$pV = NkT\left[1 - \frac{\alpha}{2^{5/2}} + \cdots\right]. \tag{4.620}$$

Using equations (4.614), (4.611), and (4.619), we get the following expansion for the energy,

$$E = \tfrac{3}{2}NkT\left[1 - \frac{\alpha}{2^{5/2}} + \cdots\right]. \tag{4.621}$$

The entropy follows from equation (4.416)

$$S = kq - k\nu N + \frac{E}{T}\cdot \tag{4.622}$$

Using equations (4.609), (4.611), (4.614), and (4.619), we get for S the following expansion:

$$S = Nk\left[\frac{5}{2} - \ln\alpha - \frac{\alpha}{2^{7/2}} + \cdots\right]. \tag{4.623}$$

We now wish to calculate the specific heats C_v and C_p and their ratio $\kappa = C_p/C_v$. For C_v we have from equations (4.614) and (4.618)

$$C_v = \left(\frac{\partial E}{\partial T}\right)_V = \frac{3}{2}Nk\left[1 + \frac{\alpha}{2^{7/2}} + \cdots\right]. \tag{4.624}$$

In order to obtain C_p we have to express δQ in terms of δT under the condition that the pressure is kept constant. This can be done in the following way. First of all we use equation (4.615) to get

$$\delta Q = \delta E + p\delta V = \delta E + \frac{2}{3}\frac{E}{V}\,\delta V = \frac{5}{3}\,\delta E, \tag{4.625}$$

since from equation (4.615) it follows that in the case of constant pressure $\delta \ln E = \delta \ln V$.

From equations (4.621) and (4.618) we have

$$\delta E = \frac{3}{2}Nk\left[1 - \frac{\alpha}{2^{5/2}} + \cdots\right]\delta T - \frac{3}{2}Nk\,\frac{\delta\alpha}{2^{5/2}} + \cdots, \tag{4.626}$$

and

$$\delta \ln \alpha = -\tfrac{3}{2}\,\delta \ln T - \delta \ln V. \tag{4.627}$$

Combining equations (4.625) to (4.627), we finally get for C_p the expansion

$$C_p = \left(T\frac{\partial S}{\partial T}\right)_p = \frac{5}{2}Nk\left[1 + \frac{3\alpha}{2^{7/2}} + \cdots\right], \tag{4.628}$$

and for the ratio of the specific heats

$$\kappa = \frac{C_p}{C_v} = \frac{5}{3}\left[1 + \frac{\alpha}{2^{5/2}} + \cdots\right]. \tag{4.629}$$

All series converge, and everywhere the first term gives the expression for the perfect Boltzmann gas.

We mentioned in §3 that in the Bose-Einstein case ν should be restricted to values smaller than $\mu\epsilon_0$. Let us consider for a moment the case where ν approaches this limiting value. We shall assume that ν is so close to $\mu\epsilon_0$ that we have

$$-\nu + \mu\epsilon_0 \ll 1 \qquad \text{and} \qquad -\nu + \mu\epsilon_0 \ll \mu(\epsilon_1 - \epsilon_0), \tag{4.630}$$

where ϵ_1 is the lowest level but one (it follows from equation [4.501] that $\epsilon_1 = 2\epsilon_0$).

If we use equations (4.216) and (4.319) to calculate the total number of particles, we have

$$N = \sum_j \frac{Z_j}{e^{-\nu+\mu E_j} - 1}\cdot \tag{4.631}$$

We shall ignore for the moment the fact that in our derivations we have used the assumption $Z_j \ll 1$ and we shall assume all Z_j to be equal to 1 so that the E_j are the energy levels of the particles. Using the inequalities (4.630), equation (4.631) then reduces to

$$N = \frac{1}{e^{-\nu+\mu\epsilon_0} - 1} + \frac{1}{e^{-\nu+\mu\epsilon_1} - 1} + \cdots \tag{4.632}$$

or

$$N \approx \frac{1}{-\nu + \mu\epsilon_0}. \tag{4.633}$$

Since the different terms on the right-hand side of equation (4.631) represent the number of atoms occupying the various energy levels, equation (4.633) expresses that for $\nu \to \mu\epsilon_0$ all atoms tend to occupy the lowest level. This phenomenon is the so-called *Einstein condensation.* It is a typical quantum effect, since for $h \to 0$, ν will go to $-\infty$. The reason why this is called a condensation and the behavior of the pressure as a function of the density will be discussed in §2 of Chapter IX.

§7. The Perfect Fermi-Dirac Gas. The discussion in this section develops parallel to that given in the preceding section as long as $e^\nu \ll 1$. We shall first give the results without any further comments. Instead of equations (4.606) to (4.614) we have now

$$\ln W_{\text{F.D.}} = \sum_j N_j(-\nu + \mu E_j) + \sum_j Z_j \ln (1 + e^{\nu - \mu E_j}), \tag{4.701}$$

$$q_{\text{F.D.}} = \sum_j Z_j \ln [1 + e^{\nu - \mu E_j}], \tag{4.702}$$

$$q_{\text{F.D.}} = 2\pi \left(\frac{2m}{h^2}\right)^{3/2} V \int_0^\infty \sqrt{\epsilon} \ln [1 + e^{\nu - \mu\epsilon}] d\epsilon, \tag{4.703}$$

$$q_{\text{F.D.}} = \left(\frac{2\pi m}{\mu h^2}\right)^{3/2} V h(\nu), \tag{4.704}$$

$$h(\nu) = -\sum_{n=1}^{\infty} \frac{(-e^\nu)^n}{n^{5/2}}, \tag{4.705}$$

$$h'(\nu) = -\sum_{n=1}^{\infty} \frac{(-e^\nu)^n}{n^{3/2}}, \tag{4.706}$$

$$N = q_{\text{F.D.}} \frac{h'(\nu)}{h(\nu)}, \tag{4.707}$$

$$p = \frac{q_{\text{F.D.}}}{\mu V}, \tag{4.708}$$

$$E = \frac{3}{2} \frac{q_{\text{F.D.}}}{\mu}. \tag{4.709}$$

From equations (4.708) and (4.709) it follows again that equation (4.615) is satisfied.

Introducing once more α by equation (4.618), we get now instead of equations (4.619) to (4.621), (4.623), (4.624), (4.628), and (4.629), the expansions

$$e^{\nu} = \alpha\left[1 + \frac{\alpha}{2^{3/2}} + \cdots\right], \tag{4.710}$$

$$pV = NkT\left[1 + \frac{\alpha}{2^{5/2}} + \cdots\right], \tag{4.711}$$

$$E = \frac{3}{2}NkT\left[1 + \frac{\alpha}{2^{5/2}} + \cdots\right], \tag{4.712}$$

$$S = Nk\left[\frac{5}{2} - \ln\alpha + \frac{\alpha}{2^{7/2}} + \cdots\right], \tag{4.713}$$

$$C_v = \frac{3}{2}Nk\left[1 - \frac{\alpha}{2^{7/2}} + \cdots\right], \tag{4.714}$$

$$C_p = \frac{5}{2}Nk\left[1 - \frac{3\alpha}{2^{7/2}} + \cdots\right], \tag{4.715}$$

$$\kappa = \frac{5}{3}\left[1 - \frac{\alpha}{2^{5/2}} + \cdots\right]. \tag{4.716}$$

All series converge so long as $e^{\nu} \leqslant 1$. We see that in first approximation Bose-Einstein and Fermi-Dirac statistics differ only in the *sign* of the deviation from the Boltzmann statistics. Higher terms are, however, no longer the same.

We shall now discuss the case where $e^{\nu} \gg 1$. This is called the case of *strong degeneracy* and the gas is called a *degenerate quantum gas*. From equation (4.603) we see that for $T = 0$, that is, at the absolute zero, the degeneracy will be complete. Let us first discuss the behavior at absolute zero.

From equations (4.703) and (4.418) we get for the total number of particles

$$N = \frac{\partial q}{\partial \nu} = 2\pi\left(\frac{2m}{h^2}\right)^{3/2} V\int_0^{\infty} \frac{\sqrt{\epsilon}\,d\epsilon}{1 + e^{-\nu+\mu\epsilon}}. \tag{4.717}$$

From this equation we see that the number of particles with energies between ϵ and $\epsilon + d\epsilon$ is given by the equation

$$dN = f(\epsilon)d\epsilon = 2\pi\left(\frac{2m}{h^2}\right)^{3/2} V\frac{\sqrt{\epsilon}\,d\epsilon}{1 + e^{-\nu+\mu\epsilon}}. \tag{4.718}$$

This equation is actually the same as equation (4.320) if we use expression (4.504) for the number of levels between ϵ and $\epsilon + d\epsilon$. We see that while $f(\epsilon)$ varies as $\sqrt{\epsilon}$ for small values of ϵ, for high energies it varies as $e^{-\mu\epsilon}$. This means that the Fermi distribution (4.718) has a "Maxwellian tail."

We introduce now by equation (4.411) the partial thermal potential $g = \nu/\mu$. Its value for $T = 0$ is denoted by g_0. In order to determine this value g_0 we split the integral in equation (4.717) into two parts and write

$$N = 2\pi \left(\frac{2m}{h^2}\right)^{3/2} V \left\{ \int_0^g \frac{\sqrt{\epsilon}\,d\epsilon}{1 + e^{-\mu(g-\epsilon)}} + \int_g^\infty \frac{\sqrt{\epsilon}\,d\epsilon}{1 + e^{\mu(\epsilon-g)}} \right\}. \qquad \textbf{(4.719)}$$

This equation is valid for any value of T (or μ). In the limit $T \to 0$, or $\mu \to \infty$, the second integral is equal to zero and the first one is equal to $\frac{2}{3}{g_0}^{3/2}$. We have thus in this way

$$N = \frac{4\pi}{3}\left(\frac{2m}{h^2}\right)^{3/2} V {g_0}^{3/2}. \qquad \textbf{(4.720)}$$

The distribution curve $f(\epsilon) = dN/d\epsilon$ is then discontinuous. We have drawn it in Figure 21.

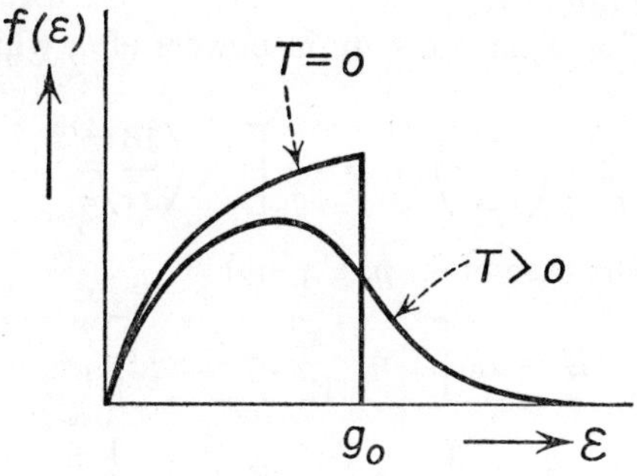

Fig. 21

For a given value of the density N/V, g_0 can be computed from equation (4.720). The energy of the system follows from equations (4.703) and (4.419) and is given by the equation

$$E = -\frac{\partial q}{\partial \mu} = 2\pi \left(\frac{2m}{h^2}\right)^{3/2} V \int_0^\infty \frac{\epsilon\sqrt{\epsilon}\,d\epsilon}{1 + e^{-\nu+\mu\epsilon}}. \qquad \textbf{(4.721)}$$

At absolute zero we get

$$E_0 = \frac{4\pi}{5}\left(\frac{2m}{h^2}\right)^{3/2} V {g_0}^{5/2} = \frac{3}{5}\frac{h^2}{2m} N \left(\frac{3N}{4\pi V}\right)^{2/3}. \qquad \textbf{(4.722)}$$

Equation (4.722) gives us the so-called zero-point energy of a Fermi-Dirac gas. We could also have calculated E_0 by using the Pauli principle and filling up the lowest energy levels until all particles had been assigned.

Combining equations (4.615) and (4.722) we find for the *zero-point pressure*

$$p_0 = \frac{2}{3}\frac{E_0}{V} = \left(\frac{3}{4\pi}\right)^{2/3} \frac{h^2}{5m}\left(\frac{N}{V}\right)^{5/3}, \tag{4.723}$$

and we see that p_0 varies as the $\frac{5}{3}$ power of the density.

That this zero-point pressure is not always negligible can be seen when we consider the "gas" of the conduction electrons in a metal. The density N/V will be of the order of 10^{24} cm^{-3} and with $m \cong 10^{-27}$ g we have

$$p_0 \sim 10^6 \text{ atmos.} \tag{4.724}$$

Equation (4.723) could also have been obtained by combining equations (4.703) and (4.422), performing an integration by parts, and letting $T \to 0$. It follows from the occurrence of h in the expression for p_0 that the zero-point pressure, like the Einstein condensation, is a typical quantum effect.

For temperatures in the neighborhood of the absolute zero we can again give series expansions. The derivation of these series is straightforward, though tedious and not always simple. The easiest way is to use Sommerfeld's method.† The expansions are in powers of β, which is given by the equation

$$\beta = \frac{2mkT}{h^2}\left(\frac{4\pi V}{3N}\right)^{2/3} = \frac{1}{\mu g_0}\left[= \left(\frac{16}{9\pi}\right)^{1/3} \alpha^{-2/3}\right]. \tag{4.725}$$

The result is in the case of E, p, C_v, and S

$$E = E_0\left[1 + \frac{5\pi^2}{12}\beta^2 + \cdots\right], \tag{4.726}$$

$$p = p_0\left[1 + \frac{5\pi^2}{12}\beta^2 + \cdots\right], \tag{4.727}$$

† Sommerfeld (*Z. Physik*, **47**, 1, 1928) proved the following theorem. The integral

$$I = \int_0^\infty \frac{du}{e^{-\alpha+u}+1}\frac{d\varphi}{du}$$

can, for large values of α, be expanded in the following series,

$$I = \varphi(\alpha) + 2\sum_{n=1}^{\infty} c_{2n}\left(\frac{d^{2n}\varphi}{du^{2n}}\right)_{u=\alpha},$$

where

$$c_n = \sum_{k=1}^{\infty} (-1)^{k+1}\frac{1}{k^n}$$

(for instance, $c_2 = \pi^2/12$, $c_4 = 7\pi^4/720$).

Equations (4.726) and (4.727) do not follow immediately from this theorem, but one must use a method similar to the one used on p. 300 to derive equation (13.121).

$$C_v = \frac{\partial E}{\partial T} = \frac{\pi^2}{2} Nk\beta + \cdots, \tag{4.728}$$

$$S = \int_0^T \frac{C_v dT}{T} = \frac{\pi^2}{2} Nk\beta + \cdots. \tag{4.729}$$

In Figure 22 we have drawn E, p, and C_v as functions of the temperature. The dotted lines indicate the behavior of a Boltzmann gas.

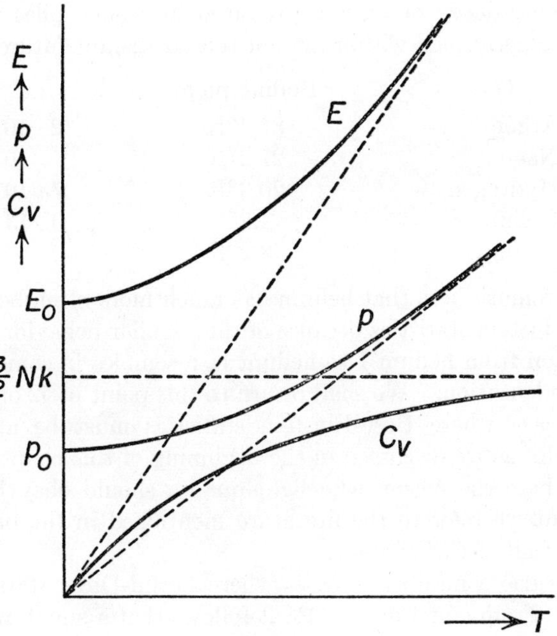

Fig. 22

§8. **Applications of the Bose-Einstein or Fermi-Dirac Statistics.** In the preceding sections we discussed the behavior of perfect gases. The question which we wish to consider in this section is the following one: When can we expect deviations from Boltzmann statistics? Let us confine ourselves to gaseous systems, or systems which to a first approximation may be treated as gases. We saw (equation [4.601]) that the condition for the applicability of Boltzmann statistics was that e^{ν} is small compared to one. We can calculate e^{ν} for various gases at their boiling point, using equation (4.603), and the result is given in the table on the next page.

We see that the only gas for which conceivably deviations from classical statistics could be detected should be helium. In the case of He_4 there seem to be some indications that the equation of state follows more closely that of a Bose-Einstein gas than that of a Fermi-Dirac gas, but the measurements are still far from conclusive. We shall return to this point in §8 of Chapter VIII. We should expect Bose-Einstein behavior from He_4, since the nucleus is built up out of 4 nucleons and there are 2 orbital electrons. Since e^{ν} in the case of He_3 is even larger due to the smaller mass of the He_3 atom and its lower boiling point, one might hope to get a definite confirmation of the statistics obeyed by He_3 through an accurate measurement of its equation of state. With the increasing availability of He_3 from the β-decay of tritium produced in atomic piles this measurement may be performed within the not too far distant future.

Gas	Boiling point	e^{ν}
Argon	87.4°K	$2 \cdot 10^{-6}$
Neon	27.2°K	10^{-4}
Hydrogen	20.3°K	$7 \cdot 10^{-3}$
Helium_4	4.2°K	0.13
Helium_3	3.2°K	0.4

We must remark here that helium has much more often been connected with Bose-Einstein statistics because of the peculiar behavior of the liquid. The transition from helium I to helium II resembles in some respects the Einstein condensation. We shall return to this point in §2 of Chapter IX.

Another case where Bose-Einstein statistics must be applied is the radiation field, as we discussed in the beginning of this chapter. We cannot discuss here the reason why light quanta should obey Bose-Einstein statistics, but we refer to the literature mentioned in the bibliographical notes at the end of this chapter.

There are also a number of cases where Fermi-Dirac statistics have to be applied. From equation (4.603) it follows that a small mass or a high density will make it necessary to abandon Boltzmann statistics. The first case where Fermi-Dirac statistics are applied is that of the "gas" of the conduction electrons in a metal. Assuming an average spacing of 1 ÅU for the atoms in the metal and one conduction electron per atom we have at room temperatures $e^{\nu} \sim 10^5$. Many properties of metals can be understood if we apply Fermi-Dirac statistics to this case. We shall return to this subject in Chapter X.

A second case where Fermi-Dirac statistics must be applied is the nuclear "gas." To a first rough approximation the nucleons inside a nucleus may be treated as a perfect Fermi-Dirac gas, or rather a mixture of two perfect Fermi-Dirac gases, that of the protons and that of the neutrons. We have here a high value of e^{ν} due to the very high nuclear density ($\rho > 10^{12}$ g cm^{-3}). We shall discuss some of the implications of this fact in Chapters XIII and XIV.

Finally, in the interior of some stars such high densities will occur that notwithstanding the very high stellar temperatures the gas is degenerate. Both Fermi-Dirac and Bose-Einstein degeneracy may occur. In Chapter XIV we shall discuss some aspects of this case, but we must refer here to the literature for a more extensive and complete discussion.

BIBLIOGRAPHICAL NOTES

General references for this chapter are

1. G. E. Uhlenbeck, Over Statistische Methoden in de Theorie der Quanta, Thesis, Leiden 1927.
2. P. Jordan, Statistische Mechanik auf Quantentheoretischer Grundlage, Braunschweig 1933.
3. E. Schrödinger, Statistical Thermodynamics, Cambridge 1948.

§1. The Bose-Einstein statistics were first introduced by Bose using a method slightly different from the elementary method:

4. S. N. Bose, Z. Physik, **26**, 178, 1924.

This paper had been translated by Einstein, who added the following note: "Boses Ableitung der Planckschen Formel bedeutet nach meiner Meinung einen wichtigen Fortschritt. Die hier benutzte Methode liefert auch die Quantentheorie des idealen Gases, wie ich an anderer Stelle ausführen will."
This application to the case of a perfect gas appeared the same year:

5. A. Einstein, Berliner Ber., **1924,** 261; **1925,** 3, 18.

Following the introduction of the exclusion principle by Pauli in 1925 in the paper

6. W. Pauli, Z. Physik, **31,** 776, 1925,

Fermi introduced it into the statistical discussion:

7. E. Fermi, Z. Physik, **36,** 902, 1926.

The connection between statistics and wave mechanics was investigated by Dirac:

8. P. A. M. Dirac, Proc. Roy. Soc. (London), **A112,** 661, 1926.

§2. The fact that the omission of the factor $N!$ is essential in order that S is an extensive quantity was noted by Gibbs. Compare, for instance,

9. J. W. Gibbs, Elementary Principles in Statistical Mechanics (Vol. II of his Collected Works), New Haven 1948, Chap. XV.

Compare also

10. L. Nordheim, Z. Physik, **40,** 492, 1924.
11. G. S. Rushbrooke, Introduction to Statistical Mechanics, Oxford 1949, pp. 36ff.

For the connection between accessible states and probabilities see refs. 1 and 8. A discussion about the splitting up of the $N!$ possible wave functions according to their symmetry properties was given by Wigner:

12. E. Wigner, Z. Physik, **40,** 492, 1926.
13. E. Wigner, Z. Physik, **40,** 883, 1927.

The reason why some particles obey Bose-Einstein and others Fermi-Dirac statistics lies rather deep. One can show that if the annihilation and creation operators corresponding to a description where "second quantization" (P. Jordan and O. Klein, Z. Physik, **45,** 751, 1927; P. Jordan and E. Wigner,

Z. Physik, **47,** 631, 1928; compare also H. A. Kramers, Hand- u. Jahrb. d. Chem. Phys., Vol. I, Leipzig 1938, §72; G. Wentzel, Quantum Theory of Fields, New York 1949, §22; C. Møller, Mimeographed Notes of Lectures on Quantum Electrodynamics given at Purdue University, 1948–1949, §§4 and 5) is introduced follow the symmetric commutation rules, the corresponding particles obey Bose-Einstein statistics, while they obey Fermi-Dirac statistics if annihilation and creation operators are anticommuting. (See, e.g., Møller, *loc. cit.*)

Pauli and Belinfante gave in 1940 (Physica, **7,** 177, 1940) the following general principles (we quote their summary and have inserted further references): "Es wird untersucht, in wie weit Spekulationen über die Statistik willkürlicher, hypothetischer Teilchen in einer relativistisch invarianten Theorie möglich sind, wenn alle oder ein Teil der folgenden drei Postulate vorausgesetzt werden: (I) die Energie ist positiv; (II) Observable an verschiedenen Raum-Zeitpunkten mit raumartiger Verbindungslinie sind kommutativ; (III) es gibt zwei äquivalente Beschreibungen der Natur, in welchen die Elementarladungen entgegengesetzte Vorzeichen haben und in welchen einander entsprechende Feldgrössen sich bei Lorentz-Transformationen in gleicher Weise transformieren. [Cf. H. A. Kramers, Proc. Kon. Ned. Akad. Wet. (Amsterdam), **40,** 814, 1937.]

"Der eine von uns [W. Pauli, Phys. Rev., **58,** 716, 1940] hatte bereits gezeigt, dass allgemein bei ganzzahligem Spin aus (II) allein Einstein-Bose-Statistik, bei halbzahligem Spin aus (I) allein Fermi-Dirac-Statistik folgt. Ferner hat der andere von uns [F. J. Belinfante, Physica, **6,** 870, 1939] gezeigt, dass für eine gewisse Klasse von Teilchen, (die alle bisher in der Natur beobachteten umfasst, und die dadurch charakterisiert ist, dass sie höchtens *einen* Undor [cf. F. J. Belinfante, Physica, **6,** 849, 1939] von gegebener Stufe beschrieben wird), aus dem durch ein spezielles Transformationsgesetz spezialisierten Postulat (III) für ganzen Spin E.-B.-Statistik, für halbzahligen Spin F.-D.-Statistik gefolgert werden kann. In der vorliegenden Note wird in den typischen Fällen von Spin 0 und Spin $\frac{1}{2}$ durch Beispiele gezeigt, dass im allgemeinen Fall mehrerer Undoren von gleicher Stufe aus (III) nicht mehr eindeutig auf die Statistik der Teilchen geschlossen werden kann, während (II) bzw. (I) für ganzen bzw. halben Spin hiezu stets hinreichend bleiben. In den speziellen Fällen des Skalarfeldes, des Vektorfeldes und des Dirac-Elektrons, wo nur ein einziger Undor gegebener Stufe in die Theorie eingeht, folgt dagegen das Transformationsgesetz der Ladungskonjugierung eindeutig, so dass hier (III) zur Festlegung der Statistik ausreicht."

§§3 and 4. We have used here notes of lectures given by H. A. Kramers in Leiden during the winter 1944–1945 for a small circle of physicists. In these lectures, Kramers introduced the *q*-potential.

§§5 to 7. These sections are applications of the formulae developed in the earlier sections. Compare also refs. 5 and 7 and

14. E. H. Kennard, Kinetic Theory of Gases, New York 1938, pp. 397 ff.

§8. For a discussion of the applicability of quantum statistics to gases see, e.g.,

15. D. ter Haar, Am. J. Phys., **17,** 399, 1949.

For an application of Bose-Einstein or Fermi-Dirac statistics to the equation of state see, e.g. (a more elaborate discussion will be given in Chap. VIII),

16. J. de Boer, Contribution to the Theory of Compressed Gases, Thesis, Amsterdam 1940.
17. J. de Boer, J. van Kranendonk, and K. Compaan, Physica, **16,** 545, 1950.
For the statistical theory of metals which will be discussed in Chap. X see, e.g.,
18. A. Sommerfeld and H. Bethe, Handb. d. Phys., Vol. **24_2,** Berlin 1933, p. 333.
For a discussion of statistics of nuclear particles (cf. Chaps. XIII and XIV) see, e.g.,
19. H. A. Bethe, Revs. Modern Phys., **9,** 69, 1937.
20. H. Wergeland, Fra Fysikkens Verden, **1945,** 223.
For astrophysical applications, one of which will be discussed in Chap. XIV, see, e.g.,
21. S. Chandrasekhar, Introduction to the Study of Stellar Structure, Chicago 1939, where further references can be found.
22. L. Biermann, Z. Naturf., **3a**, 481, 1948.

PART B

ENSEMBLE THEORY

CHAPTER V

PETIT ENSEMBLES

§1. **The Γ-space; Ensembles.** In the preceding chapters we discussed systems which consisted of independent particles and which, moreover, existed isolated from the rest of the universe. We thus neglected in our treatment various points. These points are (a) interactions within the system, except in discussing Boltzmann's H-theorem when collisions, that is, interactions between particles, played an important role; (b) interaction with surroundings; and (c) experimental limitations to the amount of information which can be obtained about a physical system. The first point will be dealt with in the present section, where we shall discuss how one can treat systems of interacting particles.

The second point is important in connection with the introduction of the concept of temperature. This concept entails necessarily a means of fixing this temperature, which in turn involves the introduction of a large thermostat in which the system is contained. However, we then have no longer an isolated system and we must expect that due to the interaction between system and thermostat, or *temperature bath*, as we shall often call the thermostat, the energy of the system is no longer constant. Indeed, there exists a certain *complementarity* between energy and temperature.† We shall see later (§§4 and 8) that, if we fix the temperature, the energy may have various values which spread around a most probable value—but in most physical cases the actual dispersion is so small as to be negligible—and that, on the other hand, if we are dealing with a really isolated system, we must expect that the temperature measured in the system will be fluctuating.

The third point which has not yet been considered with sufficient care is the fact that there are very serious limitations to the amount of information which we can obtain about a physical system which we are considering. We have mentioned, but not sufficiently stressed, that in practice only a few quantities such as the pressure, total kinetic energy, total linear momentum, and total angular momentum of the system can be measured.

† It must be emphasized that this complementarity is a classical one and does not involve the quantum of action.

In the previous chapters our discussion was such that one might get the impression that it would be possible, if we wished to do so, to determine the distribution function to any degree of detailed accuracy and hence calculate all average values in which we might be interested. Since only a few data will be available we are confronted with the problem of determining the distribution function under these circumstances. This question will be discussed in some detail in §8.

Let us discuss first of all the question of interaction between the particles in the system. Firstly, we shall briefly consider under what circumstances our neglect of the interactions would be permissible. On page 26 we said that a perfect gas, that is, a gas where one can neglect the interactions, would be a system where the total potential energy (or interaction energy) is at all times negligibly small compared to the total kinetic energy. Using the language of quantum mechanics we can put it slightly differently. The total energy of an isolated system may be given within certain limits, that is, we may know that the energy of the system lies in the interval $E - \delta$, $E + \delta$. If it is to have any sense at all still to talk about a system with a fixed energy, δ must be small compared to E.

The fact that the energy of a system can never be completely fixed is, of course, an essential point in quantum mechanics. In order to fix our ideas we may, e.g., take for δ the natural line width of the energy of the system. Or, if Δt is the smallest time interval during which observations can be made, we can take δ in accordance with the Heisenberg relations to satisfy the equation

$$\delta = \frac{h}{\Delta t}.$$

If, as is mostly the case, the system consists of many particles, the spacing ΔE of the energy levels of the particles—treated as independent entities—will be very small (compare the remarks on p. 62) and we will have $\Delta E \ll \delta$. If now the interaction between the particles is so weak that the total interaction energy U is small compared to δ, we can still treat the system as consisting of independent particles. However, in order that transitions between various states can occur at all, U must be larger than ΔE, since otherwise practically no transitions would occur. We have thus the inequalities

$$\Delta E \ll U \ll \delta \ll E. \tag{5.101}$$

One way to introduce the interaction between the particles in the system is by treating the whole system as one large molecule. If each particle has s degrees of freedom and if N is the number of particles in the system, the total number of degrees of freedom for the whole system will be sN. The state of the system will completely be determined by $2sN$ coordinates,

really the # of "dimensions"

such as

$$\begin{array}{l} q_1^1,\ q_2^1,\ q_3^1,\ \cdots,\ q_s^1;\ p_1^1,\ p_2^1,\ p_3^1,\ \cdots,\ p_s^1; \\ q_1^2,\ q_2^2,\ q_3^2,\ \cdots,\ q_s^2;\ p_1^2,\ p_2^2,\ p_3^2,\ \cdots,\ p_s^2; \\ \cdots\cdots\cdots\cdots\cdots\cdots\cdots\cdots \\ \cdots\cdots\cdots\cdots\cdots\cdots\cdots\cdots \\ q_1^N,\ q_2^N,\ q_3^N,\ \cdots,\ q_s^N;\ p_1^N,\ p_2^N,\ p_3^N,\ \cdots,\ p_s^N, \end{array}$$

where the p's and q's are the canonical momenta and coordinates of the particles.† Let $\mathcal{T}(p,q)$ be the total kinetic energy and $U(q)$ the total potential energy of the system, where p and q stand respectively for all sN p's and all sN q's. We shall only consider conservative systems so that neither $\mathcal{T}$ nor U will depend explicitly on the time. The total energy $\mathcal{H}$ is given by the equation

$$\mathcal{H} = \mathcal{T} + U = \mathcal{H}(p,q). \tag{5.102}$$

It is advantageous to number the p's and q's continuously from 1 to sN and we shall assume that this has been done unless otherwise stated. Since the p's and q's are canonically conjugate variables, we have (compare also equations [2.207])

$$\dot{p}_i = -\frac{\partial \mathcal{H}}{\partial q_i}, \quad \dot{q}_i = \frac{\partial \mathcal{H}}{\partial p_i}; \qquad i = 1, 2, \cdots, sN. \tag{5.103}$$

To each system there corresponds a point, the so-called *representative point,* in the $2sN$-dimensional phase-space. Following the Ehrenfests' notation, this space will be called Γ-*space* where Γ stands for gas.

From theoretical mechanics it is known that from equations (5.103) it follows that there are $2sN$ functions $\varphi_i(p,q)$ which are constants. They are the so-called integrals or constants of motion. One of these integrals is the total energy ϵ of the system. In general we have

$$\left.\begin{array}{ll} \varphi_1(p,q) & = \epsilon(p,q) = c_1, \\ \varphi_2(p,q) & = c_2, \\ \cdots\cdots\cdots & \cdots\cdots \\ \varphi_{2sN-1}(p,q) & = c_{2sN-1}, \\ \varphi_{2sN}(p,q) & = c_{2sN} + t, \end{array}\right\} \tag{5.104}$$

where the c_i are the $2sN$ integration constants.

† It may be remarked here that the $2sN$ coordinates need not be the coordinates and momenta of the individual particles. We shall only consider canonical variables. In that case the sN q's can be any sN quantities which completely determine the position of all particles in the system. The sN p's are determined from the kinetic energy (compare equation [2.205]).

That one can put the integration of equations (5.103) in the form (5.104) follows if one divides the first $2sN - 1$ equations of motion by the last one. The resulting $2sN - 1$ equations do not contain the time and give rise to the first $2sN - 1$ equations of (5.104). One is then left with one equation and from that one it is possible after substitution to determine t by a quadrature, and the last of equations (5.104) results.

As time goes on, the representative point of the system will describe an orbit in Γ-space. The q_i change their values because of the velocities of the particles, and the p_i because of the external and internal forces acting on the particles. The orbit will be situated on the hypersurface with equation $\epsilon(p,q) = c_1$. This hypersurface will be called an *energy surface.*

Instead of considering one system it is often advantageous and even unavoidable, as we shall discuss in §8, to consider a large number of similar systems which all contain N particles, each of which has s degrees of freedom and which all exist under the same external circumstances. In other words, all these systems will possess the same Hamiltonian (5.102), but their representative points will in general not be the same. Let us assume that there are so many systems that it is possible to speak of the density $D(p,q)$ with which the representative points are distributed in Γ-space. Such a collection of similar systems was called by Gibbs an *ensemble.*

See Schrödingers tract p. 1–10.

Since the representative points are moving in phase space, the density will in general be a function of time. Let the density, that is, the number of representative points per unit volume of Γ-space, at time t be denoted by $D(p,q,t)$. In considering the change of D with time it is important to distinguish between its rate of change at a fixed point in Γ-space and the rate of change at a point moving along an orbit in Γ-space. The first of these — which we may call the local rate of change—will be denoted by $\partial D/\partial t$, while for the second, or convected rate of change as it may be called, we use the symbol dD/dt. The relation between the two is given by the equation

$$\frac{dD}{dt} = \frac{\partial D}{\partial t} + \sum_i \left(\frac{\partial D}{\partial p_i}\dot{p}_i + \frac{\partial D}{\partial q_i}\dot{q}_i\right). \tag{5.105}$$

Let us consider for a moment the volume element $d\Omega$ in Γ-space corresponding to coordinates in the intervals p_i, $p_i + dp_i$ and q_i, $q_i + dq_i$, so that we have

$$d\Omega = \prod_i dp_i dq_i. \tag{5.106}$$

Elementary volumes in Γ-space, $d\Omega$, will sometimes be called, with Gibbs, elements of *extension in phase.*

At a later moment, $t + \delta t$, the representative points which at t were inside $d\Omega$ will have moved along their orbits and their coordinates which were p_i, q_i at t will now be $p_i + \dot{p}_i\delta t$, $q_i + \dot{q}_i\delta t$. Let $d\Omega'$ be the extension in phase at $t + \delta t$. We shall show presently that

$$\frac{dD}{dt} = 0. \tag{5.107}$$

This means that the *density in phase*, as D is called by Gibbs, remains constant in the neighborhood of a point as it moves along its orbit, or that we may treat the points in Γ-space as an incompressible fluid. A result of this will be that we have

$$d\Omega = d\Omega', \tag{5.108}$$

expressing the fact that the extension in phase occupied by a collection of representative points is constant in time. Equations (5.107) and (5.108) are two different forms of *Liouville's theorem.*

We can prove equation (5.107) by considering the right-hand side of equation (5.105) as follows. Consider the extension in phase $d\Omega$ at t and at $t + \delta t$. The number of representative points N in $d\Omega$ at t will be given by the equation

$$N = D d\Omega. \tag{5.109}$$

At $t + \delta t$ we have

$$N + \delta N = \left(D + \frac{\partial D}{\partial t}\delta t\right) d\Omega. \tag{5.110}$$

The difference δN arises from the fact that the number of points entering $d\Omega$ during δt may be different from the number of points leaving $d\Omega$ during this time interval. The number of points entering $d\Omega$ during δt through the "face" at q_i will be given by the expression

$$D\dot{q}_i \frac{d\Omega}{dq_i} \delta t, \tag{5.111}$$

while the number of points leaving $d\Omega$ during δt through the "opposite face" at $q_i + dq_i$ is given by the expression

$$\left(D + \frac{\partial D}{\partial q_i} dq_i\right)\left(\dot{q}_i + \frac{\partial \dot{q}_i}{\partial q_i} dq_i\right)\frac{d\Omega}{dq_i}\delta t. \tag{5.112}$$

In expressions (5.111) and (5.112) $d\Omega/dq_i$ stands for the "area" of the "face," that is, $d\Omega$ divided by dq_i, and not for a derivative.

Combining expressions (5.111) and (5.112), summing over all $2sN$ coordinates (q_i and p_i), and neglecting higher-order terms, we get

$$\delta N = -\sum_i \left[D\left(\frac{\partial \dot{q}_i}{\partial q_i} + \frac{\partial \dot{p}_i}{\partial p_i}\right) + \left(\frac{\partial D}{\partial q_i}\dot{q}_i + \frac{\partial D}{\partial p_i}\dot{p}_i\right)\right] d\Omega \delta t,$$

or, using equations (5.109) and (5.110),

$$\frac{\partial D}{\partial t} = -\sum_i \left(\frac{\partial D}{\partial q_i} \dot{q}_i + \frac{\partial D}{\partial p_i} \dot{p}_i \right), \tag{5.113}$$

since from equations (5.103) it follows that

$$\sum_i \left(\frac{\partial \dot{q}_i}{\partial q_i} + \frac{\partial \dot{p}_i}{\partial p_i} \right) = 0. \tag{5.114}$$

From equations (5.105) and (5.113) equation (5.107) follows.

Equation (5.113) can also be written in the following form:

$$\frac{\partial D}{\partial t} = \{\mathcal{H},D\}, \tag{5.115}$$

which expresses the rate of change of D in terms of the *Poisson bracket* of D and the Hamiltonian.

The Poisson bracket $\{a,b\}$ is defined by the equation

$$\{a,b\} = \sum_i \left[\frac{\partial a}{\partial q_i} \frac{\partial b}{\partial p_i} - \frac{\partial a}{\partial p_i} \frac{\partial b}{\partial q_i} \right].$$

An ensemble for which $\partial D/\partial t = 0$ is called a *stationary ensemble* and in the following we shall restrict ourselves mainly to that kind of ensemble. From equation (5.115) and the definition of a stationary ensemble it follows that an ensemble is stationary if

$$\{\mathcal{H},D\} = 0. \tag{5.116}$$

It is shown in theoretical mechanics that equation (5.116) is satisfied if and only if

$$D = D(\varphi_1,\varphi_2,\cdots,\varphi_{2sN-1}), \tag{5.117}$$

where the φ_i are the functions discussed above (equations [5.104]).

Instead of considering stationary ensembles with a density given by the general equation (5.117) we shall restrict ourselves to those stationary ensembles for which

$$D = D(\epsilon), \tag{5.118}$$

where $\epsilon = \varphi_1$ is the energy of the system. The reasons for this restriction are discussed in §8 of Appendix I (p. 380).

Instead of working with D we shall mostly use the normalized *coefficient of probability* ρ, which is given by the equation

$$\rho = \frac{D}{n}, \tag{5.119}$$

where n is the total number of systems in the ensemble and given by the equation

$$n = \int_\Gamma D d\Omega, \tag{5.120}$$

where in equation (5.120) and henceforth the symbol $\int_\Gamma$ will indicate integration over the whole of the available part of Γ-space.†

We shall often refer to ρ as the *density of the ensemble,* which should not be confused with the density in phase D.

With Gibbs we also introduce a function η, the *index of probability,* given by the equation

$$\eta = \ln \rho. \tag{5.121}$$

As a consequence of equation (5.107) we have

$$\frac{d\rho}{dt} = \frac{d\eta}{dt} = 0, \tag{5.122}$$

while for stationary ensembles

$$\frac{\partial\rho}{\partial t} = \frac{\partial\eta}{\partial t} = 0. \tag{5.123}$$

Finally, for the ensembles considered mainly by us we have from equation (5.118)

$$\rho = \rho(\epsilon), \quad \eta = \eta(\epsilon). \tag{5.124}$$

For future reference we remark that ρ must be a single-valued, real, and nonnegative function of the p's and q's which in virtue of equations (5.119) and (5.120) satisfies the *normalization equation*

$$\int_\Gamma \rho d\Omega = 1. \tag{5.125}$$

A function $G(p,q)$ depending on the p_i and q_i is called a *phase function* and its average value $\bar{G}$, where the average is taken over the ensemble, is defined by the equation

$$\bar{G} = \int_\Gamma G\rho d\Omega. \tag{5.126}$$

If we are dealing with a stationary ensemble, $\bar{G}$ will be a constant, that is, not dependent on time.

† In most cases, some parts of Γ-space will not be available due to external circumstances or to our choice of coordinates. In the case of a gas enclosed in a finite volume, e.g., the x_i,y_i,z_i can range only over a finite interval, while a q_i which is an angle is restricted to the interval 0 to 2π.

§2. **Stationary Ensembles.** In the present section we shall briefly introduce three kinds of stationary ensembles which we shall use in the subsequent discussion. We mentioned that we would restrict ourselves to ensembles with densities given by equation (5.124), that is, densities depending on the energy only. Let us remind ourselves at this point that in general the energy will be a function not only of the p_i and q_i, but also of external parameters, a_i, such as the volume occupied by the system or the magnitude of an external magnetic field.

Since the density must satisfy equation (5.125) we cannot use the following two expressions for ρ, which are the two simplest possibilities,

$$\rho = \text{constant}, \quad \text{or} \quad \rho = \text{constant} \times \epsilon. \qquad \textbf{(5.201)}\dagger$$

However, we can try a linear dependence of η on ϵ,

$$\eta = \frac{\psi - \epsilon}{\Theta}, \qquad \textbf{(5.202)}$$

and we have for the density

GIBBS (MACRO)CANONICAL ENSEMBLE

$$\rho = e^{\frac{\psi - \epsilon}{\Theta}}, \qquad \textbf{(5.203)}$$

where ψ and Θ are constants. Gibbs called the ensemble with density given by equation (5.203) a *canonical ensemble.* In order to distinguish it from the microcanonical ensemble to be introduced presently we shall call it a *macrocanonical ensemble.* The quantity Θ is called the *modulus* of the macrocanonical ensemble and is related to the temperature, as we shall see in the next section. The quantity ψ is independent of the p_i and q_i, but depends on Θ and the a_i, since in virtue of the normalization condition (5.125) it is determined by the equation

$$e^{-\frac{\psi}{\Theta}} = \int_\Gamma e^{-\frac{\epsilon}{\Theta}}\, d\Omega. \qquad \textbf{(5.204)}$$

We may remark here that there is a strong resemblance between the density of a macrocanonical ensemble on the one hand and the distribution function of the Maxwell-Boltzmann distribution (equation [2.107], p. 29) on the other. It looks as if a macrocanonical ensemble can be considered to be a system of "molecules" which interact weakly and therefore tend toward the Maxwell-Boltzmann distribution. Indeed, it can be shown (see Appendix I, §6, p. 361) that a system in a thermostat will show the average behavior of a system belonging to a macrocanonical ensemble.

Another reason why macrocanonical ensembles play a special role among

† It is, of course, possible that ρ satisfies equation (5.201) for a restricted range of energy values; an example is given by the microcanonical or by the F-ensemble to be introduced presently.

the stationary ensembles is that if two of them with the same modulus are coupled together, the resulting ensemble is again a macrocanonical ensemble. We shall return to this point in §6 and we refer also to §6 of Appendix I.

Apart from the macrocanonical ensembles we shall introduce two other stationary ensembles, namely, the microcanonical and the F-ensemble.

The *microcanonical ensemble* consists of systems which have all the same energy ϵ_0; its density is given by the equation

$$\rho = A\delta(\epsilon - \epsilon_0), \tag{5.205}$$

where A is a constant to be determined from the normalization condition and $\delta(x)$ is Dirac's δ-function.†

Sometimes it is convenient to define the microcanonical ensemble by equation

$$\rho = A, \qquad \epsilon_0 \leqslant \epsilon \leqslant \epsilon_0 + \Delta \tag{5.208}$$

instead of by equation (5.205).

The density of the *F-ensemble* is given by the equation

$$\rho = BF(\epsilon), \tag{5.209}$$

where the constant B is to be determined by the normalization condition and where $F(x)$ is a function defined by the equations

$$\left.\begin{aligned} F(x) &= 1, \qquad x \leqslant \epsilon_0; \\ F(x) &= 0, \qquad x > \epsilon_0. \end{aligned}\right\} \tag{5.210}$$

In Figure 23 we have drawn ρ as a function of ϵ for the three ensembles mentioned in this section.

§3. The Macrocanonical Ensemble. We mentioned in the preceding section the following theorem. *The macroscopic behavior of a system at equilibrium*

† Dirac's δ-function is defined by the equations (see, e.g., P. A. M. Dirac, Quantum Mechanics, 2d ed., Oxford 1935, §§20, 21)

$$\delta(x) = 0, \qquad x \neq 0; \qquad \int_{-\infty}^{+\infty} \delta(x)dx = 1. \tag{5.206}$$

From equations (5.206) it follows that for any function $f(x)$ we have

$$\left.\begin{aligned} &\int_{-\infty}^{+\infty} f(x)\delta(x)dx = f(0); \qquad \int_{-\infty}^{+\infty} f(x)\delta(x-a)dx = f(a); \\ &\int_a^b f(x)\delta(x-c)dx = f(c), \qquad \text{if } a < c < b; \\ &\int_a^b f(x)\delta(x-c)dx = 0, \qquad \text{if either } b < c \text{ or } c < a. \end{aligned}\right\} \tag{5.207}$$

at a temperature T will be described correctly by taking the average behavior of a system in a macrocanonical ensemble with a modulus Θ *which is related to T by the equation*

$$\Theta = kT. \tag{5.301}$$

That this is a sensible way of describing the behavior of a system in temperature equilibrium is due to the following two facts:

a) The fluctuations of most quantities from the average values are negligibly small.

b) Those fluctuations which are not small are so fast that they cannot be measured with our instruments.

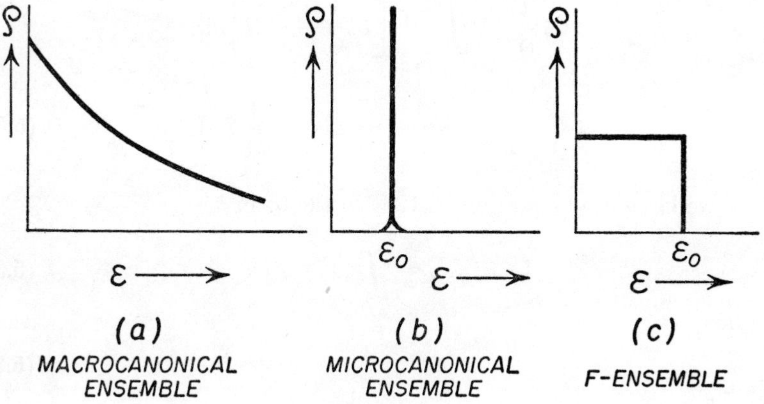

Fig. 23

Fluctuations, that is, deviations from the average value, will be discussed in the next section, when we shall have an opportunity to see how far conditions (a) and (b) are satisfied. We also refer to §8 for a further discussion of the relationship between an actual system in temperature equilibrium and macrocanonical ensembles and to §9 for a calculation leading to the actual value of fluctuations to be expected in a perfect gas.

Let us now prove our basic theorem. From the normalization of ρ we have the equation

$$e^{-\frac{\psi}{\Theta}} = \int_{\Gamma} e^{-\frac{\epsilon}{\Theta}} d\Omega. \tag{5.302}$$

As in §6 of Chapter II (p. 40) we shall introduce the generalized forces A_i by the equations

$$A_i = -\frac{\partial \epsilon}{\partial a_i}. \tag{5.303}$$

If the external parameters a_i are varied from a_i to $a_i + \delta a_i$, we have for the variation $\delta\epsilon$ of the energy

$$\delta\epsilon = -\sum A_i \delta a_i. \tag{5.304}$$

Let us now consider a new macrocanonical ensemble derived from the given one by a variation of the modulus and the external parameters. Since the normalization condition must also hold for this new ensemble we must have

$$-e^{-\frac{\psi}{\Theta}} \delta \frac{\psi}{\Theta} = \int_\Gamma e^{-\frac{\epsilon}{\Theta}} \left[-\epsilon\, \delta \frac{1}{\Theta} - \frac{1}{\Theta} \delta\epsilon \right] d\Omega,$$

that is,

$$\delta \frac{\psi}{\Theta} = \int_\Gamma e^{\frac{\psi-\epsilon}{\Theta}} \left[\epsilon\, \delta \frac{1}{\Theta} + \frac{1}{\Theta} \delta\epsilon \right] d\Omega,$$

or

$$\delta \frac{\psi}{\Theta} = \overline{\epsilon}\, \delta \frac{1}{\Theta} + \frac{1}{\Theta} \overline{\delta\epsilon} = \overline{\epsilon}\, \delta \frac{1}{\Theta} - \frac{1}{\Theta} \sum \overline{A}_i \delta a_i, \tag{5.305}$$

where we have used equation (5.126) in the form

$$\overline{G} = e^{\frac{\psi}{\Theta}} \int_\Gamma G e^{-\frac{\epsilon}{\Theta}} d\Omega. \tag{5.306}$$

Since

$$\delta \frac{\overline{\epsilon}}{\Theta} = \overline{\epsilon}\, \delta \frac{1}{\Theta} + \frac{1}{\Theta} \delta \overline{\epsilon}, \tag{5.307}$$

we can write equation (5.305) in the form

$$\delta \frac{\overline{\epsilon} - \psi}{\Theta} = -\delta\overline{\eta} = \frac{\delta\overline{\epsilon} + \overline{\delta\epsilon}}{\Theta}. \tag{5.308}$$

Using arguments similar to those given in §4 of the preceding chapter (compare also §7 of Chapter II), it follows

a) that $\overline{\delta\epsilon}$ corresponds to the work done on the system when the external parameters change from a_i to $a_i + \delta a_i$;

b) that $\delta\overline{\epsilon} + \overline{\delta\epsilon}$ is thus the heat added to the system, δQ, that is, the increase of energy not accounted for by macroscopically measurable work, this last quantity, δA, being equal to $-\overline{\delta\epsilon}$;

c) that hence Θ, being an integrating factor of δQ, must be proportional to the absolute temperature T, or

$$\Theta = kT,$$

which proves equation (5.301);

d) that $-\bar{\eta}$, apart possibly from an additive constant, corresponds to the entropy S divided by k, or

$$S = k\frac{\bar{\epsilon} - \psi}{\Theta} + \text{ct} = -k\bar{\eta} + \text{ct}; \tag{5.309}$$

e) that ψ, apart possibly from an additive constant, is the free energy F. We shall fix the additive constants by putting

$$e^{\frac{F}{kT}} = N!h^{sN}e^{\frac{\psi}{kT}}, \tag{5.310}$$

where h is Planck's constant. From equation (5.302) we then have

$$e^{-\frac{F}{kT}} = \frac{1}{N!}\int_{\Gamma} e^{-\frac{\epsilon}{kT}}\frac{d\Omega}{h^{sN}}, \tag{5.311}$$

and we see that both sides of equation (5.311) are dimensionless. The reasons for introducing $N!$ and h^{sN} are similar to the reasons for introducing the factors e/N and h^s in equation (2.718) and we shall presently see that, indeed, equation (5.311) leads to equation (2.718) in the case of systems consisting of independent particles. The factor $N!$ enters in order that the free energy and the entropy will be extensive quantities and the factor h^{sN} ensures the correct dimensions and the correct transition to quantum mechanical statistics. Of course, the complete justification can only be given from a discussion of the quantum mechanical ensemble theory which will be given in Chapter VII.

From this discussion it follows that given ψ as a function of Θ and the a_i, or given Θ and given ϵ as a function of the external parameters—in which case ψ can be computed from equation (5.302)—we have obtained an expression for the free energy of a system at equilibrium at temperature T for the given values of the a_i. It is well known that once the free energy is given as a function of T and the external parameters, the thermodynamical state of the system is determined. Most thermodynamical quantities can be derived from the free energy by differentiation. As δF and $\delta\psi$ are the same, we should expect relations between the average values of phase functions and partial derivatives of ψ. Indeed, from equation (5.305) we easily have

$$\bar{\epsilon} = \frac{\partial \dfrac{\psi}{\Theta}}{\partial \dfrac{1}{\Theta}}, \tag{5.312}$$

$$\bar{A}_i = -\frac{\partial\psi}{\partial a_i}. \tag{5.313}$$

If a_i corresponds to the volume V, equation (5.313) gives us

$$p = -\frac{\partial\psi}{\partial V}, \tag{5.314}$$

from which the equation of state can be derived once ψ is computed.

One often denotes the right-hand side of equation (5.311) by Z_Γ and this *partition function* plays a similar role to that of Z_μ of Chapter II. Expressing $\bar{\epsilon}$, $\bar{A}_i$, and p in terms of Z_Γ we have, instead of equations (5.312) to (5.314),

$$\bar{\epsilon} = -\frac{\partial \ln Z_\Gamma}{\partial(1/\Theta)}, \tag{5.315}$$

$$\bar{A}_i = \Theta\frac{\partial \ln Z_\Gamma}{\partial a_i}, \tag{5.316}$$

$$p = \Theta\frac{\partial \ln Z_\Gamma}{\partial V}. \tag{5.317}$$

Other averages can be computed by straightforward integration using equation (5.306). In that way we can, for instance, calculate the average value of the kinetic energy $\mathcal{T}$. This kinetic energy is a homogeneous quadratic expression in the p_i and hence we have (compare equation [2.211] on p. 32)

$$\mathcal{T} = \tfrac{1}{2}\sum_{i=1}^{sN} p_i\frac{\partial\mathcal{T}}{\partial p_i}. \tag{5.318}$$

By using the same methods which led to equation (2.212) we find

$$\bar{\mathcal{T}} = \tfrac{1}{2}sN\Theta = \tfrac{1}{2}sNkT, \tag{5.319}$$

expressing the *equipartition* of kinetic energy. Each degree of freedom contributes $\frac{1}{2}\Theta = \frac{1}{2}kT$ to the average kinetic energy.

Let us now consider an ensemble of systems each containing N independent particles in a volume V. Let ϵ_j be the total energy of the jth particle ($j = 1, 2, \cdots, N$) and p_i^j and q_i^j the ith generalized momentum and coordinate pertaining to the jth particle. We then have

$$\epsilon = \sum_{j=1}^{N}\epsilon_j \tag{5.320}$$

and

$$d\Omega = \prod_j d\omega_j, \tag{5.321}$$

where

$$d\omega_j = \prod_{i=1}^{s} dp_i^j dq_i^j. \tag{5.322}$$

We can now evaluate Z_Γ as

$$Z_\Gamma = \frac{1}{N!}\int_\Gamma e^{\frac{\Sigma \epsilon_j}{\Theta}} \frac{\prod_j d\omega_j}{h^{sN}} = \left[\frac{e}{N}\int e^{-\frac{\epsilon_j}{\Theta}} \frac{d\omega_j}{h^s}\right]^N = Z_\mu{}^N, \tag{5.323}$$

where Z_μ is given by equation (2.718) on page 43 and where we have used Stirling's formula for the factorial (equation [MA3.09], p. 444).

If the system consists of free monatomic particles, Z_Γ can be evaluated directly. The energy is given by the equation

$$\epsilon = \sum_j \frac{p_j^2}{2m} + \sum_j F(x_j,y_j,z_j), \tag{5.324}$$

where $F(x,y,z)$ is the function defined by equation (2.802),

$$F(x,y,z) = 0, \qquad \text{if } x,y,z \text{ lies inside } V;$$

$$F(x,y,z) = \infty, \qquad \text{if } x,y,z \text{ lies outside } V.$$

The integration over Γ-space is elementary and leads to the result (compare equations [2.803] and [5.323])

$$Z_\Gamma = \frac{1}{N!} V^N \left(\frac{2\pi m\Theta}{h^2}\right)^{\frac{3N}{2}}. \tag{5.325}$$

Using equations (5.315) and (5.317), we have

$$\bar{\epsilon}(= \bar{\mathcal{T}}) = -\frac{\partial \ln Z_\Gamma}{\partial (1/\Theta)} = \tfrac{3}{2}N\Theta, \tag{5.326}$$

$$p = \Theta \frac{\partial \ln Z_\Gamma}{\partial V} = \frac{N\Theta}{V}. \tag{5.327}$$

The last equation leads, as expected, once more to the perfect gas law.

§4. Fluctuations in a Macrocanonical Ensemble. In the preceding section formulae were derived for the average values of the total energy and the generalized forces. If we wish to ascertain what the chances are of finding these average values realized when we pick a system at random from the macrocanonical ensemble, we must compute the fluctuations of these quantities. At the same time we shall also find formulae for the correlations between the various quantities.

The easiest way of obtaining formulae for the fluctuations is to start from the normalizing equation in the form

$$\int_\Gamma e^{\frac{\psi - \epsilon}{\Theta}} d\Omega = 1. \tag{5.401}$$

Taking the derivative with respect to $1/\Theta$, we get

$$0 = {}_{\Gamma}\!\int \frac{\partial}{\partial(1/\Theta)}\left(\frac{\psi - \epsilon}{\Theta}\right) e^{\frac{\psi-\epsilon}{\Theta}}\, d\Omega = {}_{\Gamma}\!\int \left[\frac{\partial(\psi/\Theta)}{\partial(1/\Theta)} - \epsilon\right] e^{\frac{\psi-\epsilon}{\Theta}}\, d\Omega, \tag{5.402}$$

or

$$\bar{\epsilon} = \frac{\partial(\psi/\Theta)}{\partial(1/\Theta)}, \tag{5.403}$$

in accordance with equation (5.312).

Similarly, by taking the derivative with respect to a_i in equation (5.401), we get

$$0 = {}_{\Gamma}\!\int \frac{\partial}{\partial a_i}\left(\frac{\psi - \epsilon}{\Theta}\right) e^{\frac{\psi-\epsilon}{\Theta}}\, d\Omega = \frac{1}{\Theta}\,{}_{\Gamma}\!\int \left(\frac{\partial \psi}{\partial a_i} - \frac{\partial \epsilon}{\partial a_i}\right) e^{\frac{\psi-\epsilon}{\Theta}}\, d\Omega, \tag{5.404}$$

or, using equation (5.303),

$$\bar{A}_i = -\frac{\partial \psi}{\partial a_i}. \tag{5.405}$$

Differentiating equation (5.402) with respect to $1/\Theta$ gives us

$${}_{\Gamma}\!\int \left[\frac{\partial^2(\psi/\Theta)}{\partial(1/\Theta)^2} + \left\{\frac{\partial(\psi/\Theta)}{\partial(1/\Theta)} - \epsilon\right\}^2\right] e^{\frac{\psi-\epsilon}{\Theta}}\, d\Omega = 0, \tag{5.406}$$

or, using equation (5.403),

$$\overline{(\epsilon - \bar{\epsilon})^2} = -\frac{\partial^2(\psi/\Theta)}{\partial(1/\Theta)^2} = -\frac{\partial \bar{\epsilon}}{\partial(1/\Theta)}. \tag{5.407}$$

Similarly, differentiating equation (5.404) with respect to a_j, we get

$${}_{\Gamma}\!\int \left[\frac{\partial^2 \psi}{\partial a_i \partial a_j} - \frac{\partial^2 \epsilon}{\partial a_i \partial a_j} + \frac{1}{\Theta}\left(\frac{\partial \psi}{\partial a_i} - \frac{\partial \epsilon}{\partial a_i}\right)\left(\frac{\partial \psi}{\partial a_j} - \frac{\partial \epsilon}{\partial a_j}\right)\right] e^{\frac{\psi-\epsilon}{\Theta}}\, d\Omega = 0, \tag{5.408}$$

or, using equations (5.405) and (5.303),

$$\overline{(A_i - \bar{A}_i)(A_j - \bar{A}_j)} = \Theta\left[\overline{\frac{\partial^2 \epsilon}{\partial a_i \partial a_j}} - \frac{\partial^2 \psi}{\partial a_i \partial a_j}\right], \tag{5.409}$$

which is valid both for $i = j$ and for $i \neq j$.

Finally we get by differentiating either equation (5.402) with respect to a_i or equation (5.404) with respect to $1/\Theta$

$$\overline{(A_i - \bar{A}_i)(\epsilon - \bar{\epsilon})} = \frac{\partial^2 \psi}{\partial a_i \partial \frac{1}{\Theta}}. \tag{5.410}$$

We shall see later on that in many cases ψ and its derivatives, and thus also $\bar{\epsilon}$ and $\bar{A}_i$, will be proportional to the number of particles in the system,

N. In that case it follows from equations (5.407), (5.409), and (5.410) that all the quantities

$$\frac{\overline{(\epsilon - \bar{\epsilon})^2}}{\bar{\epsilon}^2}, \quad \frac{\overline{(A_i - \bar{A}_i)(A_j - \bar{A}_j)}}{\bar{A}_i\bar{A}_j}, \quad \frac{\overline{(A_i - \bar{A}_i)(\epsilon - \bar{\epsilon})}}{\bar{A}_i\bar{\epsilon}}$$

will be of the order of $1/N$ and hence negligibly small if N is sufficiently large.

It sometimes happens, however, that fluctuations can be very large. At an ideal wall, for instance, the force $(-\partial U/\partial q)$ will be infinite (compare Fig. 5 on p. 10 where we have a similarly idealized potential energy) and the pressure will fluctuate violently. It is then, however, practically always possible to show that the fluctuations of the time average B_i defined by the equation

$$B_i = \frac{1}{\tau}\int_t^{t+\tau} A_i dt, \tag{5.411}$$

are small, or that

$$\frac{\overline{(B_i - \bar{B}_i)^2}}{\bar{B}_i^2} \sim \frac{1}{N} \ll 1. \tag{5.412}$$

The fact that any actual measurement of the pressure will take a finite time means that anyhow it is more in accordance with physical reality to consider the B_i than the A_i.

§5. The Entropy in a Macrocanonical Ensemble. In §3 we saw that the entropy S of a system was related to the average value $\bar{\eta}$ of the index of probability through equation (5.309). There are two other ways to correlate the entropy with quantities relating to the ensemble. We shall reserve for later discussion (see pp. 159 ff.) the fact, which may seem strange at first sight, that it is possible to define the entropy in statistical mechanics in so many different ways.

Let the smallest possible value of the energy for given values of the external parameters be $\epsilon_{\min}$, which in general will be a function of the a_i. Since in general it will always be possible to choose all p_i equal to zero, independent of the values of the q_i, so that $\mathcal{T}_{\min} = 0$, we have

$$\epsilon_{\min}(a_i) = U_{\min}(a_i). \tag{5.501}$$

We now introduce a quantity Ω by the equation

$$\Omega = \int_{\epsilon_{\min}(a_i)}^{\epsilon} d\Omega. \tag{5.502}$$

From this equation we see, firstly, that Ω is the extension in phase between the two energy surfaces corresponding to $\epsilon_{\min}$ and ϵ and, secondly, that Ω depends both on ϵ and on the a_i, the latter through $\epsilon_{\min}$, that is,

$$\Omega = \Omega(\epsilon, a_i). \tag{5.503}$$

We also introduce a function ϕ defined by the equation

$$e^{\phi} = \frac{\partial \Omega}{\partial \epsilon}, \tag{5.504}$$

or

$$\phi(\epsilon, a_i) = \ln \frac{\partial \Omega}{\partial \epsilon}. \tag{5.505}$$

We shall need presently the value of e^{ϕ} for $\epsilon = \epsilon_{\min}$. We shall assume for the sake of simplicity that the kinetic energy $\mathcal{T}$ depends on the p_i only. We now introduce the following two elementary volumes

$$d\Omega_p = \prod_{i=1}^{sN} dp_i, \qquad d\Omega_q = \prod_{i=1}^{sN} dq_i, \tag{5.506}$$

which in the simplified case considered here are, apart from a multiplying constant, what Gibbs calls respectively an element of *extension in velocity* and an element of *extension in configuration.*

Furthermore, we write

$$\Omega_p = \int_0^{\mathcal{T}} d\Omega_p, \qquad \Omega_q = \int_{U_{\min}}^{U} d\Omega_q, \tag{5.507}$$

and we introduce two quantities ϕ_p and ϕ_q by the equations

$$e^{\phi_p} = \frac{\partial \Omega_p}{\partial \mathcal{T}}, \qquad e^{\phi_q} = \frac{\partial \Omega_q}{\partial U}. \tag{5.508}$$

From equations (5.502) and (5.507) it follows that

$$\Omega = \iint d\Omega_p d\Omega_q = \int_{U_{\min}}^{U=\epsilon} \Omega_p d\Omega_q, \tag{5.509}$$

where Ω_p depends on the q_i through the fact that the upper limit $\mathcal{T}$ in the integral in equation (5.507) must satisfy the relation

$$\mathcal{T} + U = \epsilon. \tag{5.510}$$

Taking the derivative with respect to ϵ in equation (5.509) and using the fact that

$$\frac{\partial \Omega_p}{\partial \epsilon} = \frac{\partial \Omega_p}{\partial \mathcal{T}},$$

we get

$$e^{\phi} = \frac{\partial \Omega}{\partial \epsilon} = \int_{U_{\min}}^{U=\epsilon} e^{\phi_p} d\Omega_q, \tag{5.511}$$

and hence in virtue of equation (5.501)

$$e^{\phi}\Big|_{\epsilon=\epsilon_{\min}} = 0. \tag{5.512}$$

If a phase function G is a function of the energy only, we have for its average value

$$\overline{G} = \int_{\Gamma} G(\epsilon)\rho(\epsilon)d\Omega, \tag{5.513}$$

or

$$\overline{G} = \int_{\epsilon_{\min}}^{\infty} G(\epsilon)\rho(\epsilon)e^{\phi}d\epsilon. \tag{5.514}$$

We must draw attention here to the different ways by which the right-hand sides of equations (5.513) and (5.514) depend on the a_i. In the first equation, $\overline{G}$ depends on the a_i through ϵ, but in the second equation $\overline{G}$ depends on the a_i through ϕ and the lower limit of integration while ϵ is an integration variable.

From the normalization equation we get in this way

$$e^{-\frac{\psi}{\Theta}} = \int e^{-\frac{\epsilon}{\Theta}+\phi}d\epsilon. \tag{5.515}$$

In the preceding section we saw that the fluctuations in energy in a macrocanonical ensemble are in general very small. This means that practically all members of the ensemble will possess energies which are practically equal to $\bar{\epsilon}$, and so equation (5.515) can be written in the form

$$e^{-\frac{\psi}{\Theta}} = \left[e^{-\frac{\epsilon}{\Theta}+\phi}\right]_{\epsilon=\bar{\epsilon}} \cdot \Delta, \tag{5.516}$$

where Δ is the "half-width" of the energy fluctuations which is of the order of magnitude $\bar{\epsilon}/\sqrt{N} \backsim \sqrt{N}$ (compare the discussion at the end of the preceding section),

$$\Delta^2 = C\,\overline{(\epsilon - \bar{\epsilon})^2}. \tag{5.517}$$

In order to derive equation (5.516) we first note that since the energy fluctuations are small, $\bar{\epsilon}$ will be the energy possessed by the largest number of systems in the ensemble. Since the fraction of systems, $f(\epsilon)d\epsilon$, with energies between ϵ and $\epsilon + d\epsilon$ is given by the equation

$$f(\epsilon)d\epsilon = e^{\frac{\psi-\epsilon}{\Theta}+\phi}d\epsilon, \tag{5.518}$$

as follows from the definitions of ρ and ϕ, $\bar{\epsilon}$ will also be the energy for which $e^{-\frac{\epsilon}{\Theta}+\phi}$ will be maximum, or

$$\frac{1}{\Theta} = \left.\frac{\partial\phi}{\partial\epsilon}\right|_{\epsilon=\bar{\epsilon}}. \tag{5.519}$$

Developing $\phi - (\epsilon/\Theta)$ in a Taylor series, we get

$$\phi - \frac{\epsilon}{\Theta} = \phi\Big|_{\epsilon=\bar{\epsilon}} - \frac{\bar{\epsilon}}{\Theta} + \frac{1}{2}\left.\frac{\partial^2\phi}{\partial\epsilon^2}\right|_{\epsilon=\bar{\epsilon}}(\epsilon - \bar{\epsilon})^2 + \cdots, \tag{5.520}$$

where we used equation (5.519). From equation (5.520) it follows that to a first approximation

$$e^{-\frac{\epsilon}{\Theta}+\phi} = \left[e^{-\frac{\epsilon}{\Theta}+\phi}\right]_{\epsilon=\bar{\epsilon}} \cdot e^{\frac{1}{2}\frac{\partial^2\phi}{\partial\epsilon^2}\Big|_{\epsilon=\bar{\epsilon}}(\epsilon-\bar{\epsilon})^2}. \tag{5.521}$$

Substituting equation (5.521) into equation (5.515) and integrating, we get approximately (by integrating from 0 to ∞ instead of from $\epsilon_{\min}$ to ∞)

$$e^{-\frac{\psi}{\Theta}} = \left[e^{-\frac{\epsilon}{\Theta}+\phi}\right]_{\epsilon=\bar{\epsilon}} \cdot \left(-\frac{2}{\pi}\frac{\partial^2\phi}{\partial\epsilon^2}\Big|_{\epsilon=\bar{\epsilon}}\right)^{-\frac{1}{2}}. \tag{5.522}$$

On the other hand, substituting equation (5.521) into the expression for $\overline{(\epsilon-\bar{\epsilon})^2}$, we get

$$\overline{(\epsilon-\bar{\epsilon})^2} = \frac{\int e^{\frac{\psi-\epsilon}{\Theta}+\phi}(\epsilon-\bar{\epsilon})^2 d\epsilon}{\int e^{\frac{\psi-\epsilon}{\Theta}+\phi} d\epsilon} \cong \frac{\int (\epsilon-\bar{\epsilon})^2 e^{\frac{1}{2}\frac{\partial^2\phi}{\partial\epsilon^2}\Big|_{\epsilon=\bar{\epsilon}}(\epsilon-\bar{\epsilon})^2} d\epsilon}{\int e^{\frac{1}{2}\frac{\partial^2\phi}{\partial\epsilon^2}\Big|_{\epsilon=\bar{\epsilon}}(\epsilon-\bar{\epsilon})^2} d\epsilon}$$

$$\cong \left(-\frac{\partial^2\phi}{\partial\epsilon^2}\Big|_{\epsilon=\bar{\epsilon}}\right)^{-1}. \tag{5.523}$$

Combining equations (5.522) and (5.523), we get equation (5.516).

We may remark here that equation (5.521) expresses that the distribution in energy is to a first approximation a Gaussian distribution.

From equation (5.516) it follows that

$$\frac{\bar{\epsilon}-\psi}{\Theta} = \phi(\bar{\epsilon},a_i) + \ln\Delta. \tag{5.524}$$

Since $\ln\Delta$ is in general of the order of magnitude $\ln N$ while $\bar{\epsilon}$ and ψ are of the order of magnitude N, we may neglect the last term on the right-hand side of equation (5.524). Using equation (5.309) for the entropy we have, apart possibly from an additive constant,

$$\frac{S}{k} = \phi(\bar{\epsilon},a_i) = \ln\frac{\partial\Omega}{\partial\epsilon}\Big|_{\epsilon=\bar{\epsilon}}. \tag{5.525}$$

From the well-known relation between entropy and temperature (compare equation [5.308]),

$$\frac{1}{T} = \frac{\partial S}{\partial\epsilon}\Big|_{\epsilon=\bar{\epsilon}}, \tag{5.526}$$

we get, using equation (5.525),

$$\frac{1}{\Theta} = \frac{1}{kT} = \frac{\partial S/k}{\partial\epsilon}\Big|_{\epsilon=\bar{\epsilon}} = \frac{\partial\phi}{\partial\epsilon}\Big|_{\epsilon=\bar{\epsilon}}, \tag{5.527}$$

which we derived a moment ago by slightly different arguments (equation [5.519]).

If we calculate the average value of $\partial\phi/\partial\epsilon$ over the ensemble, we get

$$\overline{\frac{\partial\phi}{\partial\epsilon}} = \int \frac{\partial\phi}{\partial\epsilon} e^{\frac{\psi-\epsilon}{\Theta}+\phi} d\epsilon = \left[e^{\frac{\psi-\epsilon}{\Theta}+\phi} \right]_{\epsilon_{\min}}^{\infty} + \frac{1}{\Theta}\int e^{\frac{\psi-\epsilon}{\Theta}+\phi} d\epsilon,$$

or

$$\overline{\frac{\partial\phi}{\partial\epsilon}} = \frac{1}{\Theta}, \tag{5.528}$$

where we have used equation (5.512) to show that the integrated part is zero and where we have also used equation (5.515).

Comparing equations (5.527) and (5.528), we see that the average value of $\partial\phi/\partial\epsilon$ is the same as its value when the energy has its most probable value. This property is equally true for other quantities and is a consequence of the fact that the dispersion in energy is extremely small.

We mentioned before that most systems by far in the ensemble have an energy in the neighborhood of $\bar{\epsilon}$. From equation (5.518) we see that this means that e^{ϕ} must increase steeply when ϵ increases from $\epsilon_{\min}$ to $\bar{\epsilon}$. Let us compare a macrocanonical ensemble with $\eta = (\psi - \epsilon)/\Theta$ and average energy $\bar{\epsilon}$ with an F-ensemble with density given by the equation

$$\rho_F = a e^{\frac{\psi-\bar{\epsilon}}{\Theta}} F(\epsilon), \tag{5.529}$$

where $F(\epsilon)$ is given by equation (5.210) and where a is a constant.

Taking averages over the F-ensemble, we have for the average value $\overline{G}_F$ of a phase function, which depends only on the energy,

$$\overline{G}_F = \int_{\Gamma} \rho_F G(\epsilon) d\Omega = \int_{\epsilon_{\min}}^{\bar{\epsilon}} a e^{\frac{\psi-\bar{\epsilon}}{\Theta}} G(\epsilon) e^{\phi} d\epsilon, \tag{5.530}$$

or, since e^{ϕ} has a steep maximum for $\epsilon \cong \bar{\epsilon}$,

$$\overline{G}_F \approx a\Delta e^{\frac{\psi-\bar{\epsilon}}{\Theta}+\phi(\bar{\epsilon})} G(\bar{\epsilon}). \tag{5.531}$$

On the other hand, the average taken over the macrocanonical ensemble is given by the equation

$$\overline{G} = \int_{\Gamma} e^{\frac{\psi-\epsilon}{\Theta}} G(\epsilon) d\Omega \approx e^{\frac{\psi-\bar{\epsilon}}{\Theta}+\phi(\bar{\epsilon})} G(\bar{\epsilon})\Delta. \tag{5.532}$$

We see that the two ensembles will lead to about the same average values and thus be more or less equivalent, if

$$a \approx 1. \tag{5.533}$$

The normalization of the F-ensemble gives

$$1 = \int_{\epsilon_{\min}}^{\bar{\epsilon}} ae^{\frac{\psi - \bar{\epsilon}}{\Theta}} d\Omega = ae^{\frac{\psi - \bar{\epsilon}}{\Theta}} \int_{\epsilon_{\min}}^{\bar{\epsilon}} d\Omega = ae^{\frac{\psi - \bar{\epsilon}}{\Theta}} \Omega(\bar{\epsilon}). \tag{5.534}$$

Taking the logarithm and neglecting $\ln a$ with respect to the other terms and using equation (5.309) for the entropy, we get, apart from a possible additive constant,

$$\frac{S}{k} = \ln \Omega(\bar{\epsilon}); \tag{5.535}$$

for the temperature we get the equation

$$\frac{1}{\Theta} = \left.\frac{\partial S/k}{\partial \epsilon}\right|_{\epsilon=\bar{\epsilon}} = \left.\frac{\partial \ln \Omega}{\partial \epsilon}\right|_{\epsilon=\bar{\epsilon}} = \left.\frac{e^{\phi}}{\Omega}\right|_{\epsilon=\bar{\epsilon}}. \tag{5.536}$$

§6. The Coupling of Two Macrocanonical Ensembles. In §2 we mentioned that one way to couple two stationary ensembles in such a way that the resulting ensemble is again a stationary ensemble is to couple two macrocanonical ensembles with the same modulus. We shall now justify that statement. The discussion in this section will once more follow closely Gibbs' considerations.

Let us consider two ensembles. The first one may have a density ρ_1, index of probability η_1, energy ϵ_1, and if it is macrocanonical, modulus Θ_1, while the corresponding quantities in the second ensemble will have indices 2. Let us couple these two ensembles at $t = t'$. This coupling consists of forming a new ensemble with systems which are obtained by combining one system from the first ensemble with one system from the second ensemble. The coupling is supposed to be a physical one so that energy can be exchanged between the two systems which are combined to form a system of the new ensemble. The density, index of probability, and energy of the new ensemble will be denoted by ρ_{12}, η_{12}, and ϵ_{12}. After a while, at $t = t''$, the two systems are separated and we have again two separate ensembles. At t' we have clearly

$$\rho_{12}' = \rho_1' \cdot \rho_2', \tag{5.601}$$

and we must show that, if

$$\rho_1 = e^{\frac{\psi_1 - \epsilon_1}{\Theta_1}}, \qquad \rho_2 = e^{\frac{\psi_2 - \epsilon_2}{\Theta_2}}, \tag{5.602}$$

the equation

$$\rho_{12}' = \rho_{12}'' \tag{5.603}$$

will be satisfied only if $\Theta_1 = \Theta_2$. Henceforth, as in the equations (5.601) and (5.603), primes and double primes will indicate values at $t = t'$ and $t = t''$ respectively.

That equation (5.603) is satisfied if $\Theta_1 = \Theta_2 = \Theta_{12}$ follows easily from equations (5.601), (5.602), and the equation

$$\epsilon_{12} = \epsilon_1 + \epsilon_2, \tag{5.604}$$

whence we have

$$\rho_{12} = e^{\frac{\psi_1 - \epsilon_1}{\Theta_1}} \cdot e^{\frac{\psi_2 - \epsilon_2}{\Theta_2}} = e^{\frac{\psi_{12} - \epsilon_{12}}{\Theta_{12}}} \tag{5.605}$$

($\psi_{12} = \psi_1 + \psi_2$), which is a stationary macrocanonical distribution.

Let us now consider what would happen if we coupled two macrocanonical ensembles with different moduli. We see immediately that the resulting ensemble is not a stationary one, since the density is not a function of ϵ_{12}, but contains ϵ_1 and ϵ_2 separately. We shall prove that, if

$$\Theta_1 > \Theta_2, \tag{5.606}$$

a system from the first ensemble will on the average have lost energy to the system from the second ensemble, with which it was combined between t' and t''. Since Θ is a measure for the temperature, this corresponds to the thermodynamical fact that energy will pass from a system of higher temperature to a system of lower temperature.

We must remark here that in order that energy can be transported from a system of the first ensemble to a system from the second ensemble, it is necessary that there exist an interaction energy ϵ_{int} so that instead of equation (5.604) we really have

$$\epsilon_{12} = \epsilon_1 + \epsilon_2 + \epsilon_{\text{int}}. \tag{5.607}$$

However, we shall assume, firstly, that $\epsilon_{\text{int}} \ll \epsilon_{12}$, and, secondly, that the coupling takes place in such a way that the systems are brought together and pulled apart so gradually that both at t' and at t'' equation (5.604) is satisfied, that is,

$$\epsilon_{12}' = \epsilon_1' + \epsilon_2' \quad \text{and} \quad \epsilon_{12}'' = \epsilon_1'' + \epsilon_2''. \tag{5.608}$$

Before proving that, on the average, energy from the first ensemble will go over to the second ensemble if equation (5.606) is satisfied, we shall prove a few necessary lemmas.

Consider an ensemble which is such that all its systems consist of two parts, denoted by indices a and b while an index ab indicates the whole system. We then have

$$\int_\Gamma \rho_{\text{ab}} d\Omega_{\text{ab}} = \int_\Gamma e^{\eta_{\text{ab}}} d\Omega_{\text{ab}} = 1, \tag{5.609}$$

where

$$d\Omega_{\text{ab}} = d\Omega_{\text{a}} d\Omega_{\text{b}}. \tag{5.610}$$

Introducing

$$\rho_a = e^{\eta_a} = \int_\Gamma e^{\eta_{ab}} d\Omega_b, \tag{5.611}$$

$$\rho_b = e^{\eta_b} = \int_\Gamma e^{\eta_{ab}} d\Omega_a, \tag{5.612}$$

we see that from equation (5.609) it follows that

$$\int_\Gamma e^{\eta_a} d\Omega_a = \int_\Gamma e^{\eta_b} d\Omega_b = 1. \tag{5.613}$$

We also see that ρ_a and ρ_b evidently denote the densities of the subensembles made up out of part a and part b.

Lemma I. In the case of an ensemble such as that just discussed one has

$$\bar{\eta}_{ab} \geqslant \bar{\eta}_a + \bar{\eta}_b, \tag{5.614}$$

where the averages are taken over the corresponding ensembles or subensembles.

Proof. First of all let us note that the expression $u \cdot e^u + 1 - e^u$ is positive for $u \neq 0$ and is zero for $u = 0$.

Secondly, let us evaluate $\bar{\eta}_{ab} - \bar{\eta}_a - \bar{\eta}_b$. Using equations (5.611) and (5.612), we have

$$\begin{aligned}\bar{\eta}_{ab} - \bar{\eta}_a - \bar{\eta}_b &= \int_\Gamma \eta_{ab} e^{\eta_{ab}} d\Omega_{ab} - \int_\Gamma \eta_a e^{\eta_a} d\Omega_a - \int_\Gamma \eta_b e^{\eta_b} d\Omega_b \\ &= \int_\Gamma (\eta_{ab} - \eta_a - \eta_b) e^{\eta_{ab}} d\Omega_{ab}.\end{aligned} \tag{5.615}$$

From equation (5.613) we have

$$\int_\Gamma e^{\eta_a} d\Omega_a \cdot \int_\Gamma e^{\eta_b} d\Omega_b = \int_\Gamma e^{\eta_a + \eta_b} d\Omega_{ab} = 1, \tag{5.616}$$

and using equations (5.615), (5.616), and (5.609), we get finally

$$\bar{\eta}_{ab} - \bar{\eta}_a - \bar{\eta}_b = \int_\Gamma (xe^x + 1 - e^x) e^{\eta_a + \eta_b} d\Omega_{ab} \geqslant 0, \qquad (x = \eta_{ab} - \eta_a - \eta_b) \tag{5.617}$$

in virtue of the fact that the integrand is nonnegative. This proves our lemma.

Lemma II. Consider two ensembles with indices of probability given by the equations

$$\eta_1 = \frac{\psi - \epsilon}{\Theta}, \qquad \eta_2 = \frac{\psi - \epsilon}{\Theta} + \Delta\eta, \tag{5.618}$$

that is, one macrocanonical ensemble and one arbitrary ensemble. We then have

$$\overline{\left(\eta + \frac{\epsilon}{\Theta}\right)_1} \leqslant \overline{\left(\eta + \frac{\epsilon}{\Theta}\right)_2}. \tag{5.619}$$

Proof. We have from equation (5.618)

$$\overline{\left(\eta + \frac{\epsilon}{\Theta}\right)_2} - \overline{\left(\eta + \frac{\epsilon}{\Theta}\right)_1} = \int_\Gamma \left[\left(\frac{\psi}{\Theta} + \Delta\eta\right) e^{\eta_1 + \Delta\eta} - \frac{\psi}{\Theta} e^{\eta_1}\right] d\Omega. \quad \mathbf{(5.620)}$$

Moreover, from the normalization condition one has

$$\int_\Gamma e^{\eta_1 + \Delta\eta} d\Omega = \int_\Gamma e^{\eta_1} d\Omega, \quad \mathbf{(5.621)}$$

and, combining equations (5.620) and (5.621) the right-hand side of equation (5.620) is found to be equal to

$$\int_\Gamma \Delta\eta e^{\eta_1 + \Delta\eta} d\Omega = \int_\Gamma \left[\Delta\eta e^{\Delta\eta} + 1 - e^{\Delta\eta}\right] e^{\eta_1} d\Omega \geqslant 0, \quad \mathbf{(5.622)}$$

from which our second lemma follows.

We can now consider the joining together and pulling apart of the two ensembles. From equation (5.601) it follows that

$$\eta_{12}' = \eta_1' + \eta_2', \quad \mathbf{(5.623)}$$

and thus

$$\bar{\eta}_{12}' = \bar{\eta}_1' + \bar{\eta}_2', \quad \mathbf{(5.624)}$$

where in going over from equation (5.623) to equation (5.624) we have used the fact that ρ_1 and ρ_2 are normalized.†

At t'' we have (see equation [5.614])

$$\bar{\eta}_{12}'' \geqslant \bar{\eta}_1'' + \bar{\eta}_2''. \quad \mathbf{(5.625)}$$

We saw in §3 that for a macrocanonical ensemble $-\bar{\eta}$, apart from possible additive and multiplying constants, corresponded to the entropy. We can also easily see that, in general, $\bar{\eta}$ should correspond to Boltzmann's H, since

$$\bar{\eta} = \int_\Gamma \eta e^\eta d\Omega = \int_\Gamma \rho \ln \rho d\Omega. \quad \mathbf{(5.626)}$$

From the second law of thermodynamics, or from a generalized H-theorem (see §6 of Appendix I, p. 366), we should then expect that

$$\bar{\eta}_{12}'' \leqslant \bar{\eta}_{12}'. \quad \mathbf{(5.627)}$$

Since at t' the two ensembles were macrocanonical while this is no longer necessarily so at t'', the conditions under which Lemma II is valid are

† From equation (5.623) one has

$$\int_\Gamma \eta_{12}' \rho_{12} d\Omega_{12} = \int_\Gamma \eta_1' \rho_{12} d\Omega_{12} + \int_\Gamma \eta_2' \rho_{12} d\Omega_{12}$$
$$= \int_\Gamma \eta_1' \rho_1 d\Omega_1 \cdot \int_\Gamma \rho_2 d\Omega_2 + \int_\Gamma \rho_1 d\Omega_1 \int_\Gamma \eta_2' \rho_2 d\Omega_2.$$

satisfied and we have from inequality (5.619)

$$\bar{\eta}_1{}' + \frac{\bar{\epsilon}_1{}'}{\Theta_1} \leqslant \bar{\eta}_1{}'' + \frac{\bar{\epsilon}_1{}''}{\Theta_1} \tag{5.628}$$

and

$$\bar{\eta}_2{}' + \frac{\bar{\epsilon}_2{}'}{\Theta_2} \leqslant \bar{\eta}_2{}'' + \frac{\bar{\epsilon}_2{}''}{\Theta_2} \cdot \tag{5.629}$$

Combining equations (5.624), (5.625), and (5.627) to (5.629), we get

$$\frac{\bar{\epsilon}_1{}'' - \bar{\epsilon}_1{}'}{\Theta_1} + \frac{\bar{\epsilon}_2{}'' - \bar{\epsilon}_2{}'}{\Theta_2} \geqslant 0. \tag{5.630}$$

From equations (5.608) and the principle of conservation of energy, we have

$$\bar{\epsilon}_1{}'' - \bar{\epsilon}_1{}' + \bar{\epsilon}_2{}'' - \bar{\epsilon}_2{}' = 0, \tag{5.631}$$

and hence, combining equations (5.630) and (5.631),

$$(\bar{\epsilon}_1{}'' - \bar{\epsilon}_1{}')\left(\frac{1}{\Theta_1} - \frac{1}{\Theta_2}\right) \geqslant 0. \tag{5.632}$$

From equations (5.606) and (5.632) we then have

$$\bar{\epsilon}_1{}' \geqslant \bar{\epsilon}_1{}'',$$

or the system with the larger modulus will, on the average, have lost energy to the other system.

We have just seen that if two macrocanonical ensembles are physically coupled, they will form a stationary ensemble if their moduli are equal, and that the one with the larger modulus will on the average lose energy to the other one if their moduli are not equal.

If we couple two microcanonical ensembles, the resulting ensemble will also be a microcanonical ensemble; hence one might ask whether there is any reason to prefer the macrocanonical to the microcanonical ensembles as we have done. The reason is that while in both cases the resulting ensemble is again a stationary one, separation at t'' reproduces the situation before t' in the case of macrocanonical ensembles, but not in the case of microcanonical ones. This last point we can see as follows. Consider two systems A and B which together form one system of the combined ensemble. If ϵ_1 is the energy of the first and ϵ_2 that of the second microcanonical ensemble, system A had an energy ϵ_1 and system B an energy ϵ_2 before t'. During the interval t',t'' the two systems were coupled and could exchange energy. When they are separated at t'' there is no reason to assume that all systems A still have the same energy, and hence they will no longer form a microcanonical ensemble.

The case is different, however, when two macrocanonical ensembles are coupled. Since according to our assumptions the interaction between the systems of the two coupled ensembles is negligibly small, we can at any time (also between t' and t'') calculate the average values of the powers of ϵ_1 and we find then that they correspond at any time to the average values in a macrocanonical ensemble with modulus Θ so that, indeed, after t'' we will again have two macrocanonical ensembles.

The average value of ϵ_1^n can be calculated as follows. Let $p_1', \cdots, p_{s'N'}', q_1', \cdots, q_{s'N'}'$ be the coordinates pertaining to the first ensemble and $p_1'', \cdots, p_{s''N''}'', q_1'', \cdots, q_{s''N''}''$ those pertaining to the second ensemble. We have then

$$\epsilon_1 = \epsilon_1(p',q'), \quad \epsilon_2 = \epsilon_2(p'',q''), \quad \epsilon_{\text{tot}} = \epsilon_1(p',q') + \epsilon_2(p'',q'')$$

and

$$d\Omega_{\text{tot}} = d\Omega' \cdot d\Omega'',$$

where the index "tot" indicates the combined ensemble.

The average value of ϵ_1^n in the combined ensemble then satisfies the equations

$$\begin{aligned} \langle\epsilon_1^n\rangle_{\text{Av tot}} &= \int_\Gamma \epsilon_1^n(p',q')\rho_{\text{tot}}d\Omega_{\text{tot}} \\ &= \int_\Gamma \epsilon_1^n(p',q')\rho' d\Omega' \cdot \int_\Gamma \rho'' d\Omega'' \\ &= \int_\Gamma \epsilon_1^n(p',q')\rho' d\Omega' = \langle\epsilon_1^n\rangle_{\text{Av 1}}. \end{aligned}$$

§7. Ergodic Systems and Microcanonical Ensembles. In this section we shall consider microcanonical ensembles. We saw in §1 and know from theoretical mechanics that the energy of a system is one of its integrals. We might therefore be tempted to prefer microcanonical to macrocanonical ensembles, especially as long as our considerations are classical so that in principle we could hope to determine the energy of the system under observation as accurately as we wished. In a moment we shall see another reason for introducing microcanonical ensembles, but a final discussion of the relative merits of the micro- and macrocanonical ensembles will be given in §8 when we discuss the relation between actually observed physical systems and ensembles.

Consider a system with a fixed energy, that is, an isolated system. Its representative point in Γ-space will describe an orbit on the energy surface

$$\epsilon(p,q) = c_1, \tag{5.701}$$

where c_1 is the value of the energy. The orbit itself is completely determined by the equations of motion and in each point of the energy surface the direction in which the orbit will proceed is completely fixed by the values of the coordinates of the representative point.†

If there are two systems, A and B, for which the first $2sN - 1$ integrals of motion in equations (5.104) are the same, but for which c_{2sN} is not the same,

$$c_{1\text{A}} = c_{1\text{B}}; \qquad c_{2\text{A}} = c_{2\text{B}}; \qquad c_{2sN-1,\text{A}} = c_{2sN-1,\text{B}};$$
$$c_{2sN,\text{A}} = c_{2sN,\text{B}} + \Delta,$$

the orbits of their representative points will be the same, the only difference being that one orbit is traversed with a time lag Δ with respect to the other orbit. The averages of any phase function $G(p,q)$ will be the same for the two systems.

There are mechanical systems for which the orbits of their representative points cover a multidimensional region in Γ-space everywhere densely. Boltzmann suspected this and introduced a class of mechanical systems with the property that the orbit of their representative point will pass *through every point* of the energy surface. Such a system is called an *ergodic system* and the theorem stating that most systems will behave as ergodic ones is called the *ergodic theorem*.‡ Boltzmann never attempted to prove the ergodic theorem. At present it is known that ergodic systems in this sense do not exist. The proof of this was given in 1913 independently by Rosenthal and Plancherel.

Since the Ehrenfests suspected that ergodic systems did not exist, they introduced so-called *quasi-ergodic* systems. The orbit of the representative point of a quasi-ergodic system will come arbitrarily close to any point on the energy surface. Fermi has actually shown that a quite general class of mechanical systems is quasi-ergodic. We do not wish to enter at this point into a discussion of the merits and drawbacks of a quasi-ergodic theorem, but refer to Appendix I.

An ergodic system would show the following properties.

a) All orbits on a given energy surface are identical. This follows since, on the one hand, every orbit passes through all points of the energy surface, while, on the other hand, the direction of the orbit is uniquely determined in every point.

---

† From this property of the orbits in Γ-space it follows that two orbits in Γ-space can never cross.

‡ "Ergodic" comes from the Greek: ἔργον = work (used here in the sense of energy), ὁδός = path. Maxwell and other British writers call the ergodic theorem the assumption of the *continuity of path*. We refer to Appendix I for a thorough discussion of all questions pertaining to the ergodic theorem and for references to the extensive literature on this problem.

b) The different orbits on a given energy surface can thus differ only in the value of the constant c_{2sN}, that is, in the moment at which each point is passed.

c) Defining the time average $\tilde{G}$ of a phase function by the equation

$$\tilde{G} = \lim_{T\to\infty} \frac{1}{2T}\int_{-T}^{+T} G(p,q)dt, \tag{5.702}$$

where p,q denote the values of the coordinates of the representative point at the time t, we see that $\tilde{G}$ will be the same for all orbits on a given energy surface.

If a system were ergodic, the time average of any phase function taken over a sufficiently long time interval would be independent of the values of any of the φ_i but the energy,† and it would be equal to the average taken over the corresponding energy surface, that is, taken over a microcanonical ensemble. We get, then, the result that the time average of a phase function is equal to the average of that phase function over a microcanonical ensemble. In view of the importance of that result, we shall derive it in a slightly different manner.

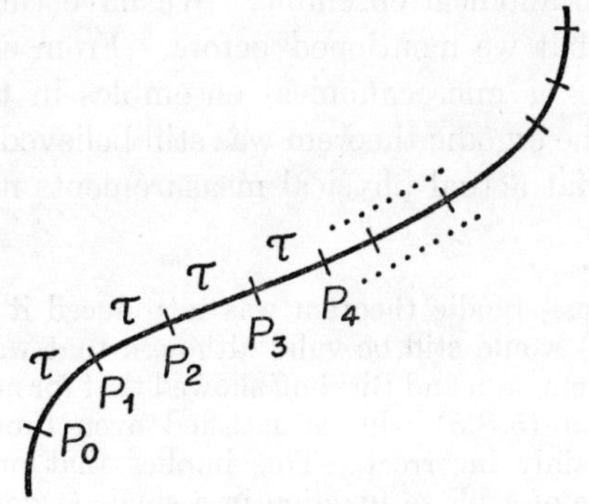

Fig. 24

Let us consider a system of given energy and let us consider its orbit on the appropriate energy surface (see Fig. 24). Let P_0 be the position of the representative point at $t = t_0$, P_1 at $t_0 + \tau$, P_2 at $t_0 + 2\tau$, $\cdots$, while P_{-1}, P_{-2}, $\cdots$ were the positions at $t_0 - \tau$, $t_0 - 2\tau$, $\cdots$, in general, P_i at $t_0 + i\tau (i = 0, \pm 1, \pm 2, \cdots)$. The points P_i form a stationary ensemble. Any collection of points in Γ-space forms an ensemble and since the P_i at a

---

† This in itself points to the improbability of ergodic systems and is actually taken by Tolman to be a sufficient proof of their nonexistence; see, however, p. 357.

later time, say $t_0 + n\tau$, can be obtained from the P_i at t_0 by putting

$$P_i(t = t_0 + n\tau) = \mathrm{P}_{i-n}(t = t_0), \tag{5.703}$$

the ensemble is stationary.

Let us now consider the average $\langle G\rangle_{\mathrm{Av}}$ of a phase function $G(p,q)$ over the P_i,

$$\langle G\rangle_{\mathrm{Av}} = \frac{\cdots + G_{-2} + G_{-1} + G_0 + G_1 + G_2 + \cdots}{\cdots + 1 + 1 + 1 + 1 + 1 + \cdots}, \tag{5.704}$$

where G_i is the value of $G(p,q)$ at P_i, and let us take the limit $\tau \to 0$. The right-hand side of equation (5.704) will then become the time average $\widetilde{G}$ while the left-hand side will become the average over a microcanonical ensemble which we shall denote here and henceforth by a double bar. We have thus

$$\overline{\overline{G}} = \widetilde{G}. \tag{5.705}$$

We must remark here that the ensemble formed by the P_i will go over into a microcanonical ensemble only if the system is ergodic, since in that case the only stationary ensemble with a continuous density and with constant energy is the microcanonical ensemble. We have thus not proved anything more than what we mentioned before. From equation (5.705) we see the importance of microcanonical ensembles in the older statistical discussions, when the ergodic theorem was still believed in, especially when we keep in mind that actual physical measurements nearly always determine time averages.

When the quasi-ergodic theorem was introduced it was hoped that equation (5.705) would still be valid although that was never proved. However, von Neumann and Birkhoff showed that for nearly all physical systems equation (5.705) will be satisfied even though the ergodic theorem is certainly incorrect. This implies that one can calculate the time average of a phase function in a single system by taking the average over a microcanonical ensemble with the same energy.

From the fact that it can be proved (see §5 of Appendix I) that equation (5.705) is valid for most physical systems even though they are not ergodic and from the fact that, while one measures time averages, ensemble averages can nearly always be much more easily computed, it follows that it might be advantageous to consider in slightly more detail the microcanonical ensemble. We shall then see that averages over a microcanonical ensemble will be the same as averages taken over a suitably chosen macrocanonical ensemble. We see thus that we can for actual calculations practically always confine ourselves to macrocanonical ensembles, which is rather gratifying, since they are more amenable to mathematical treatment and since there are also other arguments which point to macrocanonical ensembles as we have seen and shall see again in the next section.

With Gibbs we shall introduce the microcanonical ensemble by using a mathematical trick, namely by introducing the density†

$$\rho(\epsilon) = \lim_{\alpha\to\infty} e^{c-\alpha^2(\epsilon-\epsilon_0)^2}, \tag{5.706}$$

where c is a constant to be determined from the normalization condition.

Consider now the identity

$$\int_\Gamma e^{-\alpha^2(\epsilon-\epsilon_0)^2} d\Omega = \int_{\epsilon_{\min}(a_i)}^{\infty} e^{-\alpha^2(\epsilon-\epsilon_0)^2+\phi(\epsilon,a_i)} d\epsilon. \tag{5.707}$$

If we take the derivative with respect to a_j both of the left-hand side and of the right-hand side of this identity, the result is

$$-\Big[\overline{A}_j(\epsilon)e^{-\alpha^2(\epsilon-\epsilon_0)^2+\phi}\Big]_{\epsilon_{\min}}^{\infty} + \int_{\epsilon_{\min}}^{\infty}\left(\frac{\partial\overline{A}_j}{\partial\epsilon} + \overline{A}_j\frac{\partial\phi}{\partial\epsilon}\right)e^{-\alpha^2(\epsilon-\epsilon_0)^2+\phi}d\epsilon$$
$$= \int_{\epsilon_{\min}}^{\infty}\frac{\partial\phi}{\partial a_j}e^{-\alpha^2(\epsilon-\epsilon_0)^2+\phi}d\epsilon - \left[e^{-\alpha^2(\epsilon-\epsilon_0)^2+\phi}\frac{\partial\epsilon}{\partial a_j}\right]_{\epsilon_{\min}}. \tag{5.708}$$

Equation (5.708) is derived as follows. First of all we note the different ways in which the left-hand side and the right-hand side of equation (5.707) depend on the a_i (compare the remark after equation [5.514] on p. 115). The left-hand side of equation (5.708) is then obtained by first taking the derivative with respect to a_j, then introducing $e^\phi d\epsilon$ instead of $d\Omega$, and finally integrating by parts. The first term on the right-hand side of equation (5.708) derives from the fact that ϕ depends on a_j and the second term from the fact that the lower limit on the integral depends on a_j. Finally we used the identity

$$\int_\Gamma G e^{-\alpha^2(\epsilon-\epsilon_0)^2} d\Omega = \int_{\epsilon_{\min}}^{\infty} \overline{\overline{G}}(\epsilon)e^{-\alpha^2(\epsilon-\epsilon_0)^2+\phi}d\epsilon, \tag{5.709}$$

where $\overline{\overline{G}}(\epsilon)$ is the average of G over a microcanonical ensemble with energy ϵ.

Using equation (5.512), we see that the integrated parts in equation (5.708) are zero, and multiplying under the integration signs by e^c and taking the limit $\alpha \to \infty$, we get the equation

$$e^\phi\frac{\partial\overline{A}_j}{\partial\epsilon} + \overline{A}_j e^\phi\frac{\partial\phi}{\partial\epsilon} = e^\phi\frac{\partial\phi}{\partial a_j}\left(=\frac{\partial^2\Omega}{\partial a_j\partial\epsilon}\right). \tag{5.710}$$

† It is well known that the right-hand side of equation (5.706) is a possible way to define the δ-function; see, e.g., H. A. Kramers, Hand- u. Jahrb. d. Chem. Phys., Vol. I, Leipzig 1938, p. 105.

This equation can be integrated and the result is†

$$\bar{\bar{A}}_j e^{\phi} = \frac{\partial \Omega}{\partial a_j}, \tag{5.711}$$

or

$$\bar{\bar{A}}_j = e^{-\phi} \frac{\partial \Omega}{\partial a_j}. \tag{5.712}$$

The variation of Ω is now given by the equation

$$\delta\Omega = e^{\phi}(\delta\epsilon + \sum_j \bar{\bar{A}}_j \delta a_j). \tag{5.713}$$

This last equation can be written in the form

$$\delta \ln \Omega = \frac{\delta\epsilon + \sum_j \bar{\bar{A}}_j \delta a_j}{e^{-\phi}\Omega}, \tag{5.714}$$

and comparison with the thermodynamical equation for the variation of the entropy shows that we can take $\ln \Omega$ as being proportional to the entropy of the system and $e^{-\phi}\Omega$ as a measure for the temperature. Since that gives us the same as expressions (5.535) and (5.536), which were derived for macrocanonical ensembles, we have found the result that the averages over a microcanonical ensemble with energy ϵ_0 are the same as those taken over a macrocanonical ensemble for which $\bar{\epsilon} = \epsilon_0$.‡ We shall consider in somewhat more detail the relationship between micro- and macrocanonical ensembles in the next section.

§8. The Relationship between Ensembles and Actually Observed Systems. One might ask what reason there is to introduce ensembles at all since in actual cases one is always dealing with one system. Indeed, Gibbs introduced ensembles in order to use them for statistical considerations rather than to illustrate the behavior of physical systems, even though he did not adhere strictly to his original intentions as set out in the introduction to his monograph. Einstein considered rather more carefully the possibility that the average behavior of a system in a macrocanonical ensemble would represent the actual behavior of a system in thermodynamical equilibrium. However, the Ehrenfests, Ornstein,§ and Uhlenbeck‖ considered ensemble

† There should be an integration constant $K_j(a_i)$ on the right-hand side of equation (5.711). One can, however, prove by writing down the variation of Ω (compare equation [5.713]), considering such variations of the a_i and of ϵ that $\delta\epsilon_{\min} = 0$, and using equation (5.512) that all the K_j are equal to zero.

‡ It must be borne in mind that, e.g., in equation (5.712) all expressions on the right-hand side must be taken for $\epsilon = \epsilon_0$.

§ L. S. Ornstein, Toepassing der Statistische Mechanica van Gibbs op Molekulair-theoretische Vraagstukken, Thesis, Leiden 1908.

‖ G. E. Uhlenbeck, Over Statistische Methoden in de Theorie der Quanta, Thesis, Leiden 1927.

theory still mainly as a mathematical trick to lighten the calculation of average values of phase functions with a given total energy and given total number of particles, much in the same way as our discussion of equation (5.705) in the preceding section. Uhlenbeck therefore considers Gibbs' method and the Darwin-Fowler method† as more or less equivalent. However, Tolman succeeded in his monograph in showing the importance of ensemble theory from a physical point of view and we shall give some of his arguments in the present section, although referring to his monograph for a thorough discussion of this point.

At the beginning of this book we mentioned the difficulties which arise from the fact that the total number of degrees of freedom of practically any physical system is so enormously large. One cubic centimeter of helium gas under normal conditions (0°C, 1 atmos) contains 3.10^{19} atoms, and we see immediately that it will be impossible to determine the positions and velocities of all the particles in the system.‡ In practice only a few data are given about a system—or rather, obtained by physical measurements—and we should like to make predictions about the future behavior of the system, taking into account the limited knowledge gained from our observations. The only possible way of making predictions is by using statistical methods. If all necessary data could be obtained, we should be concerned with problems of ordinary classical mechanics—be it of extraordinary mathematical complexity—but since they can not, we are reduced to making statements about the *most probable* behavior of the system. In order to find out what this most probable behavior is, we compare various systems for which the measured quantities have the same value but which otherwise differ widely. This means, as will be seen at a glance, that we introduce a *representative ensemble* to describe the behavior of our system. We shall consider two cases in slightly more detail.

In the first case, let us assume that we have a perfectly isolated system§ of which we know the total energy and the total number of particles. We know then that the representative point of this system in Γ-space should lie on an energy surface and we are thus tempted to use as the representative ensemble a microcanonical ensemble. However, by doing so we have made the following basic assumption. We only knew that the representative point should lie on the energy surface, but in order to construct a representative ensemble we must make an assumption about the a priori

† See Appendix IV.

‡ The situation is the same in quantum mechanics, even though we have there the additional complication of complementarity of the coordinates and their conjugate momenta.

§ We neglect for a moment the fact that it is impossible to perform any experiments on a perfectly isolated system and remind ourselves of the fact that in classical physics it is possible to consider the case of a perfectly isolated system as an idealization.

probability of finding the representative point inside a given surface element of the energy surface. The assumption made at this moment can only be justified by the subsequent successes of the theory to account for the observed facts. The assumption which leads to the microcanonical ensemble and which, in fact, is the usual one made by all authors is that of *equal a priori probability for equal volumes in* Γ*-space.* Once this assumption is made, the microcanonical ensemble is the only ensemble which can represent the system under discussion. We refer to §8 of Appendix I for a discussion of the adopted assumption about the a priori probabilities.

The second case which we wish to consider is that of a system in temperature equilibrium. In that case the representative ensemble will be a macrocanonical ensemble. Once again use is made of the basic assumption of equal a priori probabilities for equal volumes in Γ-space. Furthermore, we use the fact that the average behavior of a system in a macrocanonical ensemble—which in view of the smallness of the fluctuations in a macrocanonical ensemble is the same as the most probable behavior of a system in a macrocanonical ensemble—corresponds indeed to the behavior of a system at equilibrium at a given temperature as we saw in §3.

We shall now consider briefly the relation between micro- and macrocanonical ensembles. Consider thereto a very large isolated system, which can thus be represented by a microcanonical ensemble, and consider the behavior of a subsystem of the original system which is in interaction with the other parts of that system. Let $p_1, \cdots, p_s, q_1, \cdots, q_s$ be the coordinates defining the subsystem and $p_1, \cdots, p_s, p_{s+1}, \cdots, p_S, q_1, \cdots, q_s, q_{s+1}, \cdots, q_S$ be those of the total system. The energies of the subsystem and the rest system, that is, the total system minus the subsystem, may be denoted by ϵ and ϵ' respectively. We shall furthermore assume the interaction energy to be negligible.

The question which we wish to consider is the following one. What is the density distribution of the representative points of the subsystem in its own Γ-space, under the condition that the total system is in statistical equilibrium and is isolated, which means that $\epsilon + \epsilon'$ is constant? Let $\rho(p_1, \cdots, p_s, q_1, \cdots, q_s)d\Omega$ be the fraction of cases where the representative point of the subsystem lies within the volume element $d\Omega$ of its Γ-space. Let $\rho'(p_{s+1}, \cdots, p_S, q_{s+1}, \cdots, q_S)d\Omega'$ be the fraction of cases where the representative point of the rest system lies within the volume element $d\Omega'$ of the corresponding Γ-space. We then have the normalization conditions

$$\int_\Gamma \rho d\Omega = \int_\Gamma \rho' d\Omega' = \int_\Gamma \rho\rho' d\Omega d\Omega' = 1. \tag{5.801}$$

The condition of constant total energy is

$$\int_\Gamma \rho\rho'(\epsilon + \epsilon')d\Omega d\Omega' = \int_\Gamma \rho\epsilon d\Omega + \int_\Gamma \rho'\epsilon' d\Omega' = E. \qquad \textbf{(5.802)}$$

The condition for statistical equilibrium follows from equation (5.625) on page 121. Remembering that $\eta = \ln \rho$, we have

$$\int_\Gamma \rho\rho'(\eta + \eta')d\Omega d\Omega' = \int_\Gamma \rho \ln \rho d\Omega + \int_\Gamma \rho' \ln \rho' d\Omega' = \text{constant}. \qquad \textbf{(5.803)}$$

The equilibrium distribution now follows in the usual way by considering slightly varied distributions $\rho + \delta\rho$ and $\rho' + \delta\rho'$ and demanding that equations (5.801) to (5.803) remain satisfied. By a reasoning completely analogous to the one leading to the Maxwell distribution (p. 20) we find

$$\rho = e^{\frac{\psi - \epsilon}{\Theta}}. \qquad \textbf{(5.804)}$$

We have thus proved the important fact that *any part of an isolated system in statistical equilibrium can be represented by a macrocanonical ensemble.* The analogy with the Maxwell distribution is not accidental, since we have there just an example of a subsystem (one atom) in an isolated system (the gas). We may add that in a similar way one can prove that a subsystem of a larger system in temperature equilibrium will also behave like the average system of a macrocanonical ensemble.

Another case of a subsystem of an isolated system is that of a system controlled by a thermostat. The system and thermostat together can be considered to be an isolated system and we can then expect that the system itself can be represented by a macrocanonical ensemble—a fact which we mentioned and used earlier in this chapter. Many authors† prefer to consider a macrocanonical ensemble in such a way that the system under consideration is one of the ensemble while the other systems in the ensemble form together the thermostat or "temperature bath." Although this is sometimes a useful approach, it seems to us to miss the important point that a system is represented by an ensemble because of the incompleteness of the available observational data.

At the end of this section let us briefly discuss the idea that energy and temperature are complementary quantities. The term "complementarity" is used here in a different manner from its use when it enters in the discussion of the Heisenberg relations. While in quantum mechanics we cannot define two canonically conjugate quantities simultaneously with arbitrary accuracy, the point here is that we cannot reduce the fluctuations

† See, e.g., E. Schrödinger, Statistical Thermodynamics, Cambridge 1948.

in both temperature and energy arbitrarily. We discussed one side of this question, namely, that *in a system in temperature equilibrium energy fluctuations occur.* On the other hand, if we consider an isolated system, say, a volume of helium gas, its total energy is fixed. Is it possible to speak about the temperature of such a system? In order to do this we must envisage a temperature measurement, for instance, by considering a small part of the gas and measuring its mean kinetic energy per atom.† Since we have just seen that such a subsystem will behave as the average member of a macrocanonical ensemble, we shall find fluctuations in the value of the mean kinetic energy per atom, and hence in the temperature. *In an isolated system we must expect temperature fluctuations.*

§9. Application of the Theory of Petit Ensembles to a Perfect Gas. Although Part C will deal in detail with various applications of the theory developed in Parts A and B, we shall briefly discuss the simple case of a perfect gas in order to illustrate the theory of petit ensembles.

The discussion was started in §3, where an expression for $e^{\psi/\Theta}$, or rather for the partition function Z_Γ, was derived. We had there (equations [5.325] and [5.310])

$$e^{-\frac{\psi}{\Theta}} = V^N(2\pi m\Theta)^{\frac{3N}{2}}. \tag{5.901}$$

From this equation we can calculate, for instance, the fluctuations in the energy, using equation (5.407), which gives

$$\overline{(\epsilon - \bar{\epsilon})^2} = -\frac{\partial^2(\psi/\Theta)}{\partial(1/\Theta)^2} = \tfrac{3}{2}N\Theta^2, \tag{5.902}$$

and combining this with the result for the average energy

$$\bar{\epsilon} = \tfrac{3}{2}N\Theta, \tag{5.903}$$

we have

$$\frac{\overline{(\epsilon - \bar{\epsilon})^2}}{\bar{\epsilon}^2} = \frac{2}{3N}, \tag{5.904}$$

showing that the dispersion is indeed very small as soon as N is large.

Let us now consider the fluctuations in the pressure. We mentioned on page 113 that in this case we cannot use formula (5.409) as long as we use ideal walls, that is, as long as we use the function $F(x_i,y_i,z_i)$ of equation (2.802) for the potential energy function. We must now consider the time average of the pressure and its fluctuations. We can do this in two steps. The first step consists in reminding ourselves of the fact that for a

† We cannot introduce an external thermometer, because this would destroy the isolation of the system.

system of many degrees of freedom we have found in §7 that we obtain the same results whether we consider a macro- or a microcanonical ensemble. The second step follows then immediately, since we also saw that time averages and averages taken over the corresponding microcanonical ensemble are the same (p. 126). We can now use the formulae for the averages in a microcanonical ensemble and we have thus

$$\tilde{p} = \overline{\overline{p}} = e^{-\phi}\frac{\partial\Omega}{\partial V}, \tag{5.905}$$

and since

$$e^{\phi} = \frac{\partial\Omega}{\partial\epsilon}, \tag{5.906}$$

we have

$$\tilde{p} = \frac{\dfrac{\partial\Omega}{\partial V}}{\dfrac{\partial\Omega}{\partial\epsilon}}. \tag{5.907}$$

In the case of a perfect gas Ω can easily be computed from the equations

$$\Omega(\epsilon,V) = \int_{\epsilon=0}^{\epsilon} d\Omega = \int_{\epsilon=0}^{\epsilon} \prod_i d\mathbf{p}_i \prod_i d\mathbf{x}_i, \tag{5.908}$$

$$\epsilon = \sum_i \left(\frac{\mathbf{p}_i{}^2}{2m} + F(x_i,y_i,z_i)\right). \tag{5.909}$$

The integration over the x_i, y_i, and z_i gives a factor V^N and the integral over the $\mathbf{p}_i$ is the formula for the volume of a $3N$-dimensional sphere with radius $\sqrt{2m\epsilon}$. The formula for this volume is different for even or odd N, but we are only interested in the dependence of Ω on ϵ and V and can therefore write

$$\Omega(\epsilon, V) = K\epsilon^{\frac{3N}{2}} V^N, \tag{5.910}$$

where K is a constant.

From equations (5.907) and (5.910) we get the familiar equation (see equation [4.615])

$$\tilde{p} = \frac{2}{3}\frac{\epsilon}{V}. \tag{5.911}$$

From equations (5.911) and (5.904) we get now for the fluctuations in the time average of the pressure

$$\frac{\overline{(\tilde{p} - \overline{\tilde{p}})^2}}{\overline{\tilde{p}}^2} = \frac{\overline{(\epsilon - \overline{\epsilon})^2}}{\overline{\epsilon}^2} = \frac{2}{3N}, \tag{5.912}$$

which proves that, in this case at least, the fluctuations are negligible for large N.

BIBLIOGRAPHICAL NOTES

This chapter is largely based on the following references:

1. J. W. Gibbs, Elementary Principles in Statistical Mechanics (Vol. II of his Collected Works), New Haven 1948.
2. R. C. Tolman, The Principles of Statistical Mechanics, Oxford 1938.
3. P. and T. Ehrenfest, Enzyklopädie der mathematischen Wissenschaften, Vol. IV, Pt. 32, Leipzig-Berlin 1911.

See also

4. A Commentary on the Scientific Works of J. W. Gibbs, edited by A. Haas, New Haven 1936; especially the articles R, S, T, and U by A. Haas and P. S. Epstein.

Independently of Gibbs, Einstein introduced ensemble theory at about the same time:

5. A. Einstein, Ann. Physik, **9**, 417, 1902.
6. A. Einstein, Ann. Physik, **11**, 170, 1903.

It should also be mentioned here that Boltzmann had made use of ensembles, especially, of course, in connection with the ergodic theorem. See, for instance,

7. L. Boltzmann, Wien. Ber., **63**, 679, 1871.

§1. Liouville's theorem was announced in 1838:

8. J. Liouville, J. de Math., **3**, 348, 1838.

CHAPTER VI

CLASSICAL GRAND ENSEMBLES

§1. The Canonical Grand Ensemble. In the last chapter of his famous monograph Gibbs considers systems in which chemical reactions can take place. If such systems are considered, it is clearly no longer advisable to retain the condition of constant number of particles. In the preceding chapter we considered the consequences of throwing overboard the condition of constant energy when we introduced the macrocanonical ensembles and it seems logical as the next step to abandon the constant total number of particles. Before we enter into the discussion of the mathematical formalism, we should briefly discuss the physical basis of this step. By some authors it is felt that just as the introduction of the macrocanonical ensemble and the concomitant loss of the condition of constant energy made calculations much easier, in the same way it might be expected—and it turns out to be the case—that our mathematical discipline will be much easier to handle once we get rid of the condition of constant total number of particles. However, one can give a much deeper and more physical reason, extending Tolman's arguments, by saying that one practically never observes the total number of particles in a system and hence is reduced to setting up representative ensembles which contain systems of varying total number of particles. These ensembles will be called with Gibbs *grand ensembles* and ensembles with a constant number of particles will be called *petit ensembles.* All the ensembles discussed in the preceding chapter were petit ensembles.

The need for grand ensembles is immediately apparent when one considers the case studied by Gibbs where, indeed, in one system the number of particles varies due to chemical reactions taking place in the system. A similar situation arises in systems at very high temperatures when pair creation and annihilation may occur (see, for instance, Chapter XIV).

Finally, we may imagine that the system under consideration is embedded not only in a temperature bath with which it can exchange energy, but also in a "particle bath" or a "particle bank" with which it can exchange particles. From the discussion in this chapter, especially in §3, it follows that such a particle bath should rather be called an "activity bath" or a "fugacity bath," if we wish to keep as close an analogy with the term "temperature bath" as possible.

We shall start out to develop the theory of the grand ensembles in a rather general way and assume that our system contains k different kinds of particles. The number of particles of the ith kind will be denoted by $\mathfrak{n}_i$, and the density of our representative grand ensemble will now not only be a function of the appropriate p's and q's, but also of the $\mathfrak{n}_i$,

$$\rho = \rho(\mathfrak{n}_1,\mathfrak{n}_2,\cdots,\mathfrak{n}_k;p,q), \tag{6.101}$$

where, of course, the number of degrees of freedom, that is, the number of the p's and q's, depends on the actual values of the $\mathfrak{n}_i$. If each particle of the ith kind possesses s_i degrees of freedom, the total number of degrees of freedom s of a system characterized by $\mathfrak{n}_1, \mathfrak{n}_2, \cdots, \mathfrak{n}_k$ will be given by the equation

$$s = \sum_i \mathfrak{n}_i s_i. \tag{6.102}$$

The density of a grand ensemble is defined in such a way that

$$\rho(\mathfrak{n}_1,\mathfrak{n}_2,\cdots,\mathfrak{n}_k;p_1,\cdots,p_s,q_1,\cdots,q_s)dp_1\cdots dp_s dq_1\cdots dq_s$$

is the fraction of systems in the ensemble with $\mathfrak{n}_i$ particles of the ith kind and with the p_i and q_i within the volume element $dp_1 \cdots dp_s dq_1 \cdots dq_s$. We shall write for the sake of brevity

$$d\Omega = dp_1 \cdots dp_s dq_1 \cdots dq_s, \tag{6.103}$$

where we have to remember that $d\Omega$ depends on the $\mathfrak{n}_i$, since s depends on the $\mathfrak{n}_i$.

From the above definition of the density it follows that ρ satisfies the normalization condition

$$\sum_{\mathfrak{n}_1=0}^{\infty}\sum_{\mathfrak{n}_2=0}^{\infty}\cdots\sum_{\mathfrak{n}_k=0}^{\infty}\int_{\Gamma}\rho(\mathfrak{n}_1,\mathfrak{n}_2,\cdots,\mathfrak{n}_k;p,q)d\Omega = 1. \tag{6.104}$$

At this moment we must consider for a short while the implications of the fact that in a system characterized by the $\mathfrak{n}_i$ the group of particles of the ith kind contains $\mathfrak{n}_i$ identical entities. There are two ways of describing the phase of the system according to whether or not two situations which differ only in the interchange of two particles belonging to the same group are considered to be different. If they are considered to correspond to different phases we call the phase defined in that way the *specific phase*, but if they are considered to give us the same phase, we are dealing with *generic phases*. Both terms were introduced by Gibbs in the last chapter of his monograph. It is seen easily that for given $\mathfrak{n}_i$ each generic phase is made up out of $\prod \mathfrak{n}_i!$ different specific phases.

We shall only be interested in stationary grand ensembles and, moreover, in *canonical grand ensembles* which are defined by the following specific density:

$$\rho_{\text{spec}} = \frac{1}{\mathfrak{n}_1!\mathfrak{n}_2!\cdots\mathfrak{n}_k!} e^{-q+\nu_1\mathfrak{n}_1+\nu_2\mathfrak{n}_2+\cdots+\nu_k\mathfrak{n}_k-\frac{\epsilon}{\Theta}} \qquad \textbf{(6.105)}$$

where $\epsilon = \epsilon(\mathfrak{n}_i;p,q;a_i)$ is the total energy of the system. The quantity Θ is again called the *modulus* of the ensemble. The quantities q and ν_i do not depend on the p's and q's, but may depend on Θ and the external parameters a_i. We shall see their physical meaning presently.

From equation (6.105) it follows that the generic density ρ_{gen} is given by the equation

$$\rho_{\text{gen}} = \sum \rho_{\text{spec}} = e^{-q+\nu_1\mathfrak{n}_1+\nu_2\mathfrak{n}_2+\cdots+\nu_k\mathfrak{n}_k-\frac{\epsilon}{\Theta}}, \qquad \textbf{(6.106)}$$

where we have used the fact that the energies of all the specific phases corresponding to the same generic phase will be the same.

Even as a macrocanonical (petit) ensemble can be considered to be built up out of microcanonical ensembles, each canonical grand ensemble is the aggregate of a large number of macrocanonical petit ensembles, as can be seen from equation (6.105) or (6.106), since for each of the petit ensembles the $\mathfrak{n}_i$ are fixed and the formula reduces to the familiar formula for the density of a macrocanonical ensemble.

The quantity q, which is called by Kramers the *grand potential*, is determined by the normalization condition (6.104) and we have

$$e^q = \sum_{\mathfrak{n}_1}\cdots\sum_{\mathfrak{n}_k} \frac{e^{\nu_1\mathfrak{n}_1+\cdots+\nu_k\mathfrak{n}_k}}{\mathfrak{n}_1!\cdots\mathfrak{n}_k!} \int_{\Gamma} e^{-\frac{\epsilon}{\Theta}} d\Omega. \qquad \textbf{(6.107)}$$

Using for the integral in equation (6.107) formula (5.204) from the theory of the macrocanonical ensembles, we can write equation (6.107) in the form

$$e^q = \sum_{\mathfrak{n}_i}\cdots\sum_{\mathfrak{n}_k} \frac{e^{\nu_1\mathfrak{n}_1+\cdots+\nu_k\mathfrak{n}_k-\frac{\psi}{\Theta}}}{\mathfrak{n}_1!\cdots\mathfrak{n}_k!}. \qquad \textbf{(6.108)}$$

From equation (6.107) or (6.108) we see that

$$q = q(\Theta,\nu_i,a_i). \qquad \textbf{(6.109)}$$

We shall denote the average over a canonical grand ensemble by a circumflex accent ($\wedge$). The average of a phase function $G(p,q;\mathfrak{n}_i)$, which now will in general also be a function of the $\mathfrak{n}_i$, is given by the equation

$$\hat{G} = \sum_{\mathfrak{n}_i} \int_{\text{spec}} G(p,q;\mathfrak{n}_i)\rho_{\text{spec}} d\Omega = \sum_{\mathfrak{n}_i} \int_{\text{gen}} G(p,q;\mathfrak{n}_i)\rho_{\text{gen}} d\Omega, \qquad \textbf{(6.110)}$$

where $\int_{\text{spec}}$ indicates the integration over all different specific phases and $\int_{\text{gen}}$ the integration over all different generic phases only.

Let us consider the variation of q as a function of the variations of Θ (or rather $1/\Theta$), the ν_i and the a_i. From equations (6.107), (6.105), and (6.110) we get, after a straightforward calculation,

$$\delta q = \sum_i \hat{\mathfrak{n}}_i \delta\nu_i - \hat{\epsilon}\, \delta\frac{1}{\Theta} - \frac{1}{\Theta}\widehat{\delta\epsilon}, \tag{6.111}$$

where

$$\widehat{\delta\epsilon} = -\sum_i \hat{A}_i \delta a_i, \tag{6.112}$$

$$A_i = -\frac{\partial\epsilon}{\partial a_i}. \tag{6.113}$$

We can write equation (6.111) in the form

$$\delta\left[-q + \sum_i \hat{\mathfrak{n}}_i\nu_i - \frac{\hat{\epsilon}}{\Theta}\right] = \sum_i \nu_i\delta\hat{\mathfrak{n}}_i - \frac{1}{\Theta}(\delta\hat{\epsilon} - \widehat{\delta\epsilon}), \tag{6.114}$$

and by the same arguments as those used in §7 of Chapter II, §4 of Chapter IV, or §3 of Chapter V we find that

$$\Theta = kT, \tag{6.115}$$

$$\frac{S}{k} = q - \sum_i \hat{\mathfrak{n}}_i\nu_i + \frac{\hat{\epsilon}}{\Theta}, \tag{6.116}$$

where T is the temperature and S the entropy.†

Comparing equations (6.116) and (6.106), we see that, apart from a multiplying constant, the entropy is equal to the average of the logarithm of the generic density,

$$S = -k\,\widehat{\ln \rho_{\text{gen}}}.$$

We can compare this result with the relationship which we found in Chapter I between Boltzmann's H and the entropy. There we saw that H, which is the average of the logarithm of the density function, and $-S/k$ were the same.

By a reasoning analogous to the one given in §8 of the preceding chapter we can now prove that a subsystem of a larger system in statistical equilibrium will show the same behavior as the average member of a canonical grand ensemble. Instead of equation (5.803) we now use the fact that in statistical equilibrium the entropy will be

† It is perhaps well to remind ourselves that when we talk glibly about "the entropy" we really mean "the entropy of the system which is represented by the canonical grand ensemble under discussion," and similarly about other quantities.

extremum, and apart from equations similar to equations (5.801) and (5.802) we have an equation stating that the total number of particles of a given kind is constant. We leave the details of this discussion to the reader.†

From equation (6.116) it follows that the free energy F expressed in terms of q, Θ, $\hat{\mathfrak{n}}_i$, and ν_i is given by the equation

$$F = \hat{\varepsilon} - ST = -q\Theta + \sum_i \hat{\mathfrak{n}}_i g_i, \tag{6.117}$$

where

$$g_i = \nu_i \Theta. \tag{6.118}$$

The variation of F/Θ is given by the equation

$$\delta \frac{F}{\Theta} = \sum_i \nu_i \delta \hat{\mathfrak{n}}_i + \hat{\varepsilon}\, \delta \frac{1}{\Theta} + \frac{1}{\Theta} \delta \hat{\epsilon}, \tag{6.119}$$

and we see that the g_i are the partial free energies,

$$g_i = \left(\frac{\partial F}{\partial \hat{\mathfrak{n}}_i}\right)_{\Theta, a_i}. \tag{6.120}$$

Let us assume for a moment that the volume V is one of the external parameters and let us assume further that it is the only one. Introducing the thermal potential G,

$$G = F + pV = -q\Theta + \sum_i \hat{\mathfrak{n}}_i g_i + pV, \tag{6.121}$$

and considering the variation of G/Θ,

$$\delta \frac{G}{\Theta} = \sum_i \nu_i \delta \hat{\mathfrak{n}}_i + \hat{\varepsilon}\, \delta \frac{1}{\Theta} + \frac{V}{\Theta} \delta p, \tag{6.122}$$

we see that the g_i are also the partial thermal potentials,

$$g_i = \left(\frac{\partial G}{\partial \hat{\mathfrak{n}}_i}\right)_{\Theta, p}. \tag{6.123}$$

It may be mentioned in passing that the ν_i are related to the absolute activities, λ_i, by the equation

$$\lambda_i = e^{\nu_i}. \tag{6.124}$$

If the system under consideration is homogeneous in all kinds of particles, G will be a homogeneous function of the first degree in the $\hat{\mathfrak{n}}_i$, and we have

$$G = \sum_i \hat{\mathfrak{n}}_i \frac{\partial G}{\partial \hat{\mathfrak{n}}_i} = \sum_i g_i \hat{\mathfrak{n}}_i. \tag{6.125}$$

† See also H. A. Kramers, Proc. Kon. Ned. Akad. Wet. (Amsterdam), **41**, 17, 1938.

Combining equations (6.121) and (6.125), we get

$$q = \frac{pV}{kT}. \qquad (6.126)†$$

It will have been noticed that the grand potential resembles in many ways the q-potential discussed in Chapter IV. Indeed, equation (6.126) is the same as equation (4.422), while equations (6.111) and (6.116) have as their counterparts equations (4.417) and (4.416). In order to see the analogy between equations (6.116) and (4.416) more clearly we write equation (6.116) in the form

$$q = \frac{ST + \sum_i g_i \hat{\mathfrak{n}}_i - \hat{\varepsilon}}{\Theta}. \qquad (6.127)$$

From equation (6.111) it follows that the grand potential can be used to derive various averages, as follows (compare equations [4.418] to [4.420]):

$$\hat{\mathfrak{n}}_i = \frac{\partial q}{\partial \nu_i}, \qquad (6.128)$$

$$\hat{\varepsilon} = -\frac{\partial q}{\partial \frac{1}{\Theta}}, \qquad (6.129)$$

$$\hat{A}_i = \Theta \frac{\partial q}{\partial a_i}. \qquad (6.130)$$

In the special case where $a_i = V$ we have from equation (6.130)

$$p = kT \frac{\partial q}{\partial V}, \qquad (6.131)$$

which will give us the equation of state, once q has been computed. Of course, in the case of a homogeneous system, the equation of state follows directly from equation (6.126), which is then the same as equation (6.131), since in this particular case q will be directly proportional to V.

§2. Fluctuations in a Canonical Grand Ensemble. In order to show that canonical grand ensembles can be used to describe systems in statistical equilibrium we must consider the fluctuations of the various quantities around their average values and show that these in general will be small, at least if the total number of particles involved is large. Let us immediately remark here that sometimes subsystems of a larger system will be

† The grand potential q is related to the quantity Ω introduced by Gibbs by the equation $\Omega = -q\Theta$.

considered, and then the fluctuations may not be small but quite substantial, for instance, when we consider density fluctuations in a gas at a temperature near the critical temperature. In that case, however, these fluctuations are real and it is thus a virtue and not a drawback of the canonical grand ensembles that they contain the possibility of fluctuations.

The calculation of the fluctuations in the $\mathfrak{n}_i$, the A_i, and ϵ is completely analogous to the calculation of the fluctuations in the preceding chapter, and we shall therefore only indicate the way in which these fluctuations can be calculated and give the results.

Taking the derivative of the normalizing condition with respect to ν_i, a_i, of $1/\Theta$, respectively, gives us the equations (6.128) to (6.130). Taking once more the derivative with respect to the same variables, we get, respectively,†

$$\widehat{(\mathfrak{n}_i - \hat{\mathfrak{n}}_i)^2} = \frac{\partial^2 q}{\partial \nu_i^2}\left(= \frac{\partial \hat{\mathfrak{n}}_i}{\partial \nu_i}\right), \tag{6.201}$$

$$\widehat{(A_i - \hat{A}_i)^2} = \Theta^2 \frac{\partial^2 q}{\partial a_i^2} + \Theta \widehat{\frac{\partial^2 \epsilon}{\partial a_i^2}}, \tag{6.202}$$

$$\widehat{(\epsilon - \hat{\epsilon})^2} = \frac{\partial^2 q}{\partial (1/\Theta)^2}\left(= -\frac{\partial \hat{\epsilon}}{\partial (1/\Theta)}\right). \tag{6.203}$$

In general q will be proportional to the total number of particles, and

$$\frac{\widehat{(\epsilon - \hat{\epsilon})^2}}{\hat{\epsilon}^2} \quad \text{and} \quad \frac{\widehat{(A_i - \hat{A}_i)^2}}{\hat{A}_i^2}$$

† The normalizing condition can be written in the form

$$\sum_{\mathfrak{n}_i} \int_\Gamma \left(\prod_i \frac{e^{\nu_i \mathfrak{n}_i}}{\mathfrak{n}_i!}\right) e^{-q - \frac{\epsilon}{\Theta}}\, d\Omega = 1.$$

Taking the derivative with respect to a_i, e.g., gives

$$\sum_{\mathfrak{n}_i} \int_\Gamma \left(\prod_i \frac{e^{\nu_i \mathfrak{n}_i}}{\mathfrak{n}_i!}\right) e^{-q - \frac{\epsilon}{\Theta}} \left(-\frac{\partial q}{\partial a_i} - \frac{1}{\Theta}\frac{\partial \epsilon}{\partial a_i}\right) d\Omega = 0,$$

and using equations (6.110), (6.105), and (6.113), equation (6.130) follows.

Taking once more the derivative with respect to a_i, we get

$$\sum_{\mathfrak{n}_i} \int_\Gamma \left(\prod_i \frac{e^{\nu_i \mathfrak{n}_i}}{\mathfrak{n}_i!}\right) e^{-q - \frac{\epsilon}{\Theta}} \left[\left(-\frac{\partial q}{\partial a_i} - \frac{1}{\Theta}\frac{\partial \epsilon}{\partial a_i}\right)^2 - \frac{\partial^2 q}{\partial a_i^2} - \frac{1}{\Theta}\frac{\partial^2 \epsilon}{\partial a_i^2}\right] d\Omega = 0,$$

from which equation (6.202) follows. The equations (6.201) and (6.203) can be derived in a similar manner.

will be of the order of magnitude of $1/N$, where $N = \sum_i \hat{\mathfrak{n}}_i$, while

$$\frac{\widehat{(\mathfrak{n}_i - \hat{\mathfrak{n}}_i)^2}}{\hat{\mathfrak{n}}_i^2}$$

will be of the order of magnitude $1/\hat{\mathfrak{n}}_i$.

In the last section of this chapter we shall use the results which we have just obtained to calculate the dispersions of both ϵ and $\mathfrak{n}$ in the case of a perfect gas.

§3. The Coupling of Two Canonical Grand Ensembles. In §6 of the preceding chapter we discussed in some detail the coupling of two petit ensembles. Since the situation is much the same in the case of grand ensembles, we shall discuss only those points where new features are appearing. Consider two canonical grand ensembles, A and B, and assume for the sake of simplicity that in each of the two systems only one kind of particle is present. Their specific densities are

$$\overset{\mathrm{A}}{\rho}_{\mathrm{spec}} = \frac{1}{\mathfrak{n}_{\mathrm{A}}!} e^{q_{\mathrm{A}}+\nu_{\mathrm{A}}\mathfrak{n}_{\mathrm{A}}-\frac{\epsilon_{\mathrm{A}}}{\Theta_{\mathrm{A}}}}, \qquad \overset{\mathrm{B}}{\rho}_{\mathrm{spec}} = \frac{1}{\mathfrak{n}_{\mathrm{B}}!} e^{q_{\mathrm{B}}+\nu_{\mathrm{B}}\mathfrak{n}_{\mathrm{B}}-\frac{\epsilon_{\mathrm{B}}}{\Theta_{\mathrm{B}}}}, \tag{6.301}$$

and their generic densities are

$$\overset{\mathrm{A}}{\rho}_{\mathrm{gen}} = e^{q_{\mathrm{A}}+\nu_{\mathrm{A}}\mathfrak{n}_{\mathrm{A}}-\frac{\epsilon_{\mathrm{A}}}{\Theta_{\mathrm{A}}}}, \qquad \overset{\mathrm{B}}{\rho}_{\mathrm{gen}} = e^{q_{\mathrm{B}}+\nu_{\mathrm{B}}\mathfrak{n}_{\mathrm{B}}-\frac{\epsilon_{\mathrm{B}}}{\Theta_{\mathrm{B}}}}. \tag{6.302}$$

If the two ensembles are physically coupled to form an ensemble AB and if we may neglect the interaction energy, we see that the specific density of the ensemble AB is given by the equation

$$\overset{\mathrm{AB}}{\rho}_{\mathrm{spec}} = \overset{\mathrm{A}}{\rho}_{\mathrm{spec}}\overset{\mathrm{B}}{\rho}_{\mathrm{spec}} = \frac{1}{\mathfrak{n}_{\mathrm{A}}!\mathfrak{n}_{\mathrm{B}}!} e^{q_{\mathrm{A}}+\nu_{\mathrm{A}}\mathfrak{n}_{\mathrm{A}}-\frac{\epsilon_{\mathrm{A}}}{\Theta_{\mathrm{A}}}} e^{q_{\mathrm{B}}+\nu_{\mathrm{B}}\mathfrak{n}_{\mathrm{B}}-\frac{\epsilon_{\mathrm{B}}}{\Theta_{\mathrm{B}}}}, \tag{6.303}$$

and its generic density by the equation

$$\overset{\mathrm{AB}}{\rho}_{\mathrm{gen}} = \overset{\mathrm{A}}{\rho}_{\mathrm{gen}}\overset{\mathrm{B}}{\rho}_{\mathrm{gen}} = e^{q_{\mathrm{A}}+\nu_{\mathrm{A}}\mathfrak{n}_{\mathrm{A}}-\frac{\epsilon_{\mathrm{A}}}{\Theta_{\mathrm{A}}}} e^{q_{\mathrm{B}}+\nu_{\mathrm{B}}\mathfrak{n}_{\mathrm{B}}-\frac{\epsilon_{\mathrm{B}}}{\Theta_{\mathrm{B}}}}. \tag{6.304}$$

We see from equations (6.303) and (6.304) that as long as the particles in the system A are different from those in system B, we have for the ensemble AB the correct relation between specific and generic densities. Moreover, if $\Theta_{\mathrm{A}} = \Theta_{\mathrm{B}}$, the ensemble AB will again be a canonical grand ensemble. However, if the systems A and B contain the same kind of particles, we see that the ensemble AB is only canonically distributed as far as the generic phases are concerned—provided $\Theta_{\mathrm{A}} = \Theta_{\mathrm{B}}$ and $\nu_{\mathrm{A}} = \nu_{\mathrm{B}}$, the two familiar conditions of equality of temperature and thermal potential—but not as far as specific phases are concerned. We see here the importance of the generic phases which was clearly recognized by Gibbs.

We can also understand now why $\widehat{\ln \rho_{\text{gen}}}$ and not $\widehat{\ln \rho_{\text{spec}}}$ might play the role of Boltzmann's H. Once this point of the pre-eminence of the generic phases is accepted, we must start from equation (6.304) and if the particles in the systems A and B are the same, we must write for the specific density, instead of equation (6.303),

$$\rho_{\text{spec}}^{\text{AB}} = \frac{1}{\mathfrak{n}_{\text{AB}}!}\rho_{\text{gen}}^{\text{AB}} = \frac{1}{\mathfrak{n}_{\text{AB}}!}e^{q_{\text{AB}}+\nu_{\text{AB}}\mathfrak{n}_{\text{AB}}-\frac{\epsilon_{\text{AB}}}{\Theta_{\text{AB}}}}, \tag{6.305}$$

where

$$\left.\begin{array}{lll} \mathfrak{n}_{\text{AB}} = \mathfrak{n}_{\text{A}} + \mathfrak{n}_{\text{B}}, & q_{\text{AB}} = q_{\text{A}} + q_{\text{B}}, & \epsilon_{\text{AB}} = \epsilon_{\text{A}} + \epsilon_{\text{B}}, \\ \nu_{\text{AB}} = \nu_{\text{A}} = \nu_{\text{B}}, & \Theta_{\text{AB}} = \Theta_{\text{A}} = \Theta_{\text{B}}. & \end{array}\right\} \tag{6.306}$$

The choice of

$$S = -k\,\widehat{\ln \rho_{\text{gen}}} \tag{6.307}$$

entails the introduction of the factor $1/N!$ in equation (5.311) on page 109 as can be seen as follows. From equation (6.307) and the equation $F = \hat{\epsilon} - (S/k)\Theta$ we get

$$e^{-\frac{F}{kT}} = e^{q-\sum\nu_i\hat{\mathfrak{n}}_i}. \tag{6.308}$$

If now the $\hat{\mathfrak{n}}_i$ are sufficiently large so that their dispersion is negligible, the canonical grand ensemble will practically be a macrocanonical ensemble and we can substitute in all equations $\mathfrak{n}_i \simeq \hat{\mathfrak{n}}_i$. This corresponds to the equivalence of the macro- and microcanonical ensembles which we discussed in the preceding chapter. Equation (6.308) leads in that way to the formula

$$e^{-\frac{F}{kT}} = \frac{1}{\prod_i \hat{\mathfrak{n}}_i!}\left(\int_\Gamma e^{-\frac{\epsilon}{\Theta}}\right)_{\mathfrak{n}_i=\hat{\mathfrak{n}}_i}, \tag{6.309}$$

which reduces to equation (5.311) in the case of only one kind of particle—apart from the factor h^{sN}, which we should have introduced throughout in order to get formulae which are the limiting cases of the quantum mechanical formulae to be derived in the next chapter.

We may remark here that although we see from this discussion the plausibility of the introduction of the factor $1/N!$ in Z_Γ and thus also that of the factor e/N in Z_μ, the only decisive argument is the one given by considering quantum statistics and considering the classical limit of the quantum mechanical expressions. Since these lead to the factors $1/N!$ and e/N we can be sure of their correctness instead of feeling rather safe in including them.

§4. Application of the Theory of the Classical Grand Ensembles to the Case of a Perfect Gas; Gibbs's Paradox. Although the results which we shall obtain are not new and were derived previously in Chapters I, II, IV, and V, we shall once more illustrate the theory by considering the case of a perfect gas enclosed in a volume V. The energy of the system is given by the equation

$$\epsilon = \sum_{i=1}^{\mathfrak{n}} \left(\frac{\mathrm{p}_i^2}{2m} + F_i \right), \tag{6.401}$$

where

$$F_i \equiv F(x_i, y_i, z_i) = 0, \quad \text{if } x_i, y_i, z_i \text{ lies inside } V,$$

and

$$F(x_i, y_i, z_i) = \infty, \quad \text{if } x_i, y_i, z_i \text{ lies outside } V.$$

From equation (6.107) we get for the grand potential the equation

$$e^q = \sum_{\mathfrak{n}=0}^{\infty} \frac{1}{\mathfrak{n}!} e^{\nu \mathfrak{n}} \int_{\Gamma} e^{-\frac{1}{\Theta}\sum_i \left(\frac{\mathrm{p}_i^2}{2m} + F_i\right)} d\Omega. \tag{6.402}$$

Integration over the x_i, y_i, and z_i gives a factor $V^{\mathfrak{n}}$, and we get

$$e^q = \sum_{\mathfrak{n}} \frac{1}{\mathfrak{n}!} e^{\nu \mathfrak{n}} V^{\mathfrak{n}} \left[\int_{-\infty}^{+\infty} e^{-\frac{u^2}{2m\Theta}} du \right]^{3\mathfrak{n}},$$

or

$$e^q = \sum_{\mathfrak{n}} \frac{1}{\mathfrak{n}!} \left[e^{\nu} V (2\pi mkT)^{3/2} \right]^{\mathfrak{n}},$$

which leads to the equation (compare equation [4.510])

$$q = e^{\nu} V (2\pi mkT)^{3/2}. \tag{6.403}$$

Using equation (6.128), we get for $\hat{\mathfrak{n}}$

$$\hat{\mathfrak{n}} = \frac{\partial q}{\partial \nu} = q, \tag{6.404}$$

and combining this with equation (6.126), we have

$$\hat{\mathfrak{n}} = \frac{pV}{kT}, \quad \text{or} \quad pV = \hat{\mathfrak{n}} kT, \tag{6.405}$$

the perfect gas law.

We find from equation (6.201) for the fluctuations in the number of particles

$$\widehat{(\mathfrak{n} - \hat{\mathfrak{n}})^2} = \frac{\partial^2 q}{\partial \nu^2} = \hat{\mathfrak{n}}, \tag{6.406}$$

which shows that, indeed,

$$\frac{\widehat{(\mathfrak{n}-\hat{\mathfrak{n}})^2}}{\hat{\mathfrak{n}}^2}=\frac{1}{\hat{\mathfrak{n}}}. \tag{6.407}$$

The average energy and its fluctuations satisfy the equations

$$\hat{\epsilon}=-\frac{\partial q}{\partial\dfrac{1}{\Theta}}=\tfrac{3}{2}q\Theta=\tfrac{3}{2}\hat{\mathfrak{n}}kT(=\tfrac{3}{2}pV), \tag{6.408}$$

$$\widehat{(\epsilon-\hat{\epsilon})^2}=\frac{\partial^2 q}{\partial\left(\dfrac{1}{\Theta}\right)^2}=\frac{15}{4}\hat{\mathfrak{n}}\Theta^2, \tag{6.409}$$

$$\frac{\widehat{(\epsilon-\hat{\epsilon})^2}}{\hat{\epsilon}^2}=\frac{5}{3\hat{\mathfrak{n}}}. \tag{6.410}$$

The free energy and the entropy of the system are given by the equations

$$F=-qkT+\nu\hat{\mathfrak{n}}=\hat{\mathfrak{n}}kT[\ln p-\tfrac{5}{2}\ln T-\tfrac{3}{2}\ln M+\text{constant}], \tag{6.411}$$

and

$$S=qk-k\nu\hat{\mathfrak{n}}-\frac{\hat{\epsilon}}{T}=\hat{\mathfrak{n}}k[\tfrac{5}{2}\ln T-\ln p+\tfrac{3}{2}\ln M+\text{constant}], \tag{6.412}$$

where M is the molecular weight of the gas and where we have used for ν the equation

$$e^{\nu}=\hat{\mathfrak{n}}V^{-1}(2\pi mkT)^{-3/2}, \tag{6.413}$$

which follows from equations (6.403) and (6.404).

At this moment we can discuss the famous paradox which bears Gibbs's name. We write thereto equation (6.412) in the following form

$$S=\hat{\mathfrak{n}}k[\ln V-\ln\hat{\mathfrak{n}}+\tfrac{3}{2}\ln T+\tfrac{3}{2}\ln M+c], \tag{6.414}$$

where c is a numerical constant.

The term $-k\hat{\mathfrak{n}}\ln\hat{\mathfrak{n}}$ derives from the fact that we are using the generic density to define the entropy. If we had taken the specific density instead, or if we had omitted the factor e/N in Z_μ, we should have had, instead of equation (6.414), the expression

$$S'=\hat{\mathfrak{n}}k[\ln V+\tfrac{3}{2}\ln T+\tfrac{3}{2}\ln M+c'], \tag{6.415}$$

where c' is another constant.

Let us now join together two systems indicated by indices A and B and let $T_A=T_B=T$. If the particles in the two systems are different, the entropy of the joint system AB will be given by the equation

$$S_{AB}' = \hat{n}_A k[\ln V_A + \tfrac{3}{2}\ln T + \tfrac{3}{2}\ln M_A + c'] + \hat{n}_B k[\ln V_B + \tfrac{3}{2}\ln T + \tfrac{3}{2}\ln M_B + c'], \quad \textbf{(6.416)}$$

or

$$S_{AB}' = S_A' + S_B'. \quad \textbf{(6.417)}$$

If, however, the particles in the two systems are the same and if we take for the sake of simplicity $V_A = V_B$, $\hat{n}_A = \hat{n}_B = N$, we must consider $2N$ particles in a volume $2V$ and we get for S_{AB}'

$$S_{AB}' = 2Nk\,[\ln 2V + \tfrac{3}{2}\ln T + \tfrac{3}{2}\ln M + c'] = S_A' + S_B' \boxed{+2kN\ln 2}. \quad \textbf{(6.418)}$$

We get here the paradoxical result that the entropy of the joint system is not the same as the sum of the entropies of the separate systems if the particles in the two systems are the same. This paradox is resolved if we use formula (6.414) and not equation (6.415). We then get, instead of equation (6.418),

$$S_{AB} = 2Nk\,[\ln 2V - \ln 2N + \tfrac{3}{2}\ln T + \tfrac{3}{2}\ln M + c] = S_A + S_B!! \quad \textbf{(6.419)}$$

The resolution of this paradox is, in the last instance, another example of the successes of quantum mechanics in getting rid of some unsolved problems of classical physics, even though in this case there were strong arguments in favor of the generic densities.

BIBLIOGRAPHICAL NOTES

This chapter is mainly based on the following references:

1. J. W. Gibbs, Elementary Principles in Statistical Mechanics (Vol. II of his Collected Works), New Haven 1948, Chap. XV.
2. H. A. Kramers, Proc. Kon. Ned. Akad. Wet. (Amsterdam), **41,** 10, 1938.
3. Lectures given by H. A. Kramers in Leiden during the winter of 1944–1945.
   See also
4. R. H. Fowler, Proc. Cambridge Phil. Soc., **34,** 382, 1938.
5. E. A. Guggenheim, J. Chem. Phys., **7,** 103, 1939.
6. R. C. Tolman, Phys. Rev., **57,** 1160, 1940.
7. R. Becker, Z. Physik. Chem., **196,** 181, 1950.
   Recently, Münster has discussed the relation between phase transitions and grand ensembles:
8. A. Münster, Z. Naturf., **6a,** 139, 1951.
9. A. Münster, Z. Naturf., **7a,** 613, 1952.

CHAPTER VII

THE ENSEMBLES IN QUANTUM STATISTICS

§1. The Density Matrix. It is, of course, well known that modern theoretical physics is to a large extent dominated by quantum mechanics. Nevertheless there are large fields of physics where one can use classical theory because the quantum mechanical corrections are far too small to enter into the discussion. Large parts of statistical mechanics belong to classical physics.† On the other hand, statistical mechanics is one of the branches of physics where the successes of quantum mechanics have been most noteworthy. We saw as instances of the successful intervention of quantum mechanics the solution of Gibbs' paradox and of the paradox of the specific heats. Other instances are the theory of metals (Chap. X) and many branches of modern astrophysics (see, for instance, Chap. XIV). The discussion of quantum statistics was started in Chapters III and IV, where we discussed, firstly, the quantum mechanical analogy to the Maxwell-Boltzmann distribution and, secondly, the implications of the exclusion principle. However, we still must discuss quantum mechanical ensemble theory, and this will be done in the present chapter.

In discussing quantum mechanical ensemble theory one must be extremely careful to make a clear distinction between the statistical aspects inherent in quantum mechanics and the statistical aspects introduced by the ensembles. The statistical nature of quantum mechanics is connected with the fact that quantum mechanics gives us a wave function to describe a system and that from this wave function one then constructs a probability density, a probability current, and probable (or average) values of physical quantities. Only in exceptional cases will it be possible to ascribe to a quantity a completely defined value. If this is the case, it results in a complete lack of definition of the *complementary* quantity. In general both of the two complementary quantities will be defined only within certain limits and these limits cannot be chosen independently but

† For instance, the discussion in Chapters XII and XV is completely classical, as is also most of the discussion in Chapters VIII and IX.

must satisfy the so-called Heisenberg relations. We do not wish to discuss this point in any more detail, since it really belongs to a discussion of the principles of quantum mechanics. In the following we shall assume that the reader is familiar with this aspect of quantum mechanics and will use it whenever necessary.

We now wish to consider the statistical aspects of the ensembles in quantum statistics. We consider thereto a large number of identical systems. Let $\mathcal{H}$ be the energy operator (or Hamiltonian) and let ψ^k be the normalized wave function describing the kth system. This wave function will then satisfy the Schrödinger equation

$$\mathcal{H}\psi^k = i\hbar\dot{\psi}^k. \tag{7.101}$$

It is useful to introduce a complete set of orthonormal functions φ_n into which the wave functions or any other function can be developed.†

Expanding ψ^k in terms of the φ_n, we have

$$\psi^k = \sum_n a_n^{\,k}\varphi_n, \tag{7.102}$$

where

$$a_n^{\,k} = \int \varphi_n^*\psi^k d\tau, \tag{7.103}$$

where a star indicates the conjugate complex‡ and where $d\tau$ is a volume element of the coordinate space.

The coefficients $a_n^{\,k}$ can be used to describe the kth system instead of ψ^k. The two representations are equivalent and the transformed Schrödinger equation which the $a_n^{\,k}$ must satisfy is

$$i\hbar\dot{a}_n^{\,k} = \sum_m H_{nm}a_m^{\,k}, \tag{7.104}$$

where the H_{nm} are the matrix elements of the Hamiltonian,

$$H_{nm} = \int \varphi_n^*\mathcal{H}\varphi_m d\tau. \tag{7.105}$$

The physical significance of the $a_n^{\,k}$ is that they are probability amplitudes, $|\,a_n^{\,k}\,|^2$ being the probability that the kth system is characterized by the function φ_n. From the normalization of the ψ^k and the fact that the φ_n form a complete orthonormal set we have

$$\sum_n |\,a_n^{\,k}\,|^2 = 1. \tag{7.106}$$

† In order not to complicate our equations we shall not explicitly introduce degeneracy or continuous spectra. It is not difficult to extend all formulae to the most general case, and we leave that to the reader.

‡ We are not taking spin into account here; this can, however, easily be done.

In the classical ensemble theory we discussed a density function $\rho(p,q)$. Now we introduce a density operator which we shall define by its matrix elements. The *density matrix* is defined through its elements by

$$\rho_{mn} = \frac{1}{N}\sum_{k=1}^{N} a_m{}^k a_n{}^{k*}, \tag{7.107}$$

where N is the number of systems in the ensemble.

From equation (7.104) we can find the equation which ρ_{mn} must satisfy. This equation is

$$i\hbar\dot{\rho}_{mn} = \sum_l (H_{ml}\rho_{ln} - \rho_{ml}H_{ln}). \tag{7.108}$$

In deriving equation (7.108) we used the fact that $\mathcal{H}$ is a Hermitian operator, that is, that

$$H_{kl} = H_{lk}{}^*. \tag{7.109}$$

Defining the commutator $[\mathcal{A},\mathcal{B}]_-$ of two operators $\mathcal{A}$ and $\mathcal{B}$ by the equation

$$[\mathcal{A},\mathcal{B}]_- = \mathcal{A}\mathcal{B} - \mathcal{B}\mathcal{A}, \tag{7.110}$$

or, in matrix notation,

$$[\mathcal{A},\mathcal{B}]_{-,kl} = \sum_m [A_{km}B_{ml} - B_{km}A_{ml}], \tag{7.111}$$

we can write equation (7.108) in matrix form, as follows,

$$i\hbar\dot{\boldsymbol{\rho}} = [\mathcal{H},\boldsymbol{\rho}]_-. \tag{7.112}$$

This equation is the quantum mechanical analogy of Liouville's theorem (equations [5.107] or [5.115]) of the classical theory. Of course, it is well known that the commutators are the quantum mechanical counterparts of the Poisson brackets of classical mechanics.

The average value $\bar{G}$ of a physical quantity is defined by the equation

$$\bar{G} = \frac{1}{N}\sum_{k=1}^{N}\int \psi^{k*}\mathcal{G}\psi^k d\tau, \tag{7.113}$$

where $\mathcal{G}$ is the quantum mechanical operator corresponding to the classical quantity G. Equation (7.113) shows that $\bar{G}$ is twice an average. First we take the quantum mechanical average of G in a system described by the wave function ψ^k, and, secondly, we take the average over the ensemble.

Introducing the $a_n{}^k$ instead of the ψ^k, we can write equation (7.113) in the form

$$\bar{G} = \frac{1}{N}\sum_{k=1}^{N}\sum_{m,n} a_m{}^k a_n{}^{k*} G_{nm}, \tag{7.114}$$

or, introducing the density matrix by means of equation (7.107),

$$\bar{G} = \sum_{m,n} \rho_{mn} G_{nm},$$

or

$$\bar{G} = \sum_m (\rho G)_{mm} = \text{Trace } \boldsymbol{\rho}\mathcal{G}. \tag{7.115}$$

A special case of this equation is the normalization condition which we get by putting $G \equiv 1$,

$$\text{Trace } \boldsymbol{\rho} = 1. \tag{7.116}$$

This equation can also be proven directly from the definition of $\boldsymbol{\rho}$ and equation (7.106),

$$\text{Trace } \boldsymbol{\rho} = \sum_m \rho_{mm} = \frac{1}{N} \sum_k a_m^k a_m^{k*} = \frac{1}{N} \sum_{k=1}^{N} 1 = 1.$$

We shall restrict our discussion once again mainly to stationary ensembles. In that case $\boldsymbol{\rho}$ and the energy operator $\mathcal{H}$ must commute. Moreover, we shall assume that $\boldsymbol{\rho}$ is a function of the energy only,

$$\boldsymbol{\rho} = \boldsymbol{\rho}(\mathcal{H}), \tag{7.117}$$

and even that

$$\boldsymbol{\rho} = e^{\frac{\psi - \mathcal{H}}{\Theta}}. \tag{7.118}$$

This last equation has a meaning only if we understand it as being an abbreviated notation for

$$\boldsymbol{\rho} = e^{\frac{\psi}{\Theta}} \sum_{n=0}^{\infty} \frac{1}{n!} \left[-\frac{\mathcal{H}}{\Theta} \right]^n. \tag{7.119}$$

§2. Pure Case and Mixed Case ("Reiner Fall" and "Gemisch"). Let us briefly consider once again the reasons for introducing ensembles. As in the classical case the necessity to introduce representative ensembles arises from the fact that our knowledge about the physical system under consideration is practically always far removed from the maximum attainable knowledge. The situation is now, however, slightly complicated because of the added statistical aspects coming from quantum mechanics. In an ideal (and practically always idealized) case we may know that our system is in a characteristic state of one of the quantum mechanical operators. Let us assume for the sake of simplicity that this operator is the energy operator so that we know that the system is in a stationary state.† In that case we are dealing with a "Reiner Fall," as von Neumann calls it.

† It is easy to extend the discussion to include the cases where the system is in a characteristic state of two or more commuting operators.

We shall call it a *pure case*. All the systems in the representative ensemble will possess the same wave function, namely, that corresponding to the characteristic state in question, and of the two averaging processes which are prescribed by equation (7.113) only one remains, namely, that of taking the quantum mechanical average. In fact, we are in a situation where ensemble theory does not need to be used. This situation has no classical analogy because we are still in a position where we must use statistical considerations, even though our knowledge is maximal.†

In general, however, the situation will not be so favorable and then we must construct a representative ensemble. Each system in the ensemble will then have a wave function which is a superposition, or mixture, of the various characteristic functions of, for instance, the energy operator, and the averages both over ψ^k and over the ensemble must be taken in order to evaluate $\overline{G}$. We are now dealing with a "Gemisch" or *mixed case*. As in the classical case, we must make certain assumptions about a priori probabilities in order to be able to construct the representative ensemble. The assumption which is made is the following one. We assume equal a priori probabilities and random a priori phases for the various nondegenerate states. A discussion of this assumption will be given in §8 of Appendix I (see also the discussion on p. 130). Once the representative ensemble has been set up, we are in the same position as in the classical case and can then make predictions about the most probable behavior of our system by considering the average behavior of a system in the ensemble. An important point is again the smallness of the fluctuations.

Before considering in the next two sections the properties of the quantum mechanical macrocanonical petit and canonical grand ensembles we shall derive the necessary and sufficient condition that the density matrix describes a pure case. Let us assume that we have chosen our orthonormal set φ_n in such a way that $\boldsymbol{\rho}$ is a diagonal matrix, or

$$\rho_{mn} = \rho_m \delta_{mn}, \tag{7.201}$$

where δ_{mn} is Kronecker's $\boldsymbol{\delta}$,

$$\delta_{mn} = 0, \quad m \neq n; \qquad \delta_{mn} = 1, \quad m = n. \tag{7.202}$$

† We have tacitly assumed that the stationary state in question is nondegenerate or, if it is a degenerate state, that it is at the same time a characteristic state of other operators (e.g., the operators corresponding to the square and the z-component of the angular momentum) in such a way that there is only one wave function which can describe the state of the system.

To some extent we might say that ordinary mechanics is the classical analogy to a pure case, as was pointed out to me by Professor H. Margenau. There remains, however, the distinction that the need for statistical considerations in the quantum mechanical case is inherent in quantum mechanics, while in the classical case it is due to limitations to our power of solving a large number of simultaneous differential equations.

From equation (7.107) it then follows that

$$\rho_m = \frac{1}{N}\sum_{k=1}^{N} | a_m{}^k |^2, \tag{7.203}$$

and we see that ρ_m is the probability of finding an arbitrary system from the ensemble in the state characterized by φ_m. Since all $| a_m{}^k |^2$ are positive and at most equal to one,

$$0 \leqslant \rho_m \leqslant 1. \tag{7.204}$$

The last equal sign holds only if for all k

$$| a_m{}^k |^2 = 1, \tag{7.205}$$

which entails that all systems are in the state characterized by φ_m as wave function. Hence, $\rho_m = 1$ is a sufficient condition for a pure case. If $\rho_m = 1$,

$$\rho_n{}^2 = \rho_n \tag{7.206}$$

for any n, or, in matrix notation,

$$\boldsymbol{\rho}^2 = \boldsymbol{\rho}. \tag{7.207}$$

Since from equation (7.204) it follows that all characteristic values of $\boldsymbol{\rho}$ are positive and smaller than or at most equal to one, equation (7.207) can be satisfied only if one characteristic value is equal to one and all the others are equal to zero. Hence equation (7.207) is a different way of expressing a sufficient condition for a pure case.

It is also possible to show that equation (7.207) is a necessary condition for a pure case. If we are dealing with a pure case, all $a_m{}^k$ with a given m are the same, and we have

$$\rho_{mn} = \frac{1}{N}\sum_{k=1}^{N} a_m{}^k a_n{}^{k*} = a_m a_n{}^*. \tag{7.208}$$

Using equation (7.106) we can then show that

$$[\rho^2]_{mn} = \sum_l \rho_{ml}\rho_{ln} = \sum_l a_m a_l{}^* a_l a_n{}^* = a_m a_n{}^* = \rho_{mn}, \tag{7.209}$$

whence follows equation (7.207) as a necessary condition.

§3. Macrocanonical Petit Ensembles in Quantum Statistics. In order that we shall be able fully to apply quantum statistics it is necessary to develop first the formalism of quantum mechanical ensemble theory to the same extent as we developed that of classical ensemble theory in the preceding two chapters. In principle everything is contained in the discussion of §1, but we shall enlarge slightly on that discussion. Let us first consider petit ensembles, and more specifically macrocanonical petit ensembles with a density matrix

$$\rho = e^{\frac{\psi - \mathcal{H}}{\Theta}}, \tag{7.301}$$

where ρ and $\mathcal{H}$ are operators, ψ and Θ are c-numbers, that is, quantities which commute with any operator, and where the right-hand side of equation (7.301) is understood in the way discussed at the end of §1. From the normalizing equation (7.116) we get for ψ the equation

$$e^{-\frac{\psi}{\Theta}} = \text{Trace } e^{-\frac{\mathcal{H}}{\Theta}}, \tag{7.302}$$

where we have used the fact that ψ and Θ are c-numbers. Equation (7.302) is the quantum mechanical equivalent of equation (5.302) on page 107. Once again we shall only indicate the proof that ψ is the free energy and that apart from a multiplying constant Θ is equal to the temperature. We must bear in mind that $\mathcal{H}$ will depend on the external parameters a_i and that the generalized forces are now operators given by the equations

$$\mathcal{A}_i = -\frac{\partial \mathcal{H}}{\partial a_i}. \tag{7.303}$$

We can write equation (7.302) in the form

$$\text{Trace } \rho = e^{\frac{\psi}{\Theta}} \text{ Trace } e^{-\frac{\mathcal{H}}{\Theta}} = 1, \tag{7.304}$$

and, considering two situations with slightly different values of Θ and the a_i, we get

$$\delta \frac{\psi}{\Theta} = \delta \frac{1}{\Theta} \text{ Trace } \rho\mathcal{H} - \frac{1}{\Theta} \sum_i \delta a_i \text{ Trace } \rho\mathcal{A}_i, \tag{7.305}$$

or, using equation (7.115) for average values,

$$\delta \frac{\psi}{\Theta} = \bar{H} \delta \frac{1}{\Theta} - \frac{1}{\Theta} \sum_i \bar{A}_i \delta a_i. \tag{7.306}$$

Writing

$$\overline{\delta A} = \sum_i \bar{A}_i \delta a_i, \tag{7.307}$$

equation (7.306) can be written in the form

$$\delta \frac{\psi}{\Theta} = \bar{H} \delta \frac{1}{\Theta} - \frac{1}{\Theta} \overline{\delta A}. \tag{7.308}$$

This equation is completely analogous to equation (5.305) on page 108 and it follows therefore that ψ can be considered to be the free energy, that

$$\Theta = kT, \tag{7.309}$$

and that the entropy S is given by the equation

$$S = k\frac{\overline{H} - \psi}{\Theta}. \tag{7.310}$$

Comparing equations (7.302) and (5.311) we see that Trace $e^{-\mathcal{H}/\Theta}$ now takes the place of the partition function of classical theory.

Before we go over to the quantum mechanical grand ensembles we may apply the formalism of the quantum mechanical macrocanonical ensemble to the case of a system of independent particles and we shall for the moment neglect exclusion effects.

The Hamiltonian of a system consisting of N independent particles is the sum of the Hamiltonians of the particles,

$$\mathcal{H} = \sum_{i=1}^{N} \mathcal{H}_i, \tag{7.311}$$

where $\mathcal{H}_i$ is the energy operator of the ith particle.

In order to simplify our calculations we shall assume that the φ_n are the characteristic functions of the Hamiltonian. This brings the energy matrix on diagonal form,

$$H_{kl} = E_k\delta_{kl}, \tag{7.312}$$

and the density matrix is hence also diagonal,

$$\rho_{kl} = \delta_{kl}e^{\frac{\psi - E_k}{\Theta}}, \tag{7.313}$$

so that we get from equation (7.302)

$$e^{-\frac{\psi}{\Theta}} = \sum_k \gamma_k e^{-\frac{E_k}{\Theta}}, \tag{7.314}$$

where γ_k is the multiplicity of the energy level E_k. We see that equation (7.314) resembles closely equation (3.413) on page 59 with one important difference, namely, that in equation (3.413) the ϵ_n were the energy levels of single molecules whereas now the E_k are the energy levels of the whole system. This corresponds to the transition from μ-space to Γ-space. Since the particles in the system are independent, we have (compare equation [7.311])

$$E_k = \sum_{i=1}^{N} \epsilon_i. \tag{7.315}$$

If we group together all particles with the same energy, say, ϵ_s, this equation can be written in the form

$$E_k = \sum_{\sum n_s = N} n_s\epsilon_s, \tag{7.316}$$

where now all ϵ_s are different.

The degeneracy γ_k arises from two factors. The first one is the fact that the levels ϵ_s may be degenerate, say, with a degeneracy g_s. The second factor comes from the degeneracy which derives from the fact that N particles can be divided into groups containing, respectively, $n_1, n_2, \cdots, n_s, \cdots$ in several different ways. We get altogether

$$\gamma_k = \frac{N!}{\prod_s n_s!} \prod_s g_s^{n_s}, \tag{7.317}$$

and substituting equations (7.316) and (7.317) into equation (7.314), we get

$$e^{-\frac{\psi}{\Theta}} = \sum_s \sum_{n_s} N! \left(\prod_s \frac{g_s^{n_s}}{n_s!} \right) e^{-\frac{\sum n_s \epsilon_s}{\Theta}},$$

or

$$e^{-\frac{\psi}{\Theta}} = \left[\sum_s g_s e^{-\frac{\epsilon_s}{\Theta}} \right]^N. \tag{7.318}$$

The expression inside the square brackets is the partition function for one particle. In §5 of Chapter IV (p. 83) we calculated this partition function under the assumption that the energy levels were lying so densely that the sum could be replaced by an integral. There is no point in writing down the result here, since we see immediately from equation (7.318) that for a system of N independent particles the free energy is equal to N times the free energy of one particle, as would be expected. We are thus back to the situation encountered in Chapter III and no new features will be found.

As in the case of the classical macrocanonical ensembles it is possible to calculate the fluctuations in energy and generalized forces. The formulae which are derived by the same methods as before are entirely the same as those found in §4 of Chapter V, the only difference being in the actual value of ψ. We refer therefore to the discussion of that section (pp. 111 ff.).

§4. Canonical Grand Ensembles in Quantum Statistics. We come now to perhaps the most powerful tool of modern statistical mechanics, the quantum mechanical canonical grand ensembles. In Part C we shall have ample opportunity to apply this tool.

In the preceding chapter we discussed the classical grand ensembles and saw that in many cases these must be preferred to the petit ensembles. It is thus desirable to develop their quantum mechanical counterparts. Since in quantum mechanics the indistinguishability of identical particles finds its ready expression in the exclusion principle, we shall now have no reason to distinguish between specific and generic densities. This makes the quantum mechanical ensemble theory simpler than the classical one.

Moreover, due to the statistical aspects of quantum mechanics the physical interpretation of the quantum mechanical ensemble theory will be much more natural.

We shall assume that our system is confined to a finite volume so that the energy levels will form a discrete spectrum. The energy levels will, of course, depend on the $\mathfrak{n}_i$, the number of particles of the various kinds which may be present in the system. We shall write for the energy levels $E(\mathfrak{n}_i;\, n)$ where n numbers the levels.

The density matrix of a stationary ensemble must now commute not only with $\mathfrak{H}$ but also with the number operators $\boldsymbol{\mathfrak{n}}_i$. These $\boldsymbol{\mathfrak{n}}_i$ are the well-known Jordan-Klein and Jordan-Wigner matrices from quantum mechanics.† Their characteristic values are the integers $\mathfrak{n}_i$.

We shall discuss only canonical grand ensembles. Their density operator is given by the equation

$$\boldsymbol{\rho} = e^{-q+\sum_i \mathfrak{n}_i\nu_i - \frac{\mathfrak{H}}{\Theta}}, \tag{7.401}$$

where q, Θ, and the ν_i are c-numbers. The grand potential q is determined by the normalization condition and we have

$$e^q = \text{Trace } e^{\sum_i \mathfrak{n}_i\nu_i - \frac{\mathfrak{H}}{\Theta}}, \tag{7.402}$$

where in equations (7.401) and (7.402) the exponentials are defined by the power series.

If we choose for the φ_n the characteristic functions of both $\mathfrak{H}$ and all the $\boldsymbol{\mathfrak{n}}_i$, equation (7.402) becomes

$$e^q = \sum_{\mathfrak{n}_i,n} e^{\sum \mathfrak{n}_i\nu_i - \frac{E(\mathfrak{n}_i,n)}{\Theta}}, \tag{7.403}$$

which is the quantum mechanical equivalent of equation (6.107) on page 137. Since $\mathfrak{H}$, and thus also the $E(\mathfrak{n}_i;n)$, depends on the external parameters we see that q is a function of Θ and the ν_i and a_i, as in the classical case,

$$q = q(\Theta,\nu_i,a_i). \tag{7.404}$$

The average $\hat{G}$ of a quantity G over the canonical grand ensemble is given by equation (7.113) which can be put in the form

$$\hat{G} = \sum_{\mathfrak{n}_i} \sum_{n} G(\mathfrak{n}_i;n)\rho(\mathfrak{n}_i;n), \tag{7.405}$$

where $\rho(\mathfrak{n}_i;n)$ is the diagonal element of the density matrix which, due to

† P. Jordan and O. Klein, Z. Physik, **45,** 751, 1927. P. Jordan and E. P. Wigner, Z. Physik, **47,** 631, 1928.

our choice of the φ_n, is on diagonal form, and where $G(\mathfrak{n}_i;n)$ is the quantum mechanical expectation value of G for the state characterized by $\mathfrak{n}_i$ and n,

$$G(\mathfrak{n}_i;n) = \int \psi^*(\mathfrak{n}_i;n)\mathfrak{G}\psi(\mathfrak{n}_i;n)d\tau. \tag{7.406}$$

Using equation (7.401) for $\boldsymbol{\rho}$, equation (7.405) can be written in the form

$$\hat{G} = e^{-q} \sum_{\mathfrak{n}_i} e^{\sum \mathfrak{n}_i\nu_i} \sum_n G(\mathfrak{n}_i;n) e^{-\frac{E(\mathfrak{n}_i;n)}{\Theta}}. \tag{7.407}$$

In order to see the physical meaning of Θ and the ν_i one considers again two situations with slightly different values of Θ, ν_i, and a_i. We shall give only the relevant results without their derivations, since the calculations are exactly the same as those given on numerous previous occasions. We have for the variation of q the equation

$$\delta q = \sum_i \hat{\mathfrak{n}}_i\delta\nu_i - \hat{\varepsilon}\,\delta\frac{1}{\Theta} + \frac{1}{\Theta}\sum_j \hat{A}_j\delta a_j. \tag{7.408}$$

The entropy S and free energy F are given by the equations

$$\frac{S}{k} = q - \sum_i \hat{\mathfrak{n}}_i\nu_i + \frac{\hat{\varepsilon}}{\Theta}, \tag{7.409}$$

$$F = \hat{\varepsilon} - ST = -q\Theta + \Theta\sum_i \hat{\mathfrak{n}}_i\nu_i. \tag{7.410}$$

Introducing

$$g_i = \nu_i\Theta, \tag{7.411}$$

we can show that the g_i are the partial free energies or the partial thermal potentials,

$$g_i = \left(\frac{\partial F}{\partial \hat{\mathfrak{n}}_i}\right)_{\Theta,a_j} = \left(\frac{\partial G}{\partial \hat{\mathfrak{n}}_i}\right)_{\Theta,p}, \tag{7.412}$$

where $G = F + pV$ is the thermal potential.

The temperature T is related to Θ by the familiar equation

$$\Theta = kT, \tag{7.413}$$

and in the case of a homogeneous system we have

$$q = \frac{pV}{kT}. \tag{7.414}$$

The grand potential gives us all thermodynamic quantities and we have, for instance, from equation (7.408)

$$\hat{\mathfrak{n}}_i = \frac{\partial q}{\partial \nu_i}, \tag{7.415}$$

$$\hat{\epsilon} = -\frac{\partial q}{\partial \dfrac{1}{\Theta}}, \tag{7.416}$$

$$\hat{A}_j = \Theta \frac{\partial q}{\partial a_j}, \tag{7.417}$$

$$p = \Theta \frac{\partial q}{\partial V}. \tag{7.418}$$

One can calculate the fluctuations similarly. The easiest way is to use the normalization condition and take the derivative with respect to two of the quantities $1/\Theta$, ν_i, or a_i. In this way we get, for instance,

$$\widehat{(\mathfrak{n}_i - \hat{\mathfrak{n}}_i)^2} = \frac{\partial^2 q}{\partial {\nu_i}^2}, \qquad \widehat{(\epsilon - \hat{\epsilon})^2} = \frac{\partial^2 q}{\partial \left(\dfrac{1}{\Theta}\right)^2}, \qquad \text{etc.} \tag{7.419}$$

In general the dispersions will be small if the $\hat{\mathfrak{n}}_i$ are large, and in such cases we are dealing with ensembles with practically completely determined values of E and the $\mathfrak{n}_i$.

Before applying the formulae of this section to a perfect gas and investigating the consequences of the exclusion principle we shall briefly discuss a few aspects of quantum mechanical ensemble theory. Both points which we shall examine also enter classical ensemble theory, be it sometimes in a slightly different way, and we have discussed them before in connection with the classical theory.

The first point is the question of fluctuations. In a phenomenological thermodynamical theory all quantities such as temperature and energy, thermal potentials and numbers of particles of a given kind, volume and pressure, and so on, have well-defined values. However, if a canonical grand ensemble is considered, only the first of each of these pairs has a sharply defined value, the second quantity of each pair fluctuating around an average value. In some cases these fluctuations enter because our very inadequate knowledge about the physical system forces us to use a representative ensemble and we cannot expect to obtain completely defined predictions from very incomplete data. Sometimes, however, the fluctuations may not only present the uncertainty of our predictions, but also correspond to a physical phenomenon. If we consider, for instance, our system embedded in a large thermostat which at the same time can exchange particles with the system, the fluctuations in energy and numbers of particles will occur and under favorable circumstances even be measurable.† In most cases these fluctuations will be extremely small and actually too small to be observable. This is important, since we can then safely apply the theory to thermodynamical systems.

It might be feared that some fluctuations, for instance, in the pressure or in other forces might be large (compare similar considerations on p. 113). There are two reasons why these fluctuations are not important. First of all, the large fluctuations often arise only due to modifications introduced to simplify calculations, such as, for instance, idealized walls and rigid molecules. Secondly, any measurement of a physical quantity will require a finite time interval so that we are not really concerned with $\hat{G}$, but with the time average of $\hat{G}$. From quantum mechanics it follows, however, that fluctuations in a time average are extremely small and decrease rapidly with increasing length of the period over which the average is taken.‡

It is possible to take a point of view complementary to the one taken when one considers canonical grand ensembles. One then considers systems with a constant energy and constant numbers of particles. Such systems are represented by microcanonical petit ensembles and it is possible to consider those in quantum mechanics, though we shall not do so. If the temperature or the thermal potentials are measured, they will show fluctuations of the same order of magnitude as the fluctuations in energy and particle numbers in a canonical grand ensemble. As long as the number of particles in the system is very large, all fluctuations will be negligible and the results obtained by using microcanonical petit ensembles are the same as those obtained by using canonical grand ensembles.

The second point which we wish to discuss at this juncture is the entropy. Our considerations will be similar to those of §5 of Chapter V. Let dZ be the total number of energy levels for which the energy lies between ϵ and $\epsilon + d\epsilon$ and for which the $\mathfrak{n}_i$ have values between $\mathfrak{n}_i$ and $\mathfrak{n}_i + d\mathfrak{n}_i$. If we write

$$dZ = W(\mathfrak{n}_i;\epsilon)d\epsilon\prod_i d\mathfrak{n}_i, \tag{7.420}$$

the normalization equation can be written in the form

$$\int e^{-q+\sum_i \mathfrak{n}_i\nu_i - \frac{\epsilon}{\Theta}} W(\mathfrak{n}_i;\epsilon)d\epsilon\prod_i d\mathfrak{n}_i = 1, \tag{7.421}$$

† It is possible to consider our system to be one of an ensemble, the other members of the ensemble forming the temperature and particle bath. We mentioned on p. 131 that we do not wish to stress this point of view, since it does not fully acknowledge the importance of representative ensembles.

‡ Compare, e.g., H. A. Kramers, Hand- u. Jahrb. d. Chem. Phys., Vol. I, Leipzig 1938, §52.

where, if necessary, the integral on the left-hand side must be treated as a Stieltjes integral.

Consider now a situation where the $\hat{\mathfrak{n}}_i$ are so large that the fluctuations are negligible. In that case the values of ϵ and $\mathfrak{n}_i$ for which the integrand in equation (7.421) is maximum will be practically equal to $\hat{\epsilon}$ and $\hat{\mathfrak{n}}_i$ and we can write equation (7.421) in the form

$$\left[e^{-q+\sum_i \mathfrak{n}_i\nu_i - \frac{\epsilon}{\Theta}} W(\mathfrak{n}_i;\epsilon)\right]_{\substack{\mathfrak{n}_i=\hat{\mathfrak{n}}_i\\ \epsilon=\hat{\epsilon}}} \Delta\epsilon\prod_i\Delta\mathfrak{n}_i = 1, \tag{7.422}$$

where $\Delta\epsilon$ and the $\Delta\mathfrak{n}_i$ are the half-widths of the fluctuations, or

$$(\Delta\hat{\epsilon})^2 = C\widehat{(\epsilon-\hat{\epsilon})^2}, \quad (\Delta\hat{\mathfrak{n}}_i)^2 = C_i\widehat{(\mathfrak{n}_i-\hat{\mathfrak{n}}_i)^2}, \tag{7.423}$$

where C and the C_i are constants of the order of magnitude 1, and where we have approximately

$$\Delta\epsilon \sim \frac{\hat{\epsilon}}{\sqrt{\sum\hat{\mathfrak{n}}_i}}, \qquad \Delta\mathfrak{n}_i \sim \sqrt{\hat{\mathfrak{n}}_i}. \tag{7.424}$$

Taking the logarithm of both sides of equation (7.422), we have

$$q - \sum_i \hat{\mathfrak{n}}_i\nu_i + \frac{\hat{\epsilon}}{\Theta} = \ln\,[W(\hat{\mathfrak{n}}_i;\hat{\epsilon})\Delta\epsilon\prod_i\Delta\mathfrak{n}_i]. \tag{7.425}$$

The left-hand side of this equation is equal to S/k, as can be seen from equation (7.409), and we have thus

$$S = k\ln\,[W(\hat{\mathfrak{n}}_i;\hat{\epsilon})\Delta\epsilon\prod_i\Delta\mathfrak{n}_i]. \tag{7.426}$$

From the well-known relation between entropy and probability it follows that $W(\mathfrak{n}_i;\epsilon)$ can be considered to be the probability of finding certain values of ϵ and $\mathfrak{n}_i$, or that $W(\mathfrak{n}_i;\epsilon)\Delta\epsilon\prod_i\Delta\mathfrak{n}_i$ is the probability of finding ϵ and $\mathfrak{n}_i$ within certain limits. This corresponds closely to the definition of W. Indeed, $W(\mathfrak{n}_i;\epsilon)\Delta\epsilon\prod_i\Delta\mathfrak{n}_i$ was defined as being the number of energy states corresponding to ϵ and $\mathfrak{n}_i$ within given limits, and this together with the fact that earlier we saw that all stationary states should have equal a priori probabilities shows that, indeed, $W(\mathfrak{n}_i;\epsilon)\Delta\epsilon\prod_i\Delta\mathfrak{n}_i$ can be considered to be the probability for the energy and the numbers of particles lying inside given intervals. We can express this slightly differently by stating that the entropy measures our *ignorance* or *lack of knowledge* or *lack of (detailed) information,* since $W(\mathfrak{n}_i;\epsilon)\Delta\epsilon\prod_i\Delta\mathfrak{n}_i$ gives us the number of possibilities which are left, once we know that ϵ and $\mathfrak{n}_i$ are confined to certain given intervals. A similar situation is present in the classical case (compare equation [5.524] where $(\partial\Omega/\partial\epsilon)\Delta$ gives us a measure for the volume in Γ-space in which the representative point can be found once the energy is stated to lie within a given interval).

The relationship between entropy and lack of information has led many authors, notably Shannon, to introduce "entropy" as a measure for the information transmitted by cables and so on, and in this way entropy has figured largely in recent discussions in information theory. It must be stressed here that the entropy introduced in information theory is *not* a thermodynamical quantity and that the use of the same term is rather misleading. It was probably introduced because of a rather loose use of the term "information."

In this connection we may briefly discuss *Maxwell's demon.* Maxwell introduced in 1871 his famous demon, "a being whose faculties are so sharpened that he can follow every molecule in its course, and would be able to do what is at present impossible to us. . . . Let us suppose that a vessel is divided into two portions A and B by a division in which there is a small hole, and that a being who can see the individual molecules opens and closes this hole, so as to allow only the swifter molecules to pass from A to B, and only the slower ones to pass from B to A. He will, thus, without expenditure of work raise the temperature of B and lower that of A, in contradiction to the second law of thermodynamics."

Maxwell's demon has been widely discussed and various authors have set out to show that various attempts to circumvent the second law by using the demon are bound to fail.† Although their discussions differ in some respects they have a few points in common. The first point is the observation that one should take the demon to be part of the total system and then one must consider the total entropy of the original system and the demon. The second point which was most clearly developed for the first time by Szilard‡ is that the demon, in order to be able to operate the trapdoor through which the molecules pass, must receive information. Its own entropy increases therefore and it is now the question whether the increase of the demon's entropy is smaller or larger than the decrease of the entropy of the gas. Both Szilard and Brillouin§ consider possible arrangements and show that in those cases the net change of entropy is positive. Szilard analyzes the problem very thoroughly and shows that one can describe a generalized Maxwell's demon as follows. By some means an operation on a system is determined by the result of a measurement on the system which immediately precedes the operation. In Maxwell's original scheme the operation was the opening of the trapdoor and the measurement

† Let us briefly point out that these proofs of the general validity of the second law are different from the proofs of the general validity of the Heisenberg relations in quantum mechanics. In both cases one sets up an idealized experiment which should be suited to get around the theoretical limitations, but while in quantum mechanics one proves that it is *never* possible to break the limitations, in the thermodynamical case one can prove only that *on the average* it is not possible to violate the second law.

‡ L. Szilard, Z. Physik, **53,** 840, 1929.

§ L. Brillouin, J. Appl. Phys., **22,** 334, 1951.

was the determination of the velocity of an approaching molecule. The result of the operation will be a decrease of entropy, but the preceding measurement will be accompanied by an increase in entropy, and once again one must consider the balance.

Wiener† takes a simpler point of view.‡ He considers the situation, where the demon acts, as a metastable state and writes: "In the long run, the Maxwell demon is itself subject to a random motion corresponding to the temperature of its environment and it receives a large number of small impressions until it falls into 'a certain vertigo' and is incapable of clear perceptions. In fact, it ceases to act as a Maxwell demon." This point of view is probably too simplified and we prefer that of Szilard's and refer the reader to his paper for a more extensive discussion.

In Chapter V (pp. 116 ff.) we saw that there were several ways of defining the entropy. This is also the case here and one can prove that due to the very steep increase of $W(\mathfrak{n}_i;\epsilon)$ with both ϵ and $\mathfrak{n}_i$, the entropy can also be defined by the equation

$$S = k \ln V, \tag{7.427}$$

where

$$V = \int_{\epsilon_{\min}}^{\hat{\epsilon}} \int_{\mathfrak{n}_i=0}^{\hat{\mathfrak{n}}_i} \cdots \int W(\mathfrak{n}_i;\epsilon)\, d\epsilon \prod_i d\mathfrak{n}_i. \tag{7.428}$$

Equation (7.427) corresponds to equation (5.535) of the classical theory.

We have included the factor $\Delta\epsilon \prod_i \Delta\mathfrak{n}_i$ in equation (7.426) in order that the expression under the logarithm would be dimensionless. Actually, equation (7.427) is probably an easier one to use for calculations, since otherwise $\Delta\epsilon$ and the $\Delta\mathfrak{n}_i$ must be computed first. In Chapter V we were not concerned with the actual value of the entropy and therefore did not pay any attention to the fact that neither $\partial\Omega/\partial\epsilon$ nor Ω is dimensionless. We could have corrected this by writing instead of equations (5.525) and (5.535)

$$S = k \ln \left[\frac{\partial\Omega}{\partial\epsilon} \cdot \Delta \cdot h^{-3sN} \right] \tag{7.429}$$

and

$$S = k \ln (\Omega \cdot h^{-3sN}), \tag{7.430}$$

where we can see now even more clearly the correspondence between the classical and the quantum mechanical case. In equation (7.427), for instance, V is the total number of states with $\epsilon < \hat{\epsilon}$ and $\mathfrak{n}_i < \hat{\mathfrak{n}}_i$, while in equation (7.430), which relates to a petit ensemble, Ω is the total volume in Γ-space with $\epsilon < \bar{\epsilon}$. The factor h^{-3sN} arises from the fact that each non-

† N. Wiener, Cybernetics, New York 1948, p. 72.

‡ See also Brillouin, *loc. cit.*, §I.

degenerate state corresponds to a volume h^{3sN} in Γ-space, and we see that, indeed, the two equations (7.427) and (7.430) will give the same result in the limiting case of very high temperatures or very low densities, when all quantum mechanical effects are negligible.

§5. **The Perfect Boltzmann Gas.** To conclude the theoretical part of this book we shall discuss the case of a perfect gas, using the method of the quantum mechanical grand ensembles. It will be seen that although no new results emerge, certain advantages are obtained. We remarked on page 85 that all gases will behave like a Boltzmann gas at sufficiently high temperatures. We shall therefore first consider a perfect gas without taking into account exclusion effects, even though this is an apparent contradiction, since the exclusion principle is an integral part of quantum mechanics. However, this can be justified by observing that the formulae obtained in the present section are, indeed, the limiting cases of the formulae obtained when the exclusion effects are duly considered. We shall not discuss the limiting process, but refer to Chapter IV, where a similar situation occurred.

In the case of a perfect gas of only one constituent we can drop the indices on the $\mathfrak{n}_i$ and ν_i. The total energy and number of particles are given by the equations

$$\epsilon = \sum_s n_s \epsilon_s, \tag{7.501}$$

$$\mathfrak{n} = \sum_s n_s, \tag{7.502}$$

where n_s is the number of particles in the energy level ϵ_s.

The degeneracy γ' of a state with energy ϵ is given by the equation (compare equation [7.317])

$$\gamma' = \mathfrak{n}! \prod_s \frac{{g_s}^{n_s}}{n_s!}. \tag{7.503}$$

We mentioned that we are not including in our discussion the exclusion principle. However, since we are interested in obtaining formulae which will turn out to be the limiting cases of the formulae obtained when the exclusion principle is taken into account, we must realize that due to symmetry effects there is only one specific phase for each generic phase and we must introduce an extra factor $1/\mathfrak{n}!$ into the equation for the degeneracy, as we did in Chapter IV (p. 72). Instead of equation (7.503) we thus have

$$\gamma = \prod_s \frac{{g_s}^{n_s}}{n_s!}, \tag{7.504}$$

and we get from equation (7.403) for the grand potential the equation

$$e^q = \sum_{\mathfrak{n}=0}^{\infty} e^{\mathfrak{n}\nu} \sum_{\Sigma n_s = \mathfrak{n}} \gamma e^{-\frac{1}{\Theta}\Sigma n_s \epsilon_s}, \tag{7.505}$$

or

$$e^q = \sum_{n_s=0}^{\infty} \cdots \sum \left(\prod_s \frac{g_s^{n_s}}{n_s!}\right) e^{\Sigma n_s\left(\nu - \frac{\epsilon_s}{\Theta}\right)},$$

$$= \prod_s \sum_{n_s=0}^{\infty} \frac{g_s^{n_s}}{n_s!} e^{n_s\left(\nu - \frac{\epsilon_s}{\Theta}\right)},$$

$$= e^{\sum_s g_s e^{\nu - \frac{\epsilon_s}{\Theta}}},$$

or

$$q = \sum_s g_s e^{\nu - \frac{\epsilon_s}{\Theta}}. \tag{7.506}$$

Equation (7.506) looks very much the same as equation (4.507) on page 83. There is, however, one important difference. While the energies in equation (4.507) were representative values for a group of levels, the energies in equation (7.506) are the separate levels. Moreover, for the derivation of equation (7.506) it is not necessary to assume that the levels are lying densely. Equation (7.506) has thus a much wider field of application.

The average number of particles $\hat{\mathfrak{n}}$ is given by equation (7.415) and we have

$$\hat{\mathfrak{n}} = \frac{\partial q}{\partial \nu} = q. \tag{7.507}$$

We can use equation (7.419) for the fluctuations in the number of particles and find thus

$$\widehat{(\mathfrak{n} - \hat{\mathfrak{n}})^2} = \frac{\partial^2 q}{\partial \nu^2} = q = \hat{\mathfrak{n}}, \tag{7.508}$$

or

$$\frac{\widehat{(\mathfrak{n} - \hat{\mathfrak{n}})^2}}{\hat{\mathfrak{n}}^2} = \frac{1}{\hat{\mathfrak{n}}}. \tag{7.509}$$

We can calculate also the fluctuations in the numbers of particles occupying the various energy levels. The energy values ϵ_s are then considered as external parameters, since we have from equation (7.501)

$$n_s = \frac{\partial \epsilon}{\partial \epsilon_s}, \tag{7.510}$$

and we see that $-\epsilon_s$ plays the role of an external parameter. From equations (7.417) and (7.506) we get thus for $\hat{n}_s$ the formula

$$\hat{n}_s = \Theta \frac{\partial q}{\partial(-\epsilon_s)} = g_s e^{\nu - \frac{\epsilon_s}{\Theta}}. \tag{7.511}$$

We see that we obtain the formula for the Maxwell-Boltzmann distribution and we have found here probably the most sophisticated derivation of that formula. Not only that but we are now also in a position to compute the fluctuations around the Maxwell-Boltzmann distribution. We have for the fluctuations of n_s the equation (compare equation [6.202] on p. 141)

$$\widehat{(n_s - \hat{n}_s)^2} = \Theta^2 \frac{\partial^2 q}{\partial \epsilon_s^{\,2}} + \Theta \widehat{\frac{\partial^2 \epsilon}{\partial \epsilon_s^{\,2}}}. \tag{7.512}$$

Since

$$\frac{\partial^2 \epsilon}{\partial \epsilon_s^{\,2}} = 0,$$

equation (7.512) gives us

$$\widehat{(n_s - \hat{n}_s)^2} = \Theta^2 \frac{\partial^2 q}{\partial \epsilon_s^{\,2}} = g_s e^{\nu - \frac{\epsilon_s}{\Theta}} = \hat{n}_s, \tag{7.513}$$

and we see that, as soon as $\hat{n}_s$ is large compared to one, the fluctuations in n_s will be small.

The results for the n_s and for $\mathfrak{n}$ were independent of the kind of particles which were present in the gas. This will no longer be true when we wish to consider the average energy and its fluctuations. Let us therefore assume now that we are dealing with a perfect monatomic gas. We can then use the fact that for all temperatures the energy levels will be lying so densely (see p. 62) that the sum in equation (7.506) can be replaced by an integral and then, of course, we get the same equation for q as in Chapter IV,

$$q = \left(\frac{2\pi m\Theta}{h^2}\right)^{3/2} e^{\nu} V. \tag{7.514}$$

From equation (7.514) follows in the usual way the perfect gas law, and for the average energy we have

$$\hat{\epsilon} = \tfrac{3}{2}\hat{\mathfrak{n}}\Theta. \tag{7.515}$$

The fluctuations in the energy follow again from equation (7.419), and we have

$$\widehat{(\epsilon - \hat{\epsilon})^2} = \frac{\partial^2 q}{\partial \left(\frac{1}{\Theta}\right)^2} = \frac{3}{2}\cdot\frac{5}{2} q\Theta^2, \tag{7.516}$$

or, using equations (7.507) and (7.515),

$$\frac{\widehat{(\epsilon - \hat{\epsilon})^2}}{\hat{\epsilon}^2} = \frac{5}{3\hat{\mathfrak{n}}}. \qquad \textbf{(7.517)}$$

That the fluctuations in the energy are now larger than those given by equation (5.904) on page 132 is due to the fact that there is an additional source of fluctuations, namely, the number of particles.

§6. The Perfect Bose-Einstein Gas. Apart from the calculations of the fluctuations the preceding section brought no new results. This could have been expected, since exclusion effects had been neglected and finally even the sum in equation (7.506) replaced by an integral, thus carefully removing any chance we may have had to obtain new results. In the present and the following section we shall see how the exclusion principle will change the considerations of the preceding section. The results will be practically the same as those obtained in Chapter IV, but our results will be less restricted, just as equation (7.506) was more general than equation (4.507). We shall assume for the sake of simplicity that all energy levels ϵ_s are nondegenerate, or that all g_s are equal to one.

The case of a perfect Bose-Einstein gas is rather simple. We can use equation (7.505) for the grand potential, but γ is now not given by equation (7.504) but is equal to one for all values of ϵ, or

$$\gamma = 1. \qquad \textbf{(7.601)}$$

We have then for q the equation

$$e^q = \sum_{\mathfrak{n}=0}^{\infty} e^{\mathfrak{n}\nu} \sum_{\sum n_s = \mathfrak{n}} e^{-\frac{1}{\Theta}\sum n_s\epsilon_s}, \qquad \textbf{(7.602)}$$

or

$$e^q = \sum_{n_s=0}^{\infty} \cdots \sum e^{\sum_s n_s\left(\nu - \frac{\epsilon_s}{\Theta}\right)}$$

$$= \prod_s \left(1 - e^{\nu - \frac{\epsilon_s}{\Theta}}\right)^{-1},$$

or

$$q = -\sum_s \ln\left[1 - e^{\nu - \frac{\epsilon_s}{\Theta}}\right]. \qquad \textbf{(7.603)}$$

Again, this equation is practically the same as equation (4.607) on page 85, but it was not necessary in deriving equation (7.603) to assume the energy levels to lie densely, and the ϵ_s are the energy levels and not a representative average of a group of energy levels as the E_j in equation (4.607) were.

We find for $\hat{\mathfrak{n}}$ and the fluctuations in $\mathfrak{n}$

$$\hat{\mathfrak{n}} = \frac{\partial q}{\partial \nu} = \sum_s \left(e^{-\nu + \frac{\epsilon_s}{\Theta}} - 1\right)^{-1}, \tag{7.604}$$

and

$$\widehat{(\mathfrak{n} - \hat{\mathfrak{n}})^2} = \frac{\partial^2 q}{\partial \nu^2} = \hat{\mathfrak{n}} + \sum_s \left(e^{-\nu + \frac{\epsilon_s}{\Theta}} - 1\right)^{-2} \tag{7.605}$$

We see here that the fluctuations are larger than in the case of a Boltzmann gas.

Of special interest are again the $\hat{n}_s$ and the fluctuations in the n_s, and we have

$$\hat{n}_s = -\Theta \frac{\partial q}{\partial \epsilon_s} = \frac{1}{e^{-\nu + \frac{\epsilon_s}{\Theta}} - 1}, \tag{7.606}$$

and

$$\widehat{(n_s - \hat{n}_s)^2} = \Theta^2 \frac{\partial^2 q}{\partial {\epsilon_s}^2} = \hat{n}_s + {\hat{n}_s}^2 \tag{7.607}$$

We do not wish to enter into a discussion of this last equation but defer it to §2 of Chapter IX, when we discuss the so-called Einstein condensation.

Let us now restrict ourselves to the case of a perfect monatomic gas. We can then use the results of Chapter IV for q, since the sum in equation (7.603) can be replaced by an integral, and we have

$$q = \left(\frac{2\pi m\Theta}{h^2}\right)^{3/2} V g(\nu), \tag{7.608}$$

where

$$g(\nu) = \sum_{n=1}^{\infty} \frac{e^{n\nu}}{n^{5/2}}. \tag{7.609}$$

Using this formula for q we get easily from equations (7.419)

$$\frac{\widehat{(\mathfrak{n} - \hat{\mathfrak{n}})^2}}{\hat{\mathfrak{n}}^2} = \frac{g''(\nu)}{g'(\nu)} \cdot \frac{1}{\hat{\mathfrak{n}}}, \quad \left(g'(\nu) = \frac{dg}{d\nu}, \quad g''(\nu) = \frac{d^2 g}{d\nu^2}\right) \tag{7.610}$$

and

$$\frac{\widehat{(\epsilon - \hat{\epsilon})^2}}{\hat{\epsilon}^2} = \frac{5}{3\hat{\mathfrak{n}}} \frac{g'(\nu)}{g(\nu)}, \tag{7.611}$$

where we used the fact that

$$\hat{\mathfrak{n}} = \frac{\partial q}{\partial \nu} = q \frac{g'(\nu)}{g(\nu)}. \tag{7.612}$$

Since $g''(\nu)$ diverges for $\nu \to 0$, the fluctuations in $\mathfrak{n}$ can become arbitrarily large as soon as $\nu \to 0$.

§7. The Perfect Fermi-Dirac Gas. The calculations are similar to those of the preceding section. We have now for γ

$$\gamma = 1, \qquad \sum n_s^2 = \mathfrak{n}; \qquad \gamma = 0, \qquad \sum n_s^2 > \mathfrak{n}, \tag{7.701}$$

and we have thus

$$e^q = \sum_{\mathfrak{n}=0}^{\infty} e^{\mathfrak{n}\nu} \sum_{\substack{\sum n_s = \mathfrak{n} \\ \sum n_s^2 = \mathfrak{n}}} e^{-\frac{1}{\Theta}\sum n_s \epsilon_s}, \tag{7.702}$$

or

$$e^q = \sum_{n_s=0}^{1} \cdots \sum e^{\sum_s n_s\left(\nu - \frac{\epsilon_s}{\Theta}\right)}$$

$$= \prod_s \left(1 + e^{\nu - \frac{\epsilon_s}{\Theta}}\right)$$

or

$$q = \sum_s \ln\left[1 + e^{\nu - \frac{\epsilon_s}{\Theta}}\right]. \tag{7.703}$$

This equation corresponds to equation (4.702), and again equation (7.703) is less restricted than its counterpart of Chapter IV.

Since the calculations are completely analogous to those of §6, we shall give only the more important results. We have for the fluctuations in $\mathfrak{n}$

$$\overline{(\mathfrak{n} - \hat{\mathfrak{n}})^2} = \hat{\mathfrak{n}} - \sum_s \left(e^{-\nu + \frac{\epsilon_s}{\Theta}} + 1\right)^{-2} < \hat{\mathfrak{n}}, \tag{7.704}$$

which shows that the fluctuations are now smaller than in the Boltzmann case.

We have for $\hat{n}_s$ and the fluctuations in the n_s

$$\hat{n}_s = \frac{1}{e^{-\nu + \frac{\epsilon_s}{\Theta}} + 1}, \tag{7.705}$$

$$\overline{(n_s - \hat{n}_s)^2} = \hat{n}_s - \hat{n}_s^2. \tag{7.706}$$

Since the n_s can only be zero or one, n_s is certainly not a large number, and although the fluctuations in the n_s are smaller than in the Boltzmann case, the relative fluctuations $[\overline{(n_s - \hat{n}_s)^2}/\hat{n}_s^2]$ can never be very small—unless $\hat{n}_s$ is practically equal to one, that is, unless we are dealing with the lowest energy levels which are practically completely occupied as long as the temperature is not extremely high. However, it is possible to consider a group of levels so that the average number of particles in this group of levels is large compared to one. Let

$$N_k = \sum{}' n_s, \tag{7.707}$$

where the prime on the summation sign indicates that the summation extends over the kth group of energy levels. We have now

$$N_k = \sum{}' \frac{\partial \epsilon}{\partial \epsilon_s} \tag{7.708}$$

and

$$\hat{N}_k = \Theta \sum{}' \frac{\partial q}{\partial \epsilon_s} = \sum{}' \frac{1}{e^{-\nu+\frac{\epsilon_s}{\Theta}} + 1}. \tag{7.709}$$

We have for the fluctuations in the N_k

$$\widehat{(N_k - \hat{N}_k)^2} = \Theta^2 \sum{}' \frac{\partial^2 q}{\partial \epsilon_s{}^2},$$

since the fluctuations in the n_s are independent, or

$$\widehat{(N_k - \hat{N}_k)^2} = \hat{N}_k - \sum{}' \left(e^{-\nu+\frac{\epsilon_s}{\Theta}} + 1\right)^{-2}, \tag{7.710}$$

and we see that the relative fluctuations in the N_k are indeed small compared to one, as soon as $\hat{N}_k$ is large.

Considering once more the case of a perfect monatomic gas, we can replace the sum in equation (7.703) by an integral and we get for q the equation

$$q = \left(\frac{2\pi m\Theta}{h^2}\right)^{3/2} V h(\nu), \tag{7.711}$$

where

$$h(\nu) = -\sum_{n=1}^{\infty} \frac{(-e^{\nu})^n}{n^{5/2}}. \tag{7.712}$$

After an easy calculation we get for the fluctuations in the energy

$$\frac{\widehat{(\epsilon - \hat{\epsilon})^2}}{\hat{\epsilon}^2} = \frac{5}{3\hat{n}} \frac{h'(\nu)}{h(\nu)}, \tag{7.713}$$

where we have used for $\hat{n}$ the equation

$$\hat{n} = q \frac{h'(\nu)}{h(\nu)}. \tag{7.714}$$

BIBLIOGRAPHICAL NOTES

Pauli was the first to introduce canonical grand ensembles in quantum statistics:

1. W. Pauli, Z. Physik, **41,** 81, 1927.

Our treatment, especially in the last four sections, is based on Kramers' work:

2. H. A. Kramers, Proc. Kon. Ned. Akad. Wet. (Amsterdam), **41,** 10, 1938.
3. Lectures given by H. A. Kramers in Leiden during the winter of 1944–1945.

§1. The density matrix was introduced by von Neumann and Dirac:

4. J. von Neumann, Mathematische Grundlagen der Quantenmechanik, Berlin 1932.
5. P. A. M. Dirac, The Principles of Quantum Mechanics, Oxford 1935, §37.

§2. See ref. 4.

PART C

APPLICATIONS

CHAPTER VIII

THE EQUATION OF STATE

§1. Classical Theory of the Equation of State. In the preceding chapters we have often considered the case of a perfect gas. However, it is well known that actual gases are far from perfect. In the present chapter we shall consider the case of actual or imperfect gases. We shall, however, for the sake of simplicity assume that we are dealing with monatomic gases. We shall also assume that the forces between the atoms are central forces which can be derived from a potential energy function $\phi(r)$ and, moreover, that the potential energy pertaining to two atoms is independent of the positions of the other atoms in the gas. In other words, the intermolecular forces are additive. In the present chapter we shall especially be concerned with gases which differ only slightly from perfect gases, while in the next chapter we shall consider gases under such circumstances that condensation can set in. Throughout the present chapter we shall use the method of the grand ensembles and our first task will be the calculation of the grand potential q, since the equation of state then follows from equation (6.126),

$$p = \frac{kT}{V} q. \tag{8.101}$$

The energy of a system of $\mathfrak{n}$ particles is, according to our assumptions, given by the equation

$$\epsilon = \sum_k \left(\frac{\mathbf{p}_k^{\,2}}{2m} + F_k\right) + \sum_{k<l} \phi(r_{kl}), \tag{8.102}$$

where r_{kl} is the distance between the kth and the lth atom, where k and l run from 1 to $\mathfrak{n}$, where the last summation extends over all pairs of atoms in the gas, and where

$$\left.\begin{aligned} F_k &= 0, \text{ if the } k\text{th atom lies inside the volume } V \\ \text{and} \quad & \\ F_k &= \infty, \text{ if the } k\text{th atom lies outside the volume } V. \end{aligned}\right\} \tag{8.103}$$

As long as our considerations are classical, we have for the grand potential the equation

$$e^q = \sum_{\mathfrak{n}=0}^{\infty} \frac{1}{\mathfrak{n}!} e^{\mathfrak{n}\nu} \int \cdots \int e^{-\mu\epsilon} \prod_{i=1}^{\mathfrak{n}} \frac{d\mathbf{p}_i d\mathbf{x}_i}{h^3}, \tag{8.104}$$

which is equation (6.107) apart from a factor $h^{3\mathfrak{n}}$ (compare the remark on p. 143). We have put in equation (8.104)

$$\mu = \frac{1}{\Theta} = \frac{1}{kT}. \tag{8.105}$$

The integration over the p's is elementary, and we get

$$e^q = \sum_{\mathfrak{n}=0}^{\infty} \frac{1}{\mathfrak{n}!} \frac{e^{\mathfrak{n}\nu}}{v_0^{\mathfrak{n}}} \int \cdots \int e^{-\mu \sum_{k<l} \phi(r_{kl})} d\mathbf{x}_1 \cdots d\mathbf{x}_{\mathfrak{n}}, \tag{8.106}$$

where due to the occurrence of the F_k all the $\mathbf{x}_i$ are now confined to V and where v_0 is given by the equation

$$v_0 = \left(\frac{h^2}{2\pi mkT}\right)^{3/2}. \tag{8.107}$$

On page 85 we saw that, apart from a numerical factor $(3/2\pi)^{3/2}$, v_0 was equal to the cube of the De Broglie wave length corresponding to the average kinetic energy in the gas. We also saw there that the classical theory could be used as long as $\mathfrak{n}v_0 \ll V$, and we can thus expect that the results of the present section will be valid as long as $\mathfrak{n}v_0 \ll V$. We shall verify this statement in §4.

The potential energy $\phi(r)$ is practically equal to zero as soon as r is larger than a few Ångström units. We shall assume for the sake of simplicity that we have rigorously

$$\phi(r) = 0, \qquad r > D, \tag{8.108}$$

where D is of the order of magnitude of 10 ÅU. As long as the gas is not too compressed, the average volume available per atom will be large compared to D^3 and practically all configurations will be such that most atoms are lying at a distance larger than D from all the other atoms, a few will be lying in pairs, even fewer will form groups (or clusters) of three, and so on. A *cluster* of n atoms is formed if one can reach from any one of the n atoms all the other $n - 1$ atoms by traveling over a chain of atoms where two consecutive atoms in the chain are always lying at a distance apart less than D and if the other atoms in the gas are all at a distance larger than D from all of the n atoms in the cluster. The term "cluster" was first introduced by Mayer.

Using this idea of clusters we can use Ursell's method to expand the right-hand side of equation (8.106) in powers of $\hat{n}v_0/V$. We write thereto

$$\frac{1}{v_0^N} e^{-\mu \sum_{k<l} \phi(r_{kl})} = W_N(\mathbf{x}_1, \cdots, \mathbf{x}_N), \tag{8.109}$$

where k and l run from 1 to N. We introduce now functions $U_N(\mathbf{x}_1,\cdots,\mathbf{x}_N)$ by the equations

$$\left.\begin{aligned} W_1(\mathbf{x}_1) &= U_1(\mathbf{x}_1), \\ W_2(\mathbf{x}_1,\mathbf{x}_2) &= U_1(\mathbf{x}_1)U_1(\mathbf{x}_2) + U_2(\mathbf{x}_1,\mathbf{x}_2), \\ W_3(\mathbf{x}_1,\mathbf{x}_2,\mathbf{x}_3) &= U_1(\mathbf{x}_1)U_1(\mathbf{x}_2)U_1(\mathbf{x}_3) + U_2(\mathbf{x}_1,\mathbf{x}_2)U_1(\mathbf{x}_3) \\ &\quad + U_2(\mathbf{x}_2,\mathbf{x}_3)U_1(\mathbf{x}_1) + U_2(\mathbf{x}_3,\mathbf{x}_1)U_1(\mathbf{x}_2) \\ &\quad + U_3(\mathbf{x}_1,\mathbf{x}_2,\mathbf{x}_3), \\ &\cdots\cdots\cdots\cdots\cdots\cdots\cdots\cdots \\ W_N(\mathbf{x}_1,\cdots,\mathbf{x}_N) &= \sum U_{n_1}U_{n_2}\cdots U_{n_i}, \qquad (\sum_k n_k = N) \end{aligned}\right\} \tag{8.110}$$

where the summation on the right-hand side of the last equation extends, first, over all possible partitiones of N as a sum of positive integers and, second, for a given partitio over all possible ways in which N atoms can be divided into groups consisting, respectively, of n_1, n_2, $\cdots$ atoms. If a partitio is such that among the n_i there are λ_1 1's, λ_2 2's, $\cdots$, λ_k k's, $\cdots$, the number of terms corresponding to that particular partitio will be equal to $N!C(\lambda_1,\lambda_2,\cdots)$ where

$$C(\lambda_1,\lambda_2,\cdots) = \frac{1}{\prod_k \lambda_k!(k!)^{\lambda_k}}. \tag{8.111}$$

The reason for introducing the U_N instead of the W_N is that U_N is equal to zero as soon as the N atoms do not belong to one cluster. This can be seen as follows. First of all, we see from equation (8.109) that as soon as the N atoms fall into two clusters of N_1 and N_2 atoms, respectively, we have

$$W_N = W_{N_1} \cdot W_{N_2}, \tag{8.112}$$

where W_{N_1} depends on the coordinates of the atoms in the first cluster only and W_{N_2} on those of the atoms in the second cluster only. This is a consequence of the fact that in the sum in the exponential there will be no terms where k and l belong to different clusters.

The property of the U_N to be zero if the N atoms do not belong to the same cluster follows now by induction. Let it be true for U_1, U_2, $\cdots$, U_N. Consider W_{N+1}. We must prove that $U_{N+1} = 0$ if the coordinates $\mathbf{x}_1$, $\cdots$, $\mathbf{x}_{N+1}$ fall into two clusters $\mathbf{x}_1$, $\cdots$, $\mathbf{x}_{N_1}$ and $\mathbf{x}_{N_1+1}$, $\cdots$, $\mathbf{x}_{N_1+N_2}$, where $N_1 + N_2 = N + 1$ and where N_1 and N_2 are at most equal to N. We can write $W_{N+1} = W_{N_1}W_{N_2}$. Expressing the W's in terms of the U's we have on the left-hand side of this equation apart from U_{N+1} no terms which contain U's with coordinates belonging to different clusters, since those U's are according to our premises equal to zero. Since there are no terms on the right-hand side with coordinates belonging to different clusters, U_{N+1} must be equal to zero. Since the theorem is true for $N = 2$, as can easily be verified from equations (8.110), our theorem is proved.

We shall need later on the equations giving us the U's in terms of the W's. These equations follow from the equations (8.110), and we have

$$\left.\begin{aligned} U_1(\mathbf{x}_1) &= W_1(\mathbf{x}_1), \\ U_2(\mathbf{x}_1,\mathbf{x}_2) &= W_2(\mathbf{x}_1,\mathbf{x}_2) - W_1(\mathbf{x}_1)W_1(\mathbf{x}_2), \\ U_3(\mathbf{x}_1,\mathbf{x}_2,\mathbf{x}_3) &= W_3(\mathbf{x}_1,\mathbf{x}_2,\mathbf{x}_3) - W_2(\mathbf{x}_1,\mathbf{x}_2)W_1(\mathbf{x}_3) \\ &\quad - W_2(\mathbf{x}_2,\mathbf{x}_3)W_1(\mathbf{x}_1) - W_2(\mathbf{x}_3,\mathbf{x}_1)W_1(\mathbf{x}_2) \\ &\quad + 2W_1(\mathbf{x}_1)W_1(\mathbf{x}_2)W_1(\mathbf{x}_3), \\ &\cdots\cdots\cdots\cdots\cdots \end{aligned}\right\} \tag{8.113}$$

We introduce now integrals I_n by the equation

$$I_n = \int U_n(\mathbf{x}_1,\cdots,\mathbf{x}_n)d\mathbf{x}_1 \cdots d\mathbf{x}_n. \tag{8.114}$$

These I_n vanish if the n atoms do not belong to the same cluster. If we therefore integrate over the $\mathbf{x}_i$ one by one, only the last integration will give us a factor V, since only one of the n atoms will have the full volume at its disposal. We can thus write

$$I_n = \frac{V}{v_0} n! b_n, \tag{8.115}$$

where v_0 is given by equation (8.107) and where now the b_n are dimensionless quantities which depend on the temperature but not on the volume.

Combining equations (8.106), (8.109) to (8.111), (8.114), and (8.115), we have after some calculations

$$\begin{aligned} q &= \sum_{\mathfrak{n}} \frac{e^{\mathfrak{n}\nu}}{\mathfrak{n}!} \int W_{\mathfrak{n}}(\mathbf{x}_1,\cdots,\mathbf{x}_{\mathfrak{n}})d\mathbf{x}_1 \cdots d\mathbf{x}_{\mathfrak{n}} \\ &= \sum_{\mathfrak{n}} \frac{e^{\mathfrak{n}\nu}}{\mathfrak{n}!} \sum_{\lambda_i} \mathfrak{n}! C(\lambda_1,\lambda_2,\cdots) I_1^{\lambda_1} I_2^{\lambda_2} \cdots \\ &= \prod_k \sum_{\lambda_k=0}^{\infty} \frac{(b_k e^{k\nu} V/v_0)^{\lambda_k}}{\lambda_k!} \\ &= e^{\frac{V}{v_0}\sum_{n=1}^{\infty} b_n e^{n\nu}}, \end{aligned}$$

or

$$q = \frac{V}{v_0} \sum_{n=1}^{\infty} b_n e^{n\nu}. \tag{8.116}$$

We may remark here that equations (7.514), (7.608), and (7.711) are special cases of equation (8.116) with, respectively,

$b_1 = 1,\ b_n = 0 (n > 1)$ for a perfect Boltzmann gas;

$b_n = n^{-5/2}$ for a perfect Bose-Einstein gas; and

$b_n = (-1)^{n+1} n^{-5/2}$ for a perfect Fermi-Dirac gas.

From equation (8.101) we have for the pressure

$$p = \frac{kT}{v_0} \sum_n b_n e^{n\nu}. \tag{8.117}$$

This equation gives p as a power series in the activity (e^ν), but it is more usual and more convenient for comparing the theoretical and experimental equations of state to express p as a power series in the density, or $1/V$. Let us denote the average number of atoms $\hat{n}$ by N. We have for N from equation (7.415)

$$N = \frac{\partial q}{\partial \nu} = \frac{V}{v_0} \sum_{n=1}^{\infty} n b_n e^{n\nu}, \tag{8.118}$$

or

$$\frac{N v_0}{V} = \sum_{n=1}^{\infty} n b_n e^{n\nu}. \tag{8.119}$$

Combining equations (8.117) and (8.119), we have

$$pV = NkT \frac{\sum b_n e^{n\nu}}{\sum n b_n e^{n\nu}} = NkT(1 - b_2 e^\nu - (2b_3 - 4b_2^2)e^{2\nu} + \cdots), \tag{8.120}$$

where we have used the fact that

$$b_1 = 1, \tag{8.121}$$

as can be seen easily from equations (8.115), (8.114), (8.113), and (8.109).

Using equation (8.119), we can write the equation of state in the form

$$pV = NkT \sum_{n=0}^{\infty} a_n \left(\frac{N v_0}{V}\right)^n, \tag{8.122}$$

where one has

$$\left.\begin{aligned} a_0 &= 1, \\ a_1 &= -b_2, \\ a_2 &= -2b_3 + 4b_2^2, \\ a_3 &= -3b_4 + 18 b_2 b_3 - 20 b_2^3, \\ &\cdots\cdots\cdots\cdots\cdots\cdots\cdots\cdots. \end{aligned}\right\} \tag{8.123}$$

Equations (8.123) can be obtained by the pedestrian way of assuming e^ν to be a power series in Nv_0/V and substituting this power series into equation (8.119), putting the coefficients on the left- and the right-hand side equal to each other and finally substituting the power series which we have obtained in this way into equation (8.117). A much more elegant method is the following one, which is due to Kramers.

Let us introduce the notation

$$e^\nu = z, \qquad \frac{Nv_0}{V} = x, \qquad F(z) = \sum_{n=1}^{\infty} b_n z^n, \qquad F' = \frac{dF}{dz}. \tag{8.124}$$

We then have from equation (8.119)

$$x = zF'(z), \tag{8.125}$$

and we are interested in the expansion

$$\frac{F}{zF'(z)} = \frac{F}{x} = \sum a_n x^n, \tag{8.126}$$

where the a_n are the same as in equation (8.122).

Let z_0 be the value of z which satisfies equation (8.125). Consider now the integral

$$\frac{1}{2\pi i}\oint F(z)d\ln(zF'(z) - x),$$

where the path of integration is in the complex z-plane around the origin and around z_0. From the theory of complex functions it follows that this integral is equal to $F(z_0)$. If we write

$$zF'(z) - x = zF'(z)\left[1 - \frac{x}{zF'(z)}\right],$$

we can use the series expansion for $\ln(1 - y)$ and we get in this way

$$F(z_0) = \frac{1}{2\pi i}\oint F(z)d\left[\ln zF'(z) - \sum_{n=0}^{\infty}\frac{1}{n+1}\left(\frac{x}{zF'(z)}\right)^{n+1}\right]$$

$$= \frac{1}{2\pi i}\sum_{n=0}^{\infty}\frac{x^{n+1}}{n+1}\oint\frac{\{F'(z)\}^{-n}dz}{z^{n+1}},$$

where we have integrated by parts. We see that $(n+1)a_n$ is the coefficient of z^n in $\{F'(z)\}^{-n}$. Equations (8.123) then follow straightaway.†

§2. The Second and Third Virial Coefficients in Classical Statistics.

The usual way to write the equation of state is the following.

$$pV = NkT\left[1 + \frac{B}{V} + \frac{C}{V^2} + \cdots\right], \tag{8.201}$$

where B, C, $\cdots$ are called the second, third, $\cdots$ virial coefficient. The

† The same method can be used to obtain, for instance, the power series in equation (4.620) on p. 87.

reason for this name was discussed on pages 8–10. Comparing equation (8.201) with equation (8.122) we see that the virial coefficients are connected with the a_n by the equations

$$\left.\begin{aligned} B &= Nv_0 a_1, \\ C &= (Nv_0)^2 a_2, \\ &\cdots\cdots\cdots\cdots. \end{aligned}\right\} \tag{8.202}$$

Using equations (8.123) we can express the virial coefficients in the b_n, and hence finally in terms of the potential energy ϕ,

$$\left.\begin{aligned} B &= -Nv_0 b_2, \\ C &= -(Nv_0)^2(2b_3 - 4b_2{}^2), \\ &\cdots\cdots\cdots\cdots\cdots\cdots\cdots\cdots. \end{aligned}\right\} \tag{8.203}$$

Substituting for b_2 from equations (8.115), (8.114), (8.113), and (8.109), we have for the second virial coefficient

$$\begin{aligned} B &= -\frac{Nv_0{}^2}{2V} I_2 \\ &= -\frac{Nv_0{}^2}{2V}\int U_2 d\mathbf{x}_1 d\mathbf{x}_2 \\ &= -\frac{Nv_0{}^2}{2V}\left[\int W_2 d\mathbf{x}_1 d\mathbf{x}_2 - \int W_1 d\mathbf{x}_1 \int W_1 d\mathbf{x}_2\right], \end{aligned}$$

or

$$B = \frac{N}{2V}\left[\int d\mathbf{x}_1 \int d\mathbf{x}_2 - \int e^{-\mu\phi(r_{12})} d\mathbf{x}_1 d\mathbf{x}_2\right]. \tag{8.204}$$

Instead of $\mathbf{x}_2$ we can introduce the polar coordinates r_{12}, ϑ and φ which determine the vector $\mathbf{x}_2 - \mathbf{x}_1$. Integration over $\mathbf{x}_1$ produces a factor V and integration over ϑ and φ a factor 4π and we can thus write equation (8.204) in the form

$$B = 2\pi N \int_0^\infty [1 - e^{-\mu\phi(r)}] r^2 dr. \tag{8.205}$$

This equation was first derived from ensemble theory by Ornstein in his thesis.

If B is known as a function of the temperature, equation (8.205) gives us in principle an equation from which the potential energy function $\phi(r)$ can be determined. In practice this can never be done but one can use, for instance, the following procedure which was introduced by Lennard-Jones extending a method of Keesom's.† One assumes that the potential energy function is one of the type

$$\phi(r) = \frac{\lambda}{r^n} - \frac{\mu}{r^m}, \tag{8.206‡}$$

where n is larger than m, thus giving repulsion for small r and attraction for large r. Introducing instead of λ and μ the depth of the potential hole, κ, and the "diameter" of the atoms, σ, where σ is the root of the equation

$$\phi(\sigma) = 0, \tag{8.207}$$

equation (8.206) can be written in the form

$$\phi(r) = c\kappa\left[\frac{1}{r^{*n}} - \frac{1}{r^{*m}}\right], \tag{8.208}$$

where

$$r^* = \frac{r}{\sigma} \tag{8.209}$$

and

$$c^{-1} = \left(\frac{m}{n}\right)^{\frac{m}{n-m}} - \left(\frac{m}{n}\right)^{\frac{n}{n-m}}. \tag{8.210}$$

Substituting expression (8.208) into equation (8.205), one obtains B as a function of σ and κ for given values of n and m. One now first of all determines n and m. One assumes the attractive forces to be London forces, which give $m = 6$. One then introduces molecular units (compare equation [8.209]) by introducing σ, κ, and κ/k as units of length, energy, and temperature. Quantities expressed in molecular units will be denoted by an asterisk, so that we have, for instance,

$$B = \sigma^3 B^*, \tag{8.211}$$

$$T = \frac{\kappa}{k} T^*. \tag{8.212}$$

One plots now, for given n, $\ln B^*$ against $\ln T^*$ and on transparent paper one plots the experimental $\ln B$ against $\ln T$ curve. If it is possible by moving the experimental curve over the calculated curve to bring the two curves to coincide at all temperatures, the n used will be the correct one. By this method Lennard-Jones found that for A, Ne, He, H_2 and N_2 any value of n between 8 and 14 would give an equally good agreement between

† See, e.g., W. H. Keesom, Physik. Z., **22**, 129, 643, 1921.

‡ A discussion of the merits of this and other potential energy functions will be given in Appendix V.

the observed and calculated curves.† It is then easiest to assume $n = 12$, since this simplifies all calculations considerably and in the following we shall assume that $m = 6$, $n = 12$, which give us for the potential energy function the equation

$$\phi^* = \frac{\phi}{\kappa} = 4\left[\frac{1}{r^{*12}} - \frac{1}{r^{*6}}\right]. \tag{8.213}$$

Once n and m are known, the differences in abscissae and ordinates will give us κ and σ (compare equations [8.211] and [8.212]). In this way the values of κ and σ of the following table were found.

TABLE OF κ AND σ‡

Gas	κ in 10^{-16} erg	σ in ÅU
A	165	3.4
Ne	49	2.7
He	14	2.6
N_2	132	3.7
H_2	51	2.9

‡ From J. de Boer, Contribution to the Theory of Compressed Gases, Thesis, Amsterdam 1940, pp. 31, 38. The values for He and H_2 are obtained by the method described in §§5 and 8.

Once κ and σ are determined, the potential energy function is known and in principle the other virial coefficients can be calculated and compared with experiments. The only one which has been calculated is the third virial coefficient for which we have from equations (8.203), (8.115), (8.114), (8.113), and (8.109)§

$$C = \frac{N^2}{3}\int (1 - e^{-\mu\phi_{12}})(1 - e^{-\mu\phi_{23}})(1 - e^{-\mu\phi_{31}})d\mathbf{x}_{12}d\mathbf{x}_{13}, \tag{8.214}$$

where $\phi_{ik} \equiv \phi(r_{ik})$.

Values of C for A and N_2 have been calculated by numerical integration

† In the cases of He and H_2, quantum effects are important, especially at low temperatures. The determination of n must therefore be made at high temperatures. We shall return to this point later on.

§ In obtaining equation (8.214) one uses the fact that one of the $\mathbf{x}_i$ in formula (8.114) can roam freely through the whole of V and that we can thus introduce as integration variables $\mathbf{x}_1, \mathbf{x}_{12}, \mathbf{x}_{13}, \cdots$, where the integration over $\mathbf{x}_1$ gives a factor V while in the other integrations one uses the fact that $\mathbf{x}_{kl} = \mathbf{x}_{1l} - \mathbf{x}_{1k}$. Moreover, one writes I_2^2 in the form

$$I_2^2 = \frac{1}{3}\frac{V^2}{v_0^4}\left[\int (e^{-\mu\phi_{12}} - 1)d\mathbf{x}_{12}\int (e^{-\mu\phi_{13}} - 1)d\mathbf{x}_{13}\right.$$
$$\left. + \int (e^{-\mu\phi_{23}} - 1)d\mathbf{x}_{23}\int (e^{-\mu\phi_{21}} - 1)d\mathbf{x}_{21} + \int (e^{-\mu\phi_{31}} - 1)d\mathbf{x}_{31}\int (e^{-\mu\phi_{32}} - 1)d\mathbf{x}_{32}\right].$$

by De Boer and Michels† and by the use of approximate expressions by Montroll and Mayer.‡ The agreement with experimental values of C is not too bad, but we refer the reader to the original papers for a detailed discussion.

§3. The Law of Corresponding States in Classical Statistics. In classical thermodynamics van der Waals introduced the law of corresponding states in order to be able to predict unknown properties of substances, about which only a few data were known, from the more complete knowledge about other substances.§ This law stated that the equation of state, if expressed in the reduced quantities $\mathfrak{p}$, $\mathbf{V}$, and $\mathbf{T}$, would be the same for all substances, or

$$\mathfrak{p} = f(\mathbf{V},\mathbf{T}), \tag{8.301}$$

where

$$\mathfrak{p} = \frac{p}{p_{cr}}, \qquad \mathbf{V} = \frac{V}{V_{cr}}, \qquad \mathbf{T} = \frac{T}{T_{cr}}, \tag{8.302}$$

if p_{cr}, V_{cr}, and T_{cr} are the values of the pressure, volume, and temperature at the critical point, and where in equation (8.301) $f(\mathbf{V},\mathbf{T})$ is a universal function.

There is, however, another law of corresponding states which is valid for all substances for which the potential energy $\phi(r)$ is of the same form, or more precisely, where apart from scale factors the potential energy function is the same. In formula, we shall assume that we are comparing substances for which the potential energy function is given by the equation

$$\phi(r) = \alpha\psi(\beta r), \tag{8.303}$$

where ψ is a universal function and where α and β may differ from one substance to another. As an example we can take the gases H_2, He, Ne, N_2, and A for which $\phi(r)$ is given by equation (8.208) with $m = 6$, $n = 12$. The quantities α and β are now equal to κ and $1/\sigma$ and

$$\psi(x) = 4\left(\frac{1}{x^{12}} - \frac{1}{x^6}\right). \tag{8.304}$$

Let us assume that α has the dimension of an energy so that ψ is a dimensionless function and that β has the dimensions of an inverse length so that βr is also dimensionless. We introduce reduced (dimensionless)

† J. de Boer and A. Michels, Physica, **6**, 97, 1939.

‡ E. W. Montroll and J. E. Mayer, J. Chem. Phys., **9**, 626, 1941.

§ We refer for a discussion of this thermodynamical law of corresponding states to H. Kamerlingh Onnes and W. H. Keesom, Enzyklopädie der mathematischen Wissenschaften, Vol. V, Pt. 10, Leipzig-Berlin 1912, §§26, 27.

variables

$$r^* = \beta r, \tag{8.305}$$

$$\mu^* = \mu\alpha, \tag{8.306}$$

and also

$$W_n^* = v_0^{*n} W_n = \beta^{3n} e^{-\mu^* \sum \psi(r_{kl}^*)}, \tag{8.307}$$

where

$$v_0^* = v_0 \beta^3 = \Lambda^{*3} \mu^{*3/2}, \tag{8.308}$$

and

$$\Lambda^* = \frac{\beta h}{\sqrt{2\pi m\alpha}} \cdot \tag{8.309}$$

Similarly,

$$U_n^* = v_0^{*n} U_n. \tag{8.310}$$

From equations (8.115), (8.114), (8.113), and (8.109) it now follows that

$$\frac{V}{v_0} b_n = \chi_n(\mu^*, V^*)(v_0^*)^{-n}, \tag{8.311}$$

where the functions χ_n do no longer depend on α or β. Substituting expression (8.311) into equations (8.116) and (8.118), we have

$$q = \sum_{n=1}^{\infty} \chi_n(\mu^*, V^*)(e^{\nu}/v_0^*)^n \tag{8.312}$$

and

$$N = \sum_{n=1}^{\infty} n\chi_n(\mu^*, V^*)(e^{\nu}/v_0^*)^n. \tag{8.313}$$

From those two equations we can eliminate e^{ν}/v_0^*, and the final result will be

$$q = q(\mu^*, V^*),$$

so that we get for the equation of state

$$p^* V^* = NT^* \chi(\mu^*, V^*), \tag{8.314}$$

where χ is a universal function for a given potential energy function ψ and where

$$V^* = \beta^3 V, \tag{8.315}$$

$$T^* = \frac{1}{\mu^*}, \tag{8.316}$$

$$p^* = \frac{p}{\beta^3 \alpha} \cdot \tag{8.317}$$

Equation (8.314) gives us the law of corresponding states in the form first derived by De Boer and Michels. Although it might be thought that equation (8.314) is less general than equation (8.301), it must be mentioned here that Kamerlingh Onnes and Keesom† emphasized the fact that equation (8.301) was probably valid only for just that class of substances for which the potential energy functions are related to each other by equation (8.303).

It follows easily that equation (8.301) holds for those substances for which the potential energy function is given by equation (8.303). The equation of state in reduced variables is given by equation (8.314) and the critical data T_{cr}, V_{cr}, and p_{cr} should follow from this equation and we have thus uniquely determined T_{cr}^*, V_{cr}^*, and p_{cr}^*. Since these three quantities are uniquely determined, we can introduce

$$\mathfrak{p} = \frac{p^*}{p_{cr}^*}, \qquad \mathfrak{V} = \frac{V^*}{V^*_{cr}}, \qquad \mathfrak{T} = \frac{T^*}{T_{cr}^*}, \tag{8.318}$$

and equation (8.314) reduces to equation (8.301).

In §7 we shall discuss the quantum mechanical counterpart of equation (8.314) and then we shall also discuss how the law of corresponding states has been used to predict properties of as yet uninvestigated substances.

§4. Quantum Mechanical Theory of the Equation of State. The situation in quantum mechanics is not very different from the one in classical theory. Once again we must obtain an expression for the grand potential q and the equation of state follows then directly from equation (8.101).

Let $\mathcal{H}_\mathfrak{n}$ be the Hamiltonian of a system of $\mathfrak{n}$ particles; it is the operator corresponding to the classical expression (8.102). Instead of equation (8.104) we now have for e^q from equations (7.402) and (7.403) on page 156

$$e^q = \text{Trace } e^{\mathfrak{n}\nu - \mu\mathcal{H}}, \tag{8.401}$$

$$e^q = \sum_{\mathfrak{n}=0}^{\infty} e^{\mathfrak{n}\nu} \text{Trace } e^{-\mu\mathcal{H}_\mathfrak{n}}, \tag{8.402}$$

$$e^q = \sum_{\mathfrak{n}=0}^{\infty} e^{\mathfrak{n}\nu} \sum_{n} e^{-\mu E(\mathfrak{n};n)} \tag{8.403}$$

We must bear in mind in dealing with equations (8.402) and (8.403) that in the case of Boltzmann statistics we must add an extra factor $1/\mathfrak{n}!$ in order that the Boltzmann statistics becomes, indeed, the limiting case of

† *Loc. cit.*

the Bose-Einstein or Fermi-Dirac statistics (compare the remarks on p. 76).

It need hardly be emphasized that the exact calculation of all energy levels $E(\mathfrak{n};n)$ is a practically impossible task and we must hope that, at any rate in the case of a dilute gas, other methods might give us useful approximations. This, in fact, turns out to be the case, as we shall see in this section.

We introduce again functions W_N, this time by putting

$$N! \text{ Trace } e^{-\mu\mathcal{H}_N} = \int W_N d\mathbf{x}_1 \cdots d\mathbf{x}_N. \tag{8.404}$$

From this equation it follows that

$$W_N(\mathbf{x}_1,\cdots,\mathbf{x}_N) = N! \sum_n \varphi_n^* e^{-\mu\mathcal{H}_N} \varphi_n, \tag{8.405}$$

where the φ_n are a complete set of orthonormal functions. One must be extremely careful at this juncture, since it is here that the differences between the Boltzmann, Bose-Einstein, and Fermi-Dirac statistics enter. The whole of the complete set of orthonormal functions is involved in the case of Boltzmann statistics, but only symmetric or antisymmetric functions may be included in the cases of Bose-Einstein or Fermi-Dirac statistics. Moreover, in the case of Boltzmann statistics we must introduce the extra factor $1/N!$ mentioned a few paragraphs ago and take, instead of equation (8.405),

$$W_{N,\text{Bo}} = \sum_n \varphi_n^* e^{-\mu\mathcal{H}_N} \varphi_n. \tag{8.406}$$

The sum on the right-hand side of equation (8.405) is called a *Slatersum*, since Slater first introduced these sums in quantum statistics.†

Comparing equations (8.402), (8.404), (8.405), (8.106), and (8.109), we see that the W_N here play the same role as in §1. We can again introduce functions U_N, using equations (8.110). If we can prove that as soon as the N atoms involved in the U_N or W_N form two clusters of, respectively, N_1 and N_2 atoms

$$W_N = W_{N_1} \cdot W_{N_2}, \tag{8.407}$$

the U_N will again be zero unless all N atoms belong to one cluster. We shall prove this property of the W_N presently. Once this is proved, we can follow the analysis of §1 step by step and the final result will again be equation (8.116), the only difference being that we now have slightly different equations for the U_N and W_N.

† J. C. Slater, Phys. Rev., **38**, 237, 1931.

In order to prove the product property of the W_N we use an argument due to Kramers. Introduce the functions

$$\Delta_{N,\mathrm{Bo}}(\mathbf{x}_k,\mathbf{x}_k') = \sum_n \varphi_n^*(\mathbf{x}_k')\varphi_n(\mathbf{x}_k), \tag{8.408}$$

$$\Delta_{N,\mathrm{BE}}(\mathbf{x}_k,\mathbf{x}_k') = \frac{1}{N!}\sum_{\mathrm{P}}\sum_n \varphi_n^*(\mathbf{x}_k')\varphi_n(\mathbf{x}_{\mathrm{P}k}), \tag{8.409}$$

$$\Delta_{N,\mathrm{FD}}(\mathbf{x}_k,\mathbf{x}_k') = \frac{1}{N!}\sum_{\mathrm{P}}\epsilon_{\mathrm{P}}\sum_n \varphi_n^*(\mathbf{x}_k')\varphi_n(\mathbf{x}_{\mathrm{P}k}), \tag{8.410}$$

where $\mathbf{x}_k$ and $\mathbf{x}_k'$ stand for the N $\mathbf{x}_i$ and $\mathbf{x}_i'$, where Pk stands for a permutation of the k, where $\sum_{\mathrm{P}}$ indicates a summation over all $N!$ possible permutations, and where ϵ_{P} is again $+1$ or -1 according to whether the permutation of the k is even or odd. It is seen from equations (8.409) and (8.410) that we have carefully selected only those φ_n which are either completely symmetrical or completely antisymmetrical in the $\mathbf{x}_k$.

If the φ_n form a complete set of orthonormal functions we have†

$$\sum_n \varphi_n^*(\mathbf{x}_k')\varphi_n(\mathbf{x}_k) = \prod_{k=1}^{N} \delta(\mathbf{x}_k' - \mathbf{x}_k), \tag{8.411}$$

with

$$\delta(\mathbf{x}' - \mathbf{x}) = \delta(x' - x)\delta(y' - y)\delta(z' - z), \tag{8.412}$$

where the δ's on the right-hand side are the Dirac δ-functions (see p. 106).

Substituting equation (8.411) into equations (8.408) to (8.410), we have

$$\Delta_{N,\mathrm{Bo}}(\mathbf{x}_k,\mathbf{x}_k') = \prod_k \delta(\mathbf{x}_k' - \mathbf{x}_k), \tag{8.413}$$

$$\Delta_{N,\mathrm{BE}}(\mathbf{x}_k,\mathbf{x}_k') = \frac{1}{N!}\sum_{\mathrm{P}}\prod_k \delta(\mathbf{x}_k' - \mathbf{x}_{\mathrm{P}k}), \tag{8.414}$$

$$\Delta_{N,\mathrm{FD}}(\mathbf{x}_k,\mathbf{x}_k') = \frac{1}{N!}\sum_{\mathrm{P}}\epsilon_{\mathrm{P}}\prod_k \delta(\mathbf{x}_k' - \mathbf{x}_{\mathrm{P}k}). \tag{8.415}$$

We can now write the equations for W_N in the following form

$$W_{N,\mathrm{Bo}} = \left[e^{-\mu\mathcal{H}_N}\prod_k \delta(\mathbf{x}_k' - \mathbf{x}_k)\right]_{\mathbf{x}_k'=\mathbf{x}_k}, \tag{8.416}$$

$$W_{N,\mathrm{BE}} = \left[e^{-\mu\mathcal{H}_N}\sum_{\mathrm{P}}\prod_k \delta(\mathbf{x}_k' - \mathbf{x}_{\mathrm{P}k})\right]_{\mathbf{x}_k'=\mathbf{x}_k}, \tag{8.417}$$

$$W_{N,\mathrm{FD}} = \left[e^{-\mu\mathcal{H}_N}\sum_{\mathrm{P}}\epsilon_{\mathrm{P}}\prod_k \delta(\mathbf{x}_k' - \mathbf{x}_{\mathrm{P}k})\right]_{\mathbf{x}_k'=\mathbf{x}_k}, \tag{8.418}$$

where the right-hand side of these equations must be read as meaning that the operator $\mathcal{H}_N$ operates on the $\mathbf{x}_k$ only and after this operation all $\mathbf{x}_k'$ are put equal to the corresponding $\mathbf{x}_k$.

† See, e.g., H. A. Kramers, Hand- u. Jahrb. d. Chem. Phys., Vol. I, Leipzig 1938, p. 128.

Let us first consider a perfect gas. We then have

$$\mathcal{H}_N = \mathcal{T}_N = -\frac{\hbar^2}{2m}\sum_k \nabla_k^2, \tag{8.419}$$

where $\mathcal{T}_N$ is the kinetic energy operator and ∇_k^2 the Laplacian corresponding to the kth atom. Consider now $e^{-\mu(\hbar^2/2m)\nabla^2}\delta(\mathbf{x}'-\mathbf{x})$. Using for the δ-function its Fourier integral in the form

$$\delta(\mathbf{x}'-\mathbf{x}) = \lim_{M\to\infty}\iiint_{-M}^{+M} e^{2\pi i\mathbf{k}\cdot(\mathbf{x}'-\mathbf{x})}d\mathbf{k}, \tag{8.420}$$

we get

$$e^{-\mu\frac{\hbar^2}{2m}\nabla^2}\delta(\mathbf{x}'-\mathbf{x}) = \lim_{M\to\infty}\iiint_{-M}^{+M} e^{-\mu\frac{\hbar^2}{2m}\mathbf{k}^2+2\pi i\mathbf{k}\cdot(\mathbf{x}'-\mathbf{x})}\,d\mathbf{k}$$

$$= \frac{1}{v_0}e^{-\frac{m}{2\hbar^2\mu}(\mathbf{x}'-\mathbf{x})^2}. \tag{8.421}$$

Substituting from equation (8.421) into equations (8.416) to (8.418), we get

$$W_{N,\mathrm{Bo}} = v_0^{-N}, \tag{8.422}$$

$$W_{N,\mathrm{BE}} = v_0^{-N}\sum_{\mathrm{P}} e^{-\frac{m}{2\hbar^2\mu}\sum_k(\mathbf{x}_k-\mathbf{x}_{\mathrm{P}k})^2}, \tag{8.423}$$

$$W_{N,\mathrm{FD}} = v_0^{-N}\sum_{\mathrm{P}} \epsilon_{\mathrm{P}} e^{-\frac{m}{2\hbar^2\mu}\sum_k(\mathbf{x}_k-\mathbf{x}_{\mathrm{P}k})^2}. \tag{8.424}$$

Suppose now that the N atoms form two clusters consisting of N_1 and N_2 atoms. In the quantum mechanical case we can only say that two atoms are no longer interacting when not only $r_{kl} > D$, but also $r_{kl} > v_0^{1/3}$. The last condition expresses the fact that it is only possible to consider two atoms as noninteracting if they are further apart than the De Broglie wavelength corresponding to their relative motion, since otherwise quantum mechanical diffraction effects will occur. All the N_1 atoms in the first cluster are thus supposed to be separated from all the N_2 atoms in the second cluster by a distance at least equal to $v_0^{1/3}$. (Since we are at the moment considering the case of a perfect gas, the range of the potential energy function does not yet enter into the discussion.) If now the N atoms form two clusters, all terms where the kth atom and the Pkth atom are in different clusters will be negligibly small and we can write equations (8.422) to (8.424) in the form

$$W_{N,\mathrm{Bo}} = v_0^{-N} = v_0^{-N_1}\cdot v_0^{-N_2} = (W_{N_1,\mathrm{Bo}})\cdot(W_{N_2,\mathrm{Bo}}), \tag{8.425}$$

$$W_{N,\mathrm{BE}} = \left(v_0^{-N_1}\sum_{\mathrm{P}_1} e^{-\frac{m}{2\hbar^2\mu}\sum_{k_1}(\mathbf{x}_{k_1}-\mathbf{x}_{\mathrm{P}_1k_1})^2}\right)\left(v_0^{-N_2}\sum_{\mathrm{P}_2} e^{-\frac{m}{2\hbar^2\mu}\sum_{k_2}(\mathbf{x}_{k_2}-\mathbf{x}_{\mathrm{P}_2k_2})^2}\right)$$

$$= (W_{N_1,\mathrm{BE}})(W_{N_2,\mathrm{BE}}), \tag{8.426}$$

$$W_{N,\mathrm{FD}} = \left(v_0{}^{-N_1}\sum_{\mathrm{P}_1}\epsilon_{\mathrm{P}_1}e^{-\frac{m}{2\hbar^2\mu}\sum_{k_1}(\mathbf{x}_{k_1}-\mathbf{x}_{\mathrm{P}_1k_1})^2}\right)\left(v_0{}^{-N_2}\sum_{\mathrm{P}_2}\epsilon_{\mathrm{P}_2}e^{-\frac{m}{2\hbar^2\mu}\sum_{k_2}(\mathbf{x}_{k_2}-\mathbf{x}_{\mathrm{P}_2k_2})^2}\right)$$

$$= (W_{N_1,\mathrm{FD}})(W_{N_2,\mathrm{FD}}), \qquad \mathbf{(8.427)}$$

where the sums over P_1 (and k_1) and P_2 (and k_2) extend only over the first and second cluster, respectively.

Let us now assume that $\mathcal{H}_N$ also contains a term corresponding to interactions. The proof of equation (8.407) now consists of two steps. First of all we note that, if the N atoms fall into two clusters, we have

$$\mathcal{H}_N = \mathcal{H}_{N_1} + \mathcal{H}_{N_2}, \quad \text{or} \quad e^{-\mu\mathcal{H}_N} = e^{-\mu\mathcal{H}_{N_1}}e^{-\mu\mathcal{H}_{N_2}}. \qquad \mathbf{(8.428)}$$

This equation in itself is sufficient to prove the product property of $W_{N,\mathrm{Bo}}$. In the cases of the Bose-Einstein and Fermi-Dirac formulae we have first of all the validity of equation (8.428) and, secondly, we will get exponentials like those in equations (8.423) and (8.424) due to the kinetic energy operator and once more all terms with the kth and the Pkth atom in different clusters will give rise to negligible terms.

We have thus proved the product property of W_N and formula (8.116) for q follows in a straightforward manner.

Before discussing in the next sections in more detail the quantum mechanical expression for the second virial coefficient we shall briefly sketch the proof that, indeed, the formulae of §1 are limiting cases of the formulae obtained in the present section. We shall use a variation of the proof due to Kirkwood. The method used is due to Kramers and we shall describe it more fully in the next section.

Using equations (8.405), (8.408), and (8.410), we can write W_N in the form

$$W_N = N!e^{-\mu\mathcal{H}_N}\Delta, \qquad \mathbf{(8.429)}$$

where Δ is given by equation (8.414) or (8.415). From equation (8.429) we see that in the limit $\mu \to 0$, W_N goes over into $N!\Delta$, or, writing $\mathbf{x}_i$ for $\mathbf{x}_1, \cdots, \mathbf{x}_N$,

$$N!\Delta(\mathbf{x}_i,\mathbf{x}_i) = [W_N(\mathbf{x}_i;\mu)]_{\mu=0}, \qquad \mathbf{(8.430)}$$

and we can write equation (8.429) as follows

$$W_N(\mathbf{x}_i;\mu) = e^{-\mu\mathcal{H}_N}W_N(\mathbf{x}_i;0). \qquad \mathbf{(8.431)}$$

It can now easily be verified that the function $W_N(\mathbf{x}_i;\mu)$ must satisfy the so-called Bloch equation†

$$\frac{\partial W_N}{\partial \mu} = -\mathcal{H}_N W_N. \qquad \mathbf{(8.432)}$$

† F. Bloch, Z. Physik, **74**, 295, 1932.

Introducing

$$\tau = \frac{\hbar}{\sqrt{2m}}, \qquad \boldsymbol{\xi}_k = \frac{\mathbf{x}_k}{\tau}, \qquad \Phi = \sum \phi(r_{kl}), \tag{8.433}$$

and ∇_k' as the vector with components $\partial/\partial\xi_k$, $\partial/\partial\eta_k$, and $\partial/\partial\zeta_k$, we can write equation (8.432) in the form

$$\frac{\partial W_N}{\partial \mu} = \left[\sum_k \nabla_k'^2 - \Phi\right] W_N. \tag{8.434}$$

We now introduce functions g_N by the equations

$$g_N(\mathbf{x}_i,\mathbf{x}_{i0}) = \ln\left\{e^{-\mu\mathcal{H}_N} \prod_{k=1}^{N} \delta(\mathbf{x}_k - \mathbf{x}_{k0})\right\}, \tag{8.435}$$

so that

$$W_N = \sum_{\mathrm{P}} \delta_{\mathrm{P}} e^{g_N(\mathbf{x}_i,\mathbf{x}_{\mathrm{P}i})}, \tag{8.436}$$

where

$$\left.\begin{aligned} \delta_{\mathrm{P}} &= 1 \quad \text{in the Bose-Einstein case,} \\ \text{and} \qquad \delta_{\mathrm{P}} &= \epsilon_{\mathrm{P}} \quad \text{in the Fermi-Dirac case.} \end{aligned}\right\} \tag{8.437}$$

It is easily verified that the g_N satisfy the equations

$$\frac{\partial g_N}{\partial \mu} = \sum_k \nabla_k'^2 g_N + \sum_k (\nabla_k' g_N)^2 - \Phi g_N. \tag{8.438}$$

If Φ were a constant, this equation would be solved by the expression

$$g_N = -\frac{1}{4\mu} \sum_k (\boldsymbol{\xi}_k - \boldsymbol{\xi}_{k0})^2 - N \ln v_0 - \mu\Phi, \tag{8.439}$$

where v_0 is given by equation (8.107), and we have used the fact that $g_N(0)$ is determined by equations (8.435) and (8.430). We have also used the fact that for constant Φ we can use the result of equation (8.421).

If Φ is not a constant, it is possible to show (compare similar considerations in the next section) that g_N can be written as

$$g_N = -\frac{1}{4\mu} \sum_k (\boldsymbol{\xi}_k - \boldsymbol{\xi}_{k0})^2 - N \ln v_0 - \mu\Phi + \text{power series in } \mu\tau^2. \tag{8.440}$$

The first term on the right-hand side of equation (8.440) can be written as

$$-\frac{1}{4\mu} \sum_k (\boldsymbol{\xi}_k - \boldsymbol{\xi}_{k0})^2 = -\frac{\pi}{v_0^{2/3}} \sum_k (\mathbf{x}_k - \mathbf{x}_{k0})^2,$$

and we see that in the classical limit, where we may assume $v_0 \to 0$, only those terms in the sum on the right-hand side of equation (8.436) will enter where all $\mathbf{x}_{Pi}$ are equal to $\mathbf{x}_i$, that is, only the identical permutation will enter. Since $4\pi\mu\tau^2$ is equal to $v_0^{2/3}$ we see that in the classical limit $(v_0 \to 0)$

$$\ln W_N \to g_N(\mathbf{x}_i,\mathbf{x}_i) \to -N \ln v_0 - \mu\Phi,$$

which gives us the classical expression (8.109).

§5. The Second Virial Coefficient in Quantum Statistics at High Temperatures. Using equations (8.203), (8.115), (8.114), (8.113), (8.405), and (8.408) to (8.410), we have for the second virial coefficient the equation

$$\begin{aligned} B &= -Nv_0 b_2 \\ &= -\frac{Nv_0^2}{2V}\int U_2 d\mathbf{x}_1 d\mathbf{x}_2 \\ &= -\frac{Nv_0^2}{2V}\int [W_2(\mathbf{x}_1,\mathbf{x}_2) - W_1(\mathbf{x}_1)W_1(\mathbf{x}_2)]d\mathbf{x}_1 d\mathbf{x}_2 \end{aligned}$$

or

$$B = -\frac{Nv_0^2}{2V}\int [2e^{-\mu\mathcal{H}_2}\Delta_{2,\mathrm{qu}}(\mathbf{x}_i,\mathbf{x}_i') - e^{-\mu\mathcal{T}_2}\Delta_{2,\mathrm{Bo}}(\mathbf{x}_i,\mathbf{x}_i')]_{\mathbf{x}_i=\mathbf{x}_i'} d\mathbf{x}_1 d\mathbf{x}_2, \tag{8.501}$$

where $\Delta_{2,\mathrm{qu}}$ is either $\Delta_{2,\mathrm{BE}}$ or $\Delta_{2,\mathrm{FD}}$ according to the case which we are considering. From equation (8.501) we see that the quantum effects and the effects due to the interactions between the atoms are mixed and not simply additive as we might perhaps have expected. It is possible to split B into two parts, the first part corresponding to a perfect quantum gas and the second one containing both quantum and interaction effects. We write for this purpose

$$B = B_{\mathrm{perf}} + B_{\mathrm{imp}}, \tag{8.502}$$

$$B_{\mathrm{perf}} = -\frac{Nv_0^2}{2V}\int [e^{-\mu\mathcal{T}_2}(2\Delta_{2,\mathrm{qu}} - \Delta_{2,\mathrm{Bo}})]_{\mathbf{x}_i=\mathbf{x}_i'} d\mathbf{x}_1 d\mathbf{x}_2, \tag{8.503}$$

$$B_{\mathrm{imp}} = -\frac{Nv_0^2}{V}\int [(e^{-\mu\mathcal{H}_2} - e^{-\mu\mathcal{T}_2})\Delta_{2,\mathrm{qu}}]_{\mathbf{x}_i=\mathbf{x}_i'} d\mathbf{x}_1 d\mathbf{x}_2. \tag{8.504}$$

Using equations (8.413) to (8.415) and equation (8.421), we have for B_{perf}

$$\begin{aligned} B_{\mathrm{perf}} &= \mp\frac{Nv_0^2}{2V}\int [e^{-\mu\mathcal{T}_2}\delta(\mathbf{x}_1 - \mathbf{x}_2')\delta(\mathbf{x}_2 - \mathbf{x}_1')]_{\mathbf{x}_i=\mathbf{x}_i'} d\mathbf{x}_1 d\mathbf{x}_2 \\ &= \mp\frac{N}{2V}\int e^{-\frac{m}{\hbar^2\mu}(\mathbf{x}_1-\mathbf{x}_2)^2} d\mathbf{x}_1 d\mathbf{x}_2 \\ &= \mp\frac{N}{2}\int e^{-\frac{m}{\hbar^2\mu}\mathbf{x}^2} d\mathbf{x} = \mp\frac{N}{2}\left(\frac{\pi\hbar^2\mu}{m}\right)^{3/2}, \end{aligned}$$

or

$$B_{\text{perf}} = \mp \frac{N v_0}{2^{5/2}}, \tag{8.505}$$

where the upper sign refers throughout to the Bose-Einstein case and the lower sign to the Fermi-Dirac case. It can easily be verified that equation (8.505) is in agreement with the results of equations (4.620) and (4.711) on pages 87 and 90.

In order to evaluate B at high temperatures it is more convenient to use the complete expression (8.501). The second term inside the square brackets can be calculated using equations (8.413) and (8.421) and we get

$$B = \frac{N}{2V}\int (1 - 2v_0{}^2[e^{-\mu\mathcal{H}_2}\Delta_{2,\text{qu}}]_{\mathbf{x}_i=\mathbf{x}_i'})\,d\mathbf{x}_1 d\mathbf{x}_2. \tag{8.506}$$

We can now introduce instead of $\mathbf{x}_1$ and $\mathbf{x}_2$ the coordinates of the center of gravity and the components of the vector $\mathbf{x}_{12}$ ($\mathbf{x}_{12} = \mathbf{x}_2 - \mathbf{x}_1$). Integration over the center of gravity coordinates and substitution of expressions (8.414) and (8.415) for $\Delta_{2,\text{qu}}$ give us the following equation for B,

$$B = \frac{N}{2}\int (1 - e^{-\mu\phi(r_{12})}F(\mathbf{x}_{12}))\,d\mathbf{x}_{12}, \tag{8.507}$$

where†

$$e^{-\mu\phi}\,F(\mathbf{x}) = \left(\frac{\mu h^2}{\pi m}\right)^{3/2}[e^{-\mu(\mathcal{T}_{12}+\phi)}(\delta(\mathbf{x}-\mathbf{x}') \pm \delta(\mathbf{x}+\mathbf{x}'))]_{\mathbf{x}=\mathbf{x}'} \tag{8.508}$$

with upper and lower sign referring respectively to the Bose-Einstein and Fermi-Dirac cases and with

$$\mathcal{T}_{12} = -\frac{\hbar^2}{m}\nabla^2. \tag{8.509‡}$$

We now use the method of the end of the preceding section. Equation (8.508) is of the form

$$f(\mathbf{x};\mu) = e^{-\mu(\mathcal{T}_{12}+\phi)}f(\mathbf{x};0), \tag{8.510}$$

and $f(\mathbf{x};\mu)$ satisfies the Bloch equation§

$$\frac{\partial f}{\partial \mu} = -(\mathcal{T}_{12} + \phi)f = \frac{\hbar^2}{m}\nabla^2 f - \phi f. \tag{8.511}$$

† In the derivation of equations (8.507) and (8.508) we use equation (8.421).

‡ The mass is now the reduced mass; hence a difference of a factor 2 in the coefficient of ∇^2.

§ We may draw attention to the fact that equation (8.511) can be interpreted as an equation for heat transport. The variable μ plays the role of the time coordinate, $\hbar^2/m$ that of the thermal conductivity, f that of the temperature, and $-\phi f$ that of the (negative) energy output at a point with coordinates $\mathbf{x}$.

We introduce a function $g(\mathbf{x},\mathbf{x}_0)$ by the equation

$$g(\mathbf{x},\mathbf{x}_0) = \ln [e^{-\mu(\mathcal{J}_{12}+\phi)}\delta(\mathbf{x} - \mathbf{x}_0)], \tag{8.512}$$

so that

$$e^{-\mu\phi}F(\mathbf{x}) = \left(\frac{\mu h^2}{\pi m}\right)^{3/2} [e^{g(\mathbf{x},\mathbf{x})} \pm e^{g(\mathbf{x},-\mathbf{x})}]. \tag{8.513}$$

Introducing new variables† by putting

$$\tau = \frac{\hbar}{\sqrt{m}}, \qquad \mathbf{x} = \tau\boldsymbol{\xi}, \qquad \mathbf{x}_0 = \tau\boldsymbol{\xi}_0, \qquad \nabla' = \tau\nabla, \tag{8.514}$$

we have for g the equation

$$\frac{\partial g}{\partial \mu} = \nabla'^2 g + (\nabla' g)^2 - \phi, \tag{8.515}$$

which must be solved with the boundary condition

$$g(\mu=0) = \ln \delta(\mathbf{x} - \mathbf{x}_0). \tag{8.516}$$

The solution of equation (8.515) in the case of constant ϕ is (compare equation [8.439])

$$g = -\frac{(\boldsymbol{\xi} - \boldsymbol{\xi}_0)^2}{4\mu} - \frac{3}{2}\ln 4\pi\mu\tau^2 - \mu\phi, \tag{8.517}$$

and in the case of variable ϕ we write

$$g = -\frac{(\boldsymbol{\xi} - \boldsymbol{\xi}_0)^2}{4\mu} - \frac{3}{2}\ln 4\pi\mu\tau^2 + \sum_{n=1}^{\infty} a_n\mu^n. \tag{8.518}$$

Substitution of this expression into equation (8.515) gives us the following equations for the a_n, which can be solved successively,

$$\left.\begin{aligned}
(\boldsymbol{\sigma}\cdot\nabla'\sigma a_1) &= -\sigma\phi,\\
(\boldsymbol{\sigma}\cdot\nabla'\sigma a_2) &= \sigma^2\nabla'^2 a_1,\\
(\boldsymbol{\sigma}\cdot\nabla'\sigma a_3) &= \sigma^3\nabla'^2 a_2 + \sigma^3(\nabla' a_1)^2,\\
(\boldsymbol{\sigma}\cdot\nabla'\sigma a_4) &= \sigma^4\nabla'^2 a_3 + 2\sigma^4(\nabla' a_1)\cdot(\nabla' a_2),\\
(\boldsymbol{\sigma}\cdot\nabla'\sigma a_5) &= \sigma^5\nabla'^2 a_4 + \sigma^5(\nabla' a_2)^2 + 2\sigma^5(\nabla' a_1)\cdot(\nabla' a_3),\\
&\cdots\cdots\cdots\cdots\cdots\cdots
\end{aligned}\right\} \tag{8.519}$$

where

$$\boldsymbol{\sigma} = \boldsymbol{\xi} - \boldsymbol{\xi}_0 \quad \text{and} \quad \sigma = |\boldsymbol{\xi} - \boldsymbol{\xi}_0|. \tag{8.520}$$

† It should be noted that the τ of equations (8.514) and (8.433) differ by a factor $\sqrt{2}$.

These equations are all of the form

$$(\boldsymbol{\sigma} \cdot \nabla' A) = \sigma B(\sigma,\boldsymbol{\omega}), \tag{8.521}$$

where

$$\boldsymbol{\omega} = \frac{\boldsymbol{\sigma}}{\sigma}, \tag{8.522}$$

with the solution

$$A = \int_0^{\sigma} B(\sigma,\boldsymbol{\omega})d\sigma, \tag{8.523}$$

where during the integration $\boldsymbol{\omega}$ is kept fixed.

We are interested in the solution of g for small values of μ (or high temperatures). At high temperatures we may expect that quantum effects will enter as small corrections and we expand now $\phi(\tau\boldsymbol{\sigma})$ in a Taylor series

$$\phi = \sum_{n=0}^{\infty} \frac{\tau^n}{n!} (\boldsymbol{\sigma} \cdot \nabla_0)^n \phi, \tag{8.524}$$

where ∇_0 indicates that after ∇ has operated on ϕ, the value for $\sigma = 0$ must be taken.

Using equations (8.519), (8.523), and (8.524), we find after some tedious though straightforward calculations the following expansions which are given up to the fourth power of τ.†

$$\left.\begin{aligned}
a_1 &= -\phi_0 - \frac{\tau}{2}(\boldsymbol{\sigma} \cdot \nabla_0)\phi - \frac{\tau^2}{3!}(\boldsymbol{\sigma} \cdot \nabla_0)^2\phi \\
&\quad - \frac{\tau^3}{4!}(\boldsymbol{\sigma} \cdot \nabla_0)^3\phi - \frac{\tau^4}{5!}(\boldsymbol{\sigma} \cdot \nabla_0)^4\phi + \cdots, \\
a_2 &= -\frac{\tau^2}{6}\nabla_0{}^2\phi - \frac{\tau^3}{12}(\boldsymbol{\sigma} \cdot \nabla_0)\nabla_0{}^2\phi - \frac{\tau^4}{40}(\boldsymbol{\sigma} \cdot \nabla_0)^2\nabla_0{}^2\phi + \cdots, \\
a_3 &= \frac{\tau^2}{12}(\nabla_0\phi)^2 + \frac{\tau^3}{12}(\nabla_0\phi \cdot (\boldsymbol{\sigma} \cdot \nabla_0)\nabla_0\phi) \\
&\quad + \frac{\tau^4}{360}[-6\nabla_0{}^4\phi + 9(\nabla_0\phi \cdot (\boldsymbol{\sigma} \cdot \nabla_0)^2\nabla_0\phi) \\
&\quad + 8((\boldsymbol{\sigma} \cdot \nabla_0)\nabla_0\phi)^2] + \cdots, \\
a_4 &= \frac{\tau^4}{180}[\nabla_0{}^2(\nabla_0\phi)^2 + 4(\nabla_0\phi \cdot \nabla_0{}^3\phi)] + \cdots, \\
a_5 &= -\frac{\tau^4}{120}(\nabla_0\phi \cdot \nabla_0(\nabla_0\phi)^2) + \cdots.
\end{aligned}\right\} \tag{8.525}$$

† In deriving equations (8.525) one must bear in mind that the ∇' in equations (8.519) operate only on σ and that $\nabla'^2((\boldsymbol{\sigma} \cdot \nabla_0)\nabla_0\phi)^2 = \nabla_0{}^2(\nabla_0\phi)^2 - 2(\nabla_0\phi \cdot \nabla_0{}^3\phi)$.

In order to obtain the function $F(\mathbf{x})$ we need both $g(\mathbf{x},\mathbf{x})$ and $g(\mathbf{x},-\mathbf{x})$. From equation (8.517) we see that $g(\mathbf{x},-\mathbf{x})$ will contain a term $-\mathbf{x}^2/\mu\tau^2$ and the corresponding term in $F(\mathbf{x})$ will contain a factor $e^{-\mathbf{x}^2/\mu\tau^2}$ which is negligible at the temperatures and dilutions where our expansions can be used. We may thus neglect this term, which corresponds to the influence of the exclusion principle and are now only interested in $g(\mathbf{x},\mathbf{x})$ for which we have from equations (8.517) and (8.525)

$$g(\mathbf{x},\mathbf{x}) + \frac{3}{2}\ln 4\pi\mu\tau^2 + \mu\phi = \mu^2\tau^2\left[-\frac{1}{6}\nabla^2\phi + \frac{\mu}{12}(\nabla\phi)^2\right]$$

$$+\mu^3\tau^4\left[-\frac{1}{60}\nabla^4\phi + \frac{\mu}{180}\nabla^2(\nabla\phi)^2 + \frac{\mu}{45}(\nabla\phi\cdot\nabla^3\phi) - \frac{\mu^2}{120}(\nabla\phi\cdot\nabla(\nabla\phi)^2)\right] + \cdots. \tag{8.526}$$

Substituting into equation (8.513) we have finally, after expanding the exponentials,

$$F(\mathbf{x}) = 1 + \frac{\hbar^2}{m}\left[-\frac{\mu^2}{6}\nabla^2\phi + \frac{\mu^3}{12}(\nabla\phi)^2\right] + \frac{\hbar^4}{m^2}\left[-\frac{\mu^3}{60}\nabla^4\phi\right.$$
$$+\frac{\mu^4}{360}\{2\nabla^2(\nabla\phi)^2 + 8(\nabla\phi\cdot\nabla^3\phi) + 5(\nabla^2\phi)^2\}$$
$$\left.-\frac{\mu^5}{360}\{5\nabla^2\phi(\nabla\phi)^2 + 3(\nabla\phi\cdot\nabla(\nabla\phi)^2)\} + \frac{\mu^6}{288}(\nabla\phi)^4\right] + \cdots. \tag{8.527}$$

Substituting expression (8.527) into equation (8.507), we obtain for B a power series in $\hbar^2$,

$$B = B_{\text{cl}} + B_1 + B_2 + \cdots, \tag{8.528}$$

where B_{cl} is the classical expression for the second virial coefficient and where B_n is proportional to $\hbar^{2n}$. In the case of helium (and hydrogen) the contributions from B_1 and B_2 cannot be neglected. In the last section of the present chapter we shall discuss how De Boer used a comparison between B given by equation (8.528) and the experimentally determined second virial coefficient to obtain the potential energy function for helium. It turns out that one only needs terms up to $\hbar^4$ in B. Kramers has drawn attention to the fact that one should be extremely wary about including higher powers of $\hbar$, since it is far from certain that the power series in $\hbar$ will converge.†

§6. The Second Virial Coefficient in Quantum Statistics at Low Temperatures. At low temperatures we can use formula (8.502) for B and we have from

† Compare the analogous position of the power series which occurs in the WKB method.

equations (8.502), (8.505), and (8.504)

$$B = B_{\text{perf}} + B_{\text{imp}}, \tag{8.601}$$

$$B_{\text{perf}} = \mp \frac{Nv_0}{2^{5/2}}, \tag{8.602}$$

$$B_{\text{imp}} = -\frac{Nv_0{}^2}{V}\int\left[(e^{-\mu\mathcal{H}_2} - e^{-\mu\mathcal{T}_2})\Delta_{2,\text{qu}}\right]_{\mathbf{x}_i=\mathbf{x}_i'} d\mathbf{x}_1 d\mathbf{x}_2. \tag{8.603}$$

Our task is now the evaluation of B_{imp}. From equations (8.409), (8.410), (8.405), and (8.404) it follows that B_{imp} can be written in the form

$$B_{\text{imp}} = -\frac{Nv_0{}^2}{V}[\text{Trace } e^{-\mu\mathcal{H}_2} - \text{Trace } e^{-\mu\mathcal{T}_2}], \tag{8.604}$$

or, introducing as the φ_n the characteristic functions of $\mathcal{H}_2$ and $\mathcal{T}_2$, respectively,

$$B_{\text{imp}} = -\frac{Nv_0{}^2}{V}[\sum_k e^{-\mu\epsilon_k} - \sum_k e^{-\mu\epsilon_k{}^0}], \tag{8.605}$$

where the ϵ_k are the characteristic values of the Hamiltonian of two particles including a potential energy term while the $\epsilon_k{}^0$ are those of the same Hamiltonian without the potential energy term.

Let us assume for a moment that the volume V is not finite, but infinite. Introducing center of gravity and relative coordinates,

$$\mathbf{X} = \tfrac{1}{2}(\mathbf{x}_1 + \mathbf{x}_2), \qquad \mathbf{x}_{12} = \mathbf{x}_2 - \mathbf{x}_1, \tag{8.606}$$

we can write the characteristic functions of $\mathcal{H}_2$ and $\mathcal{T}_2$ in the form†

$$\varphi_k(\mathbf{x}_1,\mathbf{x}_2) = e^{\frac{i}{\hbar}(\mathbf{P}\cdot\mathbf{X})}\frac{R_{n,l}(r)}{r}\delta_l Y_l{}^m(\boldsymbol{\omega}), \tag{8.607}$$

$$\epsilon_k = \frac{\mathbf{P}^2}{4m} + E_{n,l}, \tag{8.608}$$

where $r = |\mathbf{x}_{12}|$, $\boldsymbol{\omega} = \mathbf{x}_{12}/r$, $Y_l{}^m$ is a spherical harmonic, and

$$\left.\begin{aligned} &\delta_l = 1, \quad l = \text{even}; \quad \delta_l = 0, \quad l = \text{odd for the Bose-Einstein case,}\\ &\delta_l = 0, \quad l = \text{even}; \quad \delta_l = 1, \quad l = \text{odd for the Fermi-Dirac case.}\end{aligned}\right\} \tag{8.609}$$

† The reason for $4m$ instead of $2m$ in equation (8.608) is that the center of gravity moves with mass $2m$.

The fact that m has two different meanings in equations (8.607) and (8.608) should not be confusing.

The reason for the occurrence of δ_l is the fact that we can tolerate only completely symmetrical or completely antisymmetrical wave functions. Since at an interchange of $\mathbf{x}_1$ and $\mathbf{x}_2$, $\mathbf{X}$ and r remain unchanged, while $\boldsymbol{\omega}$ goes over into $-\boldsymbol{\omega}$, and since†

$$Y_l^m(\boldsymbol{\omega}) = (-1)^l Y_l^m(-\boldsymbol{\omega}), \tag{8.610}$$

the δ_l must be given by equation (8.609).

The functions $R_{n,l}$ satisfy the following equations:

$$\frac{d^2R}{dr^2} + \left[\frac{m}{\hbar^2}(E_{n,l} - \phi(r)) - \frac{l(l+1)}{r^2}\right]R = 0, \tag{8.611}$$

$$\frac{d^2R^0}{dr^2} + \left[\frac{m}{\hbar^2}E^0_{n,l} - \frac{l(l+1)}{r^2}\right]R^0 = 0, \tag{8.612}$$

where the first and second equation refer respectively to the case with and without interaction. The reason for m instead of $2m$ in equations (8.611) and (8.612) is that we are concerned with the reduced mass.

We shall assume for the sake of simplicity that there are no discrete levels. This assumption is certainly incorrect in the case of Ne and A, but there the temperatures involved are never so low that we cannot use the considerations of the preceding section. In the case of He it is still a moot point whether or not a bound state exists. If the values of κ and σ given in the table on page 179 are correct, there is no discrete level, but potential energy functions proposed by other authors‡ would lead to a stationary state. This would mean that at low temperatures part of the atoms will have formed diatomic molecules. The contribution to the second virial coefficient can easily be taken into account.

Up to this moment we have treated the energy spectrum as being continuous, while in actual fact it will be discrete due to the boundary conditions at the walls of the containing volume. We are thus indeed dealing with sums. We can write equation (8.605) as follows,§

$$B_{\text{imp}} = -\frac{Nv_0^2}{V}\left[\sum_{\text{c.o.g.}} e^{-\mu\epsilon_{\text{c.o.g.}}}\right]\left[\sum_l \delta_l(2l+1)\left\{\sum_n e^{-\mu E_{n,l}} - \sum_n e^{-\mu E^0_{n,l}}\right\}\right], \tag{8.613}$$

where the first sum on the right-hand side refers to the center of gravity

† See, e.g., H. A. Kramers, Hand- u. Jahrb. d. Chem. Phys., Vol. I, Leipzig 1938, p. 171, eq. (148).

‡ H. S. W. Massey and R. A. Buckingham, Proc. Roy. Soc. (London), **A168**, 378, 1938; **A169**, 205, 1938. R. A. Buckingham, J. Hamilton, and H. S. W. Massey, Proc. Roy. Soc. (London), **A179**, 103, 1941.

§ The factor $2l + 1$ in the second sum on the right-hand side of equation (8.613) derives from the degeneracy of the Y_l^m.

motion and can easily be evaluated, since it is the partition function of a free particle of mass $2m$ in a volume V,

$$\sum_{\text{c.o.g.}} e^{-\mu\epsilon_{\text{c.o.g.}}} = 2^{3/2}\frac{V}{v_0}. \tag{8.614}$$

Instead of the correct boundary condition, which would be that φ_k vanishes as soon as $\mathbf{x}_1$ or $\mathbf{x}_2$ comes outside the volume, we shall use the boundary conditions

$$R_{n,l}(r_0) = 0, \qquad R^0{}_{n,l}(r_0) = 0, \tag{8.615}$$

where r_0 is large compared to the range D of the potential energy.

If r_0 is sufficiently large, we can replace the summations over n by suitable integrations. The numbers of energy levels $E_{n,l}$ and $E^0{}_{n,l}$ between E and $E + dE$ may be denoted respectively by $g_1(E;l)dE$ and $g_2(E;l)dE$, and we shall write

$$g(E;l) = g_1(E;l) - g_2(E;l).$$

We then have from equations (8.613) and (8.614)

$$B_{\text{imp}} = -2^{3/2}Nv_0\sum_l \delta_l(2l+1)\int_0^\infty e^{-\mu E}g(E;l)dE. \tag{8.616}$$

We must now evaluate the function $g(E;l)$. It is advantageous to introduce instead of E the wave number k by the equation

$$k^2 = \frac{m}{\hbar^2}E, \tag{8.617}$$

so that equations (8.611), (8.612), and (8.616) become

$$\frac{d^2R}{dr^2} + \left\{k^2 - \frac{m}{\hbar^2}\phi(r) - \frac{l(l+1)}{r^2}\right\}R = 0, \tag{8.618}$$

$$\frac{d^2R^0}{dr^2} + \left(k^2 - \frac{l(l+1)}{r^2}\right)R^0 = 0, \tag{8.619}$$

$$B_{\text{imp}} = -2^{3/2}Nv_0\sum_l \delta_l(2l+1)\int_0^\infty e^{-\frac{\mu\hbar^2k^2}{m}}g(k;l)dk, \tag{8.620}$$

where $g(k;l)$ is now the density of the energy levels in the k-scale. This density can be determined by considering the behavior of R and R^0 for large values of r. In that case the term with $\phi(r)$ can be neglected and we have

$$R = \sin[kr + \eta(k,l)], \tag{8.621}$$

$$R^0 = \sin[kr + \eta^0(k,l)]. \tag{8.622}$$

The boundary conditions (8.615) then give us

$$kr_0 + \eta^0(k,l) = n\pi, \tag{8.623}$$

$$kr_0 + \eta(k,l) = n\pi. \tag{8.624}$$

Let Δk and Δk^0 be the change in wave number when n changes by one, so that we have

$$\frac{1}{\Delta k} = g_1(k;l), \qquad \frac{1}{\Delta k^0} = g_2(k;l), \tag{8.625}$$

and

$$g(k;l) = \frac{1}{\Delta k} - \frac{1}{\Delta k^0}\cdot \tag{8.626}$$

From equations (8.623) and (8.624) we have

$$\left(r_0 + \frac{\partial \eta^0}{\partial k}\right)\Delta k^0 = \pi, \tag{8.627}$$

$$\left(r_0 + \frac{\partial \eta}{\partial k}\right)\Delta k = \pi, \tag{8.628}$$

from which it follows that

$$g(k;l) = \frac{1}{\pi}\left(\frac{\partial \eta}{\partial k} - \frac{\partial \eta^0}{\partial k}\right)\cdot \tag{8.629}$$

The solution of equation (8.619) which vanishes for $r = 0$ (condition of regularity of the wave function at the origin) is given by the equation†

$$R^0 = \frac{\sqrt{\pi k r}}{2} J_{l+1/2}(kr) \underset{r\to\infty}{\longrightarrow} \sin\,(kr - \tfrac{1}{2}l\pi), \tag{8.630}$$

where J_n is the Bessel function of order n, and we see that η^0 is independent of k so that for B_{imp} we finally have from equations (8.620) and (8.629)

$$B_{\text{imp}} = -\frac{2^{3/2}}{\pi} N v_0 \sum_l \delta_l (2l+1) \int_0^\infty e^{-\frac{\mu\hbar^2 k^2}{m}} \frac{d\eta}{dk}\, dk, \tag{8.631}$$

or, after integrating by parts,

$$B_{\text{imp}} = -16\sqrt{\pi} N \left(\frac{\mu\hbar}{m}\right)^{5/2} \int_0^\infty e^{-\frac{\mu\hbar^2 k^2}{m}} \sum_l \delta_l (2l+1)\eta_l(k) k\,dk, \tag{8.632}$$

where

$$\eta_l(k) = \eta(k,l) - \eta^0(k,l). \tag{8.633}$$

† See, e.g., E. Jahnke and F. Emde, Tables of Functions, Leipzig 1933, p. 146.

The phase shifts η_l must be obtained by a numerical integration of equation (8.618). From equation (8.632) we see that only those values of k will give an appreciable contribution to the second virial coefficient for which k^2 is at most of the order $m/\mu\hbar^2$. This means that the lower the temperature (or the larger μ) is, the smaller are the values of k which will contribute materially to B. If we now consider equation (8.618), we see first of all that for large values of l, the term $l(l+1)/r^2$ will dominate over the term $m\phi(r)/\hbar^2$, and from equation (8.629) we see that for those values of l, $g(k;l)$ will practically be equal to zero. Second, we see that the smaller the values of k in which we are interested, the smaller the values of l for which there is still an appreciable phase shift.† Since the number of terms in the sum on the right-hand side of equation (8.632) increases with temperature and since all phase shifts must be obtained by numerical integration, it follows that expression (8.632) can be used only at low temperatures. At this moment there does not exist a method which will give values of B at temperatures lower than those for which equation (8.528) can still be trusted and higher than those for which equation (8.632) can still be evaluated within a finite time interval.

§7. The Law of Corresponding States in Quantum Statistics.

In §3 we discussed the law of corresponding states which existed for substances which had a potential energy function of the form

$$\phi(r) = \alpha\psi(\beta r) \tag{8.701}$$

where ψ is a universal function and where α with the dimensions of an energy and β with the dimensions of an inverse length differed from substance to substance. We found that as long as quantum effects could be neglected the equation of state could be written in the form

$$p^* = f(V^*,T^*), \tag{8.702}$$

where f was a universal function and where the reduced quantities p^*, V^*, and T^* were related to the pressure, volume, and temperature by the equations

$$p^* = \frac{p}{\beta^3\alpha}, \tag{8.703}$$

$$V^* = \beta^3 V, \tag{8.704}$$

$$T^* = \frac{k}{\alpha}T. \tag{8.705}$$

† This corresponds to the fact that in the classical case low energy values and large values of the angular momentum entail large values of the minimum distance apart.

As early as 1921 it was realized by Byk that in the region of relatively low temperatures quantum effects could not continue to be neglected. Equation (8.702) no longer holds and must be replaced by the equation

$$p^* = f(V^*, T^*, \Lambda^*), \tag{8.706}$$

where once more f is a universal function and where Λ^* is given by the equation

$$\Lambda^* = \frac{h\beta}{\sqrt{2\pi m\alpha}}. \tag{8.707}$$

One can easily verify that, apart from a numerical factor of the order of unity, Λ^* is the reduced De Broglie wavelength of a particle moving with an average kinetic energy corresponding to 1°K.

Equation (8.706) can be derived in the same way that equation (8.702) was derived in §3. We must again study the behavior of the W_N. Using equation (8.405) for the W_N and choosing for the φ_n the characteristic functions of the $\mathcal{H}_N$, we have

$$\int W_N d\mathbf{x}_1 \cdots d\mathbf{x}_N = N! \sum_n e^{-\mu\epsilon_n}, \tag{8.708}$$

where the ϵ_n are the characteristic values of $\mathcal{H}_N$. These characteristic values must be found by solving the Schrödinger equation

$$\mathcal{H}_N \varphi_n = \epsilon_n \varphi_n, \tag{8.709}$$

or

$$\left[-\sum_k \frac{\hbar^2}{2m} \nabla_k^2 + \sum \phi(r_{kl}) \right] \varphi_n = \epsilon_n \varphi_n \tag{8.710}$$

with the boundary conditions that φ_n is zero at the walls of the volume V.

Introducing reduced variables

$$\left. \begin{aligned} \epsilon_n^* = \frac{\epsilon_n}{\alpha}, \qquad \mathbf{x}_k^* = \beta \mathbf{x}_k, \qquad \nabla_k^* = \frac{\nabla_k}{\beta} \\ r^* = \beta r, \qquad \phi(r) = \alpha\psi(r^*), \end{aligned} \right\}, \tag{8.711}$$

we can write equation (8.710) in the form

$$\left[-\frac{\Lambda^{*2}}{4\pi} \sum_k \nabla_k^{*2} + \sum \psi(r_{kl}^*) - \epsilon_n^* \right] \varphi_n = 0, \tag{8.712}$$

and the boundary condition now involves V^*.

From equation (8.712) it follows that

$$\epsilon_n^* = \epsilon_n^*(V^*, \Lambda^*), \tag{8.713}$$

and introducing

$$\mu^* = \mu\alpha, \tag{8.714}$$

we see that

$$\frac{V}{v_0} b_N = \chi_N(\mu^*, V^*, \Lambda^*). \tag{8.715}$$

In the same way that equation (8.314) followed in §3 from equation (8.311) we now get

$$p^*V^* = NT^*\chi(\mu^*, V^*, \Lambda^*), \tag{8.716}$$

which proves equation (8.706).

De Boer and collaborators have used the quantum mechanical law of corresponding states to discuss the solid and liquid states of the inert gases. We refer to their papers for this discussion. The most striking application of the quantum mechanical law of corresponding states has, however, been the prediction of the properties of He^3. We shall briefly outline how this was done by De Boer and Lunbeck.

In the classical case all gases for which equation (8.701) holds will have the same values of p_{cr}^* and T_{cr}^*. As soon as quantum effects become important this will no longer be true, and both p_{cr}^* and T_{cr}^* will be functions of Λ^*. De Boer and Lunbeck now plotted p_{cr}^* (and T_{cr}^*) as a function of Λ^* for X, Kr, A, N_2, Ne, H_2, and He^4 and extrapolated then to the Λ^*-value of He^3. We have given the values of Λ^*, p_{cr}^*, T_{cr}^*, p_{cr}, and T_{cr} for these gases in the following table, and also the extrapolated and the experimental values in the case of He^3. The uncertainty in the predicted values of the critical data of He^3 is due to the uncertainty of the extrapolation.

CRITICAL DATA OF DIFFERENT GASES†

Gas	Λ^*	p_{cr}^*	T_{cr}^*	p_{cr} (atmos)	T_{cr} (°K)
X	0.03	0.122	1.26	58	290
Kr	0.04	0.117	1.26	54	209
A	0.07	0.116	1.25	48	151
N_2	0.09	0.132	1.30	33.5	126
Ne	0.24	0.114	1.26	26.9	44.8
H_2	0.69	0.063	0.90	12.8	33.2
He^4	1.05	0.027	0.51	2.26	5.25
He^3 (predicted)	1.22	0.011–0.016	0.31–0.35	0.93–1.35	3.1–3.5
He^3 (experimental)				1.17	3.35

† From J. de Boer and R. J. Lunbeck, Physica, **14**, 510, 1948. Experimental values of p_{cr} and T_{cr} for He^3 from B. M. Abraham, D. W. Osborne, and B. Weinstock, Phys. Rev., **80**, 366, 1950.

From this table it is seen that the law of corresponding states was able to predict with amazing accuracy the critical data of He^3.

In a similar way De Boer and Lunbeck derived the vapor pressure curve of liquid He^3. Fixing the value of p^*, the corresponding values of T^* were plotted as a function of Λ^* and then extrapolated to the value of Λ^* corresponding to He^3. In this case they were able to predict the vapor pressure curve for temperatures above 2°K. The values of the vapor pressure are given in the following table. Very soon after their predictions had been published the vapor pressure of He^3 was measured by workers at Los Alamos and at the Argonne Laboratory† and their experimental values agreed with the predicted ones within the margins given by De Boer and Lunbeck.

VAPOR PRESSURE OF He^3

T(°K)		2.0	2.4	2.8	3.0	3.2	3.3
p in cm Hg	predicted§	14	27	48	59	75	82
	experimental‖	15.2	29.1	49.1	61.8	76.4	84.5

§ De Boer and Lunbeck, *loc. cit.*
‖ Abraham, Osborne, and Weinstock, *loc. cit.*

De Boer and Lunbeck also gave a vapor pressure formula for temperatures below 2°K. They used the thermodynamical formula‡

$$\ln p = \frac{\chi_0}{kT} + \frac{5}{2}\ln T + \mathfrak{C} + \frac{3}{2}\ln M + \frac{1}{k}\int_0^T \frac{\chi}{T^2}\,dT, \qquad (8.717)$$

where χ is the internal energy of the liquid per atom, χ_0 its value at 0°K, $\mathfrak{C}$ the constant given by equation (2.808) on page 44, and M the molecular weight. At temperatures below 2°K the last term may be neglected. Expressing p in cm of mercury and using logarithms to the base 10, De Boer and Lunbeck wrote equation (8.717) in the form

$$\log p = -\frac{1.12}{T} + \frac{5}{2}\log T + 1.01, \qquad (8.718)$$

where they had used the extrapolation method to evaluate χ_0. The experimental vapor pressure curve determined by Abraham, Osborne, and Weinstock satisfies the equation

$$\log p_{\text{exp}} = -\frac{0.98}{T} + \frac{5}{2}\log T + 0.92. \qquad (8.719)$$

Again, the agreement between the predicted and the experimental data is excellent.

† S. G. Sydoriak, E. R. Grilly, and E. F. Hammel, Phys. Rev., **75**, 303, 1949; Abraham, Osborne, and Weinstock, *loc. cit.*

‡ See, e.g., E. H. Kennard, Kinetic Theory of Gases, New York 1938, p. 408. Compare also the discussion on p. 402.

§8. **The Equation of State of Helium.** In this last section we wish to discuss how the theory of §§1, 2, and 4–6 has been applied to the case of helium. As we have emphasized in those sections, the problem is twofold. The first problem is the determination of the potential energy function; the second problem is the calculation of the virial coefficients once $\phi(r)$ has been agreed upon.

There are two different ways of approaching the problem of the determination of the potential energy function. Since helium atoms are comparatively simple systems, various authors have attempted to derive from first principles the interaction potential between two helium atoms.† The result is then a potential energy of the form

$$\phi(r) = ae^{-br} - (cr^{-6} + dr^{-8} + er^{-10}). \qquad \textbf{(8.801)}$$

The $\phi(r)$ so obtained can be used to evaluate the second virial coefficient as has been done, for instance, by Massey and co-workers,‡ who tried a number of different values for a, b, c, and d. However, as soon as one tries different values for these constants, one deals no longer with a potential which is determined from first principles and one can with equal justification use a Lennard-Jones potential (8.208) as has been done by De Boer. In this second method of determining $\phi(r)$ one starts from a carefully chosen $\phi(r)$ in which there are a number of yet to be determined parameters (see §2). As long as quantum effects can be neglected, the determination of the unknown parameters is straightforward. However, in the case of helium, quantum effects play an important part up to temperatures of the order of 400°K and the classical expression for the second virial coefficient can no longer be used. We may remind ourselves at this point that assuming classical statistics to be applicable and assuming a potential energy function of the form

$$\phi(r) = 4\kappa\left[\left(\frac{\sigma}{r}\right)^{12} - \left(\frac{\sigma}{r}\right)^{6}\right], \qquad \textbf{(8.802)}$$

one can determine κ and σ by the method described in §2, that is, by plotting $\ln B^*$ against $\ln T^*$ and comparing this plot with the experimental $\ln B$ against $\ln T$ graph. The reduced quantities B^* and T^* are given by the equations

$$B^* = \sigma^{-3}B, \qquad \textbf{(8.803)}$$

$$T^* = \frac{k}{\kappa}T, \qquad \textbf{(8.804)}$$

† J. C. Slater, Phys. Rev., **32**, 349, 1928; J. C. Slater and J. G. Kirkwood, Phys. Rev., **37**, 682, 1931; and H. Margenau, Phys. Rev., **38**, 747, 1931.

‡ H. S. W. Massey and R. A. Buckingham, Proc. Roy. Soc. (London), **A168**, 378, 1938; **A169**, 205, 1938; R. A. Buckingham, J. Hamilton, and H. S. W. Massey, Proc. Roy. Soc. (London), **A179**, 103, 1941.

and the differences in ordinates and abscissae will thus give us the "classical" values of κ and σ. De Boer found in that way

$$\kappa_{\text{cl}} = 9.5 \cdot 10^{-16} \text{ erg}, \qquad \sigma_{\text{cl}} = 2.60 \cdot 10^{-8} \text{ cm}. \tag{8.805}$$

Using these preliminary values of κ and σ, the parameter Λ^*, which expresses the influence of quantum effects and which is given by the equation (compare equation [8.309])

$$\Lambda^* = \frac{h}{\sigma\sqrt{2\pi m\kappa}}, \tag{8.806}$$

can be determined.

Expressing equation (8.507) or (8.528) in reduced variables T^*, B^*, and Λ^*, one finds that at high temperatures the reduced second virial coefficient can be written in the form

$$B^* = B_{\text{cl}}^*(T^*) + \Lambda^{*2}f_1(T^*) + \Lambda^{*4}f_2(T^*) + \cdots. \tag{8.807}$$

This equation follows from equations (8.507), (8.527), (8.303), (8.305), (8.306), (8.316), and (8.803) and from the fact that $\nabla^* = \beta^{-1}\nabla(=\sigma\nabla)$. On inspection one sees that the function $F(x)$ given by equation (8.527) is of the form

$$F(x) = 1 + \Lambda^{*2}g_1 + \Lambda^{*4}g_2 + \cdots,$$

where $g_1, g_2, \cdots$ are expressions which contain only reduced quantities.

Once Λ^* is determined, one can plot $\ln B^*$ against $\ln T^*$, using the complete expression (8.807) for B^*. Comparison of this graph with the experimental graph gives us new values of κ and σ. We can use these values to determine a new value of Λ^* and recalculate B^* as a function of T^*. This procedure is continued until a consistent set of values of κ, σ, and Λ^* is obtained. The final values obtained by De Boer in this way were

$$\kappa = 14.0 \cdot 10^{-16} \text{ erg}, \qquad \sigma = 2.56 \cdot 10^{-8} \text{ cm}, \tag{8.808}$$

which are very appreciably different from the values of equation (8.805).

It may be remarked here that in determining κ and σ only terms up to h^4 (or Λ^{*4}) had to be included in expression (8.807). The relative importance of the terms B_1 and B_2 can be seen from the following table, which gives for a number of temperatures ranging from 27°K to 256°K the value of the total second virial coefficient (Keesom's adopted values), and the values of the terms B_1 and B_2 in equation (8.528) calculated by De Boer. We see that for temperatures down to about 50°K, B_2 is at most 20 per cent of B_1 and the omission of higher-order terms is probably justified, but that for lower temperatures the method of §5 can certainly not be used. Furthermore, we see that even at 256°K B_1 gives a correction of 5 per cent and that therefore the quantum mechanical corrections play an important role even at room temperatures. This was also evident from the fact that the κ and σ of equation (8.808) differed so appreciably from those of equation (8.805).

VALUES OF B, B_1, AND B_2 IN cm^3/MOLE

T in °K	B	B_1	B_2
27.3	0.9	9.16	−4.05
40.9	5.8	4.89	−1.26
50.6	7.7	3.58	−0.71
64.0	9.2	2.60	−0.38
83.5	10.5	1.82	−0.19
113.7	11.2	1.20	−0.09
163.8	11.6	0.78	−0.04
256.0	11.5	0.48	−0.01

After κ and σ have been empirically determined by comparing the theoretical and the experimental values of the second virial coefficient at high temperatures, the potential energy function obtained in this way can be used to calculate B at low temperatures, using the method described in §6. This has been done by De Boer, using the values of equation (8.808), and the agreement between calculated and observed values of B is quite satisfactory but yet not so good that one can say definitely that the correct potential energy curve has been found. We may quote Keesom: ". . . we state that broadly speaking correspondence between theory and experimental data exists. Exact numerical agreement, however, has not yet been reached, which indicates that the exact interaction potential has yet to be found.

"As to the point whether discrete energy levels exist, we mention that Massey and Buckingham as well as Gropper† calculate that the potential energy functions they use would lead to one discrete energy level, De Boer and Michels, on the other hand, that their potential energy function leads to none. As experimental data lie between the results of the two parties, the question of the existence of discrete energy levels is left undecided."

This conclusion remained unaltered when the second virial coefficient was determined by Kistemaker for temperatures down to 1.6°K. It was hoped that his measurements might enable us to verify the fact that helium atoms obey Bose-Einstein statistics. This, however, turned out to be impossible. The difference in behavior of the second virial coefficient between the cases of Bose-Einstein and Fermi-Dirac statistics only becomes definitely discernible for atoms of mass number 4 at about 2°K, and Kistemaker's accuracy was not sufficient to decide between the two statistics. As far as He^4 is concerned, it will be extremely difficult to

† L. Gropper, Phys. Rev., **55**, 1095, 1939.

extend or improve on Kistemaker's experiments, since one must determine isotherms in a region where the saturated vapor pressure is less than 2 cm Hg (only 4 mm Hg at 1.5°K).

The situation is completely different when we consider the lightest helium isotope, He^3. Due to its lighter mass, quantum effects will be more pronounced; secondly, its vapor pressure will be much higher. At 1.5°K, for instance, the saturated vapor pressure of He^3 is still 5 cm Hg, and it should be possible to determine the second virial coefficient of He^3 with reasonable accuracy down to 1.2°K. With this in mind De Boer and collaborators have recently calculated the second virial coefficient of He^3, using the same potential energy function that was used by De Boer in calculating the second virial coefficient of He^4.

At high temperatures no quantum effects occur and the second virial coefficients of He^3 and He^4 should be the same.† At low temperatures, however, a difference will set in. The situation is slightly more complicated than in the case of He^4, since He^3 has a nuclear spin $\frac{1}{2}\hbar$.

The influence of spin was not present in our previous considerations and we must go back to the beginning of §6.‡ Instead of equation (8.607) for the characteristic functions, we now have

$$\varphi_k(1,2) = e^{\frac{i}{\hbar}(\mathbf{P}\cdot\mathbf{X})} \frac{R_{nl}(r)}{r} Y_l^m(\boldsymbol{\omega})\chi_l(1,2), \tag{8.809}$$

where $\chi_l(1,2)$ is the spin-dependent part of the wave function. Introducing the spinors ξ and η,§ which correspond to situations where the z-component of the spin has the well-defined value $\frac{1}{2}\hbar$ or $-\frac{1}{2}\hbar$, respectively, there are the following four possibilities for $\chi_l(1,2)$:‖

$$\left.\begin{aligned} \chi_l^{(1)}(1,2) &= \xi_1\xi_2\delta_l, \\ \chi_l^{(2)}(1,2) &= (\xi_1\eta_2 + \eta_1\xi_2)\delta_l, \\ \chi_l^{(3)}(1,2) &= \eta_1\eta_2\delta_l, \\ \chi_l^{(4)}(1,2) &= (\xi_1\eta_2 - \eta_1\xi_2)(1 - \delta_l), \end{aligned}\right\} \tag{8.810}$$

where δ_l is again given by equation (8.609). The factors δ_l and $(1 - \delta_l)$ arise from the symmetry requirements of the φ_k. Since we can safely neglect the influence of the spin on the energy levels, equation (8.608) still holds. The remainder of §6 is also unchanged except that we

† It might be of interest to measure the second virial coefficient of He^3 at high temperatures to verify whether the two potential energy functions are really exactly the same, as would be expected.

‡ We shall discuss only the inclusion of spin effects into the considerations leading to the expression for B_{imp} and, moreover, only for the case of spin $\frac{1}{2}$. From this discussion it should be clear how spin effects can be included in the calculation of B_{perf} or in the considerations of §5, and also how the consideration can be adapted to the case of higher spin values.

§ See H. A. Kramers, Hand- u. Jahrb. d. Chem. Phys., Vol. I, Leipzig 1938, p. 243.

‖ Compare Kramers, *loc. cit.*, §73.

must introduce the extra degeneracy due to the spin and we must thus in equations (8.613), (8.616), (8.620), (8.631), and (8.632) replace δ_l by $2\delta_l + 1[=3\delta_l + (1 - \delta_l)]$. This means that we now must calculate the phases η_l not only for the odd (or even) values, but for all values of l. The contribution to the second virial coefficient from B_{perf} (see equation [8.601]) must also be changed, and in the case of He^3 we have

$$B_{\text{perf}} = \frac{Nv_0}{2^{3/2}}. \tag{8.811}$$

BIBLIOGRAPHICAL NOTES

We refer to the following three references for extensive bibliographies:

1. H. Kamerlingh Onnes and W. H. Keesom, Enzyklopädie der mathematischen Wissenschaften, Vol. V, Pt. 10, Leipzig-Berlin 1912. This reference gives a survey of the literature about the equation of state which is complete up to 1908 and fairly complete up to 1911.
2. J. de Boer, Rep. Prog. Phys., **12,** 305, 1949. This review discusses more recent developments.
3. J. R. Partington, Physical Chemistry, Vol. I, London 1949, §VIIC.

We have followed in this chapter practically everywhere Kramers' treatment, which in many respects is so much more elegant than older methods:

4. Lectures given by H. A. Kramers in Leiden during the winter of 1944–1945.

§1. The first author who used ensemble theory to obtain the equation of state was Ornstein, who by the method of the macrocanonical ensembles derived formula (8.205) for the second virial coefficient:

5. L. S. Ornstein, Toepassing der Statistische Mechanica van Gibbs op Molekulair-theoretische Vraagstukken, Thesis, Leiden 1908.

In a paper published in 1927 Ursell developed the principles from which the further developments in the theory of the equation of state followed:

6. H. D. Ursell, Proc. Cambridge Phil. Soc., **23,** 685, 1927.

Further developments followed in the work of Mayer and collaborators, Uhlenbeck and co-workers, Born and Fuchs, and De Boer:

7. J. E. Mayer, J. Chem. Phys., **5,** 67, 1937.
8. G. E. Uhlenbeck and E. Beth, Physica, **3,** 729, 1936.
9. E. Beth and G. E. Uhlenbeck, Physica, **4,** 915, 1937.
10. B. Kahn, On the Theory of the Equation of State, Thesis, Utrecht 1938.
11. M. Born and K. Fuchs, Proc. Roy. Soc. (London), **A166,** 391, 1938.
12. J. de Boer and A. Michels, Physica, **5,** 945, 1938.
13. J. de Boer and A. Michels, Physica, **6,** 409, 1939.
14. J. de Boer, Contribution to the Theory of Compressed Gases, Thesis, Amsterdam 1940.
15. R. H. Fowler and E. A. Guggenheim, Statistical Thermodynamics, Cambridge 1939, Chap. VII.

§2. See refs. 4, 5, 8, 9, 10, 12, 13, 14, and

16. J. E. Jones, Proc. Roy. Soc. (London), **A106,** 463, 1924.
17. R. H. Fowler, Statistical Mechanics, Cambridge 1936, §§10.3–10.33.

§3. See refs. 2, 12, 14, and

18. K. S. Pitzer, J. Chem. Phys., **7,** 583, 1939.

19. E. A. Guggenheim, J. Chem. Phys., **13**, 253, 1945.
20. J. de Boer, Physica, **14**, 139, 1948.

§4. See refs. 2, 4, 8, 9, 10, 14, and
21. J. G. Kirkwood, Phys. Rev., **44**, 31, 1933.

§5. See refs. 2, 4, 8, 10, 14, and 21.

§6. See refs. 2, 4, 10, and 14.

§7. The first time a quantum mechanical law of corresponding state was considered was by Byk:
22. A. Byk, Ann. Physik, **66**, 157, 1921.
23. A. Byk, Ann. Physik, **69**, 161, 1922.
See also refs. 2, 12, 14, 20, and
24. J. de Boer and R. J. Lunbeck, Physica, **14**, 510, 1948.
25. J. de Boer and B. S. Blaisse, Physica, **14**, 149, 1948.
26. J. de Boer and R. J. Lunbeck, Physica, **14**, 520, 1948.
In the last two references the quantum mechanical law of corresponding states has been applied to the solid and the liquid state.

§8. See refs. 2, 4, 14, and, especially,
27. W. H. Keesom, Helium, Amsterdam 1942, §2.2.
The most recent measurements of the second virial coefficient of helium down to 1.6°K are those of Kistemaker:
28. J. Kistemaker and W. H. Keesom, Physica, **12**, 227, 1946.
29. J. Kistemaker, Thermodynamische Eigenschappen van Helium in de Omgeving van het λ-punt, Thesis, Leiden 1945.
The second virial coefficient of the lightest helium isotope has recently been calculated by De Boer and collaborators:
30. J. de Boer, J. van Kranendonk, and K. Compaan, Physica, **16**, 545, 1950.

The following papers were published after this chapter had been written:
31. J. S. Rowlinson, J. Chem. Phys., **19**, 827, 1951; third virial coefficient of polar gases.
32. R. J. Lunbeck and C. A. ten Seldam, Physica, **17**, 788, 1951; second and third virial coefficients of CH_3F.
33. R. J. Lunbeck, Het Principe van Overeenstemmende Toestanden in de Quantummechanica, Thesis, Amsterdam 1951; law of corresponding states.
34. S. Ono, J. Chem. Phys., **19**, 504, 1951; cluster integrals (mathematical considerations).
35. G. V. Chester, Proc. Phys. Soc. (London), **67**, 1954, in course of publication; law of corresponding states.

CHAPTER IX

CONDENSATION PHENOMENA

§1. Introduction. In the preceding chapter we started the discussion of imperfect gases by considering the behavior of these gases at large dilutions. In that case only slight deviations from the behavior of perfect gases can be expected. In the present chapter, however, we shall be con-

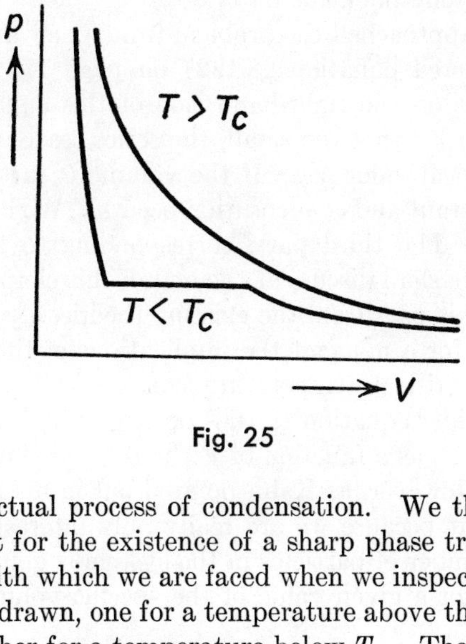

Fig. 25

cerned with the actual process of condensation. We thus want a theory which can account for the existence of a sharp phase transition. We can see the problem with which we are faced when we inspect Figure 25, where two isotherms are drawn, one for a temperature above the critical temperature T_c and the other for a temperature below T_c. The first isotherm is a smooth curve, but the second one consists of *three analytically different* parts. These parts correspond, respectively, to the pure liquid, the region of coexistence of liquid and vapor, and the pure vapor.

One of the earliest attempts to derive an isotherm consisting of three analytically different parts was the one made by van der Waals, who suggested the equation of state (see also p. 8)

$$\left(p + \frac{a}{V^2}\right)(V - b) = NkT, \tag{9.101}$$

where p, V, N, k, and T have their usual meaning and where a and b are constants which depend on the gas considered. The equation of state given by equation (9.101) does *not* consist of analytically different parts. However, at temperatures below the critical temperature the isotherms are no longer monotonic functions, but there is a part where $\partial p/\partial V$ is positive. Since this would not correspond to a state of stable equilibrium, one connects the two stable parts of the isotherm—where $\partial p/\partial V < 0$—by a line p = constant, which then is supposed to correspond to the region where vapor and liquid are coexisting. The value of the pressure in the region of coexistence is determined by thermodynamical arguments (compare the discussion on p. 265).

From this brief description of van der Waals' theory it is clear that it does not really account satisfactorily for the occurrence of the phase transition, but must rather be classified as a semiphenomenological theory (compare also the remarks made on p. 8).

In 1937 Mayer approached the problem from a new and more promising angle. He considered equation (8.122) on page 175 and showed that although the series on the right-hand side of this equation converges as long as the volume V is not too small, the series ceases to have a meaning for V below a critical value V_c. If the volume is further decreased, the pressure stays constant and condensation occurs. We have thus two parts of the isotherms. The third part, corresponding to the pure liquid, is never obtained; we shall discuss at the end of this chapter why we cannot expect to obtain this part from the existing theories.

Let us consider for a moment the implications of the fact that the isotherm below the critical temperature consists of analytically different parts. If we consider equation (8.106) on page 172, it seems strange that the grand potential q as a function of V should ever consist of analytically different parts. However, as Kahn pointed out in his thesis, this state of affairs comes about because we are really only interested in the limiting case where the number of particles in the system is going to infinity. We may expect that for a given value of the specific volume v, given by the equation

$$v = \frac{V}{N}, \tag{9.102}$$

the following limit will exist:

$$p(v,T) = \lim_{\substack{N\to\infty \\ V\to\infty \\ V/N=v}} p(V,N,T). \tag{9.103}$$

If we bear in mind that we really are only interested in such a limiting property of the pressure, it should no longer surprise us that p can consist of analytically different parts. In some special cases it can be shown by actual calculations† that the derivatives $d^n p/dv^n$ $(n > 2)$ at $v = v_c$ go to infinity with N, and thus that only in the limit $N \to \infty$ the isotherm really consists of two analytically different parts.

In §2 we shall discuss the so-called Einstein condensation. This is the condensation phenomenon which occurs in a perfect Bose-Einstein gas. In that case we can follow the behavior of the system exactly and it is possible to follow in detail the transition of a smooth isotherm for finite N to an isotherm showing two analytically different parts for infinite N. We shall also discuss in how far the Einstein condensation can have a bearing on the peculiar behavior of liquid helium below 2.19°K.

In §3 we shall discuss an approximate way of treating the condensation of an imperfect gas. This method discusses the formation of little drops in a vapor just above its saturation point and is related to the thermodynamical discussion of the condensation phenomenon given by Becker and Döring. Our reason for discussing this kind of theory is that in many ways it gives a clearer picture of the actual physical processes involved than the more rigorous theory. This rigorous theory will be discussed in the last section of the present chapter. We shall give a discussion of Mayer's theory which differs slightly from the usual presentations.

§2. The Einstein Condensation. We mentioned on page 89 that a perfect Bose-Einstein gas would show the so-called Einstein condensation. We shall now consider this phenomenon in some detail. It was first mentioned by Einstein in his original paper on the perfect Bose-Einstein gas, but lately it has come to the fore because F. London suggested in 1938 that the λ-transition of liquid helium might be a case of the Einstein condensation. We shall return to this point at the end of this section.

In many ways the behavior of a perfect Bose-Einstein gas resembles the behavior of an imperfect gas below the critical temperature, as was emphasized by Kahn. We shall see in the last section that, indeed, the theory of the present section is a special case of the general theory discussed there. However, since in the case of a perfect Bose-Einstein gas the energy levels are exactly known, the present case is much simpler. Let us first consider the case of a finite number of particles, N.

The equation of state of a perfect Bose-Einstein gas is given by equations (7.608), (7.609), and (7.414) on pages 167 and 157, and we have

$$q = \mu p V = \frac{V}{v_0} f(y), \qquad \textbf{(9.201)}$$

† The case of the condensation of a perfect Bose-Einstein gas has been discussed by Wergeland and Hove-Storhoug (D. Kgl. Norske Vid. Selsk. Forh., **15**, 181, 1943). See also D. ter Haar, Proc. Roy. Soc. (London), **A212**, 552, 1952.

where

$$f(y) = \sum_{n=1}^{\infty} \frac{y^n}{n^{5/2}} \cdot \tag{9.202}$$

In equation (9.201) q is the grand potential, v_0 is given by the equation

$$v_0 = \left(\frac{\mu h^2}{2\pi m}\right)^{3/2}, \tag{9.203}$$

μ and the activity y are related to the absolute temperature T and to the thermal potential per particle divided by μ, ν, by the equations

$$\mu = \frac{1}{kT} \tag{9.204}$$

and

$$y = e^{\nu}. \tag{9.205}$$

Furthermore, y is a function of the specific volume $v = V/N$ by the relation

$$N = y\frac{\partial q}{\partial y} = \frac{V}{v_0} yf'(y), \qquad \left(f'(y) = \sum_{n=1}^{\infty} \frac{y^n}{n^{3/2}}\right), \tag{9.206}$$

or

$$\frac{1}{v} = \frac{1}{v_0} yf'(y). \tag{9.207}$$

The power series on the right-hand side of equations (9.201) and (9.207) converge for $y \leqslant 1$, but are no longer convergent for $y > 1$.† As long as the specific volume v is larger than a critical value v_c given by the equation

$$\frac{1}{v_c} = \frac{1}{v_0} f'(1) = \frac{2.61}{v_0}, \tag{9.208}$$

we can use equations (9.201) and (9.207) to obtain the equation of state. However, one has to consider with some special care the case where $v < v_c$.

Let us now consider the case where the specific volume is reduced below v_c. It can be shown that the isotherm consists of two parts. The first part, where $v \geqslant v_c$, is given by equation (9.201), or

$$p = \frac{kT}{v_0} f(y), \qquad v \geqslant v_c, \tag{9.209}$$

† It has been shown by Opechowski (Physica, **4**, 722, 1937) that the following expansions are valid when y lies in the neighborhood of 1:

$$f(y) = 2.36(-\ln y)^{3/2} + 1.34 + 2.61 \ln y - 0.73(\ln y)^2 + \cdots,$$

$$yf'(y) = -3.54(-\ln y)^{1/2} + 2.61 - 1.46 \ln y - 0.10(\ln y)^2 + \cdots.$$

where y as a function of v follows from equation (9.207). The second part of the isotherm is given by the equation

$$p = \frac{kT}{v_0} f(1), \qquad v < v_c. \tag{9.210}$$

Curve b of Figure 26 depicts one of these isotherms. We have drawn in the same figure for comparison the isotherm of a perfect Boltzmann gas at the same temperature (curve c). Curve a in Figure 26 is finally the

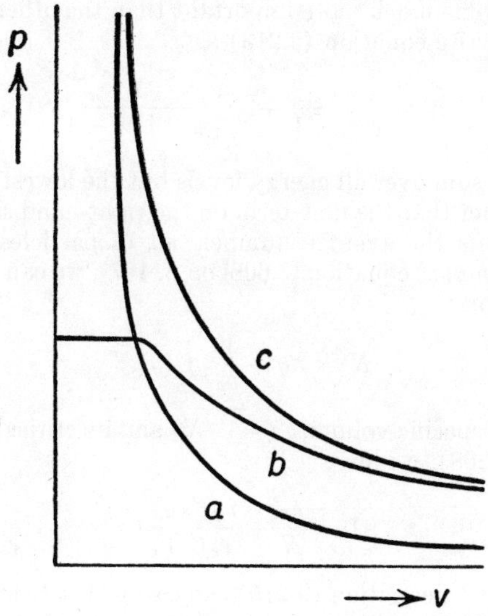

Fig. 26

curve on which all condensation points lie. The equation of this curve is obtained by eliminating T from equations (9.201) and (9.207) and putting $y = 1$, and we have in this way

$$pv^{5/3} = \frac{h^2}{2\pi m} \frac{f(1)}{[f'(1)]^{5/3}}. \tag{9.211}$$

Equations (9.209) and (9.210) are exactly valid only in the limiting case where $N \to \infty$. They can be proved most easily by first considering the case of finite N and afterward letting N go to infinity. We shall briefly sketch the argument. We must make use of the fact that although equations (9.201) and (9.207) have been derived by replacing sums over energy levels by integrals, the energy spectrum will really be discrete as long as the volume remains finite, and instead of equations (9.201) and (9.207) we should really use equations (7.603) and (7.604) on pages 166 and 167, or

$$q = -\sum_s \ln(1 - e^{\nu - \mu\epsilon_s}), \tag{9.212}$$

$$N = \sum_s \frac{1}{e^{-\nu + \mu\epsilon_s} - 1}. \tag{9.213}$$

If v approaches v_c, ν will approach 0, and it is dangerous to replace the sums in equations (9.212) and (9.213) by integrals. We shall, for the sake of simplicity, shift the zero of the energy levels in such a way that the lowest energy level, ϵ_0, is zero. Since ν will be in the neighborhood of zero, the first term in the sum on the right-hand side of equation (9.213) will become much more important than the other terms and we shall therefore write equation (9.213) as

$$N = \frac{1}{e^{-\nu} - 1} + \sum_{s \neq 0} \frac{1}{e^{-\nu + \mu\epsilon_s} - 1}, \tag{9.214}$$

or replacing the sum over all energy levels but the lowest by an integral and using the fact that the first term on the right-hand side of equation (9.214) represents the average number, n_0, of particles in the lowest energy level (compare equation [7.606] on p. 167), we can write equation (9.214) in the form

$$N = n_0 + \frac{V}{v_0} y f'(y). \tag{9.215}$$

Introducing the specific volume v $(= V/N)$ and its critical value v_c given by equation (9.208), we have

$$1 = \frac{n_0}{N} + \frac{v y f'(y)}{v_c f'(1)}. \tag{9.216}$$

As long as $v > v_c$, equation (9.216) can easily be satisfied and, indeed, only a small fraction of the particles will occupy the lowest level so that equations (9.216) and (9.207) are identical. However, if $v < v_c$, equation (9.216) must replace equation (9.207). In that case we should expect y to be about equal to one—which can be verified by a careful analysis—and using for n_0 equation (7.606) and using the fact that $y \approx 1$, we can write equation (9.216) in the form

$$1 = \frac{1}{N(1-y)} + \frac{v}{v_c}, \qquad v < v_c, \tag{9.217}$$

or

$$y = 1 - \frac{1}{N} \frac{v_c}{v_c - v}, \tag{9.218}$$

and we see that, indeed, in the limit $N \to \infty$, y will be equal to one for all values of v smaller than v_c, and equation (9.210) follows.

We must refer to the literature given in the bibliographical notes at the end of this chapter for a more detailed discussion of the behavior of the isotherm both for $v < v_c$ and for v in the neighborhood of v_c.

We have now considered the condensation which takes place when at constant temperature the specific volume is decreased. We can also consider what happens when we decrease the temperature while keeping the density (or v) constant. Condensation will then set in as soon as the temperature becomes equal to a critical temperature T_0 given by the equation (compare equations [9.208] and [9.203])

$$T_0 = \frac{h^2}{2\pi mk}[2.61v]^{-2/3} = \frac{h^2}{2\pi mk}\left(\frac{\rho}{2.61m}\right)^{2/3}, \tag{9.219}$$

or

$$T_0 = 120\rho^{2/3}M^{-5/3}\,^\circ\mathrm{K}, \tag{9.220}$$

where ρ is the density of the system in g cm^{-3} and where M is the molecular weight of the gas.

Let us briefly summarize the behavior of pressure, energy, and specific heat as functions of the temperature for given values of N and V.

First consider the pressure, from which the energy follows immediately by the relation (equation [4.615] on p. 86)

$$pV = \tfrac{2}{3}E. \tag{9.221}$$

As long as the temperature is above T_0 we have equation (9.209), or

$$p = CT^{5/2}f(y), \qquad T > T_0, \tag{9.222}$$

where†

$$C = \left(\frac{2\pi mk}{h^2}\right)^{3/2} k, \tag{9.223}$$

and where y is still a function of T by equation (9.207).

At temperatures below T_0, when y will be equal to one, we have

$$p = CT^{5/2}f(1), \qquad T \leqslant T_0. \tag{9.224}$$

The specific heat per particle, c_v, follows from equations (9.222), (9.224), and (9.221) and from the relation

$$c_v = \frac{1}{N}\frac{\partial E}{\partial T}, \tag{9.225}$$

and we have

$$c_v = \frac{3}{2}v\frac{\partial p}{\partial T}. \tag{9.226}$$

At temperatures below T_0 equation (9.226) leads to the equation

$$c_v = \tfrac{15}{4}CvT^{3/2}f(1), \qquad T \leqslant T_0. \tag{9.227}$$

† It may be noted that C is related to the chemical constant of the gas; compare §2 of Appendix III.

The value of c_v on the condensation curve, where $y = 1$ and $T = T_0$, follows from equations (9.227) and (9.219) and we have

$$c_v = \frac{15}{4}\,k\,\frac{f(1)}{f'(1)} = 1.926k, \tag{9.228}$$

which is actually more than the classical value $1.5k$. From equation (9.226) it follows that c_v is a continuous function of T, though $\partial c_v/\partial T$ is discontinuous. The Einstein condensation is thus a transition of the third

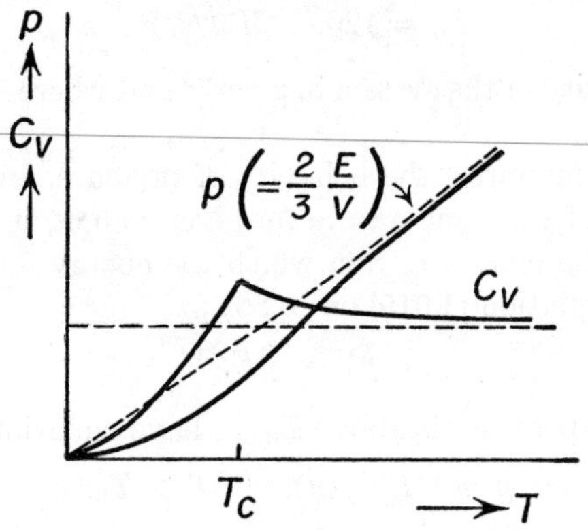

Fig. 27

order according to P. Ehrenfest's classification.† Figure 27 depicts p and c_v as functions of T.

To what extent can the Einstein condensation be compared to the condensation of an imperfect gas? In the latter case part of the system will form the liquid and thus form a different phase. This is not the case when we are considering a perfect Bose-Einstein gas. The particles which are too many, that is, those particles in excess of Nv/v_c, will all be found in the lowest energy level (compare equation [9.216]), as was first pointed out by Einstein. However, in both cases we have the same behavior of the thermal potential, namely, the approach to a limiting value which is maintained during the condensation.‡

† P. Ehrenfest, Proc. Kon. Ned. Akad. Wet. (Amsterdam), **36**, 153, 1933.

‡ It seems to me that the distinction which London makes between a condensation in momentum space in the case of the Einstein condensation and a condensation in coordinate space in the case of an imperfect gas is not justified, since the condensed phase of an imperfect gas also does not contribute to the pressure and thus also corresponds to a phase condensed in momentum space. Compare also the discussion by Becker (Z. Physik, **128**, 120, 1950), who points out that the Einstein condensation can also be considered to be a condensation in coordinate space.

From equation (9.216) we can get an expression for the number of particles in the lowest energy level, n_0, at temperatures below the condensation temperature T_0. Putting $y = 1$ and using equations (9.208), (9.203), and (9.219), we have

$$n_0 = N\left[1 - \left(\frac{T}{T_0}\right)^{3/2}\right], \qquad T < T_0. \tag{9.229}$$

We now must discuss in how far the λ-transition of liquid helium can be considered to be a case of the condensation of a perfect Bose-Einstein gas. The reasons why F. London compared the two phenomena were the following:

a) Substituting into equation (9.220) the values pertaining to liquid helium, that is, $M = 4$, $\rho = 0.146$ g cm^{-3} (the density of liquid helium), one gets

$$T_0 = 3.2°\text{K}, \tag{9.230}$$

which is of the same order of magnitude as the λ-transition point 2.19°K.

b) The general behavior of the specific heat of liquid helium resembles the behavior of the specific heat of a perfect Bose-Einstein gas.

c) Treating the particles in the lowest energy level and the other particles as constituting two different "fluids," one acquires the necessary foundations for a two-fluid theory of liquid helium which has in many respects been so successful in accounting for the behavior of liquid helium below the λ-point.

However, there seem to be more reasons against considering the λ-transition of liquid helium as an example of the condensation of a perfect Bose-Einstein gas than in favor of such a point of view. Some of the reasons against this point of view are the following†:

a) Some people object as a point of principle to treating a liquid as an ideal gas. Wergeland has, for instance, pointed out that the effects due to the indistinguishability of the particles disappear if the system has an ordered structure (compare also the discussion on pp. 71–72). However, liquid helium resembles in many respects a gas rather than a liquid. Its density is rather low, and the viscosity of liquid helium above the λ-point increases with increasing temperature like that of a gas instead of decreasing like that of a liquid.

b) The specific heat of liquid helium, though resembling superficially that of a perfect Bose-Einstein gas, is very different in its detailed behavior. The following differences may be noted. (i) The value of the specific heat per particle at the λ-point is about $12k$ instead of $1.9k$. (ii) The λ-transition seems to be a transition of the second order with a

† See, however, R. P. Feynman, Phys. Rev., **91**, 1291, 1953.

discontinuity in the specific heat itself instead of being a third-order transition. (iii) Instead of depending on the temperature as $T^{3/2}$ (equation [9.227]), c_v starts as T^3 for temperatures below 0.6°K and behaves as $T^{6.7}$ for $T > 0.6$K.†

c) In Chapter VII we found for the fluctuations in the number of particles in the lowest energy level (see equation [7.607] on p. 167) the expression

$$\overline{(n_0 - \bar{n}_0)^2} = \bar{n}_0 + \bar{n}_0^2. \tag{9.231}$$

Since at temperatures well below T_0, $\bar{n}_0 \sim N$ we see that we get from equation (9.231)

$$\overline{n_0^2} = 2\bar{n}_0^2 + \bar{n}_0 \sim 2N^2. \tag{9.232}$$

Although this equation will not hold if we are considering the system as a whole—in that case the total number of particles is fixed so that we cannot treat the system by using a grand ensemble—it will be valid for any small volume element in the system. We see thus that below the condensation point we should expect large fluctuations in density which have never been observed in liquid helium.

§3. The Liquid Drop Model of Condensation. In 1935 Becker and Döring discussed the condensation phenomenon from a thermodynamic and kinetic point of view. The main points of their theory follow. As long as for a given temperature the pressure is less than the saturated vapor pressure, most of the gas will consist of single molecules and only a small fraction of the molecules will be present as small droplets. The number of droplets of a given size decreases extremely rapidly with increasing size. The reason for this behavior is that the smaller the drop the larger the relative influence of the surface tension. As long as the pressure is below the saturation pressure the tendency of all drops will be to evaporate rather than grow, and the larger-size drops are present only due to fluctuations. However, as soon as the pressure exceeds the saturation pressure there will be a tendency for most drops to grow, and thus condensation will set in.‡

The statistical counterpart of this theory was developed by Frenkel, Band, and Wergeland. We shall give here a slightly altered version of Wergeland's theory. Our purpose will again be the study of the behavior of the isotherms, where we plot the pressure p as a function of the specific volume v.

The main idea of Wergeland's theory is to treat the system as consisting of a mixture of noninteracting droplets. Using the method of the grand

† H. C. Kramers, J. D. Wasscher, and C. J. Gorter, Physica, **18**, 329, 1952.

‡ We do not wish to enter into a detailed discussion of Becker and Döring's theory and so refer the interested reader to their paper.

ensembles, we have for the grand potential the equation

$$q = \sum_l q_l, \tag{9.301}$$

where q_l is the grand potential corresponding to the subsystem consisting only of those drops which contain l atoms (or molecules). Since we are considering the drops as noninteracting we are dealing in each subsystem with a perfect Boltzmann gas and we have thus from equation (7.506) on page 164 for q_l the equation

$$q_l = e^{\nu_l - \mu f_l}, \tag{9.302}$$

where f_l is the (free) energy of one drop and ν_l/μ the thermal potential per drop corresponding to the drops of l atoms. Since a free exchange of atoms between the drops must be possible, we have the equilibrium condition

$$\nu_l = l\nu. \tag{9.303}$$

Our first problem is to calculate f_l. We are dealing in this case with a system containing l atoms which can thus be represented by a macrocanonical ensemble and we have (compare equation [5.204] on p. 105)

$$e^{-\mu f_l} = \frac{1}{l!}\int e^{-\mu\epsilon}\,d\Omega. \tag{9.304}$$

With Wergeland we shall assume that each drop can be represented by a volume v_l in which the l atoms move independently in a smoothed-out constant negative potential $-\chi_l$, and we shall assume that χ_l and v_l vary with l as follows:†

$$\chi_l = \frac{l-1}{l}\,\chi, \qquad v_l = v_1 l^{\frac{l-2}{l-1}}. \tag{9.305}$$

We see that for large values of l, χ_l is nearly constant and v_l nearly proportional to l, as should be expected.

The integral in equation (9.304) can now easily be evaluated. The integration over the momenta gives a factor v_0^{-l}, where v_0 is again given by equation (9.203) and we get

$$e^{-\mu f_l} = \frac{v_0^{-l}}{l!}\,e^{l\mu\chi_l}\int_V d\mathbf{x}_1 \prod_{i=2}^{l}\int_{v_l} d\mathbf{x}_i, \tag{9.306}$$

where we used the fact that the drop itself has the whole volume V at its disposal, but the atoms in the drop only the volume v_l, while each atom

† We refer to Wergeland's paper for a justification of these assumptions.

contributes a factor $e^{\mu\chi_l}$. From equations (9.305) and (9.306) we finally get

$$e^{-\mu f_l} = \frac{V}{v_1}\frac{e^{-\mu\chi}}{l!}\left(\frac{v_1}{v_0}e^{\mu l\chi}\right) l^{l-2}, \tag{9.307}$$

and from equations (9.301) to (9.303) and (9.307)

$$q = \frac{V}{v_1} e^{-\mu\chi} \sum_l \frac{l^{l-2}}{l!} z^l, \tag{9.308}$$

where

$$z = \frac{v_1}{v_0} e^{\nu+\mu\chi}. \tag{9.309}$$

From equation (9.308) we get for the pressure and for the average number of atoms in the system the equations

$$p = \frac{kTq}{V} = \frac{kT}{v_1} e^{-\mu\chi} \sum_l \frac{l^{l-2}}{l!} z^l, \tag{9.310}$$

$$N = \frac{\partial q}{\partial \nu} = \frac{V}{v_1} e^{-\mu\chi} \sum_l \frac{l^{l-1}}{l!} z^l. \tag{9.311}$$

Equations (9.310) and (9.311) together give us the equation of state in parameter form. It is possible to eliminate z, and one obtains in that way the equation

$$p = \frac{NkT}{V}\left(1 - \frac{Nv_1}{2V} e^{\mu\chi}\right). \tag{9.312}$$

Equation (9.312) can be derived as follows. Define ξ, η, and ζ by the equations

$$\xi = \sum_{l=1}^{\infty} \frac{l^{l-2}}{l!} z^l, \tag{9.313}$$

$$\eta = \sum_{l=1}^{\infty} \frac{l^{l-1}}{l!} z^l, \tag{9.314}$$

$$\zeta = \sum_{l=1}^{\infty} \frac{l^l}{l!} z^l, \tag{9.315}$$

so that we have from equations (9.310) and (9.311)

$$p = \frac{kT}{v_1} e^{-\mu\chi}\xi, \tag{9.316}$$

$$N = \frac{V}{v_1} e^{-\mu\chi}\eta. \tag{9.317}$$

From equations (9.313) to (9.315) we see that the following relations exist among ξ, η, and ζ:

$$\eta = z\frac{d\xi}{dz}, \qquad \zeta = z\frac{d\eta}{dz}, \tag{9.318}$$

or

$$\xi = \int_0^\eta \eta(z)\frac{dz}{z}, \qquad \eta = \int_0^\zeta \zeta(z)\frac{dz}{z}. \tag{9.319}$$

By using for $l^l/l!$ the expression

$$\frac{l^l}{l!} = \frac{1}{2\pi i}\oint \frac{du}{u^{l+1}}e^{lu}, \tag{9.320}$$

one can write

$$\zeta = \frac{u_0}{1 - u_0}, \tag{9.321}$$

where u_0 is given by the equation

$$u_0 = ze^{u_0}, \tag{9.322}$$

and from equations (9.319) we get

$$\eta = u_0, \qquad \xi = u_0 - \tfrac{1}{2}u_0^2. \tag{9.323}$$

From equations (9.323), (9.316), and (9.317) equation (9.312) follows.

We must now consider how the condensation phenomenon occurs. Introducing again the specific volume v $(= V/N)$, we have from equation (9.311)

$$\frac{1}{v} = \frac{e^{-\mu\chi}}{v_1}\sum_l \frac{l^{l-1}}{l!}z^l. \tag{9.324}$$

The series on the right-hand side of this equation converges for $z \leqslant 1/e$, but $z = e^{-1}$ is a singularity of the function represented by the series. The same point is also a singularity of the series on the right-hand side of equation (9.310) and we see that the equation of state given by equation (9.312) will hold as long as $v > v_c$, where v_c is given by the equation†

$$\frac{1}{v_c} = \frac{e^{-\mu\chi}}{v_1}. \tag{9.325}$$

As soon as $v < v_c$, however, we must use different methods to obtain p as a function of v. It is possible to show that from equations (9.310) and (9.311) it follows that for $v < v_c$ the following equation holds:

$$p = p_c = \frac{kT}{2v_1}e^{-\mu\chi}, \qquad v < v_c. \tag{9.326}$$

† From equation (9.322) we see that for $z = 1/e$, $u_0 = 1$, so that $\eta = 1$, and equation (9.325) follows by inserting this value of η into equation (9.317).

Equation (9.326) holds exactly only in the limiting case where $N \to \infty$. Otherwise one has to add to the right-hand side of equation (9.326) terms of the order of magnitude $1/N$. It is possible to prove this by considering the equations

$$q = Vg(z), \tag{9.327}$$

$$N = Vzg'(z), \qquad g'(z) = \frac{dg}{dz}. \tag{9.328}$$

Let $g(z)$ have the following properties:

a) The function $g(z)$ has a singularity on the real axis for $z = z_0$.

b) The expression $zg'(z)$ is monotonically increasing on the real axis between $z = 0$ and $z = z_0$.

c) The singularity at $z = z_0$ is a branch point of the function $g(z)$.

As long as v $(= V/N)$ is larger than v_c given by the equation

$$\frac{1}{v_c} = z_0 g'(z_0), \tag{9.329}$$

equations (9.327) and (9.328) give us q as a function of v. However, if $v < v_c$, we have instead the equation

$$q = Vg(z_0) + \text{terms of the order } V^0, \tag{9.330}$$

and equation (9.326) follows.

It may be noted here that in the case of the perfect Bose-Einstein gas we are confronted with a similar case. The function $g(z)$ is then the function $f(y)$ given by equation (9.202) and $z_0 = 1$. In the next section we shall encounter another instance where we can use equation (9.330).

One can consider equation (9.326) as an equation giving the saturated vapor pressure as a function of the temperature (compare equation [A3.205] on p. 402).

Using equation (9.326) one can write the equation of state (9.312) in the form

$$p = \frac{NkT}{V}\left(1 - \frac{NkT}{4p_cV}\right), \tag{9.331}$$

where now only measurable quantities appear in the equation.

Wergeland has compared this equation of state with the actually observed ones for the cases of nitrogen and argon and has found that equation (9.331) represented the observational data with good accuracy in the neighborhood of the saturation pressure where the deviations from the perfect gas law are by no means small.

Equation (9.325) can be used to determine the temperature T_0 at which for a given specific volume v condensation occurs. Denoting $1/kT_0$ by μ_0, we have the equation

$$e^{\mu_0 \chi} = \frac{v}{v_1}. \tag{9.332}$$

We now wish to consider the actual numbers of droplets of various sizes at temperatures in the neighborhood of T_0. Let $\hat{m}_l$ be the average number of droplets containing l atoms. From the theory of the grand ensembles we have for $\hat{m}_l$ the equation (compare equation [7.511] on p. 165)

$$\hat{m}_l = \frac{-1}{\mu}\frac{\partial q}{\partial \epsilon_l}, \tag{9.333}$$

or, using equations (9.301), (9.302), and (9.307) to (9.309),

$$\hat{m}_l = \frac{V}{v_1} e^{-\mu\chi} \frac{l^{l-2}}{l!} z^l. \tag{9.334}$$

From equations (9.310) and (9.334) we see that the pressure is the sum of the pressures of the subsystems which are all perfect gases $\left(p = \frac{kT}{V}\sum_l \hat{m}_l\right)$, which is, of course, a consequence of our assumption of noninteracting droplets (compare also equation [9.301]).

Using equations (9.317), (9.322), and (9.323), we can write equation (9.334) in the form

$$\hat{m}_l = N \frac{l^{l-2}}{l!} \eta^{l-1} e^{-l\eta}. \tag{9.335}$$

The quantity η measures the degree of saturation, with $\eta = 1$ corresponding to the condensation point. At infinite dilution, $v \to \infty$, and $\eta \to 0$. In that case we have from equation (9.335)

$$\hat{m}_1 = N, \qquad \hat{m}_l = 0, \qquad l > 1, \tag{9.336}$$

that is, every atom is single!

At the condensation point $\hat{m}_l$ is proportional to $l^{-5/2}$† and we see that even then only the smallest drops are present in appreciable amounts.

Let us now consider temperatures just above T_0. From equations (9.332) and (9.317) we get

$$\eta = \left(\frac{v_1}{v}\right)^{\frac{\Delta T}{T}}, \tag{9.337}$$

where

$$\Delta T = T - T_0. \tag{9.338}$$

Substituting equation (9.337) into equation (9.335), we get

$$\hat{m}_l = N \frac{l^{l-2}}{l!} \left(\frac{v_1}{v}\right)^{\frac{(l-1)\Delta T}{T}} e^{-l\left(\frac{v_1}{v}\right)^{\frac{\Delta T}{T}}}, \tag{9.339}$$

† One uses equation (MA3.08) on p. 444 for the factorial.

which shows that $\hat{m}_l$ is only appreciable, even for the smallest l, in a temperature region of the order of $\Delta T \backsim T_0/l$. Figure 28 gives the ratio of m_l at $T_0 + \Delta T$ to m_l at T_0 as a function of $\Delta T/T$, where we have taken $l = 10^5$ and $v_1/v = 10^{-3}$.

The fact that there are no appreciable numbers of drops at temperatures just above T_0 corresponds to the fact that right up to the saturation point no condensation can be observed.

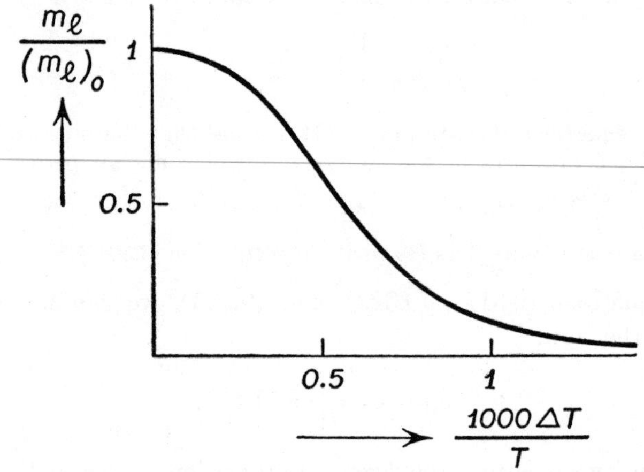

Fig. 28

The liquid drop model theory is only an approximate theory and fails to account for the existence of a critical temperature. At any temperature, condensation will occur, since the coefficients in the power series on the right-hand side of equation (9.308) do not depend on the temperature. This breakdown of the theory is not surprising, since the theory is essentially concerned with the behavior near the saturation point, where it gives, indeed, a clear picture of what is happening. However, far from the saturation point the theory will break down, since there the approximate formulae (9.305) must be applied for small values of l and they will no longer hold.

§4. **Mayer's Theory of Condensation.** We come now to the theory which was first developed by Mayer. We are again concerned with deriving an equation for the isotherms and hence we must derive the equation of state. We can actually use the results derived in the previous chapter, since there were no restrictions imposed on the derivation. We found there that the grand potential of the system was given by the equation

$$q = Vh(y), \tag{9.401}$$

where

$$h(y) = \frac{1}{v_0} \sum_{n=1}^{\infty} b_n y^n, \tag{9.402}$$

$$y = e^{\nu}, \tag{9.403}$$

and where v_0 is given by equation (9.203). The average number of particles in the system is given by the equation

$$N = Vyh'(y). \tag{9.404}$$

The equation of state follows from equations (9.401) and (9.404) and the relation between q and p. It may be noted at this point that the equations which we have just written down are valid both for the classical and for the quantum mechanical case, the only difference being in the actual form of the b_n (see the discussion in Chap. VIII). The b_n are functions of the temperature only, and especially do not depend on the volume V.

We see that equations (9.401) and (9.404) are of the same character as equations (9.201) and (9.206) in §2, or equations (9.310) and (9.311) in §3, and we can use the same argument as in §3 to prove that in the limit where $N \to \infty$ the isotherms consist of two analytically different parts, provided the function $h(y)$ satisfies the conditions (a), (b), and (c) given on page 220. As the b_n are functions of the temperature it is possible that for temperatures above a critical value T_c the function $h(y)$ is regular for all finite values of y, but for temperatures below T_c a singularity occurs, say, at $y = y_0$. If that is the case, the isotherms will give p as a monotonically decreasing function of v for $T > T_c$, but for $T < T_c$ the isotherms will consist of two different parts joining at $v = v_c$, where

$$\frac{1}{v_c} = y_0 h(y_0). \tag{9.405}$$

As long as $v > v_c$, the pressure p is a monotonically decreasing function of v, given by equations (9.401) and (9.404) and the relation $q = \mu pV$. However, for $v < v_c$ we have, apart from terms of the order $1/N$,

$$p = \frac{1}{\mu} h(y_0). \tag{9.406}$$

We must remark here that the derivation of equations (9.401) and (9.404) is general only as long as we may neglect the molecular volume. This means that we are really restricting the equation of state to specific volumes larger than the molecular volume, v_m, which is of the order of magnitude d^3, where d is the range of the intermolecular forces. As soon as we are dealing with specific volumes of the order of, or smaller than, v_m, the derivation of equation (9.401) is no longer valid, and especially it is no longer true that the b_n are independent of the volume. Similar considerations apply to the discussion of §3. It is thus not surprising that the theories discussed in the present and in the preceding section fail to account for the third part of the isotherm, corresponding to the pure liquid.

It is not possible to reach any quantitative conclusions about the existence and the value of the critical temperature as long as one does not make certain plausible assumptions about the dependence of the b_n on T, as was done by Mayer for the case of a classical gas. We refer the reader to Mayer's publications for a more detailed discussion of this point and of his theory in general.

BIBLIOGRAPHICAL NOTES

We refer to the following general references:

1. J. E. and M. G. Mayer, Statistical Mechanics, New York 1940, especially Chapters 13 and 14.
2. B. Kahn, On the Theory of the Equation of State, Thesis, Utrecht 1938.

§1. See ref. 2, §§I.1 and III.1, and also

3. B. Kahn and G. E. Uhlenbeck, Physica, **5**, 399, 1938.

§2. We refer to refs. 2 and 3 and also to

4. A. Einstein, Berliner Ber., **1925**, 3.
5. F. London, Phys. Rev., **54**, 947, 1938.
6. R. H. Fowler and H. Jones, Proc. Cambridge Phil. Soc., **34**, 573, 1938.
7. H. Wergeland and K. Hove-Storhoug, D. Kgl. Norske Vid. Selsk. Forh., **15**, 131, 1943.
8. H. Wergeland and K. Hove-Storhoug, D. Kgl. Norske Vid. Selsk. Forh., **15**, 135, 1943.
9. H. Wergeland and K. Hove-Storhoug, D. Kgl. Norske Vid. Selsk. Forh., **15**, 181, 1943.
10. H. Wergeland, D. Kgl. Norske Vid. Selsk. Forh., **17**, 51, 1944.
11. H. Wergeland, D. Kgl. Norske Vid. Selsk. Forh., **17**, 63, 1944.
12. Lectures given by H. A. Kramers in Leiden during the winter of 1944–1945.
13. H. Wergeland, D. Kgl. Norske Vid. Selsk. Forh., **19**, 80, 1947.
14. W. Band, Phys. Rev., **79**, 871, 1950.
15. R. Becker, Z. Physik, **128**, 120, 1950.
16. G. Leibfried, Z. Physik, **128**, 133, 1950.
17. A. R. Fraser, Phil. Mag., **42**, 156, 1951.
18. A. R. Fraser, Phil. Mag., **42**, 165, 1951.
19. D. ter Haar, Proc. Roy. Soc. (London), **A212**, 552, 1952.

Recently many papers have appeared, all stressing some particular detail of the theory of the Einstein condensation, or of the theory of He II as a Bose-Einstein system. We may mention refs. 15 and 16 and

20. G. Schubert, Z. Naturf., **1**, 113, 1946.
21. G. Schubert, Z. Naturf., **2a**, 250, 1947.
22. G. Leibfried, Z. Naturf., **2a**, 305, 1947.
23. T. Matsubara, Progr. Theor. Phys., **6**, 714, 1951.
24. R. B. Dingle, Adv. Phys., **1**, 111, 1952.

25. R. B. Dingle, Proc. Cambridge Phil. Soc., **45,** 275, 1949.
26. H. N. V. Temperley, Proc. Roy. Soc. (London), **A199,** 361, 1949.

Our treatment is based on refs. 12 and 19. We use throughout the method of the grand ensembles instead of restricting the number of particles in the system as is done in all references given here, except refs. 12, 15, 16, and 19.

§3. The thermodynamical theory of condensation was given by Becker and Döring in their paper:

27. R. Becker and W. Döring, Ann. Physik, **24,** 719, 1935.

The statistical analogy can be found in the following papers:

28. J. Frenkel, J. Chem. Phys., **7,** 200, 1939.
29. W. Band, J. Chem. Phys., **7,** 324, 1939.
30. J. Frenkel, J. Chem. Phys., **7,** 538, 1939.
31. W. Band, J. Chem. Phys., **7,** 927, 1939.
32. J. E. Mayer and S. F. Streeter, J. Chem. Phys., **7,** 1019, 1939.
33. S. F. Streeter and J. E. Mayer, J. Chem. Phys., **7,** 1025, 1939.
34. F. Kuhrt, Z. Physik, **131,** 185, 1952.
35. F. Kuhrt, Z. Physik, **131,** 205, 1952.
36. H. Wergeland, Avhandl. Norske Videnskaps-Akad. Oslo, Mat-Naturv. Klasse, 1943, No. 11.
37. D. ter Haar, Proc. Cambridge Phil. Soc., **49,** 130, 1953.

Our treatment is based on refs. 36 and 37.

§4. Mayer's theory appeared first in the following papers:

38. J. E. Mayer, J. Chem. Phys., **5,** 67, 1937.
39. J. E. Mayer and P. G. Ackermann, J. Chem. Phys., **5,** 74, 1937.
40. J. E. Mayer and S. F. Harrison, J. Chem. Phys., **6,** 87, 1938.
41. S. F. Harrison and J. E. Mayer, J. Chem. Phys., **6,** 101, 1938.

See also refs. 1, 2, 3, 37, and

42. M. Born and K. Fuchs, Proc. Roy. Soc. (London), **A166,** 391, 1938.
43. J. E. Mayer, J. Chem. Phys., **10,** 629, 1942.
44. B. H. Zimm, J. Chem. Phys., **19,** 1019, 1951.
45. J. E. Mayer, J. Chem. Phys., **19,** 1024, 1951.

We must draw attention to the fact that we have omitted most of the mathematical details for which we refer to refs. 19, 36, and 37. We refer to ref. 1 for an extensive discussion of Mayer's theory.

After this chapter was written the following important paper appeared:

46. C. N. Yang and T. D. Lee, Phys. Rev., **87,** 404, 1952.

See also

47. T. D. Lee and C. N. Yang, Phys. Rev., **87,** 410, 1952.

Reference 46 seems to open up the possibility for a more general discussion of the condensation phenomenon, although it still does not provide us with a simple theory.

CHAPTER X

THE ELEMENTARY ELECTRON THEORY OF METALS

§1. Introduction; the Richardson Effect. We mentioned at the end of Chapter IV that one case where one encounters a Fermi-Dirac gas is the case of the "gas" of the conduction electrons in a metal. We shall discuss this case in the present chapter, introducing as a first approximation the assumption that the electron gas may be treated as a perfect Fermi-Dirac gas inside the volume occupied by the metal.

Before we sketch the model which we shall use we may briefly give a survey of the historical development of the electron theory of metals. The first major step toward such a theory was made in 1900 by Drude, who applied the kinetic theory of gases to the electron gas and was thus able to derive the Wiedemann-Franz law, which states that the ratio of thermal to electrical conductivity is proportional to the absolute temperature, but otherwise a constant. In 1905 Lorentz further developed Drude's theory by applying better statistical methods and introducing the Maxwell distribution as the velocity distribution of the electrons inside the metal. One of the greatest difficulties of the Drude-Lorentz theory, however, was the fact that Debye's theory of the specific heats of solids accounted for the specific heat of metals *without* a contribution from the electron gas, while a classical electron gas would contribute $\frac{3}{2}k$ per electron. This difficulty was overcome when Sommerfeld in 1928 applied Fermi-Dirac instead of Boltzmann statistics to the electron gas. It is essentially Sommerfeld's theory which we shall discuss in the present chapter.

Our model of a metal is the following one (see Fig. 29). We shall assume that the conduction electrons are moving as free and independent particles in a constant negative potential, $-\chi$, produced by the metallic ions. Our problem is thus first of all to derive an expression for the energy levels of an electron when its potential energy has the form given in Figure 29.†

† We are not concerned with any detailed features of the potential energy and have therefore assumed U to be constant throughout the metal and to change discontinuously to zero at the surface of the metal. In actual cases there will be a smooth transition from $-\chi$ to 0, but the simplified potential of Fig. 29 is sufficient for our purposes.

Actually, we need only the energy level density and it turns out that, if we take as the zero of energy the value of the potential energy inside the metal, this density is the same as that of an electron in a volume V with rigid walls, as long as we are only interested in bound levels. We have thus for the number of levels, dZ, with energies between ϵ and $\epsilon + d\epsilon$

$$dZ = 4\pi \left(\frac{2m}{h^2}\right)^{3/2} V\sqrt{\epsilon}d\epsilon, \tag{10.101}$$

where m is the mass of the electron† and V the volume of the metal, and where the difference of a factor 2 between equation (10.101) and equation

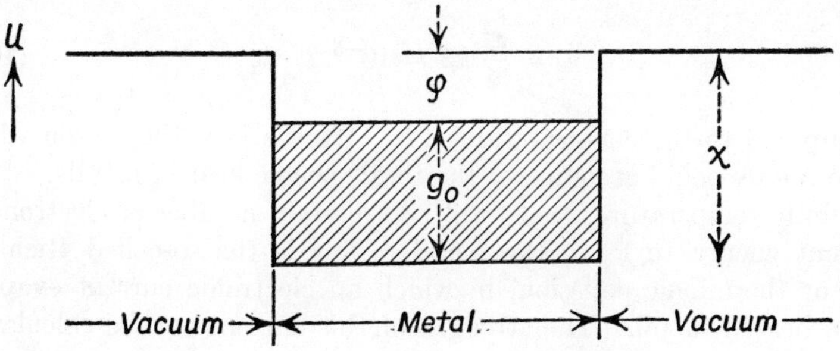

Fig. 29

(4.504) on page 82 arises since we now must take into account the fact that the electron has a spin so that every energy level is twofold degenerate.

We can now use the formulae derived in §7 of Chapter IV as long as we insert everywhere the appropriate factors 2 arising from the electron spin. We mentioned on page 94 that the electron gas would be highly degenerate and we must use the formulae for the case of strong degeneracy (pp. 91–93). Let us first consider the situation at the absolute zero. In that case we know that the electrons will occupy all the lowest levels up to an energy, g_0, which is given by equation (4.720), or

$$g_0 = \frac{h^2}{2m}\left(\frac{3N}{8\pi V}\right)^{2/3}, \tag{10.102}$$

where N is the total number of electrons in the system. We have indicated this situation schematically in Figure 29 by shading the area between $\epsilon = 0$ and $\epsilon = g_0$.‡ We introduce a quantity φ by the equation

$$\varphi = \chi - g_0. \tag{10.103}$$

† We neglect here the fact that sometimes one must use for m not the actual mass of the electron, but an effective mass.

‡ It must be emphasized here that this common way of indicating energy levels in a

This quantity, which is the energy one must impart to an electron at the top of the "Fermi sea" in order to get the electron out of the metal, is called the *work function*.

At finite temperatures we can use equations (4.725) to (4.729)—again with extra factors 2 where necessary. Introducing the variable β by the equation

$$\beta = \frac{2mk}{h^2}\left(\frac{8\pi V}{3N}\right)^{2/3} T = 2 \cdot 10^{-6} \cdot T \qquad \textbf{(10.104)}$$

(we assumed $N/V = 10^{24}$ cm^{-3}), we have, for instance, for the specific heat per electron the expression

$$c_v = \frac{\pi^2}{2} k\beta = 10^{-5}\, T \cdot k, \qquad \textbf{(10.105)}$$

as compared to the classical value $\frac{3}{2}k$. We see here the reason why the Debye theory could account for the total specific heat of metals.

At finite temperatures there will be a certain number of electrons with sufficient energy to leave the metal. This is the so-called Richardson effect or thermionic emission, in which an electronic current evaporates from a heated metal. The strength of this current can be calculated as follows. Let j be the current per unit area, or the transport of charge per unit time through 1 cm^2 of the surface of the metal, and let $f(\epsilon)d\epsilon$ be the number of electrons per unit volume with energies between ϵ and $\epsilon + d\epsilon$. We then have

$$j = e \int uf(\epsilon)d\epsilon, \qquad \textbf{(10.106)}$$

where u is the velocity component normal to the surface of the metal and where e is the electronic charge.

Introducing as variables instead of ϵ the x, y, and z components of the velocity, u, v, and w, choosing the x-axis along the normal to the surface of the metal, and introducing for $f(\epsilon)$ the distribution function given, apart from a spin factor, by equation (4.718) we have

$$j = \frac{2m^3e}{h^3} \iiint \frac{ududvdw}{e^{-\nu+\mu\epsilon} + 1}, \qquad \textbf{(10.107)}\dagger$$

potential energy diagram does *not* mean that the energy levels are functions of the position in the metal. As characteristic values of the wave equation they are numbers. The same remark applies to the schematic representation of the energy bands in Fig. 31. Compare also the discussion on p. 243.

† We transform from equation (10.106) to equation (10.107) by using the fact that we have $\epsilon = \frac{1}{2}mc^2$ $(c^2 = u^2 + v^2 + w^2)$ and thus $\sqrt{\epsilon}\, d\epsilon = \sqrt{\frac{1}{2}m^3}c^2dc$ and the fact that $dudvdw \leftrightarrow 4\pi c^2dc$.

where μ is once more related to the absolute temperature by the equation

$$\mu = \frac{1}{kT}, \tag{10.108}$$

and where ν/μ is the partial thermal potential. The integrations over v and w on the right-hand side of equation (10.107) extend from $-\infty$ to $+\infty$, but u can only be integrated from $u_0 = \sqrt{2\chi/m}$, since otherwise the electron possesses insufficient energy to leave the metal.

We may at this point briefly mention the so-called *Fermi-level*, E_F, a term widely used in metal and semiconductor theory.†‡ This Fermi-level is the *electrochemical potential* and is equal to the partial thermal potential ν/μ as can be seen as follows. Addition of δN electrons to the system will result in a change δF of the free energy equal to $(\nu/\mu)\delta N$ (compare equation [4.410] on p. 80). Consider now two systems A and B at electrical potentials V_A and V_B. An adiabatic transfer of δN electrons with charge e from A to B will result in a change δF of the free energy of the combined system which on the one hand is equal to $e(V_B - V_A)$ and on the other hand is equal to $(\nu/\mu)_B - (\nu/\mu)_A$. This shows that E_F is the electrochemical potential.

Since in the case of equilibrium between two systems the partial thermal potential must be the same in the two systems,§ it follows that two metals or semiconductors in contact should have the same value for their Fermi-levels in equilibrium.

The name "Fermi-level" derives from the fact that at the absolute zero all levels up to E_F will be occupied (compare the discussion on p. 92).

Using the relation

$$u = \frac{1}{m}\frac{\partial \epsilon}{\partial u}, \tag{10.109}$$

we can write equation (10.107) in the form

$$j = \frac{2m^2 e}{h^3}\int_{-\infty}^{+\infty} dv \int_{-\infty}^{+\infty} dw \int_{\epsilon_0}^{\infty} \frac{d\epsilon}{e^{-\nu+\mu\epsilon}+1}, \tag{10.110}$$

where

$$\epsilon_0 = \chi + \tfrac{1}{2}m(v^2 + w^2). \tag{10.111}$$

† See, e.g., W. Shockley, Electrons and Holes in Semiconductors, New York 1950, p. 231 and Chap. 16; J. C. Slater, Quantum Theory of Matter, New York 1951, Chap. 12.

‡ The Fermi-level must not be confused with the Fermi-energy, a term often used for the average energy of the electrons in the system (e.g., Slater, *op. cit.*, p. 420).

§ See, e.g., J. W. Gibbs, Elementary Principles in Statistical Mechanics (Vol. II of his Collected Works), New Haven 1948, p. 197; or R. H. Fowler and E. A. Guggenheim, Statistical Thermodynamics, Cambridge 1939, p. 65.

The result of the integration over ϵ is

$$j = \frac{2m^2e}{\mu h^3} \int_{-\infty}^{+\infty} dv \int_{-\infty}^{+\infty} dw \ln \left[1 + e^{\nu - \mu(\chi + \frac{1}{2}m(v^2+w^2))}\right]. \quad (10.112)$$

At ordinary temperatures the exponential is small compared to one and we can expand the logarithm and get in this way

$$j = \frac{2m^2e}{\mu h^3} \iint_{-\infty}^{+\infty} dv dw e^{\nu - \mu\chi - \frac{1}{2}\mu m v^2 - \frac{1}{2}\mu m w^2},$$

or

$$j = \frac{4\pi m e}{\mu^2 h^3} e^{\nu - \mu\chi}. \quad (10.113)$$

As long as the temperature is so low that the parameter β defined by equation (10.104) is small compared to one, ν is practically equal to μg_0,† and using equations (10.103) and (10.108) we get

$$j = \frac{4\pi m e}{h^3} k^2 T^2 e^{-\mu\varphi}, \quad (10.114)$$

which is the equation giving the current density of the Richardson effect.

Richardson showed experimentally that the velocity distribution of the electrons which leave the metal is practically Maxwellian. One can easily show that this will be the case even though the distribution function inside the metal is a Fermi-Dirac distribution. The distribution function of the electrons which can leave the metal is given by the Fermi-Dirac formula

$$f(\epsilon)d\epsilon = \frac{C\sqrt{\epsilon}d\epsilon}{e^{-\nu+\mu\epsilon} + 1}, \qquad \epsilon \geqslant \chi, \quad (10.115)$$

where C is a constant. The energy ϵ' of these electrons outside the metal is related to their energy ϵ inside the metal by the equation

$$\epsilon' = \epsilon - \chi, \quad (10.116)$$

and their distribution function will thus be of the form

$$f'(\epsilon')d\epsilon' = \frac{C\sqrt{\epsilon' + \chi}d\epsilon'}{e^{-\nu+\mu\chi+\mu\epsilon'} + 1} = \frac{C\sqrt{\epsilon' + \chi}d\epsilon'}{e^{\mu\varphi+\mu\epsilon'} + 1}. \quad (10.117)$$

† By an analysis similar to the one leading to equations (4.726) to (4.729) one finds that $\nu = \mu g_0\left(1 - \frac{\pi^2}{12}\beta^2\right)$.

Since $\mu\varphi \gg 1$ at the temperatures at which the experiments were made, we can neglect the 1 in the denominator. Moreover, we can neglect to a first approximation ϵ' with respect to χ and equation (10.117) reduces to the equation

$$f'(\epsilon')d\epsilon' = C'e^{-\mu\epsilon'}d\epsilon', \tag{10.118}$$

which is, indeed, a Maxwell distribution.†

§2. Lorentz's Solution of the Transport Equation.

If we wish to consider electrical and thermal conductivity in metals—as we shall do in the next section—or the Hall effect—as we shall do in §4—we are no longer dealing with pure equilibrium situations but with steady, nonequilibrium states, and we must consider Boltzmann's transport equation. We derived this equation in §5 of Chapter II and we shall consider it in the following form,

$$(\mathbf{c} \cdot \nabla f) + (\mathbf{F} \cdot \nabla_c f) = B - A, \tag{10.201}$$

where $f(\mathbf{x},\mathbf{c})$ is the distribution function, where $\mathbf{c}$ is the velocity vector with components u, v, and w, and where ∇ and ∇_c are symbolical vectors with components $\partial/\partial x$, $\partial/\partial y$, $\partial/\partial z$, and $\partial/\partial u$, $\partial/\partial v$, $\partial/\partial w$, respectively. In equation (10.201) we have put $\partial f/\partial t = 0$, since we are dealing with a steady state, the vector $\mathbf{F}$ is the force per unit mass, and $B\,du\,dv\,dw$ and $A\,du\,dv\,dw$ are respectively the numbers of electrons which per unit time acquire or lose velocities between $\mathbf{c}$ and $\mathbf{c} + \mathbf{dc}$.

We wish to obtain a solution of equation (10.201) in the case where there are homogeneous electric fields E_x and E_y in the x- and y-directions and a homogeneous magnetic field H_z in the z-direction. The force per unit mass is then the Lorentz force and is given by the equation‡

$$\mathbf{F} = -\frac{e}{m}\left[\mathbf{E} + \frac{\mathbf{c} \times \mathbf{H}}{c_0}\right], \tag{10.202}$$

or

$$F_x = -\frac{e}{m}E_x - \frac{e}{mc_0}vH_z, \tag{10.203}$$

$$F_y = -\frac{e}{m}E_y + \frac{e}{mc_0}uH_z, \tag{10.204}$$

$$F_z = 0, \tag{10.205}$$

† The fact that the distribution of the electrons leaving the metal is practically Maxwellian is due to the fact that the Fermi distribution has a Maxwellian tail (see p. 91).

‡ In the present and the next chapter we denote the velocity of light by c_0 in order not to have the same symbol for two different quantities.

which substituted in equation (10.201) leads to the equation

$$u\frac{\partial f}{\partial x} + v\frac{\partial f}{\partial y} + w\frac{\partial f}{\partial z} - \frac{\partial f}{\partial u}\left(\frac{e}{m}E_x + \frac{e}{mc_0}vH_z\right) - \frac{\partial f}{\partial v}\left(\frac{e}{m}E_y - \frac{e}{mc_0}uH_z\right) = B - A. \quad (10.206)$$

It is not possible to solve this equation rigorously, but it is possible to find a solution if we introduce the following three basic assumptions first introduced by Lorentz.

a) The collisions which the electrons undergo are only collisions with the lattice and these collisions are all elastic. That is, during the collision the direction, but not the magnitude, of the velocity of the electron is changed.

b) The electronic scattering is isotropic. This means that, if the probability per unit time that an electron will change its velocity from $\mathbf{c}$ to a velocity within the range $\mathbf{c}'$, $\mathbf{c}' + d\mathbf{c}'$ is denoted by $\Theta(\mathbf{c};\mathbf{c}')d\mathbf{c}'$,† this function Θ will be independent of the relative directions of the velocity of the electron before and after the collision.

c) The distribution function, f, in the case where electric and magnetic fields are present is related to the distribution function, f_0, in the case where there is no field present by the equation

$$f = f_0 + u\chi_1 + v\chi_2, \quad (10.207)$$

where we may treat the last two terms on the right-hand side of this equation as being small compared to the first term and where χ_1 and χ_2 are assumed to depend on the electron velocity only through its absolute magnitude, c.

If we introduce these three assumptions we can evaluate the terms A and B on the right-hand side of equation (10.206). From our definition of A and of the function $\Theta(\mathbf{c};\mathbf{c}')$, we have

$$A = f(\mathbf{x},\mathbf{c})\int \Theta(\mathbf{c};\mathbf{c}')d\mathbf{c}', \quad (10.208)$$

where the integration extends over the whole of velocity space. Similarly we have

$$B = \int f(\mathbf{x},\mathbf{c}'')\Theta(\mathbf{c}'';\mathbf{c})d\mathbf{c}''. \quad (10.209)$$

According to assumption (a) Θ is zero unless $c = c'$, and we have therefore

$$\Theta(c,\vartheta,\varphi;c',\vartheta',\varphi') = \delta(c - c')\frac{1}{c^2}\eta(c), \quad (10.210)$$

† Once again we denote by dc a volume element in velocity space and once again we draw attention to the difference between dc and $d\mathbf{c}$.

where $\delta(c - c')$ is Dirac's delta-function (see p. 106), where we have introduced polar coordinates c, ϑ, and φ instead of u, v, and w, and where we have used the fact that according to assumption (b) η cannot depend on ϑ, φ, ϑ', or φ'. The factor c^{-2} is introduced to simplify our equations. From the definition of Θ it can easily be verified that the probability per unit time that an electron with speed c in the direction prescribed by the polar angles ϑ, φ is elastically deflected into the solid angle $\sin \vartheta' d\vartheta' d\varphi'$ around ϑ',φ' is equal to $\eta \sin \vartheta' d\vartheta' d\varphi'$. It follows then that the total number of collisions made by an electron per sec is equal to $4\pi\eta$.

Introducing polar coordinates into equations (10.208) and (10.209) and using equations (10.210) and (10.207), we have

$$A = 4\pi\eta(f_0 + u\chi_1 + v\chi_2), \tag{10.211}$$

$$B = 4\pi\eta f_0. \tag{10.212}$$

Equations (10.211) and (10.212) are derived as follows. From equation (10.208) we have

$$A = f(\mathbf{x},\mathbf{c}) \int \Theta c'^2 dc' \sin \vartheta' d\vartheta' d\varphi'$$

$$= f(\mathbf{x},\mathbf{c})\eta(c) \int_0^{2\pi} d\varphi' \int_0^{\pi} \sin \vartheta' d\vartheta' = 4\pi\eta f,$$

and equation (10.211) follows. Similarly we have from equations (10.209), (10.210), assumption (c), and the relations $u = c \cos \vartheta \cos \varphi$, $v = c \cos \vartheta \sin \varphi$,

$$B = \int f(\mathbf{x},\mathbf{c}'')\Theta(\mathbf{c};\mathbf{c}'')c''^2 dc'' \sin \vartheta'' d\vartheta'' d\varphi''$$

$$= \int [f_0(\mathbf{x},\mathbf{c}'') + u''\chi_1(c'') + v''\chi_2(c'')]\delta(c - c'') \frac{c''^2}{c^2} \eta(c) \sin \vartheta'' d\vartheta'' d\varphi''$$

$$= 4\pi\eta f_0 + c\chi_1(c)\eta \int_0^{2\pi} \cos \varphi'' d\varphi'' \int_0^{\pi} \sin \vartheta'' \cos \vartheta'' d\vartheta''$$

$$+ c\chi_2(c)\eta \int_0^{2\pi} \sin \varphi'' d\varphi'' \int_0^{\pi} \sin \vartheta'' \cos \vartheta'' d\vartheta'',$$

and equation (10.212) follows.

Instead of η we shall introduce the mean free path λ, that is, the average distance traversed by an electron between two consecutive collisions. Since the total number of collisions made per sec by an electron is $4\pi\eta$, we have

$$\lambda = \frac{c}{4\pi\eta}, \tag{10.213}$$

and from equations (10.211) to (10.213) we have

$$B - A = -\frac{c}{\lambda}(u\chi_1 + v\chi_2). \tag{10.214}$$

We can now substitute from equations (10.207) and (10.214) into equation (10.206). We shall retain only the most important terms, which means that we shall everywhere neglect terms containing the χ_i with respect to similar terms containing f_0. Since f_0, χ_1, and χ_2 depend only on u, v, and w in the combination $u^2 + v^2 + w^2$, we can use the following relations:

$$\frac{\partial f_0}{\partial u} = \frac{\partial f_0}{\partial \epsilon}\frac{\partial \epsilon}{\partial u} = mu\frac{\partial f_0}{\partial \epsilon}, \quad \frac{\partial f_0}{\partial v} = mv\frac{\partial f_0}{\partial \epsilon}, \quad \frac{\partial \chi_i}{\partial u} = mu\frac{\partial \chi_i}{\partial \epsilon}, \quad \frac{\partial \chi_i}{\partial v} = mv\frac{\partial \chi_i}{\partial \epsilon}, \tag{10.215}$$

where

$$\epsilon = \tfrac{1}{2}mc^2 = \tfrac{1}{2}m(u^2 + v^2 + w^2). \tag{10.216}$$

Since it follows from symmetry considerations that f does not depend on z we get finally the equation

$$u\frac{\partial f_0}{\partial x} + v\frac{\partial f_0}{\partial y} - e\frac{\partial f_0}{\partial \epsilon}(uE_x + vE_y) - \frac{e}{mc_0}(vH_z\chi_1 - uH_z\chi_2) + \frac{c}{\lambda}(u\chi_1 + v\chi_2) = 0. \tag{10.217}$$

Since this equation must hold for any pair of values of u and v, one can put the coefficients of u and v separately equal to zero and we have thus the following equations for χ_1 and χ_2:

$$\frac{\partial f_0}{\partial x} - eE_x\frac{\partial f_0}{\partial \epsilon} + \frac{e}{mc_0}H_z\chi_2 + \frac{c}{\lambda}\chi_1 = 0, \tag{10.218}$$

$$\frac{\partial f_0}{\partial y} - eE_y\frac{\partial f_0}{\partial \epsilon} - \frac{e}{mc_0}H_z\chi_1 + \frac{c}{\lambda}\chi_2 = 0. \tag{10.219}$$

Introducing the abbreviations

$$f_1 = \frac{\partial f_0}{\partial x} - eE_x\frac{\partial f_0}{\partial \epsilon}, \tag{10.220}$$

$$f_2 = \frac{\partial f_0}{\partial y} - eE_y\frac{\partial f_0}{\partial \epsilon}, \tag{10.221}$$

$$s = \lambda\frac{eH_z}{mcc_0}, \tag{10.222}$$

we have these solutions for χ_1 and χ_2:

$$\chi_1 = \frac{-\lambda}{c(1+s^2)}(f_1 - sf_2), \tag{10.223}$$

$$\chi_2 = \frac{-\lambda}{c(1+s^2)}(sf_1 + f_2). \tag{10.224}$$

The physical meaning of the quantity s is that it is the ratio of the mean free path to the radius of curvature of an electron moving with speed c in a magnetic field H_z.

We shall use equations (10.223) and (10.224) in the following sections to derive expressions for the electrical and thermal conductivity and for the Hall coefficient.

§3. Electrical and Thermal Conductivity; Wiedemann-Franz Law. In order to calculate the coefficients of electrical and thermal conductivity we must obtain expressions for the electrical and thermal currents in terms of the distribution function. Let j_x and w_x be the total electrical and thermal currents which pass through a unit area normal to the x-direction. Since $-eu$ and $u \cdot \frac{1}{2}mc^2$ are the contributions per electron of velocity $\mathbf{c}$ to j_x and w_x, respectively, we have

$$j_x = -e\iiint uf d\mathbf{c}, \tag{10.301}$$

$$w_x = \tfrac{1}{2}m\iiint uc^2 f d\mathbf{c}. \tag{10.302}$$

Using equation (10.207) for f, the integrals on the right-hand side of equations (10.301) and (10.302) consist of three parts. The integrals containing f_0 and χ_2 are zero, since the integrands are odd functions of u and the integration extends from $u = -\infty$ to $u = +\infty$. Equations (10.301) and (10.302) reduce thus to the expressions

$$j_x = -e\iiint \chi_1(c)u^2 d\mathbf{c}, \tag{10.303}$$

$$w_x = \tfrac{1}{2}m\iiint \chi_1(c)u^2c^2 d\mathbf{c}. \tag{10.304}$$

Introducing polar coordinates and integrating over the angles we get

$$j_x = -\frac{4\pi e}{3}\int_0^\infty c^4\chi_1(c)dc, \tag{10.305}$$

$$w_x = \frac{2\pi m}{3}\int_0^\infty c^6\chi_1(c)dc, \tag{10.306}$$

and χ_1 is given by equation (10.223).

The electrical conductivity σ is defined by Ohm's law,

$$j_x = \sigma E_x. \tag{10.307}$$

We shall assume, firstly, that there is no magnetic field, so that $H_z = 0$ and also $s = 0$; secondly, that the temperature is constant throughout the metal so that $\partial f_0/\partial x = 0$. We then have from equations (10.220) and (10.223)

$$\chi_1 = \frac{e\lambda}{c} E_x \frac{\partial f_0}{\partial \epsilon}, \tag{10.308}$$

and hence from equations (10.305), (10.307), and (10.308)

$$\sigma = -\frac{4\pi e^2}{3}\int_0^\infty \lambda c^3 \frac{\partial f_0}{\partial \epsilon}\, dc. \tag{10.309}$$

Before we evaluate the right-hand side of equation (10.309), we shall derive an expression for the thermal conductivity which is defined by the equation

$$w_x = -\kappa \frac{dT}{dx}, \tag{10.310}$$

when we are considering the case where there exists a temperature gradient in the x-direction.

Since a temperature gradient is connected with an uneven electron density, there will be present an electric field E_x, and we must calculate w_x under the condition that j_x is zero. We must thus use both equation (10.305) and equation (10.306). Let us first of all determine $\partial f_0/\partial x$. This expression is now different from zero, since f_0 depends on the temperature. The dependence of f_0 on the temperature is through the variable α given by the equation

$$\alpha = \mu\epsilon - \nu, \tag{10.311}$$

and hence we have

$$\frac{\partial f_0}{\partial x} = \frac{1}{\mu}\frac{\partial f_0}{\partial \epsilon}\frac{d\alpha}{dT}\frac{dT}{dx} = -\frac{\partial f_0}{\partial \epsilon}\frac{dT}{dx}\left[\frac{\epsilon}{T} + \frac{1}{\mu}\frac{d\nu}{dT}\right]. \tag{10.312}$$

From equations (10.223), (10.220), (10.305), (10.306), and (10.312) we now get

$$j_x = -\frac{4\pi e}{3}\int_0^\infty \lambda c^3 \frac{\partial f_0}{\partial \epsilon}\left[eE_x + \frac{dT}{dx}\left(\frac{\epsilon}{T} + \frac{1}{\mu}\frac{d\nu}{dT}\right)\right] dc, \tag{10.313}$$

$$w_x = \frac{2\pi m}{3}\int_0^\infty \lambda c^5 \frac{\partial f_0}{\partial \epsilon}\left[eE_x + \frac{dT}{dx}\left(\frac{\epsilon}{T} + \frac{1}{\mu}\frac{d\nu}{dT}\right)\right] dc. \tag{10.314}$$

We are interested in the case where $j_x = 0$. We can then determine E_x from equation (10.313) and substitute into equation (10.314). It is advantageous to introduce instead of c the energy ϵ as integration variable by using equation (10.216). Furthermore we shall introduce a function $F(\epsilon)$ by writing

$$f_0(u,v,w) = \frac{2m^3}{h^3} F(\epsilon). \tag{10.315}$$

Introducing this new integration variable and the function $F(\epsilon)$ instead of f_0 and eliminating E_x from equations (10.313) and (10.314), we get

$$w_x = \frac{16\pi m}{3h^3} \frac{1}{T} \frac{dT}{dx} \frac{K_1K_3 - K_2{}^2}{K_1}, \tag{10.316}$$

where

$$K_n = \int_0^\infty \lambda \epsilon^n \frac{\partial F}{\partial \epsilon} \, d\epsilon. \tag{10.317}$$

From equations (10.310) and (10.316) we get for κ the equation

$$\kappa = \frac{16\pi m}{3h^3} \frac{K_2{}^2 - K_1K_3}{K_1T}, \tag{10.318}$$

where the K_n are given by equations (10.317) and (10.315).

The electrical conductivity can also be expressed in terms of the K_n and we have from equation (10.309)

$$\sigma = -\frac{16\pi me^2}{3h^3} K_1. \tag{10.319}$$

Up to now our discussion has been general, but at this point we must introduce the special form of the distribution function which is applicable in the case of a metal. We have in that case the Fermi-Dirac distribution

$$f_0(u,v,w) = \frac{2m^3}{h^3} \frac{1}{e^{-\nu+\mu\epsilon} + 1}, \tag{10.320}$$

or

$$F(\epsilon) = \frac{1}{e^{-\nu+\mu\epsilon} + 1}, \tag{10.321}$$

where ν is very nearly equal to μg_0.

As long as $e^{-\nu}$ is small compared to unity, the function $F(\epsilon)$ will be practically equal to one for energies up to g_0 and be practically equal to zero for energies larger than g_0 (see Fig. 30). Similarly, $\partial F/\partial \epsilon$ will be practically equal to zero except for energies in the immediate neighborhood of g_0 (see Fig. 30). At the absolute zero $-\partial F/\partial \epsilon$ will be a Dirac delta-function;

at finite temperatures it will still be a similar function. Indeed, it can be shown that the following equation holds to a fair approximation:†

$$\int_0^\infty G(\epsilon)\frac{\partial F}{\partial \epsilon}\,d\epsilon = -G(g_0) - \frac{\pi^2}{6\mu^2}\left.\frac{\partial^2 G}{\partial \epsilon^2}\right|_{\epsilon=g_0}, \tag{10.322}$$

where usually the second term on the right-hand side can be neglected with respect to the first one.

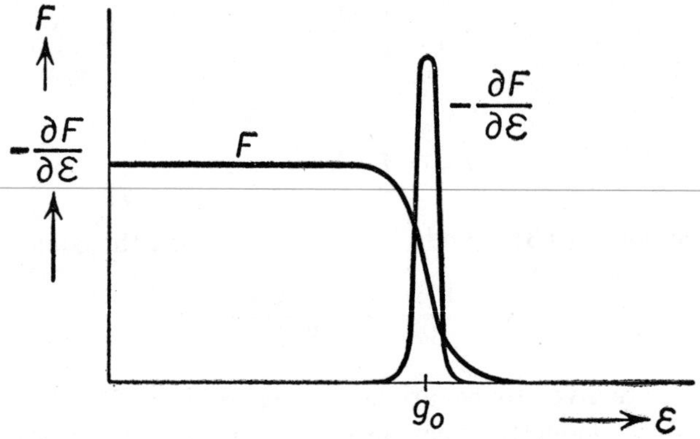

Fig. 30

Using equation (10.322) we have for the K_n the equations

$$K_n = -\bar{\lambda}g_0{}^n - \frac{\pi^2}{6}k^2T^2\left(\frac{\partial^2\lambda\epsilon^n}{\partial\epsilon^2}\right)_{\epsilon=g_0} \tag{10.323}$$

where $\bar{\lambda}$ $(=\lambda(g_0))$ is the mean free path of an electron with kinetic energy g_0.

Using equation (10.323) we get for the electrical conductivity from equation (10.319)

$$\sigma = \frac{ne^2\bar{\lambda}}{m\bar{c}}, \tag{10.324}$$

where $\bar{c}$ is the velocity of an electron with kinetic energy g_0 and where n is the number of electrons per cm^3. In deriving equation (10.324) we have used equations (10.102) and (10.216).

Similarly, we get for the thermal conductivity from equation (10.318)

$$\kappa = \frac{\pi^2}{3}\frac{k^2n\bar{\lambda}}{m\bar{c}}T. \tag{10.325}$$

† A. Sommerfeld and H. Bethe, Handb. d. Phys., Vol. $\mathbf{24}_2$, Berlin 1933, p. 346. One integrates by parts and uses the theorem on p. 92.

Combining equations (10.324) and (10.325), we get the relation

$$\frac{\kappa}{T\sigma} = \frac{\pi^2}{3}\left(\frac{k}{e}\right)^2, \tag{10.326}$$

where the right-hand side is a universal constant. This relation is the so-called *Wiedemann-Franz law* since these two physicists were the first to observe a relationship of this kind.†

§4. The Isothermal Hall Effect. Let us consider now the case where there are homogeneous electric fields both in the x- and in the y-direction and a magnetic field in the z-direction. If the metal is at a constant temperature throughout and if there is no current flowing in the y-direction and a current j_x in the x-direction, we have the case of the isothermal *Hall effect.* The Hall electromotoric force is the electromotoric force induced in the y-direction, and the Hall constant R is defined by the equation

$$E_y = Rj_xH_z, \tag{10.401}$$

under the physical conditions described by the equations

$$\frac{\partial f_0}{\partial x} = \frac{\partial f_0}{\partial y} = 0, \qquad j_y = 0. \tag{10.402}$$

Using equations (10.220), (10.221), (10.223), and (10.224) we have from equation (10.305) for j_x and a similar equation for j_y

$$j_x = -\frac{4\pi e^2}{3}\left[E_x\int_0^\infty \frac{\lambda}{1+s^2}\frac{\partial f_0}{\partial \epsilon}c^3dc - E_y\int_0^\infty \frac{\lambda s}{1+s^2}\frac{\partial f_0}{\partial \epsilon}c^3dc\right], \tag{10.403}$$

$$j_y = 0 = -\frac{4\pi e^2}{3}\left[E_x\int_0^\infty \frac{\lambda s}{1+s^2}\frac{\partial f_0}{\partial \epsilon}c^3dc + E_y\int_0^\infty \frac{\lambda}{1+s^2}\frac{\partial f_0}{\partial \epsilon}c^3dc\right]. \tag{10.404}$$

From these two equations we can express E_x and E_y in terms of j_x and we get

$$E_x = -\frac{3h^3}{16\pi me^2}\frac{L_1}{{L_1}^2 + {L_2}^2}j_x, \tag{10.405}$$

$$E_y = \frac{3h^3}{16\pi me^2}\frac{L_2}{{L_1}^2 + {L_2}^2}j_y, \tag{10.406}$$

where we have introduced once again ϵ as integration variable, where we have used equation (10.315), and where L_1 and L_2 are given by the

† G. Wiedemann and R. Franz, Ann. Physik, **89**, 497, 1853.

equations

$$L_1 = \int_0^\infty \frac{\epsilon\lambda}{1 + s^2} \frac{\partial F}{\partial \epsilon} d\epsilon, \tag{10.407}$$

$$L_2 = \int_0^\infty \frac{\epsilon\lambda s}{1 + s^2} \frac{\partial F}{\partial \epsilon} d\epsilon. \tag{10.408}$$

From equations (10.401) and (10.406), we get for the Hall constant the equation

$$R = \frac{3h^3}{16\pi me^2 H_z} \frac{L_2}{{L_1}^2 + {L_2}^2}, \tag{10.409}$$

and from equations (10.307) and (10.405) we get for the electrical conductivity when a magnetic field is present

$$\sigma(H_z) = -\frac{16\pi me^2}{3h^3} \frac{{L_1}^2 + {L_2}^2}{L_1}. \tag{10.410}$$

We can once again introduce for f_0 the Fermi-Dirac distribution, and using equation (10.322) we have

$$L_1 = -\frac{g_0\bar{\lambda}}{1 + \bar{s}^2}, \qquad L_2 = -\frac{g_0\bar{\lambda}\bar{s}}{1 + \bar{s}^2}, \tag{10.411}$$

where

$$\bar{s} = \frac{e\bar{\lambda}H_z}{m\bar{c}c_0}. \tag{10.412}$$

Using equations (10.411) and (10.410), we see that to a first approximation

$$\sigma(H_z) = \sigma(0). \tag{10.413}$$

If we take higher-order terms into account, $\sigma(H_z)$ is, however, no longer the same as $\sigma(0)$, but decreases with increasing magnetic field.

From equations (10.409), (10.411), (10.412), (10.216), and (10.102), we get for the Hall constant the equation

$$R = -\frac{1}{nec_0}. \tag{10.414}$$

The negative sign on the right-hand side of equation (10.414) arises from the fact that the electrical current is carried by the negatively charged electrons. If the carriers were positive charges, the Hall constant would be positive.

The Hall constant calculated from equation (10.414) agrees very well with the observed values in the case of monovalent metals such as Li, Na, Al, and Ag.

BIBLIOGRAPHICAL NOTES

We may refer to the following general references:

1. A. Sommerfeld and H. Bethe, Handb. d. Phys., Vol. $\mathbf{24_2}$, Berlin 1933, p. 333.
2. A. H. Wilson, The Theory of Metals, Cambridge 1936.
3. S. Chapman and T. G. Cowling, The Mathematical Theory of Non-Uniform Gases, Cambridge 1939, especially Chap. 17.
4. F. Seitz, The Modern Theory of Metals, New York 1940, especially Chap. IV.

§1. Around the turn of the century Riecke, Drude, and Lorentz developed the electron theory of metals:

5. E. Riecke, Ann. Physik, **66,** 353, 1898.
6. E. Riecke, Ann. Physik, **66,** 545, 1898.
7. P. Drude, Ann. Physik, **1,** 566, 1900.
8. M. Reinganum, Ann. Physik, **2,** 398, 1900.
9. E. Riecke, Ann. Physik, **2,** 835, 1900.
10. P. Drude, Ann. Physik, **3,** 369, 1900.
11. H. A. Lorentz, Arch. Néerland. Sci., **10,** 336, 1905 (= Collected Papers, Vol. III, The Hague 1936, p. 180).
12. H. A. Lorentz, The Theory of Electrons, Leipzig 1909, §§47–50.

The theory was further developed by Sommerfeld, who modified Lorentz's treatment by introducing Fermi-Dirac statistics:

13. A. Sommerfeld, Z. Phys., **47,** 1, 1928.
14. A. Sommerfeld and N. H. Frank, Revs. Modern Phys., **3,** 1, 1931.

See also refs. 1, 2, and 4.

The Richardson effect is described in the following paper.

15. O. W. Richardson, Phil. Mag., **23,** 594, 1912.

§2. See refs. 1–4, 11–13, and

16. R. Gans, Ann. Physik, **20,** 293, 1906.
17. Mimeographed notes of lectures given by V. A. Johnson at Purdue University, 1949.

§§3 and 4. See refs. 1, 2, 4, 13, 14, 16, and 17.

CHAPTER XI

SEMICONDUCTORS

§1. **Introduction.** If we wish to consider semiconductors, we must enter into a slightly more detailed discussion of the band structure of the energy levels in crystals. If we are concerned with the movement of electrons in a crystal and if we treat the electrons as noninteracting with each other, the first problem is to find the characteristic energy values of a particle moving in a potential energy field with periodic structure. One can show that—at any rate, if one is dealing with an infinite crystal—the energy spectrum consists of "bands."† This means that there exist energy values E_0, E_1, E_2, $\cdots$ such that all energies satisfying the inequalities

$$E_0 \leqslant E \leqslant E_1, \quad E_2 \leqslant E \leqslant E_3, \quad E_4 \leqslant E \leqslant E_5, \cdots \qquad \textbf{(11.101)}$$

are characteristic values, while none of the energies satisfying the inequalities

$$E < E_0, \quad E_1 < E < E_2, \quad E_3 < E < E_4, \cdots \qquad \textbf{(11.102)}$$

are characteristic values. The energy values satisfying (11.101) are called *allowed* energies and the energy values satisfying (11.102) are called *forbidden* energies; one also speaks of *allowed* and *forbidden bands.*

Let us consider the situation at the absolute zero. There are two possibilities. The first possibility is that the electrons fill up the lowest bands completely, but only half fill the last band which is at all occupied, and we are dealing with a metal. In that case any amount of energy can remove electrons from a level occupied at absolute zero. The second possibility is that the electrons exactly fill up the lowest bands, but that the next allowed band is completely empty. This is the case of an *intrinsic semiconductor* or an *insulator.* The difference between these two types of materials is only quantitative and depends on the energy gap $\Delta\epsilon$ between the band last filled and the first empty band. In insulators this gap is of the order of 5 to 10 ev, while in intrinsic semiconductors it is of the order of 1 ev. The gap is, for instance, 0.4 ev in the case of tellurium and 0.76 ev in

† We refer to a paper by Kramers (Physica, **2**, 483, 1935) for a general discussion of this behavior.

the case of germanium. We shall see presently the importance of the magnitude of the energy gap.

Sometimes the structure of a crystal is not completely periodic due, for instance, to impurities in the crystal. In that case it is possible that there are a few energy levels which lie in the forbidden band (see Fig. 31). If these levels are occupied by electrons and if the distance between these

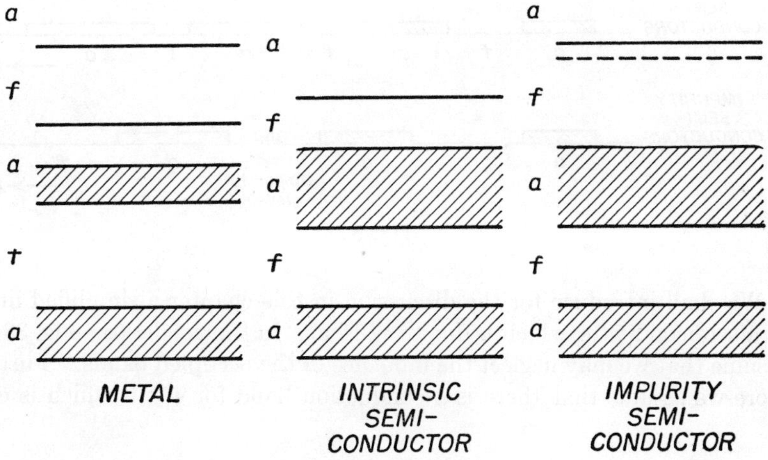

Fig. 31

levels and the first empty or *conduction band* is not too large, electrons may be excited into the allowed band and give rise to conductivity. It must be noted that the wave functions corresponding to the energy levels between two allowed bands are often localized. In Figure 31 we have indicated the cases of a metal, of an intrinsic semiconductor, and of an impurity type of semiconductor. We have indicated by *a* and *f* respectively the allowed and the forbidden bands. Levels occupied at the absolute zero are indicated by shading.

It must be emphasized that Figure 31 and similar figures in reality give twofold information. First of all, one can read from these figures the values of the characteristic energies. However, this could be done from a figure such as is given by Figure 32 without leading to confusion.† In Figure 31, however, one has additional information regarding the wave functions corresponding to the various energy levels, and one sees that the wave functions corresponding to the allowed bands have a constant ampli-

† One sees from Fig. 32 that the energy levels corresponding to the impurity levels, although often lying very closely—much more closely in fact than is indicated in Fig. 32—are different and not all equal as one might expect from Fig. 31.

tude throughout the crystal, but that the wave functions corresponding to the impurity levels are localized, thus corresponding to electrons which are bound to specific positions in the lattice.

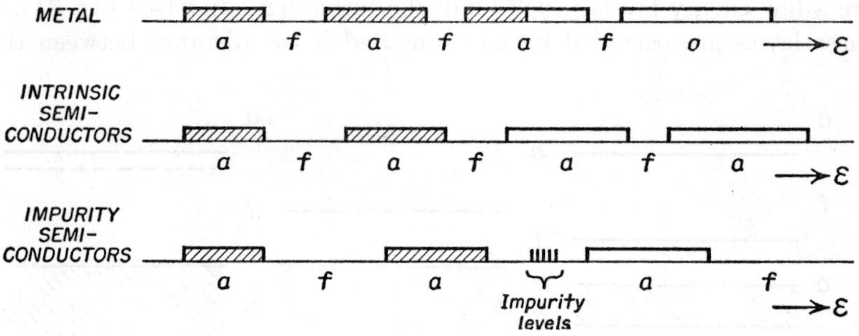

Fig. 32

We shall introduce for the discussion in this chapter a simplified model of a semiconductor which is due to Wilson. In this model (see Fig. 33) we assume that we may neglect the influence of the occupied bands. Furthermore we assume that there is a conduction band for $\epsilon \geqslant 0$ which is com-

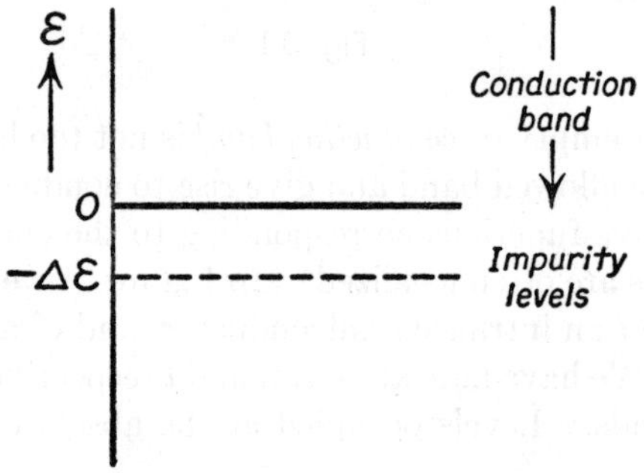

Fig. 33

pletely unoccupied at the absolute zero and that there are N_b impurity levels, all situated at $\epsilon = -\Delta\epsilon$, which are at the absolute zero completely occupied. We shall assume that the number of energy levels $Z(\epsilon)d\epsilon$ in the conduction band with energies between ϵ and $\epsilon + d\epsilon$ is essentially given by equation (4.504) on page 82, or

$$Z(\epsilon)d\epsilon = 4\pi\left(\frac{2m}{h^2}\right)^{3/2} V\sqrt{\epsilon}d\epsilon, \qquad \epsilon > 0, \tag{11.103}$$

where V is the volume of the semiconductor, where m is here an effective electron mass,† and where we have introduced an additional factor 2 to account for the electron spin.

We can express the fact that there are N_b impurity levels at $\epsilon = -\Delta\epsilon$ by writing

$$Z(\epsilon) = N_b \delta(\epsilon + \Delta\epsilon), \qquad \epsilon < 0, \tag{11.104}$$

where $\delta(x)$ is again Dirac's δ-function (see p. 106).

The number of electrons $N(\epsilon)d\epsilon$ with energies between ϵ and $\epsilon + d\epsilon$ is given by the equation (compare equation [4.320] on p. 78)

$$N(\epsilon)d\epsilon = \frac{Z(\epsilon)d\epsilon}{e^{-\nu+\mu\epsilon} + 1}, \tag{11.105}$$

where μ is again related to the absolute temperature, T, by the equation

$$\mu = \frac{1}{kT}, \tag{11.106}$$

where $Z(\epsilon)$ is given by equations (11.103) and (11.104), and where ν/μ is the partial thermal potential.

As we have in all N_b electrons, namely, the electrons occupying the impurity levels at the absolute zero, we have the equation

$$N_b = \frac{N_b}{e^{-\nu-\mu\Delta\epsilon} + 1} + 4\pi\left(\frac{2m}{h^2}\right)^{3/2} V \int_0^\infty \frac{\sqrt{\epsilon}\,d\epsilon}{e^{-\nu+\mu\epsilon} + 1}. \tag{11.107}$$

The first term on the right-hand side of this equation gives us the number of electrons occupying at a given temperature the impurity levels, while the second term gives us the number of electrons in the conduction band. We shall verify presently that practically always $e^{-\nu} \gg 1$ so that we can neglect the 1 in the denominator of the integrand in equation (11.107). Since, however, $e^{-\nu-\mu\Delta\epsilon}$ will be small compared to one, we have to a fair approximation from equation (11.107)

$$N_b e^{-\nu-\mu\Delta\epsilon} = 2\left(\frac{2\pi m}{\mu h^2}\right)^{3/2} V e^{\nu}, \tag{11.108}$$

or

$$\nu = -\tfrac{1}{2}\mu\Delta\epsilon + \frac{1}{2}\ln\left[\frac{N_b}{2V}\left(\frac{\mu h^2}{2\pi m}\right)^{3/2}\right]. \tag{11.109}$$

At room temperatures μ is of the order of 40 ev^{-1}, and since $\Delta\epsilon$ will usually be of the order of 1 ev we see that $\frac{1}{2}\mu\Delta\epsilon$ will practically always be large

† We refer to the discussion given, for instance, by Seitz of the physical meaning of the effective mass.

compared to one. The second term on the right-hand side of equation (11.109) is of the order of magnitude of unity so that to a first approximation we may write

$$\nu = -\tfrac{1}{2}\mu\Delta\epsilon. \tag{11.110}$$

From this equation and the fact that $\mu\Delta\epsilon \gg 1$ it follows that the approximations made in going over from equation (11.107) to equation (11.108) were justified.

The total number of electrons N_c in the conduction band is given by the equation

$$N_c = 4\pi\left(\frac{2m}{h^2}\right)^{3/2} V \int_0^\infty \frac{\sqrt{\epsilon}\,d\epsilon}{e^{-\nu+\mu\epsilon}+1} \cong 2\left(\frac{2\pi m}{\mu h^2}\right)^{3/2} Ve^{\nu}, \tag{11.111}$$

or, if we use equation (11.109),

$$n_c = \sqrt{2n_b}\left(\frac{2\pi m}{\mu h^2}\right)^{3/4} e^{-\frac{1}{4}\mu\Delta\epsilon}, \tag{11.112}$$

where we have introduced the electron densities n_b and n_c by writing

$$n_b = \frac{N_b}{V}, \qquad n_c = \frac{N_c}{V}. \tag{11.113}$$

The number of electrons per unit volume $f(\epsilon)d\epsilon$ with energies between ϵ and $\epsilon + d\epsilon$ follows from equations (11.105), (11.103), (11.109), and (11.112) and is given by the equation

$$f(\epsilon)d\epsilon = \frac{2}{\sqrt{\pi}} n_c \mu^{3/2} e^{-\mu\epsilon}\sqrt{\epsilon}\,d\epsilon, \qquad \epsilon > 0, \tag{11.114}$$

which is a Maxwell distribution. There is, however, one point of difference between the distribution given by equation (11.114) and the normal Maxwell distribution, namely, that n_c in equation (11.114) is temperature-dependent. We shall use equation (11.114) in the next section to derive expressions for the electrical conductivity and the Hall constant.

§2. Electrical Conductivity and Isothermal Hall Effect. The electrical conductivity σ and the isothermal Hall constant R of semiconductors can immediately be computed by using equation (10.309) for σ and equations (10.401), (10.403), and (10.404) for R. The distribution function, f_0, which gives us the distribution in velocity, follows from equation (11.114) (compare the transition from equation [10.106] to equation [10.107]), or

$$f_0(u,v,w) = n_c\left(\frac{\mu m}{2\pi}\right)^{3/2} e^{-\mu\epsilon}. \tag{11.201}$$

If we are dealing with a semiconductor, we may to a fair approximation assume the mean free path λ to be a constant, and we have thus from equations (10.309), (10.216), and (11.201)

$$\sigma = -\frac{4\pi e^2}{3}\int_0^\infty \lambda c^3 \frac{\partial f_0}{\partial \epsilon}\, dc, \tag{11.202}$$

or

$$\sigma = \frac{8}{3\pi}\frac{n_c e^2 \lambda}{m\bar{c}}, \tag{11.203}$$

where we have denoted by $\bar{c}$ the mean absolute velocity given by the equation (compare equation [1.107] on p. 3)

$$\bar{c}^2 = \frac{8}{\pi}\frac{kT}{m}. \tag{11.204}$$

Comparing the conductivity given by equation (11.203) with the conductivity of a metal given by equation (10.324), we see that the main difference lies in the fact that in the case of a semiconductor n_c takes the place of the number of electrons per unit volume, n, in the case of a metal. This means essentially a difference of a factor $e^{-\frac{1}{2}\mu\Delta\epsilon}$ which for $T = 300°\mathrm{K}$ and $\Delta\epsilon = 1$ ev amounts to a difference of a factor 10^{-8}. However, if $\Delta\epsilon$ were of the order of 5 ev to 10 ev, the factor would amount to 10^{-40} to 10^{-80} and we see now why the difference between semiconductors with $\Delta\epsilon \sim 1$ ev and insulators with $\Delta\epsilon \sim 5$ ev to 10 ev is such a fundamental one.

Let us now consider the isothermal Hall effect. The parameter s given by equation (10.222) is usually small compared to one so that we can neglect the s^2 in the denominators in the equations (10.403) and (10.404). In that case equations (10.403) and (10.404) reduce to the following two equations:

$$j_x = \sigma E_x - BE_y H_z, \tag{11.205}$$

$$0 = BE_x H_z + \sigma E_y, \tag{11.206}$$

where σ is given by equation (11.202), where

$$B = -\frac{4\pi e^3}{3mc_0}\int_0^\infty \lambda^2 c^2 \frac{\partial f_0}{\partial \epsilon}\, dc \tag{11.207}$$

(c_0 is again the velocity of light), and where BH_z/σ is of the order of magnitude of s so that we can neglect $B^2H_z^2$ with respect to σ^2. Eliminating E_x from equations (11.205) and (11.206), neglecting $B^2H_z^2$ with respect to σ^2, and using equation (10.401) for the definition of the Hall constant, R, we have

$$R = -\frac{B}{\sigma^2}. \tag{11.208}$$

From equations (11.207) and (11.201), we get for B

$$B = \frac{n_c e^3 \lambda^2}{3mc_0 kT}, \tag{11.209}$$

and for R, from equations (11.203), (11.204), (11.208) and (11.209),

$$R = -\frac{3\pi}{8n_c e c_0}. \tag{11.210}$$

From this equation we see that the Hall constant depends only on n_c and thus gives an excellent means for measuring the number of conduction electrons.

We may remark here that one can also calculate very easily the Hall constant in the case where $s^2 \gg 1$. It is, however, outside the scope of this book to discuss either this case or the intermediate case where $s \sim 1$.

§3. **The Transition from Classical to Quantum Statistics in Semiconductors.** In the preceding sections we considered the properties of semiconducting materials and we used for the distribution function the classical Maxwell distribution. Usually the behavior of semiconductors is satisfactorily described in this way. However, Lark-Horovitz and his collaborators found that the behavior of some of their semiconducting samples could not be described by classical statistics, but that Fermi-Dirac statistics had to be used. This result of the Purdue semiconductor group led Schottky and Ehrenberg† to consider in detail the model which we have used in the present chapter. We shall give here essentially their considerations. The question is at what temperatures a transition from classical to Fermi-Dirac statistics can be expected to occur. We use equations (4.601) and (4.603) on page 84 and find that degeneracy can be considered to set in at a temperature corresponding to a value μ_d, which is approximately given by the equation

$$n_c \left(\frac{\mu_d h^2}{2\pi m}\right)^{3/2} = 1. \tag{11.301}$$

Using equation (11.112) we have from this equation

$$\sqrt{2n_b}\left(\frac{\mu_d h^2}{2\pi m}\right)^{3/4} e^{-\frac{1}{2}\mu_d \Delta\epsilon} = 1. \tag{11.302}$$

† Private communication to Dr. K. Lark-Horovitz, to whom I am indebted for passing these considerations on to me.

As long as the left-hand side of this equation is smaller than one, we can apply classical statistics.† We see from equation (11.302) that both for $\mu \to 0$ (high temperatures) and for $\mu \to \infty$ (low temperatures) classical statistics can be applied, but that there may be a temperature range where one must apply Fermi-Dirac statistics.

At high temperatures the exponential is essentially constant and condition (11.302) reduces to the usual condition for degeneracy with constant density. At sufficiently high temperatures the factor containing $\mu^{3/4}$ is the dominating one, and the fact that the conduction gas is nondegenerate is due to the fact that the De Broglie wavelength of the electrons is small (compare the discussion on p. 85). At low temperatures the exponential factor dominates, and the gas is nondegenerate because of the fact that the number of conduction electrons is greatly reduced (see equation [11.112]).

In the case of most semiconductors and certainly in the case of intrinsic semiconductors $\Delta\epsilon$ is too large for degeneracy to be possible. If the number of impurity levels per unit volume, n_b, is of the order of 10^{18} cm^{-3}, as it was in most of the samples investigated by Lark-Horovitz and co-workers, the energy gap $\Delta\epsilon$ must be at most of the order of 0.01 ev in order that degeneracy can occur. If $\Delta\epsilon$ is sufficiently small, there will be a temperature interval, $T_1 < T < T_2$, in which the gas of the conduction electrons is degenerate. The temperature T_1 is, however, always extremely low. In order to get an idea of the orders of magnitude involved we can give the following two examples:

$$\left.\begin{array}{ll} n_b = 10^{18}\ \text{cm}^{-3},\ \Delta\epsilon = 10^{-3}\ \text{ev}, & T_1 = 1.5°\text{K},\quad T_2 = 170°\text{K}; \\ n_b = 10^{15}\ \text{cm}^{-3},\ \Delta\epsilon = 2\cdot 10^{-5}\ \text{ev}, & T_1 = 0.03°\text{K},\ T_2 = 2°\text{K}. \end{array}\right\} \quad \textbf{(11.303)}$$

This effect is, of course, extremely important. Apart, perhaps, from the questionable transition from classical to quantum statistics in the case of the equation of state of helium (§8 of Chapter VIII), this is the only case in which the fact that a lowering of the temperature may induce quantum effects has been demonstrated *ad oculos.* It is therefore very unfortunate that the simple model which we have used in this chapter is certainly inadequate to describe the behavior of the degenerate samples investigated by Lark-Horovitz and co-workers. (Actually none of the existing models has been able to describe these samples.) The main difficulty is that the Hall constant and thus the number of conduction electrons (and also the mean free path) is constant *in the low-temperature region* and not, as we should expect from our model, in the high-temperature region.

† It is not really permitted to apply equation (11.112), but it can be verified that the conclusions which we shall reach are qualitatively correct and even quantitatively correct, up to a possible factor which is at most 2.5.

BIBLIOGRAPHICAL NOTES

We may refer to the following general references.

1. A. Sommerfeld and H. Bethe, Handb. d. Phys., Vol. **24_2**, Berlin 1933, p. 333.
2. F. Seitz, The Modern Theory of Solids, New York 1940.
3. K. Lark-Horovitz, "Preparation of Semiconductors and Development of Crystal Rectifiers," N.D.R.C., Report 14–585, November, 1945.
4. Progress Reports of the Purdue University Semi-Conductor Research Group from 1945 onward.
5. Mimeographed notes of lectures given by V. A. Johnson at Purdue University.
6. D. A. Wright, Semi-Conductors, London 1950.
7. "Semi-Conducting Materials," Proceedings of the Reading Conference, London 1951.
8. J. S. Blakemore, Proc. Phys. Soc. (London), **A65**, 460, 1952.

§1. See refs. 2, 7, and

9. A. H. Wilson, Proc. Roy. Soc. (London), **A133**, 458, 1931.
10. A. H. Wilson, Proc. Roy. Soc. (London), **A134**, 277, 1931.
11. R. H. Fowler, Proc. Roy. Soc. (London), **A140**, 505, 1933.
12. R. H. Fowler, Proc. Roy. Soc. (London), **A141**, 56, 1933.
13. H. M. James, Purdue University Progress Report, January 1–March 31, 1952, p. 8.
14. P. T. Landsberg, Proc. Phys. Soc. (London), **A65**, 604, 1952.
15. E. A. Guggenheim, Proc. Phys. Soc. (London), **A66**, 121, 1953.

In refs. 13–15 the influence of electron spin is considered, and especially the fact that the energy levels of paired electrons may be lower than those of unpaired electrons. In order to take this into account one has to depart from the one-electron picture which we have used, and one should, as was especially emphasized by James and Guggenheim, use grand ensembles.

§2. See refs. 2 and 5 and a report by V. A. Johnson and F. M. Shipley to the United States Signal Corps, dated August, 1952.

§3. See ref. 4 and

16. K. Shifrin, J. Phys. (U.S.S.R.), **8**, 242, 1944.
17. V. A. Johnson and K. Lark-Horovitz, Phys. Rev., **71**, 374, 1947 (corrigenda in Phys. Rev., **71**, 909, 1947).
18. R. A. Hutner, E. S. Rittner, and F. K. du Pré, Philips Res. Rep., **5**, 188, 1950.

CHAPTER XII

COOPERATIVE PHENOMENA

§1. **Introduction.** If one adds to a metal A a quantity of another metal B, it sometimes happens that the crystal structure of the resulting alloy is the same as that of the pure metal A, except that some lattice sites are occupied by B atoms instead of by A atoms. Such an alloy is called a *solid solution*, or, since it can be obtained by a process of a simple one for one substitution, a *substitutional solid solution*. Although originally it was thought that the arrangement of the A and B atoms was purely random, later evidence pointed to the fact that there was a definite *order* in the way the A and B atoms were distributed over the lattice sites. The first evidence for this order was the discovery by Tammann† that samples of a certain copper-gold alloy were not affected by nitric acid if there was 50 atomic per cent copper or less, while copper but no gold was dissolved if the atomic per cent of copper was more than 50. Tammann concluded from this experiment that a 50–50 atomic mixture of copper and gold gave an ordered arrangement of atoms, while any extra copper could not be fitted in and was easily dissolved by the acid.

More conclusive evidence has been furnished by X-ray diffraction experiments. One of the earlier investigations was the work of Johansson and Linde,‡ who investigated the same alloy as Tammann, that is, Cu-Au. They found indications of an ordered structure by observing the so-called *superstructure lines*. The origin of these superstructure lines can be seen from Figure 34. In Figure 34(a) and Figure 34(c) we have pictured two possible situations in a crystal, the first one a state of disorder and the second one a state of complete order. Imagine an X-ray beam of wave length λ falling on the crystal at an angle θ, which is such that the path length difference PQR between two rays reflected by two successive planes is equal to $\frac{1}{2}\lambda$ (Fig. 34[b]). If the reflecting properties of the two planes are the same—as they will be when there is a state of disorder—no line will appear on the photographic plate. However, if a state of order exists, it is possible that a line will be produced, provided the scattering properties of

† G. Tammann, Lehrb. d. Metallographie, Leipzig 1921, p. 325.

‡ C. H. Johansson and J. O. Linde, Ann. Physik, **78**, 439, 1925.

the A and B atoms are sufficiently different as they are, for instance, in a Cu-Au alloy.

Since the scattering cross sections for neighboring elements in the periodic system are very nearly the same, the X-ray technique cannot be used for alloys such as Fe-Co. Recently, however, the new methods of neutron diffraction made it possible to observe superstructure lines in the case of Fe-Co.†

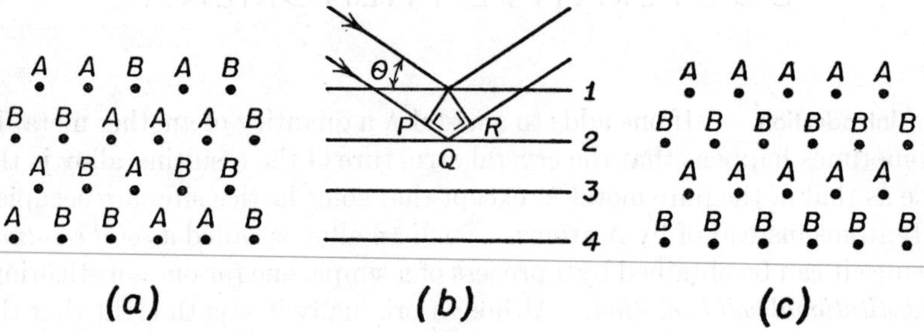

Fig. 34

Let us consider an alloy in which a regular arrangement of the atoms like the one pictured in Figure 34(c) is energetically the most favorable. Of course, if it were not the most favorable, an ordered state would practically never occur. If, then, the ordered state is the state of lowest energy, there will be a tendency for A atoms to surround themselves with B atoms and vice versa rather than a tendency for a formation of clusters of A or B atoms. At very low temperatures we may expect a state of order to exist. We shall call the lattice sites occupied by A atoms in a state of complete order α-sites and the lattice sites occupied by B atoms β-sites. An A atom on an α-site or a B atom on a β-site will be called a *right* atom and an A atom on a β-site or a B atom on an α-site will be called a *wrong* atom.

Consider the crystal at a sufficiently low temperature so that the crystal is in an ordered state. If we now raise the temperature, there will be a chance that an A atom on an α-site may interchange places with a B atom on a β-site. This entails that a certain number of atoms will become wrong and that thus a certain amount of disorder will result. If we wish to discuss the amount of order or disorder in the crystal quantitatively, we must distinguish between two kinds of order. The first kind, called *long-range order* or *order at distance*, measures how large a fraction of the A atoms is situated on α-sites. The second kind, called *short-range order* or *local order*, measures how well on the average A atoms are surrounded by B atoms. At the absolute zero there will be perfect long-range order and

† C. G. Shull and S. Siegel, Phys. Rev., **75**, 1008, 1949.

perfect short-range order, but at finite temperatures both will be destroyed. There will be, on the one hand, A atoms on β-sites and B atoms on α-sites and, on the other hand, there will be nearest neighbors of the same kind. So long as the temperature is not too high, the tendency of atoms to surround themselves with other atoms will counteract the thermal movement of the atoms in the lattice, restoring A atoms to α-sites and B atoms to β-sites.† At temperatures below a certain critical temperature, to be introduced presently, there will be more right atoms than wrong ones, the tendency for unlike neighbors maintaining a certain amount of long-range order. However, an A atom on a β-site makes it energetically more favorable for a B atom to be present on the neighboring α-sites, thus lowering the potential barrier which must be overcome in order that these α-sites can be

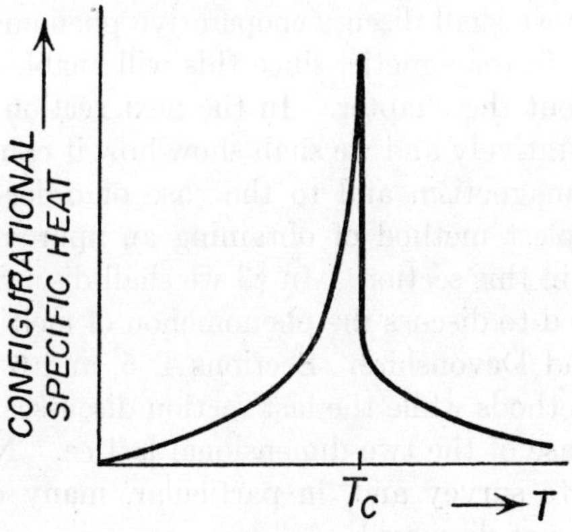

Fig. 35

occupied by B atoms. We see thus that the higher the long-range disorder, the greater will be the ease with which this disorder can be further increased. This "avalanche" effect will finally lead to a complete and abrupt disappearance of long-range order at a certain critical temperature T_c. By analogy with ferromagnetism this temperature is often called the *Curie temperature.* Above this temperature there will be as many wrong atoms as there are right atoms. Short-range order, however, will still persist to a certain degree.

Since it requires energy to produce disorder, the disordering effect can be seen in the specific heat curve. The part of the specific heat which is con-

† We may remark here that, of course, a situation where all A atoms are on β-sites and all B atoms are on α-sites is also a possible state of complete order. Since we shall be only concerned with alloys where the number of α-sites and the number of β-sites are equal, we must expect a certain symmetry to exist between situations which differ only in that α- and β-sites have been interchanged.

nected with the ordering of the crystal is called the *configurational* specific heat. A qualitative sketch of its behavior as a function of temperature is given in Figure 35. The steep rise in the neighborhood of T_c is due to the "avalanche" effect described in the preceding paragraph. That the configurational specific heat is not equal to zero at temperatures above T_c is due to the fact that a certain amount of local order still persists.

The order-disorder transformation in alloys is one of a large group of phenomena called *cooperative phenomena*. It is a characteristic of such systems that certain subsystems will cooperate to form units which hold together in spite of disrupting influences like thermal agitation. Also, this ability to hold together will depend strongly on the degree to which the subsystems have already cooperated. Apart from order in substitutional solid solutions we may mention ferromagnetism and melting. In the following sections we shall discuss cooperative phenomena in terms of the Ising model† of a ferromagnetic, since this will enable us to use the same notation throughout the chapter. In the next section we shall introduce this model quantitatively and we shall show how it can be applied both to the case of ferromagnetism and to the case of order-disorder in binary alloys. The simplest method of obtaining an approximate solution will also be discussed in this section. In §3 we shall discuss how this approximation can be used to discuss the phenomenon of melting, as was done by Lennard-Jones and Devonshire. Sections 4, 5, and 6 discuss some other approximation methods while the last section discusses a few exact results obtained in the case of the two-dimensional lattice. No attempt is made to give a complete survey and, in particular, many of the more recent developments are not discussed.

§2. The Bragg-Williams Approximation. The first approach to the problem of order-disorder was made by Bragg and Williams in 1934, and we shall describe the statistical derivation of their formulae, which they gave in 1935.‡ Before doing this, we must describe the Ising model. Although the discussion of §§2 to 5 will apply to most lattice types, we shall restrict ourselves to either the two-dimensional lattice or the simple cubic lattice.

Consider a lattice on each of the sites of which a spin is situated which is capable of two orientations We shall characterize these two orientations by assigning to each spin a parameter μ which is capable of two values $+1$ or -1. We shall, moreover, assume that each spin interacts only with its nearest neighbors. In a ferromagnetic the energy will be lowest if all spins are parallel. If two neighbors change from a parallel to an antiparallel

† E. Ising, Z. Physik, **31**, 253, 1925.
‡ Compare also W. Ehrenberg, Nature, **158**, 308, 1946.

alignment the total energy of the system is increased, say by an amount J. For the total energy of the system we have thus

$$E = -\tfrac{1}{2}J \sum_{\langle i,k\rangle} \mu_i\mu_k, \tag{12.201}$$

where $\sum_{\langle i,k\rangle}$ denotes here and henceforth a summation over all nearest neighbor pairs in the lattice.

In an antiferromagnetic lattice there will be a tendency to have antiparallel pairs, and if we always take J to be positive the energy will in that case be given by the equation

$$E = \tfrac{1}{2}J \sum_{\langle i,k\rangle} \mu_i'\mu_k'. \tag{12.202}$$

In the case of a binary alloy we shall also have an energy which is given by equation (12.202), which can be seen as follows. Let each A atom correspond to a μ' equal to $+1$ and each B atom to a μ' equal to -1. If v_{AA}, v_{BB}, and v_{AB} are the energies associated with an AA, a BB, or an AB pair respectively, one can show that the total energy will be given by equation (12.202), if J is taken to be equal to $\tfrac{1}{2}(v_{\mathrm{AA}} + v_{\mathrm{BB}}) - v_{\mathrm{AB}}$.

From the definition of the v's we have for the total energy

$$E = v_{\mathrm{AA}}Q_{\mathrm{AA}} + v_{\mathrm{BB}}Q_{\mathrm{BB}} + v_{\mathrm{AB}}Q_{\mathrm{AB}} + \text{constant},$$

where $Q_{\mathrm{AA}}, \cdots$, are the number of AA, $\cdots$, pairs in the lattice. If Q is the total number of pairs, we can rewrite the equation for the energy in the following form,

$$E = \tfrac{1}{2}Q(v_{\mathrm{AA}} + v_{\mathrm{BB}}) - JQ_{\mathrm{AB}} + \text{constant}.$$

Since $\mu_i'\mu_k'$ is $+1$ for an AA or a BB pair and -1 for an AB pair, we have

$$\sum_{\langle i,k\rangle} \mu_i'\mu_k' = Q_{\mathrm{AA}} + Q_{\mathrm{BB}} - Q_{\mathrm{AB}} = Q - 2Q_{\mathrm{AB}},$$

whence follows equation (12.202) by a suitable choice of the constant in the energy.

In the case of binary alloys equation (12.202) can be reduced to equation (12.201) by the following procedure. Choosing one arbitrary lattice site and calling it an α-site, calling all its nearest neighbors β-sites, and so on, so that each α-site is surrounded by β-sites, and the other way round, we can introduce the α- and β-sublattices of the substitutional solid solution (see Fig. 36). We shall assume that there are N lattice sites, $\tfrac{1}{2}N$ of which are α-sites and $\tfrac{1}{2}N$ of which are β-sites, and that there are $\tfrac{1}{2}N$ A atoms ($\mu' = +1$) and $\tfrac{1}{2}N$ B atoms ($\mu' = -1$). In the state of complete order all A atoms will be on α-sites and all B atoms on β-sites. Introducing μ_i by the equations

$$\begin{rcases} \mu_i = \mu_i', & \text{if } i \text{ is an } \alpha\text{-site,} \\ \mu_i = -\mu_i', & \text{if } i \text{ is a } \beta\text{-site,} \end{rcases} \tag{12.203}$$

we see that a state of complete order is described by all μ_i being equal to $+1$ (or -1, which case we shall not consider; compare the footnote on p. 253). Introducing the μ_i into expression (12.202) for the energy we obtain equation (12.201), since each pair in the lattice consists of one α- and one β-site. We see thus that by applying equations (12.203) we can reduce the problem of antiferromagnetism or of binary alloys to that of ferromagnetism.†

α	β	α	β	α
β	α	β	α	β
α	β	α	β	α
β	α	β	α	β
α	β	α	β	α

Fig. 36

Let r_α and w_α denote respectively the fraction of α-sites occupied by A atoms and by B atoms, and let r_β and w_β likewise denote the fraction of β-sites occupied by B atoms and by A atoms. It is easily seen that there exists the following relation between these four quantities,

$$r_\alpha = 1 - w_\alpha = r_\beta = 1 - w_\beta, \tag{12.204}$$

and we see that one of them will determine the other three completely.

We change two μ_i from $+1$ to -1 for every A atom on an α-site which we interchange with a B atom on a β-site. If $N_{A\beta}$ be the number of A atoms on β-sites, we have thus

$$\sum_{\langle i \rangle} \mu_i = N - 4N_{A\beta}, \tag{12.205}$$

where the sum is extended over all the sites in the lattice. We also have

$$\tfrac{1}{2}N - N_{A\beta} = \tfrac{1}{2}Nr_\alpha. \tag{12.206}$$

In deriving equation (12.205) we have made use of the fact that for complete order $\sum \mu_i = N$. Combining equations (12.205) and (12.206), we have

$$2r_\alpha = 1 + \frac{1}{N}\sum_{\langle i \rangle} \mu_i. \tag{12.207}$$

† By using this method we can avoid the difficult procedure used by Rushbrooke (Nuovo cimento, **6**, Suppl., 251, 1949) where a grand ensemble for the binary alloys is compared with a petit ensemble for a ferromagnetic.

We can now introduce the long-range order parameter R† by the equation

$$R = 2r_\alpha - 1 = \frac{1}{N}\sum_{\langle i\rangle} \mu_i. \tag{12.208}$$

We see that R ranges from a value 1 for perfect order (all μ_i equal to $+1$) to 0 for perfect disorder (as many μ_i equal to $+1$ as equal to -1).

In order to evaluate R exactly as a function of temperature one can use the following method. The energy expression (12.201) is changed to‡

$$E' = -\tfrac{1}{2}J \sum_{\langle i,k\rangle} \mu_i\mu_k - I\sum_{\langle i\rangle}\mu_i. \tag{12.209}$$

The partition function Z of the crystal is then given by the equation

$$Z = \sum_{\langle\mu\rangle} e^{K\sum_{\langle i,k\rangle}\mu_i\mu_k + C\sum_{\langle i\rangle}\mu_i}, \tag{12.210}$$

where the sum extends over all possible combinations of μ_i values, and where

$$K = \frac{J}{2kT} \tag{12.211}$$

and

$$C = \frac{I}{kT}. \tag{12.212§}$$

We can treat I as an external parameter, and it then follows from equation (12.209) that the corresponding generalized force is given by NR. We know that such a force can be derived from the partition function (see, e.g., equation [2.713]) and we have therefore

$$R = \frac{1}{N}\frac{\partial \ln Z}{\partial C}. \tag{12.213}$$

In the case of binary alloys there is no term with I in the energy, and we have in that case

$$R = \frac{1}{N}\left(\frac{\partial \ln Z}{\partial C}\right)_{C=0}. \tag{12.214‖}$$

† This parameter is usually denoted by S, but we wish to reserve this symbol for the entropy.

‡ The second term in equation (12.209) enters into the expression for the energy of a ferromagnetic in the case where an external magnetic field H is present, I being equal to mH if m is the magnetic moment per spin (see §6).

§ It can be shown that in the case of binary alloys, C is related to the thermal potential of the A atoms in a grand ensemble (compare Rushbrooke, *loc. cit.*; compare also equation [12.210] if one substitutes the μ_i' for the μ_i).

‖ We see from equation (12.214) that the long-range order is connected with the magnetization at zero field.

In order to make the problem more amenable to treatment Bragg and Williams introduced the following simplifying assumptions.

a) The thermodynamical behavior of the crystal depends on the μ_i only in its dependence on R;

b) The average energy Φ necessary to interchange an A atom on an α-site with a B atom on a β-site will depend on R in the following way,

$$\Phi = R\Phi_0, \tag{12.215}$$

where Φ_0 is the energy necessary for the interchange in the state of complete order. From our model it follows that we have

$$\Phi_0 = 2zJ, \tag{12.216}$$

where z is the number of nearest neighbors per site. We have for z the values 4, 6, 8, and 12 in the cases of a two-dimensional square lattice, a simple cubic, a body centered, and a face-centered cubic lattice, respectively.

Once one has accepted the two assumptions mentioned, it is possible to calculate in a straightforward manner the energy, specific heat, and R as a function of temperature.

First of all we shall express the energy in terms of R. If we change the number of A atoms on α-sites from $N_{A\alpha}$ to $N_{A\alpha} + dN_{A\alpha}$ we have from equations (12.206) and (12.208)

$$dN_{A\alpha} = \tfrac{1}{2}Ndr_\alpha = \tfrac{1}{4}NdR. \tag{12.217}$$

Since according to our second assumption each move will cost an energy $R\Phi_0$, the change in energy will be given by the equation

$$dE = -R\Phi_0 dN_{A\alpha} = -\tfrac{1}{4}N\Phi_0 RdR, \tag{12.218}$$

whence

$$E = E_0(1 - R^2) + E_1, \tag{12.219}$$

where E_1 is the energy corresponding to the completely ordered state and where

$$E_0 = \tfrac{1}{8}N\Phi_0. \tag{12.220}$$

If $W(R)$ is the number of ways of arranging the atoms over the lattice in a way consistent with a given value of R, the entropy will be given by the equation

$$S = k \ln W(R), \tag{12.221}$$

where k is once again Boltzmann's constant.

Since we must arrange $\frac{1}{2}Nr_\alpha$ A atoms over $\frac{1}{2}N$ α-sites and $\frac{1}{2}Nw_\beta$ A atoms over $\frac{1}{2}N$ β-sites, $W(R)$ is given by the equation

$$W(R) = \binom{\frac{1}{2}N}{\frac{1}{2}Nr_\alpha}\binom{\frac{1}{2}N}{\frac{1}{2}Nw_\beta}. \tag{12.222}$$

Using equations (12.204) and (12.208) to express r_α and w_β in terms of R and using the Stirling formula for the factorial in the form

$$\ln x! = x \ln x - x, \tag{12.223}$$

we get, after a straightforward calculation,

$$S = kN\,[\ln 2 - \tfrac{1}{2}(1 + R) \ln (1 + R) - \tfrac{1}{2}(1 - R) \ln (1 - R)]. \tag{12.224}$$

We see that S increases from 0 for $R = 1$ to $kN \ln 2$ for $R = 0$.

In order to find the equilibrium value of R at a given temperature we must minimize the free energy F with respect to R. We have then to solve R from the equation

$$\frac{\partial F}{\partial R} = 0, \tag{12.225}$$

where the free energy $F(= E - TS)$ is given by the equation

$$F = E_1 + E_0(1 - R^2) - NkT\,[\ln 2 - \tfrac{1}{2}(1 + R) \ln (1 + R) - \tfrac{1}{2}(1 - R) \ln (1 - R)]. \tag{12.226}$$

In this way we get for R the equation

$$R = \tanh \frac{R\Phi_0}{4kT}, \tag{12.227}$$

an equation which must be solved numerically or graphically.

In order to see how the second method works we introduce an auxiliary quantity X by the equation

$$X = \frac{\Phi_0}{4kT} R, \tag{12.228}$$

and we get from equation (12.227)

$$R = \tanh X. \tag{12.229}$$

We must now solve X and R from the two equations (12.228) and (12.229). We must draw attention to one point of difference between these two equations. Equation (12.228), being the definition of X, will be valid whether or not we are dealing with an equilibrium situation, but equation (12.229) obtains only if we are dealing with an equilibrium situation.

The graphical method of solution consists of drawing in an X-R plane the two curves corresponding to equations (12.228) and (12.229) (see Fig. 37). The intersection of these two curves gives us the equilibrium value of R. From Figure 37 we see first of all that $R = 0$ is always a possible solution, as follows also directly from equation (12.227). However, if the temperature is sufficiently low, there is also another solution, corresponding to the point P in Figure 37. We shall show presently that P corresponds to stable equilibrium while the equilibrium corresponding to $R = 0$ is in that case unstable. When the temperature is increased, there will come a moment when P is also situated in the origin. The corresponding temperature T_c will be called the critical temperature. Above T_c the

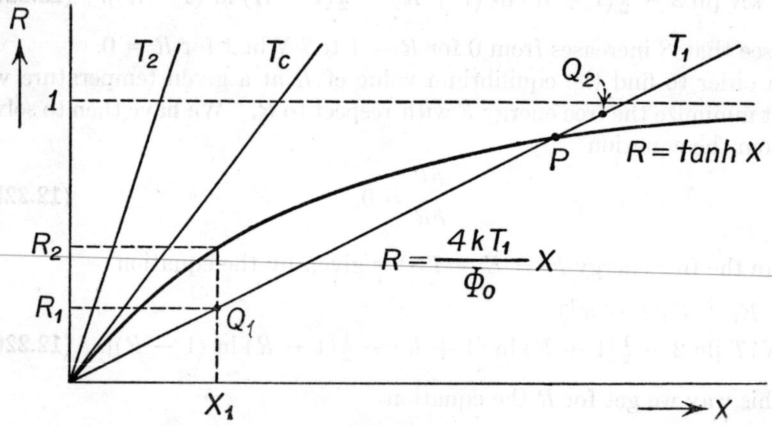

Fig. 37

only solution is $R = 0$ and there will thus be no long-range order at temperatures above T_c. The value of T_c can be calculated from the condition that for this temperature the straight line represented by equation (12.228) should be tangent in the origin to the curve represented by equation (12.229), or

$$\frac{\Phi_0}{4kT_c} = \left(\frac{dR}{dX}\right)_{X=0} = 1,$$

or

$$T_c = \frac{\Phi_0}{4k}. \tag{12.230}$$

Using equations (12.230), (12.216), and (12.211), and introducing x by the equation

$$x = e^{-2K}, \tag{12.231}$$

we see that the critical value of x is given by the equation

$$x_c = e^{-2/z}, \tag{12.232}$$

which in the case of the two-dimensional square lattice and in the case of the simple cubic lattice reduces to

$$x_c = e^{-1/2} = 0.6065 \tag{12.233}$$

and

$$x_c = e^{-1/3} = 0.7165. \tag{12.234}$$

It is now necessary to show that P corresponds to a condition of stable equilibrium. We mentioned earlier that for a nonequilibrium situation equation (12.228) is still valid. The point Q_1 (see Fig. 37) will thus represent such a nonequilibrium situation. If the temperature and the ordering

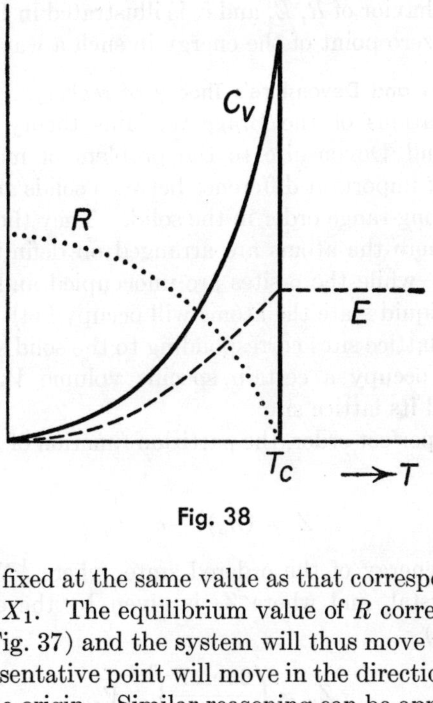

Fig. 38

energy Φ are kept fixed at the same value as that corresponding to Q_1, X is fixed at the value X_1. The equilibrium value of R corresponding to X_1 is equal to R_2 (see Fig. 37) and the system will thus move toward a *higher* R value, or the representative point will move in the direction of P and not in the direction of the origin. Similar reasoning can be applied to a point Q_2 corresponding to a value larger than its equilibrium value.

A more direct way of proving that P is a stable equilibrium is to evaluate $\dfrac{\partial^2 F}{\partial R^2}$. It then turns out that for $T < T_c$ the origin corresponds to a maximum of $F \left(\dfrac{\partial^2 F}{\partial R^2} < 0\right)$, and P to a minimum $\left(\dfrac{\partial^2 F}{\partial R^2} > 0\right)$. At temperatures above T_c the origin corresponds to a minimum. The critical temperature can be found in a similar way from the equations

$$R = 0, \qquad \frac{\partial F}{\partial R} = 0, \qquad \frac{\partial^2 F}{\partial R^2} = 0, \tag{12.235}$$

expressing the fact that the root $R = 0$ at the origin is a twofold one.

Once R is determined by the graphical method as a function of temperature, the configurational energy follows from equation (12.219) and the configurational specific heat from the equation

$$c_v = \frac{dE}{dT}. \tag{12.236}$$

The general behavior of R, E, and c_v is illustrated in Figure 38, where we have shifted the zero point of the energy in such a way that $E_1 = 0$.

§3. Lennard-Jones and Devonshire's Theory of Melting. One of the most successful applications of the Bragg-Williams theory has been that by Lennard-Jones and Devonshire to the problem of melting. Their idea was that the most important difference between solids and liquids might be the existence of long-range order in the solid. They therefore used for the solid a model where the atoms are arranged on definite sites—which we shall call α-sites—while the β-sites are unoccupied and form holes in the lattice. In the liquid state the atoms will occupy both α-sites and β-sites, that is, both the lattice sites corresponding to the solid state and the holes. Each atom will occupy a certain specific volume V_s corresponding to vibrations around its lattice site.

In the state of perfect order, the partition function of the system is given by the equation

$$Z = (Z_\mu)^{\frac{1}{2}N} e^{-\frac{E_1}{kT}}, \tag{12.301}$$

where E_1 is the energy of the ordered state, where $\frac{1}{2}N$ is the number of atoms in the crystal, and where Z_μ is given by the equation (compare equation [2.803]†)

$$Z_\mu = \left(\frac{2\pi mkT}{h^2}\right)^{3/2} V_s. \tag{12.302}$$

If the order is not complete, the partition function will contain a factor corresponding to the disorder, and instead of equation (12.301) we have

$$Z = Z_1 \cdot Z_2 \tag{12.303}$$

with

$$Z_1 = (Z_\mu)^{\frac{1}{2}N} \tag{12.304}$$

† There is no factor e/N in equation (12.302), since we are dealing with a crystal; compare the discussion on p. 72.

and

$$Z_2 = W(R)e^{-\frac{E(R)}{kT}}, \qquad (12.305)$$

where $W(R)$ and $E(R)$ are given by equations (12.219) and (12.222). Introducing the free energy by equation (12.226), equation (12.305) can also be written in the form

$$Z_2 = e^{-\frac{F(R)}{kT}}. \qquad (12.306)$$

Once the equilibrium value of R is found from equation (12.227), all quantities such as the pressure p, the internal energy E, or the entropy S follow from the partition function in the usual way. Since the partition function is a product of two factors, one pertaining to the state of complete order and one pertaining to the degree of disorder, all these quantities will consist of two terms.

We have, for instance, for the pressure

$$p = p_1 + p_2, \qquad p_i = kT\frac{\partial \ln Z_i}{\partial V}. \qquad (12.307)$$

Using equations (12.302), (12.304), (12.306), and (12.226), we get

$$p_1 = \tfrac{1}{2}NkT\frac{d \ln V_s}{dV} \qquad (12.308)$$

and

$$p_2 = -(1 - R^2)\frac{dE_0}{dV} - \frac{dE_1}{dV}, \qquad (12.309)$$

where we have used equation (12.225) to write

$$\frac{\partial F}{\partial V} = \frac{dE_1}{dV} + (1 - R^2)\frac{dE_0}{dV} + \frac{\partial F}{\partial R}\frac{\partial R}{\partial V}$$
$$= \frac{dE_1}{dV} + (1 - R^2)\frac{dE_0}{dV}.$$

In order to be able to discuss the melting process we must derive the equation of the isotherms which give p as a function of V. This means that for constant T we must find R as a function of V rather than as a function of T for constant V. Let us consider thereto the equation from which R can be determined, that is,

$$R = \tanh\frac{\Phi_0 R}{4kT}. \qquad (12.310)$$

The volume enters into this equation through Φ_0. We may, in general, expect Φ_0 to increase with decreasing volume, as long as the interatomic distances in the crystal do not become too small. Following Lennard-Jones and Devonshire, we shall assume for the sake of simplicity that

$$\Phi_0 = aV^{-l}. \tag{12.311}$$

It is then also a logical consequence of the model that

$$E_1 = bV^{-l}. \tag{12.312}$$

The specific volume V_s will, in general, increase with the volume and we shall assume for the sake of simplicity that

$$V_s = cV^m. \tag{12.313}$$

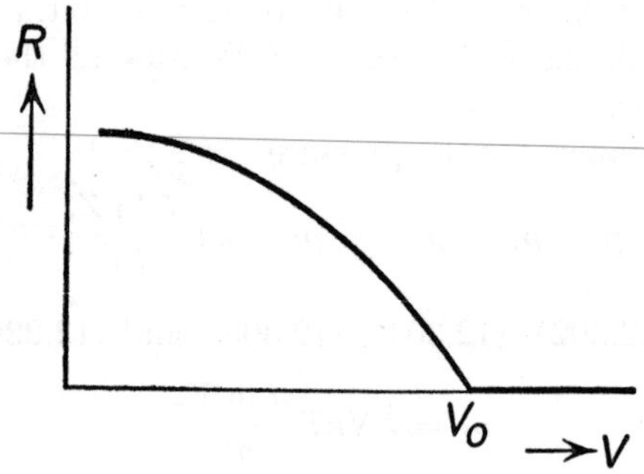

Fig. 39

In the preceding section we saw that R decreased from a value 1 at zero temperature to 0 at and above a certain critical temperature T_c. If we keep the temperature constant but vary the volume and thus Φ_0, we can expect that for high values of Φ_0 (small volumes) R will be in the neighborhood of 1, but that R will decrease with increasing volume or decreasing Φ_0. As a function of volume the qualitative behavior of R is sketched in Figure 39.

Using equations (12.308), (12.309), and (12.311) to (12.313), we have for the pressure

$$p = \frac{\frac{1}{2}NmkT}{V} + l\frac{E_1}{V} + l\frac{E_0}{V}(1 - R^2). \tag{12.314}$$

The first two terms on the right-hand side of equation (12.314) decrease smoothly with increasing V, but the last term increases for small values of V with increasing V due to the factor $(1 - R^2)$ while decreasing beyond V_0, where V_0 is the value of V for which long-range order disappears. In Figure 40 we have sketched the behavior of the sum of the first two terms, of the last term, and of the total pressure as a function of V. We see that—

for certain temperatures, at any rate—the isotherms bear some resemblance to van der Waals' isotherms in the vaporization range. As in the latter case, the actual path taken by a representative point will not be AEBDC when the volume is increased, but the straight line ABC. This line is constructed in such a way that the two areas AEB and BCD are equal. The distance AC is the change of volume during the melting process, and p_0 is the pressure at which melting takes place.

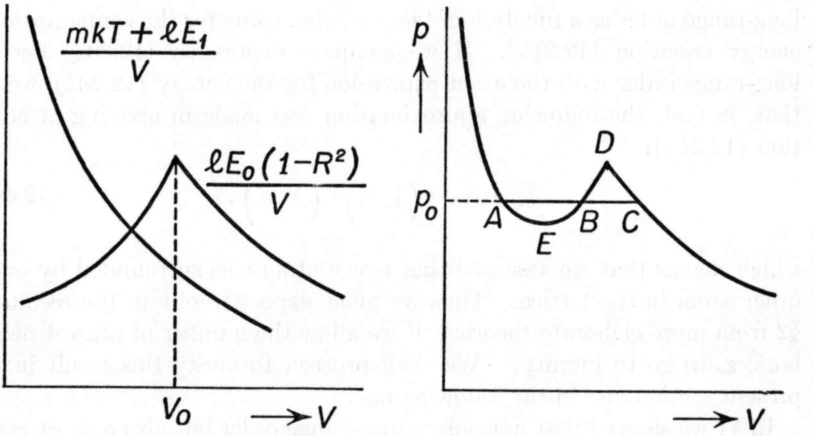

Fig. 40

Lennard-Jones and Devonshire have shown how one can obtain, instead of equations (12.312) and (12.313), exact expressions for V_s and E_1 once the interatomic forces are known for the potential energy of which they assume (see equation [1.301]):

$$U(r) = Ar^{-n} - Br^{-m}. \tag{12.315}$$

If one makes the assumption that E_0 is proportional to the repulsive energy ($l = n/3$), one can determine the constant a in equation (12.311) by putting the melting pressure at one temperature equal to the observed melting pressure at this temperature. This allows the whole melting curve to be calculated and compared with observation. The agreement has been found to be remarkably good. The assumption of central forces which is implicit in equation (12.315) for the potential energy will be best justified in the case of the inert gases. Lennard-Jones and Devonshire have calculated various quantities for argon, and some of their results are shown in the following table. It will be seen that the agreement between calculated and observed values is surprisingly good in view of the fact that the Bragg-Williams theory of order-disorder is based on a highly simplified model.

	Calculated	Observed
Change of volume on melting at 83.8°K	13.5%	12%
Change of entropy on melting at 83.8°K	$1.70k$	$1.66k$
Pressure of melting in dynes cm^{-2} at 90.3°K	$286 \cdot 10^6$	$291 \cdot 10^6$

§4. The Quasi-Chemical Method. In §2 we considered the behavior of long-range order as a function of temperature, using for the configurational energy equation (12.219). If we compare expression (12.208) for the long-range order with the exact expression for the energy (12.201), we see that, in fact, the following approximation was made in arriving at equation (12.219):

$$\sum_{\langle i,k \rangle} \mu_i \mu_k \to \left(\sum_{\langle i \rangle} \mu_i\right) \cdot \left(\sum_{\langle k \rangle} \mu_k\right), \tag{12.401}$$

which means that we assumed that every atom was surrounded by every other atom in the lattice. Thus we must expect to obtain the results of §2 from more elaborate theories, if we allow the number of nearest neighbors, z, to go to infinity. We shall proceed to verify this result in the present section and in the following one.

In §1 we showed that not only a long-range order but also a short-range order exists, and that the latter persists even if the former disappears. This short-range order measures how well, on the average, every A atom is surrounded by B atoms and vice versa. Let us consider a pair of neighboring sites which always consists of one α-site and one β-site. There are four possibilities, according to whether an A or a B atom occupies the α-site or the β-site. We shall indicate these four possibilities in the following way:

$$\left.\begin{aligned} &++,\ \text{A on } \alpha \text{ and A on } \beta, \\ &+-,\ \text{A on } \alpha \text{ and B on } \beta, \\ &-+,\ \text{B on } \alpha \text{ and A on } \beta, \\ &--,\ \text{B on } \alpha \text{ and B on } \beta. \end{aligned}\right\} \tag{12.402}$$

Let Q be the total number of pairs in the lattice and Q_{++}, Q_{+-}, Q_{-+}, and Q_{--} the total number of $++$, $+-$, $-+$, and $--$ pairs. If we neglect surface effects, Q is found by observing that every atom has z neighbors and that for every pair two atoms are involved; thus

$$Q = \tfrac{1}{2} zN. \tag{12.403}$$

Furthermore, as can easily be shown, the following relations exist:

$$\left.\begin{aligned} Q_{++} + Q_{+-} + Q_{-+} + Q_{--} &= Q, \\ Q_{++} &= Q_{--}. \end{aligned}\right\} \qquad (12.404)$$

From equations (12.403) and (12.404) we see that there are only two independently variable Q's. We shall see presently that we can express the Q's in terms of two other variables, the long-range and the short-range order parameters. The latter parameter, σ, is introduced by means of the equation

$$Q_{+-} + Q_{-+} - Q_{--} - Q_{++} = \sigma Q. \qquad (12.405)$$

In the case of perfect order, all pairs are $+-$, and σ is equal to one. If there is total disorder, all four Q's will be equal, and σ will be equal to zero.

In the sum $\sum_{\langle i,k\rangle} \mu_i\mu_k$ each $+-$ or $-+$ pair corresponds to a term $+1$ and each $++$ or $--$ pair to a term -1. Hence we can write σQ for this sum, or

$$\sigma = \frac{1}{Q} \sum_{\langle i,k\rangle} \mu_i\mu_k. \qquad (12.406)$$

Comparing equations (12.201) and (12.406), we see that the configurational energy is proportional to the short-range order† and we have

$$E = -\tfrac{1}{2}JQ\sigma. \qquad (12.407)$$

We may remark here that from equations (12.406), (12.401), and (12.208) it follows that the Bragg-Williams approximation gives the following relation between σ and R,

$$\sigma = R^2. \qquad (12.408)$$

We now have two parameters σ and R with which to describe the situation of a crystal. Let $W(R,\sigma)$ be the number of different ways in which a certain combination of values for σ and R can be realized. The free energy F is then given by the equation (compare equation [12.226])

$$F = -kT \ln W(R,\sigma) + E(\sigma). \qquad (12.409)$$

The equilibrium value of σ is then obtained by minimizing F with respect to σ,

$$\frac{\partial F}{\partial \sigma} = 0, \qquad (12.410)$$

and this equation will give us σ as a function of R.

† This is true as long as there is no external field in the case of ferromagnetism or as long as there are as many A as B atoms in the case of binary alloys.

In order to obtain the equilibrium value of R we have to use rather devious means. Let $W(R)$ be the number of ways in which a situation corresponding to a given value of R can be realized. This quantity is given by equation (12.222). We now define an energy $E'(R)$† by the equation

$$F(R) = -kT \ln W(R) + E'(R). \tag{12.411}$$

This equation is similar to the one leading to equation (12.226), and once we know $E'(R)$ we can proceed in the same way as in §2, obtaining R from condition (12.225) and the critical point from equations (12.235).

From equation (12.411) it follows that the partition function Z is given by the equation

$$Z = W(R)e^{-\frac{E'(R)}{kT}} \tag{12.412}$$

On the other hand, we also have

$$Z = \sum_{\langle R\rangle} e^{-\frac{E}{kT}}, \tag{12.413}$$

where the summation extends over all configurations with the same value of R and where E is $E(\sigma)$ after substituting for σ its equilibrium value obtained from equation (12.410). We also know that in the case of equilibrium the energy is given by the equation (compare equation [2.712])

$$E = -\frac{\partial \ln Z}{\partial \frac{1}{kT}} = \frac{\sum_{\langle R\rangle} E(\sigma)e^{-\frac{E(\sigma)}{kT}}}{\sum_{\langle R\rangle} e^{-\frac{E(\sigma)}{kT}}}, \tag{12.414}$$

where σ is once more a function of R through equation (12.410).

From equations (12.412) and (12.414) we finally get

$$E = \frac{\partial E'/T}{\partial 1/T},$$

or

$$E'(R) = T\int_{\frac{1}{T}=0}^{\frac{1}{T}} E(\sigma)d\,\frac{1}{T}, \tag{12.415}$$

where we have made use of the fact that when $T \to \infty$, $E'(R) \to 0$.

Substituting expression (12.415) for $E'(R)$ into equation (12.411), we have

$$F(R) = -kT \ln W(R) + T\int_0^{\frac{1}{T}} E(\sigma)d\,\frac{1}{T}. \tag{12.416}$$

---

† This energy is a free energy; compare equation (12.415).

We can now proceed to evaluate $F(R)$. All equations up to this point have been exact, but in obtaining an expression for $W(R,\sigma)$ we shall make certain approximations. We shall assume that we may treat all pairs in the lattice as independent entities, which is certainly not correct but may serve as a first approximation. This approximation is called the *quasi-chemical* method since it treats the pairs as independent chemical bonds. If all the pairs are assumed to be independent, $W(R,\sigma)$ should, apart from a factor depending on R, be the number of ways in which Q can be written as the sum of Q_{++}, Q_{+-}, Q_{-+}, and Q_{--}. We have thus

$$W(R,\sigma) = W_1(R)\frac{Q!}{Q_{++}!Q_{+-}!Q_{-+}!Q_{--}!}. \tag{12.417}$$

We now must express the Q's in terms of R and σ.

From equations (12.404) and (12.405) we see immediately that

$$Q_{++} = Q_{--} = \tfrac{1}{4}Q(1 - \sigma). \tag{12.418}$$

Since r_α is the fraction of α-sites correctly occupied, and since $Q_{++} + Q_{+-}$ is the number of pairs in the lattice of which the α-site is correctly occupied, we have

$$Q_{++} + Q_{+-} = r_\alpha Q. \tag{12.419}$$

Introducing R from equation (12.208) we get from equations (12.419), (12.418), and (12.404) the following expressions for Q_{+-} and Q_{-+}:

$$\left.\begin{aligned} Q_{+-} &= \tfrac{1}{4}Q(1 + 2R + \sigma), \\ Q_{-+} &= \tfrac{1}{4}Q(1 - 2R + \sigma). \end{aligned}\right\} \tag{12.420}$$

For the free energy we get, after some straightforward calculations from equations (12.409), (12.417), and (12.407), and using (12.223) for the factorials, the following expression:

$$\begin{aligned} F = -kT\,[\ln W_1(R) + Q\ln Q - Q_{++}\ln Q_{++} - Q_{+-}\ln Q_{+-} \\ - Q_{-+}\ln Q_{-+} - Q_{--}\ln Q_{--}] - \tfrac{1}{2}JQ\sigma. \end{aligned} \tag{12.421}$$

The equilibrium value of σ follows from equation (12.410), and using equations (12.418) and (12.420) we get

$$\ln\frac{Q_{++}Q_{--}}{Q_{+-}Q_{-+}} = -\frac{2J}{kT}, \tag{12.422}$$

or, introducing x by equation (12.231),

$$\frac{Q_{++}Q_{--}}{Q_{+-}Q_{-+}} = x^2. \tag{12.423}$$

Equation (12.423) is the basic equation of the quasi-chemical method.

Introducing equations (12.418) and (12.420) for the Q's, we get for σ the expression

$$\sigma = \frac{1 + x^2 - 2x\sqrt{1 - R^2 + R^2x^2}}{1 - x^2}. \qquad \textbf{(12.424)}$$

At temperatures above T_c we have $R = 0$, and hence

$$\sigma = \frac{1 - x}{1 + x}. \qquad \textbf{(12.425)}$$

Using expression (12.415) for $E'(R)$, expression (12.407) for E, and expression (12.424) for σ, we find after integration

$$-E'(R)/\tfrac{1}{2}QkT =$$

$$2 \ln \frac{u + 1}{2} + (R - 1) \ln \frac{u - R}{1 - R} - (R + 1) \ln \frac{u + R}{1 + R} + \frac{J}{kT}, \qquad \textbf{(12.426)}$$

where

$$u = \frac{1}{x}\sqrt{1 - R^2 + R^2x^2}. \qquad \textbf{(12.427)}$$

Equation (12.426) can be obtained as follows. Introducing u by equation (12.427) we get for the integral on the right-hand side of equation (12.415) the expression

$$k\int_1^u \frac{[u^2 + u(2R^2 - 1)]du}{(u + 1)(u^2 - R^2)} = k\int_1^u \left[\frac{2}{u + 1} + \frac{R - \frac{1}{2}}{u - R} - \frac{R + \frac{1}{2}}{u + R}\right] du,$$

from which follows equation (12.426) if we use the fact that

$$\frac{1}{2} \ln \frac{u^2 - R^2}{1 - R^2} = -\ln x.$$

From equations (12.411), (12.222) (using equation [12.223], compare equation [12.226]), (12.426), and (12.403), we finally get for the free energy the equation

$$F(R) = \tfrac{1}{2}kNT\Bigg[(1 + R) \ln (1 + R) + (1 - R) \ln (1 - R) - 2 \ln 2$$

$$+ \frac{z}{2}\left\{(1 + R) \ln \frac{u + R}{1 + R} + (1 - R) \ln \frac{u - R}{1 - R} - 2 \ln \frac{u + 1}{2}\right\}\Bigg]. \qquad \textbf{(12.428)}$$

The equilibrium value of R follows from $\partial F/\partial R = 0$ and we get R from equation (12.427) and the equation

$$\left(1 - \frac{z}{2}\right) \ln \frac{1 + R}{1 - R} + \frac{z}{2} \ln \frac{u + R}{u - R} = 0. \qquad \textbf{(12.429)}\dagger$$

† One must bear in mind that $\dfrac{\partial F}{\partial R} = \left(\dfrac{\partial F}{\partial R}\right)_u + \left(\dfrac{\partial F}{\partial u}\right)_R \dfrac{du}{dR}$, where $\dfrac{du}{dR}$ can be obtained from equation (12.427).

The critical temperature follows from equations (12.235), which leads to the equation

$$x_c = 1 - \frac{2}{z}, \tag{12.430}$$

where equation (12.427) has been used once again.

Equations (12.427) and (12.429) give us R as a function of x or as a function of temperature. Equation (12.424) then gives us σ and from equation (12.407) we finally get the configurational energy and hence the specific heat.

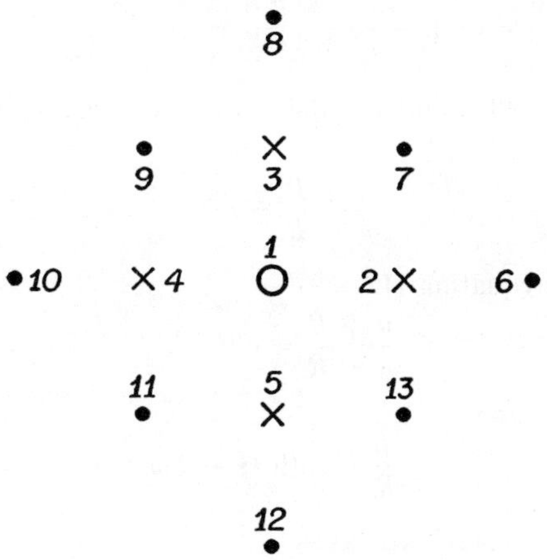

Fig. 41

In 1935 Bethe introduced two approximations which consisted of considering one atom with one or two shells of neighboring atoms (see Fig. 41). In his first approximation he studied the influence of atoms 2, 3, 4, and 5 on atom 1, and in his second approximation he studied the influence of atoms 6 to 13 on 1 to 5. He did this by writing down expressions for the partition functions pertaining to the selected number of inner atoms.

Bethe's first approximation is equivalent to the quasi-chemical method. We shall not give here the complete proof of this equivalence, but remark only that in limiting the consideration to atoms 1 to 5 Bethe is in fact dealing only with independent pairs, and since the number of pairs will be proportional to the corresponding partition function, we see that for the $++$ and $--$ pairs extra factors x are introduced, thus leading to equation (12.423). The method used by Bethe to obtain equation (12.429) from equation (12.423) is completely different from the one used here and we must refer the reader to Bethe's paper for his derivation of equation

(12.429) and also for a discussion of his second approximation. We shall, however, show briefly how one can rewrite equation (12.429) in the form given by Bethe.

Introducing δ by the equation

$$R = \tanh z\delta, \tag{12.431}$$

equation (12.429) reduces to Bethe's equation

$$x = \frac{\sinh (z - 2)\delta}{\sinh z\delta}, \tag{12.432}$$

while σ expressed in δ is given by the equation

$$\sigma = 1 - \frac{2 \sinh (z - 2)\delta}{\cosh z\delta \sinh (2z - 2)\delta}. \tag{12.433}$$

Equations (12.432) and (12.433) can be derived as follows. From equation (12.431) we have

$$\frac{1 + R}{1 - R} = e^{2z\delta},$$

and hence from equation (12.429)

$$\frac{u + R}{u - R} = e^{2(z-2)\delta},$$

or

$$\frac{u}{R} = \coth (z - 2)\delta.$$

From equation (12.427) we have

$$x = \sqrt{\frac{\dfrac{1}{R^2} - 1}{\left(\dfrac{u}{R}\right)^2 - 1}},$$

whence follows equation (12.432), since $\coth^2 \alpha - 1 = \sinh^{-2} \alpha$.

Furthermore from equations (12.424) and (12.427) we have

$$\sigma = \frac{\dfrac{1}{x^2} + 1 - 2R\dfrac{u}{R}}{\dfrac{1}{x^2} - 1}.$$

Substituting for x and u/R in terms of δ and using the relations for $\sinh (\alpha - \beta)$, $\sinh 2\alpha$, and the sum and difference of two hyperbolic sines, we obtain equation (12.433).

We can use equations (12.431) to (12.433) to show that the Bragg-Williams approximation follows if we let z go to infinity. If Φ_0 remains finite, it follows from equation (12.216) that for $z \to \infty$, J must go to zero.

Also δ must go to zero, since R is of the order of magnitude 1 (see equation [12.431]). From equation (12.432) we have for $\delta \to 0$

$$x = \cosh 2\delta - \coth z\delta \sinh 2\delta \approx 1 - \frac{2\delta}{R}, \tag{12.434}$$

and from equations (12.231) and (12.216) we have

$$x = e^{-\frac{J}{kT}} \approx 1 - \frac{J}{kT} = 1 - \frac{\Phi_0}{2zkT}. \tag{12.435}$$

Hence

$$z\delta = \frac{R\Phi_0}{4kT},$$

and equation (12.431) reduces to equation (12.227)

Also, equation (12.433) can be written in the form

$$\sigma \approx 1 - \frac{1}{\cosh^2 z\delta} = \tanh^2 z\delta = R^2, \tag{12.436}$$

which is the same as equation (12.408).

§5. **Kirkwood's Method.** In 1938 Kirkwood introduced a method which gives a series expansion of $E'(R)$ and hence of the free energy in terms of K (or $1/T$). One can obtain this series expansion in the following way. We have, on the one hand, for the partition function, by definition, equation (12.412) and, on the other hand (see equations [12.210] and [12.413]), we have

$$Z = \sum_{\langle R\rangle} e^{Ks}, \tag{12.501}$$

where s stands for $\sum_{\langle i,k\rangle} \mu_i\mu_k$ and where the summation extends over all configurations for which R has a given value. Combining equations (12.412) and (12.501), we have

$$\frac{E'(R)}{kT} = \ln W(R) - \ln \sum_{\langle R\rangle} e^{Ks}. \tag{12.502}$$

Denoting by pointed brackets the averages taken over all configurations for which R has a given value, namely,

$$\langle s^n\rangle = \frac{1}{W(R)} \sum_{\langle R\rangle} s^n, \tag{12.503}$$

we get after expanding first the exponential and then the logarithm

$$\frac{E'(R)}{kT} = -\ln\left[1 + K\langle s\rangle + \frac{K^2}{2}\langle s^2\rangle + \frac{K^3}{3!}\langle s^3\rangle + \cdots\right], \tag{12.504}$$

or

$$\frac{E'(R)}{kT} = -\sum_{n=1}^{\infty} \frac{K^n}{n!} M_n, \tag{12.505}$$

where the first four M_n are given by the equations

$$M_1 = \langle s \rangle, \tag{12.506}$$

$$M_2 = \langle s^2 \rangle - \langle s \rangle^2, \tag{12.507}$$

$$M_3 = \langle s^3 \rangle - 3\langle s^2 \rangle\langle s \rangle + 2\langle s \rangle^3, \tag{12.508}$$

$$M_4 = \langle s^4 \rangle - 4\langle s^3 \rangle\langle s \rangle - 3\langle s^2 \rangle^2 + 12\langle s^2 \rangle\langle s \rangle^2 - 6\langle s \rangle^4. \tag{12.509}$$

The point now is to evaluate the M_n as functions of R and this entails a rather large amount of work. We shall give the results of these calculations presently, but in order to illustrate how these results may be obtained we shall evaluate $\langle s^3 \rangle$ in detail. The other $\langle s^n \rangle$ follow in the same way, and we shall give in Figure 42 and in accompanying tables all the results necessary to calculate M_1 to M_4 in order to enable the reader to check our results.

If we wish to calculate $\langle s^3 \rangle$ we are dealing with Q^3 terms of the structure $(\mu_1\mu_2)(\mu_3\mu_4)(\mu_5\mu_6)$ where in each case the two μ's inside one pair of brackets correspond to one pair in the lattice. There are altogether seven different kinds of configurations where we have three pairs. These configurations are the ones numbered e to k in Figure 42. The contribution from each of these configurations will consist of three factors. The first one, f_1, will be the number of configurations in the lattice which are of the kind considered. The second factor, f_2, is the number of ways in which the pairs (in our case, three pairs) can be distributed over the configuration and the last factor, f_3, is the average value of the product of the μ's corresponding to the given value of R.

The last factor is easily calculated. Each pair consists of an α-site and a β-site. Introducing the notation

$$r = \tfrac{1}{2}(1 + R), \quad w = \tfrac{1}{2}(1 - R), \quad n = \tfrac{1}{2}N, \tag{12.510}$$

we see that for a given long-range order R there are rn α-sites with $\mu_i = +1$ and wn α-sites with $\mu_i = -1$. Let δ_k be the average value of the product of k μ's belonging to k different lattice sites which are either all α-sites or all β-sites. We have, then, for δ_k the equation

$$\delta_k = \frac{\binom{rn}{k} - \binom{rn}{k-1}\binom{wn}{1} + \binom{rn}{k-2}\binom{wn}{2} - \cdots \pm \binom{rn}{1}\binom{wn}{k-1} \mp \binom{wn}{k}}{\binom{n}{k}}. \tag{12.511}$$

This equation follows from the fact that $\binom{rn}{p}\binom{wn}{k-p}$ is the number of ways in which p of the μ's are equal to $+1$ and $k - p$ of the μ's are equal to -1, while $\binom{n}{k}$ is the total number of ways to choose k from n μ's.

From equation (12.511) we get for δ_1 to δ_4

$$\delta_1 = R, \tag{12.512}$$

$$\delta_2 = R^2 + \frac{R^2 - 1}{n - 1}, \tag{12.513}$$

$$\delta_3 = R^3 + R(R^2 - 1)\frac{3n - 2}{n^2 - 3n + 2}, \tag{12.514}$$

$$\delta_4 = R^4 + (R^2 - 1)\frac{6R^2n^2 - 11R^2n - 3n + 6(R^2 + 1)}{n^3 - 6n^2 + 11n - 6}. \tag{12.515}$$

If a lattice site is occupied more than once,we may count it once if it is occupied an odd number of times and not count it at all if it is occupied an even number of times. This follows since μ_i^2 is always equal to one. If we introduce

$$\delta_0 = 1 \tag{12.516}$$

we have for f_3 always an equation of the form

$$f_3 = \delta_i\delta_j. \tag{12.517}$$

The factor f_2 is also easily computed. It is the number of ways in which n pairs can be divided into groups consisting respectively of n_1, n_2, $\cdots$ pairs, and we have thus

$$f_2 = \binom{n}{n_1}\binom{n - n_1}{n_2}\binom{n - n_1 - n_2}{n_3}\cdots. \tag{12.518}$$

The first factor is the most difficult to evaluate and involves rather a lot of careful sorting out. We shall return to its evaluation presently, but first we give the results for f_1, f_2, and f_3 which are needed to evaluate $\langle s\rangle$, $\langle s^2\rangle$, $\langle s^3\rangle$, and $\langle s^4\rangle$. The first column in each table gives the letter by which the configuration is indicated in Figure 42

TABLE FOR $\langle s\rangle$

Configuration	f_1	f_2	f_3
a	Q	1	δ_1^2

TABLE FOR $\langle s^2\rangle$

Configuration	f_1	f_2	f_3
b	Q	1	δ_0^2
c	$(z - 1)Q$	2!	$\delta_0\delta_2$
d	$\frac{1}{2}Q(Q - 2z + 1)$	2!	δ_2^2

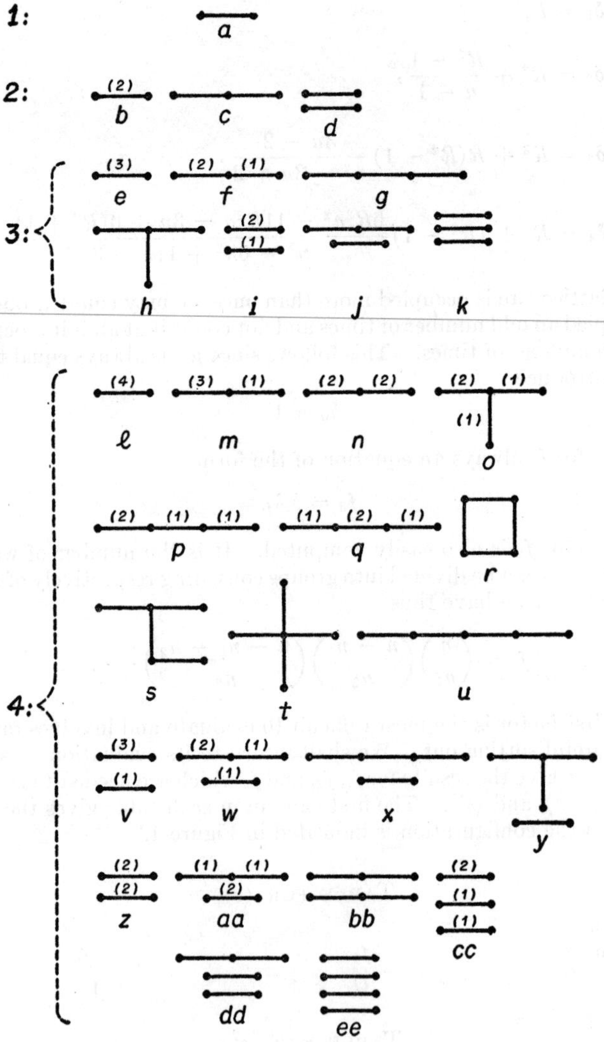
1:
a
2:
(2)
b
c
d
3:
(3)
e
(2) (1)
f
g
h
(2)
(1)
i
j
k
4:
(4)
ℓ
(3) (1)
m
(2) (2)
n
(2) (1)
(1)
o
(2) (1) (1)
p
(1) (2) (1)
q
r
s
t
u
(3)
(1)
v
(2) (1)
(1)
w
x
y
(2)
(2)
z
(1) (1)
(2)
aa
bb
(2)
(1)
(1)
cc
dd
ee

Fig. 42

TABLE FOR $\langle s^3 \rangle$

Configuration	f_1	f_2	f_3
e	Q	1	δ_1^2
f	$2(z-1)Q$	3	δ_1^2
g	$(z-1)^2Q$	3!	δ_1^2
h	$\frac{1}{3}(z-1)(z-2)Q$	3!	$\delta_1\delta_3$
i	$Q(Q-2z+1)$	3	δ_1^2
j	$(z-1)Q(Q-3z+2)$	3!	$\delta_1\delta_3$
k	$\frac{1}{3!}Q[Q^2-(6z-3)Q+10z^2-12z+4]$	3!	δ_3^2

TABLE FOR $\langle s^4 \rangle$

Configuration	f_1	f_2	f_3
l	Q	1	δ_0^2
m	$2(z-1)Q$	4	$\delta_0\delta_2$
n	$(z-1)Q$	$\binom{4}{2}$	δ_0^2
o	$(z-1)(z-2)Q$	$\binom{4}{2}\cdot 2$	$\delta_0\delta_2$
p	$2(z-1)^2Q$	$\binom{4}{2}\cdot 2$	$\delta_0\delta_2$
q	$(z-1)^2Q$	$\binom{4}{2}\cdot 2$	δ_2^2
r	$\frac{1}{4}(z-2)Q$	4!	δ_0^2
s	$(z-1)^2(z-2)Q$	4!	δ_2^2
t	$\frac{1}{12}(z-1)(z-2)(z-3)Q$	4!	$\delta_0\delta_4$
u	$[(z-2)^2z+(z-1)^2]Q$	4!	$\delta_0\delta_2$
v	$Q(Q-2z+1)$	4	δ_2^2
w	$2(z-1)Q(Q-3z+2)$	$\binom{4}{2}\cdot 2$	δ_2^2
x	$Q[(z-1)^2(Q-4z+3)+z-2]$	4!	δ_2^2
y	$\frac{1}{3}(z-1)(z-2)Q(Q-4z+3)$	4!	$\delta_2\delta_4$
z	$\frac{1}{2}Q(Q-2z+1)$	$\binom{4}{2}$	δ_0^2
aa	$(z-1)Q(Q-3z+2)$	$\binom{4}{2}\cdot 2$	$\delta_0\delta_2$
bb† (*i*)	$\frac{1}{4}(z-1)^2Q(Q-4z+4)$	4!	δ_2^2
bb† (*ii*)	$\frac{1}{4}Q[(z-1)^2Q-5z^3+14z^2-11z]$	4!	$\delta_0\delta_4$
cc	$\frac{1}{2}Q(Q^2-(6z-3)Q+10z^2-12z+4)$	$\binom{4}{2}\cdot 2$	δ_2^2
dd	$\frac{1}{2}Q[(z-1)Q^2-(z-1)(8z-5)Q+18z^3-44z^2+34z-6]$	4!	$\delta_2\delta_4$
ee	$\frac{1}{4!}Q[Q^3-(12z-6)Q^2+(52z^2-60z+19)Q-84z^3+168z^2-114z+18]$	4!	δ_4^2

† One must distinguish here two cases according to whether the central lattice points belong to different sublattices (*i*) or to the same sublattice (*ii*).

In order to illustrate how f_l is found we shall give here the considerations leading to the f_l needed for $\langle s^3 \rangle$.

Configuration e: f_l is the number of pairs in the lattice.

Configuration f: There are Q possibilities to choose the first pair and the second pair can be attached to the first pair in $2(z-1)$ different ways.

Configuration g: There are Q possibilities for the middle pair and $z-1$ possibilities for each of the outer pairs.

Configuration h: There are N possibilities for the central point and $\binom{z}{3}$ different ways of choosing the three pairs.

Configuration i: The doubly occupied pair has Q possibilities and the other pair has again Q possibilities minus those where the second pair would touch the first one. This leads to $Q - 2z + 1$ possibilities, since the $2z - 1$ pairs leading to the end points of the first pair are excluded. One can check the result in this case by observing that (f_a stands for f_{1a}, etc.)

$$f_e + f_f + f_i = f_a^2. \qquad \textbf{(12.519)}\dagger$$

Configuration j: There are $(z-1)Q$ possibilities for the two connected pairs—the extra factor $\frac{1}{2}$ as compared to f_f enters because the two pairs are now identical—and the number of pairs excluded for the single pair is $3z - 2$. One can check the result by using the equation

$$f_f + 2f_g + 3f_h + f_j = f_e \times f_a. \qquad \textbf{(12.520)}$$

Configuration k: One can calculate f_k either directly by considering the various possibilities, or more easily by using the equation

$$f_g + f_i + 2f_j + 3f_k = f_d \times f_a. \qquad \textbf{(12.521)}$$

As far as the results for $\langle s^4 \rangle$ are concerned, we must mention the fact that they apply only to the two-dimensional square or to the simple cubic lattice, while those for $\langle s^3 \rangle$ do not hold for triangular or honeycomb plane lattices, or for face centered cubic lattices. In the calculations leading to the results for $\langle s^4 \rangle$, equations like the following ones can be used either to check the results or to compute the f_l,

$$f_p + f_q + 4f_r + 2f_s + 2f_u + f_x = f_g \times f_a, \qquad \textbf{(12.522)}$$

$$f_o + 4f_t + f_s + f_y = f_h \times f_a, \qquad \textbf{(12.523)}$$

$$f_n + 2f_o + 2f_q + 4f_r + 2f_s + 6f_t + 2f_u + 2f_{bb} = f_c^2, \qquad \textbf{(12.524)}$$

$$f_p + 2f_s + f_u + f_w + 2f_x + 3f_y + f_{dd} = f_e \times f_d, \qquad \textbf{(12.525)}$$

$$f_x + f_{cc} + 2f_{dd} + 4f_{ee} = f_k \times f_a. \qquad \textbf{(12.526)}$$

The final results‡ for M_1 to M_4 are

$$M_1 = QR^2, \qquad \textbf{(12.527)}$$

† It may be mentioned here that T. S. Chang (J. Chem. Phys., **9**, 169, 1941) has calculated the f_l by the exclusive use of relations of this kind.

‡ Again the results for M_1 and M_2 are general while the results for M_3 and M_4 hold only for the two-dimensional square and the simple cubic lattice.

$$M_2 = Q(1 - R^2)^2, \tag{12.528}$$

$$M_3 = 4QR^2(1 - R^2)^2, \tag{12.529}$$

$$M_4 = 2Q(1 - R^2)^2[(3z - 9)(1 - R^2)^2 + 2(1 - 3R^2)^2]. \tag{12.530}$$

We thus get for the free energy, combining equations (12.411), (12.505), and (12.527) to (12.530),

$$\frac{F(R)}{NkT} = \tfrac{1}{2}(1 + R)\ln(1 + R) + \tfrac{1}{2}(1 - R)\ln(1 - R) - \ln 2 + \frac{z}{2}\Big[-KR^2 - \frac{K^2}{2}(1 - R^2)^2 - \frac{2K^3}{3}R^2(1 - R^2)^2 - \frac{K^4}{12}(1 - R^2)^2[(3z - 9)(1 - R^2)^2 + 2(1 - 3R^2)^2] - \cdots\Big], \tag{12.531}$$

where we have used equations (12.222) and (12.223) for $W(R)$.

Minimizing the free energy we get for the equilibrium value of R the equation

$$\ln\frac{1+R}{1-R} = zR\Big[2K - 2K^2(1-R^2) + \frac{4K^3}{3}(1-R^2)(1-3R^2) - \frac{2K^4}{3}(1-R^2)[(3z-9)(1-R^2)^2 + (1-3R^2)(2-3R^2)] + \cdots\Big], \tag{12.532}$$

and, using equations (12.235), we get the critical temperature from the following equation for K_c,

$$\frac{2}{z} = 2K_c - \frac{(2K_c)^2}{2!} + \frac{(2K_c)^3}{3!} - (3z - 7)\frac{(2K_c)^4}{4!} + \cdots. \tag{12.533}$$

This equation should be compared with equations (12.232) and (12.430), which follow from the Bragg-Williams and quasi-chemical methods. These equations can be written in the following form:

$$\frac{2}{z} = 2K_c, \tag{12.534}$$

and

$$\frac{2}{z} = 1 - e^{-2K_c} = 2K_c - \frac{(2K_c)^2}{2!} + \frac{(2K_c)^3}{3!} - \frac{(2K_c)^4}{4!} + \cdots. \tag{12.535}$$

Before commenting on the last three equations we can tabulate the values of x_c obtained by different approximation methods† in the cases of

† Other comparisons between various approximations can be found in the paper by Kramers and Wannier (Phys. Rev., **60**, 262, 1941) and D. ter Haar, Physica, **18**, 836, 1952. In these papers series expansions for the partition function are compared.

the two-dimensional square lattice (t.d.s.), the simple cubic (s.c.), the body-centered cubic (b.c.c.), and the face-centered cubic lattice (f.c.c.). The table contains values of x_c obtained by the following methods:

BW: Bragg-Williams (Kirkwood's first term)
K II: Kirkwood's first two terms
K III: Kirkwood's first three terms
K IV: Kirkwood's first four terms
Q.C.: Quasi-chemical method
Z: Zernike's first approximation†
Var: Variational method (see §6)
E: Exact value in the case of the two-dimensional square lattice (see §7); extrapolated values following from plotting the reciprocal of the specific heat obtained from exact series expansions‡ in the case of the other three lattices

TABLE OF VALUES OF x_c

Approximation	$z = 4$ (t.d.s.)	$z = 6$ (s.c.)	$z = 8$ (b.c.c.)	$z = 12$ (f.c.c.)
BW	0.607	0.717	0.779	0.848
K II	0.368§	0.655	0.746	0.832
K III	0.508	0.667	0.750	—
K IV	0.509‖	0.653	0.730#	—
Q.C.	0.500	0.667	0.750	0.833
Z	0.524	0.674	0.753	0.834
Var	0.438	—	—	—
E	0.414	0.606	0.701	0.793

§ This value of x_c does not agree with the one given by Kramers and Wannier (Phys. Rev., **60**, 262, 1941). It seems highly probable from the context that there is a misprint in their paper at this point, the more so since their value of x_c in the case K III agrees with ours. It is remarkable that in the case K II the exact value of x_c is actually passed.

‖ This value is actually the value for the case K V, where we have used Chang's results (J. Chem. Phys., **9**, 169, 1941) for the free energy. The equation for K_c in the case K IV does not have a real solution.

This value has also been evaluated by using Chang's results (*loc. cit.*).

We may end this section by making a few remarks concerning equations (12.533) to (12.535). Comparing equation (12.534) with the other two equations for K_c, we see once again that the Bragg-Williams approximation is obtained from the other approximations in the limit $z \to \infty$. As we mentioned on page 272 in that limit J and thus K is proportional to $1/z$, and we see that equation (12.534) follows from the other equations by neglecting higher-order terms in $1/z$ (or K). The same applies to equation (12.532), which goes over into equation (12.227) by neglecting all terms on the right-hand side except the first one.

† F. Zernike, Physica, **7**, 565, 1940.
‡ E. Trefftz, Z. Physik, **127**, 371, 1950.

§6. **The Variational Method.** In order to discuss the variational method introduced by Kramers and Wannier or Onsager's exact solution of the case of the two-dimensional square lattice, we start from expression (12.210) for the partition function,

$$Z = \sum e^{K\sum \mu_i\mu_k + C\sum \mu_i}. \tag{12.601}$$

Let us first consider a linear chain (Fig. 43). The probability $P(\mu_1, \mu_2, \ldots, \mu_{n-1})$ that the spins $\mu_1, \mu_2, \cdots, \mu_{n-1}$ of a chain of $n-1$ members will have given values (for instance, $\mu_1 = -1$, $\mu_2 = +1$,

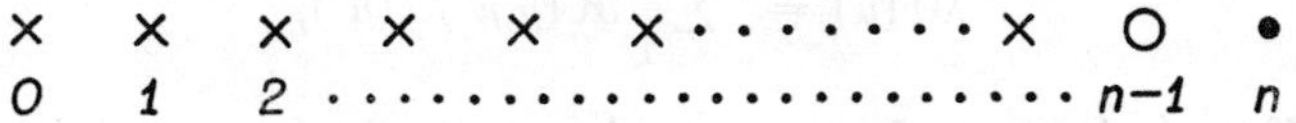

Fig. 43

$\mu_3 = +1$, $\mu_4 = -1, \cdots, \mu_{n-1} = +1$) will be proportional to the Boltzmann factor $e^{-E/kT}$, since the a priori probability (or weight) for any arrangement is the same. From expression (12.209) for the energy we have thus, using equations (12.211) and (12.212),

$$P(\mu_1, \mu_2, \cdots, \mu_{n-1}) = p_{n-1}e^{K(\mu_1\mu_2 + \mu_2\mu_3 + \cdots + \mu_{n-2}\mu_{n-1}) + C(\mu_1 + \mu_2 + \cdots + \mu_{n-1})}, \tag{12.602}$$

where p_{n-1} is a normalizing constant. Including one more spin in the chain we have

$$P(\mu_1, \mu_2, \cdots, \mu_n) = \frac{p_n}{p_{n-1}} P(\mu_1, \cdots, \mu_{n-1})e^{K\mu_{n-1}\mu_n + C\mu_n} \tag{12.603}$$

From expressions (12.602) and (12.603) we can obtain the probabilities $P(\mu_{n-1})$ and $P(\mu_{n-1}, \mu_n)$ that, respectively, μ_{n-1} and both μ_{n-1} and μ_n have given values irrespective of the $n-2$ preceding spins. We have

$$P(\mu_{n-1}) = \sum_{\mu_1=\pm1}\sum_{\mu_2=\pm1}\cdots\sum_{\mu_{n-2}=\pm1} P(\mu_1, \cdots, \mu_{n-1}), \tag{12.604}$$

and

$$P(\mu_{n-1}, \mu_n) =$$

$$\sum_{\mu_1=\pm1}\sum_{\mu_2=\pm1}\cdots\sum_{\mu_{n-2}=\pm1} \frac{p_n}{p_{n-1}} P(\mu_1, \cdots, \mu_{n-1})e^{K\mu_{n-1}\mu_n + C\mu_n}, \tag{12.605}$$

or

$$\lambda P(\mu_{n-1}, \mu_n) = P(\mu_{n-1})e^{K\mu_{n-1}\mu_n + C\mu_n}, \tag{12.606}$$

where $\lambda = p_{n-1}/p_n$.

Summing both sides of expression (12.606) over the two possible values of μ_{n-1}, we get the probability $P(\mu_n)$ that μ_n has a given value irrespective of the $n - 1$ preceding spins, or

$$\lambda P(\mu_n) = \sum_{\mu_{n-1}=\pm 1} P(\mu_{n-1}) e^{K\mu_{n-1}\mu_n + C\mu_n}. \tag{12.607}$$

If our chain is sufficiently long, $P(\mu_n)$ and $P(\mu_{n-1})$ should be the same function, $P(\mu)$. Introducing a spinor† $\mathcal{A}(\mu)$ by the equation

$$\mathcal{A}(\mu) = P(\mu) e^{-\frac{1}{2}C\mu}, \tag{12.608}$$

we can write equation (12.607)—or, since it is a matrix equation, equations (12.607)—in the form

$$\lambda \mathcal{A}(\mu) = \sum_{\mu'=\pm 1} \mathcal{H}(\mu,\mu') \mathcal{A}(\mu'), \tag{12.609}$$

where $\mathcal{H}(\mu,\mu')$ is a two-by-two matrix whose elements are given by the equation

$$\mathcal{H}(\mu,\mu') = e^{K\mu\mu' + \frac{1}{2}C(\mu+\mu')}. \tag{12.610}$$

Equation (12.609) has the form of a matrix eigenvalue equation. Let us examine the importance of the eigenvalues of $\mathcal{H}$. The normalized eigenvectors of $\mathcal{H}$ may be denoted by $\mathcal{A}_1(\mu)$ and $\mathcal{A}_2(\mu)$ and the corresponding eigenvalues by λ_1 and λ_2. Since $\mathcal{H}(\mu,\mu')$ is a function of both μ and μ' we can expand it in the form

$$\mathcal{H}(\mu,\mu') = \sum_{i,j=1}^{2} c_{ij} \mathcal{A}_i(\mu) \mathcal{A}_j(\mu'), \tag{12.611}$$

where the c_{ij} are given by the equations

$$c_{ij} = \sum_{\mu=\pm 1} \sum_{\mu'=\pm 1} \mathcal{H}(\mu,\mu') \mathcal{A}_i(\mu) \mathcal{A}_j(\mu'). \tag{12.612}$$

Since the $\mathcal{A}_i(\mu)$ are eigenvectors of $\mathcal{H}$, we have

$$\sum_{\mu'=\pm 1} \mathcal{H}(\mu,\mu') \mathcal{A}_j(\mu') = \lambda_j \mathcal{A}_j(\mu), \tag{12.613}$$

and from the orthonormality conditions‡

$$\sum_{\mu=\pm 1} \mathcal{A}_i(\mu) \mathcal{A}_j(\mu) = \delta_{ij} \tag{12.614}$$

it then follows that $c_{ij} = \lambda_i \delta_{ij}$, or

$$\mathcal{H}(\mu,\mu') = \lambda_1 \mathcal{A}_1(\mu) \mathcal{A}_1(\mu') + \lambda_2 \mathcal{A}_2(\mu) \mathcal{A}_2(\mu'). \tag{12.615}$$

Using the orthonormality relations (12.614) one can easily prove from

---

† The $P(\mu)$ and $\mathcal{A}(\mu)$ are matrices of one by two, that is, $\begin{pmatrix} P(+1) \\ P(-1) \end{pmatrix}$ and $\begin{pmatrix} \mathcal{A}(+1) \\ \mathcal{A}(-1) \end{pmatrix}$. Such matrices are called *spinors* because of their occurrence in the theory of the spinning electron.

‡ The Kronecker symbol δ_{ij} is such that $\delta_{ij} = 1$ for $i = j$ and $= 0$ for $i \neq j$.

equation (12.615) that

$$\sum_{\mu_2=\pm 1} \mathcal{H}(\mu_1,\mu_2)\mathcal{H}(\mu_2,\mu_3) = \lambda_1^2\mathfrak{A}_1(\mu_1)\mathfrak{A}_1(\mu_3) + \lambda_2^2\mathfrak{A}_2(\mu_1)\mathfrak{A}_2(\mu_3),$$

$$\sum_{\mu_2=\pm 1}\sum_{\mu_3=\pm 1} \mathcal{H}(\mu_1,\mu_2)\mathcal{H}(\mu_2,\mu_3)\mathcal{H}(\mu_3,\mu_4)$$
$$= \lambda_1^3\mathfrak{A}_1(\mu_1)\mathfrak{A}_1(\mu_4) + \lambda_2^3\mathfrak{A}_2(\mu_1)\mathfrak{A}_2(\mu_4),$$

and so on, until

$$\sum_{\mu_2,\cdots,\mu_N=\pm 1} \mathcal{H}(\mu_1,\mu_2)\mathcal{H}(\mu_2,\mu_3)\cdots\mathcal{H}(\mu_N,\mu_{N+1})$$
$$= \lambda_1^N\mathfrak{A}_1(\mu_1)\mathfrak{A}_1(\mu_{N+1}) + \lambda_2^N\mathfrak{A}_2(\mu_1)\mathfrak{A}_2(\mu_{N+1}). \quad \textbf{(12.616)}$$

Assuming $\mu_1 = \mu_{N+1}$, which corresponds either to closing the chain and forming a ring or to imposing a periodicity condition on the chain, we can sum expression (12.616) over μ_1 and obtain

$$\sum_{\langle\mu\rangle} \mathcal{H}(\mu_1,\mu_2)\mathcal{H}(\mu_2,\mu_3)\cdots\mathcal{H}(\mu_N,\mu_1) = \lambda_1^N + \lambda_2^N. \quad \textbf{(12.617)}\dagger$$

The left-hand side of equation (12.617) is just the partition function Z of a linear lattice of N spins, as can be seen from equations (12.610) and (12.601).

We get thus for this partition function of a one-dimensional lattice the equation

$$Z = \lambda_1^N + \lambda_2^N, \quad \textbf{(12.618)}$$

where the λ_i are the eigenvalues of the matrix given by equation (12.610). If N is sufficiently large, and if $|\lambda_2| < |\lambda_1|$, we may write equation (12.618) in the form‡

$$Z = \lambda_1^N. \quad \textbf{(12.619)}$$

The eigenvalues of $\mathcal{H}$ are found by solving the equation

$$\begin{vmatrix} e^{K+C} - \lambda & e^{-K} \\ e^{-K} & e^{K-C} - \lambda \end{vmatrix} = 0, \quad \textbf{(12.620)}$$

or

$$\lambda_{1,2} = e^K \cosh C \pm \sqrt{e^{2K}\sinh^2 C + e^{-2K}}. \quad \textbf{(12.621)}$$

In the case of substitutional solutions we have $C = 0$ and we get for Z

$$Z = (2\cosh K)^N, \quad \textbf{(12.622)}$$

a result which could have been obtained also from a straightforward summation of the partition function of a linear chain.

† From the rules of matrix multiplication one sees immediately that the left-hand side of this equation is equal to Trace $\mathcal{H}^N$.

‡ In calculating the order parameters or the configurational energy, only ln Z is important and in going over from (12.618) to (12.619) we neglect in ln Z terms of the order $(\lambda_2/\lambda_1)^N$ against the main term $N \ln \lambda_1$.

It can easily be verified by using equations (12.214), (12.619), and (12.621) that the long-range order is always equal to zero. This corresponds to the well-known fact that a one-dimensional lattice will not show ferromagnetism. The reason is that one wrong spin will upset completely any tendency for long-range order, since there is no way for later spins to find out whether or not they are in accordance with the order of earlier parts of the crystal. The situation is different in the two-dimensional case, since here each spin is connected with all the other spins in the lattice in a multitude of ways and not only through one nearest neighbor.

The reason for treating the rather trivial case of the linear lattice so extensively is that we now can immediately use the same method for the two- and three-dimensional cases. We shall see presently that in these cases also the calculation of the partition function can be reduced to the calculation of the largest eigenvalue of a matrix.† However, the matrices involved are no longer simple and it requires more powerful methods to obtain either an exact or an approximate solution for the largest eigenvalue. In the next section we shall discuss the exact solution in the case of the two-dimensional square lattice; in the present one we shall discuss the variational method for obtaining an approximate solution.

Let us briefly summarize what we have done to obtain the partition function of the linear chain. We built up the chain by adding spins to it one by one. If the chain is sufficiently long, the addition of one more spin does not alter the physical situation and we get an equation relating $P(\mu_n)$ to $P(\mu_{n-1})$, or, since the two are the same functions of their arguments, a matrix equation for $P(\mu)$. The largest eigenvalue of the symmetrized matrix then gives us the partition function.

In the two-dimensional case the step which must be repeated is the addition of one more column of spins (see Fig. 44), while in the three-dimensional case one adds successive plates of spins. Let us consider a two-dimensional crystal where each column contains a spins and where we add columns until the crystal contains $a \times b (= N)$ spins. Denoting the spins of the nth column by $\mu_i (i = 1,2,\cdots,a)$ and those of the $n - 1$st column by $\mu_i' (i = 1,2,\cdots,a)$,‡ we get instead of equation (12.607) the equation

$$\rho P(\mu_i) = \sum_{\mu_i' = \pm 1} \mathcal{K}(\mu_i,\mu_i')P(\mu_i'), \qquad \textbf{(12.623)}$$

where ρ appears due to the normalization, where the $P(\mu_i')$ and $P(\mu_i)$ stand for the probability that the a μ_i' or μ_i have given values, and

† This matrix approach, which was used by Kramers and Wannier, has independently been suggested by Lassettre and Howe (J. Chem. Phys., **9**, 747, 801, 1941); see also E. W. Montroll, J. Chem. Phys., **9**, 706, 1941.

‡ These μ_i' should not be confused with the μ_i' introduced by equation (12.203).

where $\mathcal{K}(\mu_i,\mu_i')$ is given by the equation

$$\mathcal{K}(\mu_i,\mu_i') = e^{K\sum_{i=1}^{a-1}\mu_i'\mu_{i+1}'+K\sum_{i=1}^{a}\mu_i\mu_i'+C\sum_{i=1}^{a}\mu_i'}. \tag{12.624}$$

Introducing $\mathfrak{A}(\mu_i)$ by the equations

$$\mathfrak{A}(\mu_i) = P(\mu_i)e^{\frac{1}{2}K\sum\mu_i\mu_{i+1}+\frac{1}{2}C\sum\mu_i}, \tag{12.625}$$

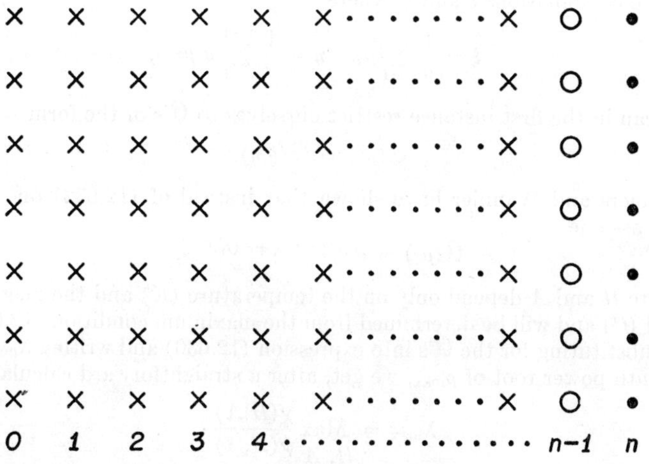

Fig. 44

equation (12.623) is brought into a symmetrical form,

$$\rho\mathfrak{A}(\mu_i) = \sum_{\langle\mu_i'\rangle} \mathcal{H}(\mu_i,\mu_i')\mathfrak{A}(\mu_i'), \tag{12.626}$$

where

$$\mathcal{H}(\mu_i,\mu_i') = e^{K[\sum\mu_i\mu_i'+\frac{1}{2}\sum\mu_i\mu_{i+1}+\frac{1}{2}\sum\mu_i'\mu_{i+1}']+\frac{1}{2}C[\sum\mu_i+\sum\mu_i']}. \tag{12.627}$$

The matrix $\mathcal{H}$ is now of the order 2^a and if we expand it in terms of its eigenvectors we can again show that the partition function Z is determined by the eigenvalues ρ_i of $\mathcal{H}$ in the following way:

$$Z = \sum_{i=1}^{2^a} \rho_i^{\,b}, \tag{12.628}$$ †

where once again a periodicity condition $(\mu_i^{(1)} = \mu_i^{(b+1)})$ is imposed on the lattice.

If b is sufficiently large, only the largest eigenvalue will contribute, and we have

$$Z = \rho^b_{\max}. \tag{12.629}$$

In order to find $\rho_{\max}$ we remind ourselves of the fact that the largest eigenvalue of a matrix can be found from the Ritz' variational principle,

† A more sophisticated way of writing this equation is $Z = \text{Trace } \mathcal{H}^b$.

stating in our case

$$\rho_{\max} = \underset{\text{all } \mathcal{A}\text{'s}}{\text{Max}} \frac{\sum\limits_{\langle \mu_i, \mu_i' \rangle} \mathcal{H}(\mu_i,\mu_i')\mathcal{A}(\mu_i)\mathcal{A}(\mu_i')}{\sum\limits_{\langle \mu_i \rangle} \mathcal{A}^2(\mu_i)}. \tag{12.630}$$

In practice one must, of course, restrict the $\mathcal{A}$'s used in considering this variational problem and one only gets an approximation to the largest eigenvalue instead of the exact value. Since in $\mathcal{H}$ the μ_i (and μ_i') occur in the combinations ξ and η, where

$$\xi = \frac{1}{a} \sum_{i=1}^{a} \mu_i, \quad \eta = \frac{1}{a} \sum_{i=1}^{a-1} \mu_i \mu_{i+1}, \tag{12.631}$$

we can in the first instance restrict ourselves to $\mathcal{A}$'s of the form

$$\mathcal{A}(\mu_i) = \mathcal{A}(\xi,\eta). \tag{12.632}$$

Kramers and Wannier have shown that instead of (12.632) one may also assume

$$\mathcal{A}(\mu_i) = e^{a[H(K,C)\eta + A(K,C)\xi]}, \tag{12.633}$$

where H and A depend only on the temperature (K) and the magnetic field (C) and will be determined from the maximum condition (12.630).

Substituting for the $\mathcal{A}$'s into expression (12.630) and writing $\lambda_{\max}$ for the ath power root of $\rho_{\max}$, we get, after a straightforward calculation,

$$\lambda_{\max} = \underset{H,\,A}{\text{Max}} \frac{\chi(H,A)}{\psi(H,A)}, \tag{12.634}$$

where

$$\chi^a = \sum_{\langle \mu_i, \mu_i' \rangle} e^{K\sum \mu_i\mu_i' + (\frac{1}{2}K + H)(\sum \mu_i \mu_{i+1} + \sum \mu_i' \mu_{i+1}') + (\frac{1}{2}C + A)(\sum \mu_i + \sum \mu_i')}, \tag{12.635}$$

and

$$\psi^a = \sum_{\langle \mu_i \rangle} e^{2H\sum \mu_i\mu_{i+1} + 2A\sum \mu_i}. \tag{12.636}$$

If we look more closely at the expressions for χ and ψ, we see that they are the partition function for a crystal consisting of two parallel chains (with a different interaction in the chains and between the chains) and the partition function for a one-dimensional chain. In the beginning of this section we saw how partition functions of crystals which are infinitely extended in only one dimension can be computed by reducing the calculation to finding the largest eigenvalue of a matrix. In that way we find for χ and ψ the equations

$$\begin{aligned} \chi^3 - 2\chi^2[e^{2K+2H} \cosh 2(A + C) + e^{-K} \cosh (K + 2H)] \\ + 4\chi \sinh (K + 2H)[e^{K+2H} \cosh (2A + C) + e^{2K} \cosh (K + 2H)] \\ -8e^K \sinh^3 (K + 2H) = 0, \end{aligned} \tag{12.637}$$

the largest root of which gives χ, and (see equation [12.621])

$$\psi = e^{2H} \cosh 2A + \sqrt{e^{4H} \sinh^2 2A + e^{-4H}}. \tag{12.638}$$

If $C = 0$ (zero field), $A = 0$ is always a possible solution, since both

$\partial\psi/\partial A$ and $\partial\chi/\partial A$ are zero for $A = 0$. Assuming $A = 0$, equation (12.637) can be reduced to

$$\chi^2 - 4\chi \cosh K \cosh (K + 2H) + 4 \sinh^2 (K + 2H) = 0. \quad \textbf{(12.639)}$$

Introducing s by the equation

$$s\lambda \cosh 2H = \sinh (K + 2H), \quad \textbf{(12.640)}$$

and using the relation

$$\cosh K \cosh (K + 2H) = \sinh K \sinh (K + 2H) + \cosh 2H, \quad \textbf{(12.641)}$$

we get from equations (12.634) and (12.638) to (12.641)

$$\lambda = \operatorname*{Max}_{s} \frac{2}{(s - \sinh K)^2 + 1 - \sinh^2 K},$$

or

$$\lambda = \frac{2}{1 - \sinh^2 K}. \quad \textbf{(12.642)}$$

This solution is valid only at high temperatures (or low values of K), as can be seen immediately from the fact that for too high values of K λ becomes negative. At temperatures below the critical temperature, the solution $A = 0$ gives a metastable solution and we must find another solution with A different from zero. The equations are much more complicated and we refer the reader to Kramers and Wannier's paper for a treatment of this case.

The critical temperature is found from equations similar to equations (12.235), that is, from

$$\frac{\partial^2\lambda}{\partial A^2} = 0, \qquad \frac{\partial\lambda}{\partial A} = 0, \qquad A = 0. \quad \textbf{(12.643)}$$

One finds for x_c 0.4384, which value was incorporated in the table at the end of the preceding section.

The treatment of a simple cubic lattice is similar to that of the two-dimensional square lattice. It is, however, slightly more complicated. After the first variational approach, one is left with a χ and a ψ, which are now the partition functions of two plates and one plate respectively, and one must apply the variational method once more in order to obtain expressions which can be evaluated. We refer to the papers quoted in the bibliographical notes for a discussion of this case.

§7. Some Exact Results for the Two-Dimensional Square Lattice. The largest eigenvalue of the matrix $\mathcal{K}$ of equation (12.624), assuming C to be zero, can be found by using spinor analysis. We must refer to the original papers for a detailed discussion, but because of the importance of this solution we shall briefly sketch how a solution can be obtained. Before that, however, we shall discuss how one can locate the critical temperature exactly without evaluating the partition function. This was done by Kramers and Wannier by considering the transformation properties of the matrix $\mathcal{K}$. We shall follow here a simple topological proof due to Onsager.

Consider two square lattices with the following properties (Fig. 45).

The spins of the first lattice are depicted by crosses and connections between nearest neighbors by full-drawn lines. In the second lattice the spins are depicted by circles and the connections by dotted lines. The second lattice—which we shall call the *dual* lattice—is obtained by putting in each square of the first one a spin. We see that then each connection of the one lattice is crossed by exactly one connection in the other lattice, and the other way round. In our case, the dual lattice is

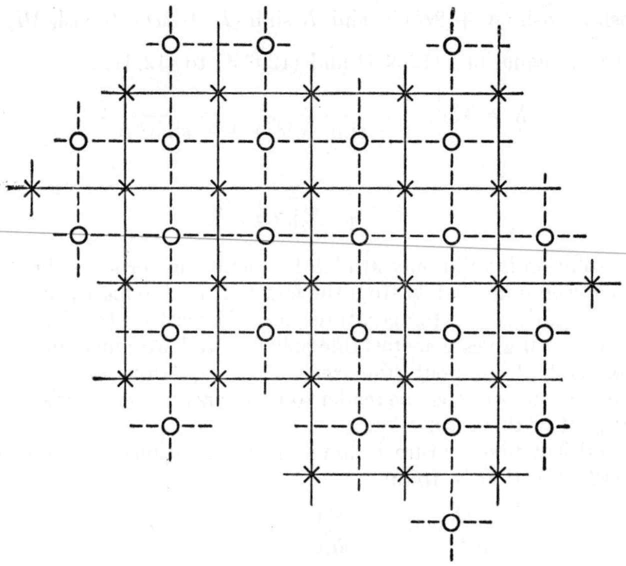

Fig. 45

identical with the original one and the square lattice is "self-dual." If the lattices are finite, it can be proved in topology that, if *all* connections are crossed so that the number of pairs Q is the same in both lattices,

$$N + N^* = Q + 2, \qquad \textbf{(12.701)}$$

where N and N^* are, respectively, the number of spins in the original and in the dual lattice.†

If there is no field ($C = 0$), the partition function which is a function of temperature has the form

$$Z(T) = \sum_{\langle\mu\rangle} e^{K \sum_{\langle i,k\rangle} \mu_i \mu_k}, \qquad \textbf{(12.702)}$$

and we see that each pair contributes a factor $e^{K\mu\mu'}$ where μ and μ' are two neighboring spins. These factors can be either e^K or e^{-K}, since $\mu\mu'$ can only be $+1$ or -1.

† One can easily see that, apart from a constant term which enters due to surface effects, $N + N^* = Q$.

We now introduce a new variable K^* by the equation

$$\sinh 2K \sinh 2K^* = 1. \tag{12.703}$$

If we put

$$K^* = \frac{J}{2kT^*}, \tag{12.704}$$

we have through equation (12.703) associated with each temperature T another temperature T^*, and if T increases from 0 to ∞, T^* decreases from ∞ to 0.

Using equation (12.703) one can show that

$$e^K = \sqrt{\tfrac{1}{2} \sinh 2K}\ (e^{K^*} + e^{-K^*})$$

and

$$e^{-K} = \sqrt{\tfrac{1}{2} \sinh 2K}\ (e^{K^*} - e^{-K^*}),$$

and we can thus replace $e^{K\mu\mu'}$ by $\sqrt{\frac{1}{2} \sinh 2K}\ (e^{K^*} + \mu\mu' e^{-K^*})$ in the partition function. Therefore, equation (12.702) is equivalent to the equation

$$Z(T) = (\tfrac{1}{2} \sinh 2K)^{\frac{Q}{2}} \sum_{\langle\mu\rangle} \prod_{r=1}^{Q} (e^{K^*} + \mu_r\mu_r' e^{-K^*}), \tag{12.705}$$

where r numbers the pairs, or the connections, in the lattice. If we develop the product, we get a sum of products containing factors $\mu_r\mu_r'$. Each product can be represented by a polygon formed by connections in the lattice, where a polygon is here understood in the very general sense of an assembly of nonintersecting lines in the plane. If the polygon is not made up out of closed circuits, its contribution to the sum will be zero, since a summation over an odd μ will vanish on summation over this μ. The magnitude of the term corresponding to a given polygon is such that each connection which is part of the polygon will contribute a factor e^{-K^*} and each connection outside the polygon will contribute a factor e^{K^*}.

Each closed circuit will divide the plane into two parts, one inside and one outside the circuit, and we can attribute spins ν_i to the lattice sites of the dual lattice in such a way that $\nu_i = +1$ if the site is inside a closed circuit, and $\nu_i = -1$ if it is outside this circuit. When the polygon consists of more than one closed circuit, the ν_i change sign each time the polygon is crossed. Due to the fact that each connection in the original lattice is crossed by one and only one connection of the dual lattice and that for each connection crossing a polygon $\nu_r\nu_r'$ will be equal to -1, but for all other connections in the dual lattice $\nu_r\nu_r'$ will be equal to $+1$, we can write for the product in equation (12.705) the expression

$$\tfrac{1}{2} \sum_{\langle\nu\rangle} e^{K^* \sum_{\langle i,k\rangle} \nu_i\nu_k}, \tag{12.706}$$

where the first summation extends over all spins of the dual lattice, where the summation in the exponent extends over all pairs of the dual lattice, and where the factor $\frac{1}{2}$ derives from the fact that we can choose arbitrarily what we wish to call the inside of a polygon.

Expression (12.706) is one half of the partition function of the dual lattice at a temperature T^* corresponding to equation (12.704). We have thus obtained a relation between the partition function of the original lattice at temperature T and the partition function of the dual lattice at temperature T^*, or, since the two lattices are the same, a relation between $Z(T)$ and $Z(T^*)$. Substituting expression (12.706) into equation (12.705), summing over the μ_i which is now trivial and gives a factor 2^N, and using relations (12.701) and (12.703), we have

$$\frac{Z(T)}{2^{N/2}\,(\cosh 2K)^{Q/2}} = \frac{Z(T^*)}{2^{N/2^*}\,(\cosh 2K^*)^{Q/2}} \tag{12.707}$$

Equation (12.707) relates the partition function at two temperatures, and if there are singular temperatures, they must exist in pairs, unless for that temperature

$$\sinh 2K_c = 1. \tag{12.708}$$

Assuming therefore that there is only one singular temperature, which is then the critical temperature, equation (12.708) gives its location. From equation (12.708) one obtains for x_c the value 0.4142 ($=\sqrt{2} - 1$).

We come now to a discussion of Onsager's work in which he determined all the eigenvalues of the matrix $\mathcal{K}(\mu_i,\mu_i')$ given by the equation

$$\mathcal{K}(\mu_i,\mu_i') = e^{K\sum\mu_i\mu_i' + K'\sum\mu_i'\mu'_{i+1}}. \tag{12.709}$$

We see that this matrix $\mathcal{K}$ consists of two factors, one, which contains $\sum\mu_i\mu_i'$, pertaining to the interaction between two columns, and a second one, which contains $\sum\mu_i'\mu'_{i+1}$, pertaining to the interaction in the last column. Since there is no reason a priori to assume the two interactions to be equally strong we have introduced a K' which is not necessarily equal to K in expression (12.709). Another way of interpreting the matrix (12.709) is by saying that the first factor means the addition of one extra column which interacts with the original crystal, and the second factor means the introduction of interaction in this last column. The addition of the last column thus takes place in two steps.

Onsager now introduces the following operators,

$$\mathfrak{C}_i = \mathit{1} \times \mathit{1} \times \cdots \times \mathfrak{C} \times \mathit{1} \times \cdots \times \mathit{1}, \tag{12.710}$$

and

$$\mathfrak{S}_i = \mathit{1} \times \mathit{1} \times \cdots \times \mathfrak{S} \times \mathit{1} \times \cdots \times \mathit{1}, \tag{12.711}$$

where there are a factors in each direct product with the matrices $\mathfrak{C}$ and $\mathfrak{S}$ on the ith place. The matrix in the jth place operates only on the argument μ_j, and the matrices $\mathfrak{C}$, $\mathfrak{S}$, and $\mathit{1}$ have the form

$$\mathfrak{C} = \begin{pmatrix} 0 & 1 \\ 1 & 0 \end{pmatrix}; \quad \mathfrak{S} = \begin{pmatrix} 1 & 0 \\ 0 & -1 \end{pmatrix}, \quad \mathit{1} = \begin{pmatrix} 1 & 0 \\ 0 & 1 \end{pmatrix}. \tag{12.712†}$$

† These matrices are related to the Pauli matrices ρ_x, ρ_y, and ρ_z, and we have $\mathfrak{C} = \rho_x$, $\mathfrak{S} = \rho_z$. (For the form of the Pauli matrices see, e.g., H. A. Kramers, Hand- u. Jahrb. d. Chem. Phys., Vol. I, Leipzig 1938, p. 284.)

From the definitions of $\mathcal{C}_i$ and $\mathcal{S}_i$ it follows easily that

$$\mathcal{C}_i\mathcal{A}(\mu_1,\cdots,\mu_i,\cdots,\mu_a) = \mathcal{A}(\mu_1,\cdots,-\mu_i,\cdots,\mu_a), \qquad (12.713)$$

and

$$\mathcal{S}_i\mathcal{A}(\mu_1,\cdots,\mu_i,\cdots,\mu_a) = \mu_i\mathcal{A}(\mu_1,\cdots,\mu_i,\cdots,\mu_a). \qquad (12.714)$$

Introducing once more K^* by equation (12.703) one can write

$$e^{K\sum \mu_i\mu_i'} = (2 \sinh 2K)^{a/2}\, \mathcal{V}_1, \qquad (12.715)$$

where the matrix $\mathcal{V}_1$ can be expressed in terms of the $\mathcal{C}_i$ as

$$\mathcal{V}_1 = e^{K^*\sum_{i=1}^{a}\mathcal{C}_i}. \qquad (12.716)†$$

Also we have

$$\mathcal{V}_2 \equiv e^{K'\sum \mu_i'\mu'_{i+1}} = e^{K'\sum \mathcal{S}_i\mathcal{S}_{i+1}}, \qquad (12.717)$$

and we see that finding the largest eigenvalue of $\mathcal{K}$ is reduced to finding the largest eigenvalue of $\mathcal{V}_2\mathcal{V}_1$.

It turns out to be advantageous to introduce instead of the $\mathcal{C}_i$ and $\mathcal{S}_i$ $2a$ operators $\mathcal{P}_i$ and $\mathcal{Q}_i$ ($i = 1,2,\cdots,a$) by the equations

$$\left.\begin{aligned} \mathcal{P}_i &= \mathcal{C} \times \mathcal{C} \times \cdots \times \mathcal{S} \times 1 \times 1 \times \cdots, \\ \mathcal{Q}_i &= \mathcal{C} \times \mathcal{C} \times \cdots \times \iota\mathcal{S}\mathcal{C} \times 1 \times 1 \times \cdots, \end{aligned}\right\} \qquad (12.718)$$

where the factor $\mathcal{S}$, or $\iota\mathcal{S}\mathcal{C}$,‡ appears on the ith place.

The matrices $\mathcal{V}_1$ and $\mathcal{V}_2$ expressed in the $\mathcal{P}_i$ and $\mathcal{Q}_i$ are

$$\mathcal{V}_1 = \prod_i e^{\iota K^*\mathcal{P}_i\mathcal{Q}_i}, \qquad \mathcal{V}_2 = \prod_i e^{-\iota K'\mathcal{P}_{i+1}\mathcal{Q}_i}\,\mathcal{B}, \qquad (12.719)$$

where the matrix $\mathcal{B}$ derives from the factor $e^{K'\mathcal{S}_a\mathcal{S}_1}$.

It can be shown that the $\mathcal{P}_i$ and $\mathcal{Q}_i$ and their products form a $2n$-dimensional representation of the group of rotations in $2n$-dimensional space. Hence the eigenvalues of the rotation group in $2n$-dimensional space will be related to the eigenvalues of the $\mathcal{P}_i$ and the $\mathcal{Q}_i$ and thus to the eigenvalues of $\mathcal{V}_1$ and $\mathcal{V}_2$. Because of the product character of $\mathcal{V}_1$ and $\mathcal{V}_2$, the eigenvalues of $\mathcal{V}_2\mathcal{V}_1$ will be the product of eigenvalues of two-dimensional matrices. One finally finds for the partition function Z

---

† One can obtain equation (12.716) as follows:

$$\begin{aligned} e^{K\mu\mu'} &= \sqrt{\tfrac{1}{2}\sinh 2K}\,(e^{K^*} + \mu\mu' e^{-K^*}) \\ &= \sqrt{\tfrac{1}{2}\sinh 2K}\,[(1 + \mathcal{C})e^{K^*} + (1 - \mathcal{C})e^{-K^*}] \\ &= \sqrt{\tfrac{1}{2}\sinh 2K}\, e^{K^*\mathcal{C}}. \end{aligned}$$

The first equal sign follows from the definition of K^* and the second one can be shown to hold by writing out the elements of the matrices on both sides; the third one follows by expanding the exponentials.

‡ Here $\iota = \sqrt{-1}$.

the equation

$$\frac{1}{N}\ln Z = \ln 2 + \frac{1}{2\pi^2}\int_0^\pi d\omega \int_0^\pi d\omega' \ln [\cosh 2K \cosh 2K' - \sinh 2K \cos \omega - \sinh 2K' \cos \omega']. \quad \textbf{(12.720)}$$

In the case where $K = K'$ this equation reduces to

$$\frac{1}{N}\ln Z = \ln (2 \cosh 2K) + \frac{1}{2\pi^2}\iint_0^\pi \ln [1 - 4\kappa \cos \omega_1 \cos \omega_2] d\omega_1 d\omega_2, \quad \textbf{(12.721)}$$

where

$$\kappa = \frac{2 \sinh 2K}{\cosh^2 2K}. \quad \textbf{(12.722)}$$

The configurational energy follows in the usual way, and we find

$$E = -\tfrac{1}{2}NJ \coth 2K \left[1 \pm \frac{2}{\pi}\sqrt{1-\kappa^2}\, K(\kappa)\right]. \quad \textbf{(12.723)}$$

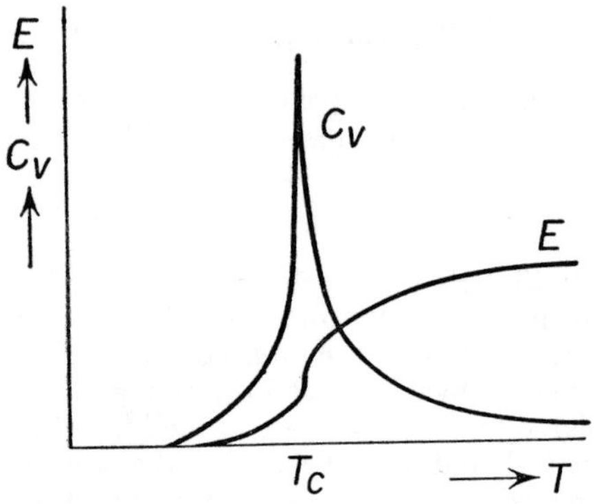

Fig. 46

The plus sign holds below and the minus sign above T_c, while $K(\kappa)$ is the complete elliptic integral of the first kind,†

$$K(\kappa) = \int_0^{\frac{\pi}{2}} \frac{d\varphi}{\sqrt{1 - \kappa^2 \sin^2 \varphi}}. \quad \textbf{(12.724)}$$

The variable κ increases from 0 at $T = 0$ to 1 at $T = T_c$ and decreases from there to 0 at infinite temperatures. The elliptic integral $K(\kappa)$ is

† See, e.g., H. and B. S. Jeffreys, Methods of Mathematical Physics, Cambridge 1946, p. 634.

logarithmically singular for $\kappa = 1$, and we have

$$K(\kappa) \sim c \ln (T - T_c), \quad \text{for} \quad T \sim T_c, \tag{12.725}$$

where c is practically a constant. The energy thus behaves in the neighborhood of T_c as $- \mid T - T_c \mid \ln (T - T_c)$ and the specific heat shows a logarithmic singularity at T_c.

In Figure 46 the behavior of the configurational energy and specific heat as a function of temperature for a two-dimensional square lattice with $K = K'$ is shown.

BIBLIOGRAPHICAL NOTES

The following general references should be noted.

1. F. C. Nix and W. Shockley, Revs. Modern Phys., **10,** 1, 1938.
2. R. H. Fowler and E. A. Guggenheim, Statistical Thermodynamics, Cambridge 1939, Chap. XIII.

§1. In ref. 1 the experimental evidence is discussed in great detail.

§2. The theory of Bragg and Williams is developed in the following three papers.

3. W. L. Bragg and E. J. Williams, Proc. Roy. Soc. (London), **A145,** 699, 1934.
4. W. L. Bragg and E. J. Williams, Proc. Roy. Soc. (London), **A151,** 540, 1935.
5. W. L. Bragg and E. J. Williams, Proc. Roy. Soc. (London), **A152,** 231, 1935.

The derivation which we have given can be found in ref. 5; see also ref. 1.

Equations (12.227) and (12.230) had earlier been derived by Gorsky; see

6. W. Gorsky, Z. Physik, **50,** 64, 1928.

§3. Lennard-Jones and Devonshire discuss critical phenomena of liquids in the following four papers:

7. J. E. Lennard-Jones and A. F. Devonshire, Proc. Roy. Soc. (London), **A163,** 53, 1937.
8. J. E. Lennard-Jones and A. F. Devonshire, Proc. Roy. Soc. (London), **A165,** 1, 1938.
9. J. E. Lennard-Jones and A. F. Devonshire, Proc. Roy. Soc. (London), **A169,** 317, 1939.
10. J. E. Lennard-Jones and A. F. Devonshire, Proc. Roy. Soc. (London), **A170,** 464, 1939.

Reference 9 applies Bethe's first approximation (reference 13) and ref. 10 Bragg and Williams' method to the melting process. It turns out that the second method is much simpler and gives about the same results. We have therefore based this section on ref. 10.

§4. The quasi-chemical method is due to Fowler and Guggenheim; see

11. R. H. Fowler and E. A. Guggenheim, Proc. Roy. Soc. (London), **A174,** 189, 1940.

See also ref. 2 and

12. G. S. Rushbrooke, Proc. Roy. Soc. (London), **A166,** 296, 1938, where some of the results are derived by using Bethe's method.

The quasi-chemical method is equivalent to Bethe's first approximation:

13. H. A. Bethe, Proc. Roy. Soc. (London), **A150,** 552, 1935.

In this paper Bethe also gives a second approximation where he considers the influence of second shell atoms on the first shell (compare Fig. 41). The equivalence of Bethe's first approximation and the quasi-chemical method was proved by Chang, see

14. T. S. Chang, Proc. Cambridge Phil. Soc., **35,** 265, 1939.

The same author also investigated the influence of taking other than nearest neighbor interactions into account, see

15. T. S. Chang, Proc. Roy. Soc. (London), **A161,** 546, 1937.

§5. Kirkwood's method can be found in the following paper:

16. J. G. Kirkwood, J. Chem. Phys., **6,** 70, 1938.

See also refs. 1 and 2 and

17. T. S. Chang, J. Chem. Phys., **9,** 169, 1941.
18. H. Bethe and J. G. Kirkwood, J. Chem. Phys., **7,** 578, 1938.
19. W. Opechowski, Physica, **4,** 181, 1937.

Kirkwood (ref. 16) and Nix and Shockley (ref. 1) give the complete calculations leading to M_1 and M_2, and Chang (ref. 17) gives those leading to M_3 while indicating how the higher M_n can be calculated. However, the necessary data to calculate M_4 have never before been published. They are given here in detail since they are also of interest for calculations leading to an exact series expansion of the partition function at temperatures above the Curie point (cf. refs. 19, 20, and 25).

§6. This section follows

20. H. A. Kramers and G. H. Wannier, Phys. Rev., **60,** 252, 263, 1941.

The case of a simple cubic lattice is treated in

21. P. Groen, Orde en Wanorde in de Eenvoudigste Roosters, Thesis, Amsterdam 1942.
22. B. Martin and D. ter Haar, Physica, **18,** 569, 1952 (cf. Phys. Rev., **77,** 721, 1950).

See also

23. A. J. Wakefield, Proc. Cambridge Phil. Soc., **47,** 419, 1951.
24. A. J. Wakefield, Proc. Cambridge Phil. Soc., **47,** 799, 1951.
25. D. ter Haar, Physica, **18,** 836, 1952.
26. D. ter Haar, Physica, **19,** 611, 1953.

§7. The exact solution was first given by Onsager in 1944:

27. L. Onsager, Phys. Rev., **65,** 117, 1944.

The treatment given here is, however, a sketch of the methods developed by Kaufman and Houtappel rather than of the original method of Onsager's, see

28. B. Kaufman, Phys. Rev., **76,** 1232, 1949.
29. R. M. F. Houtappel, Physica, **16,** 425, 1950 (= Thesis, Leiden 1950).

In reference 29 the partition functions of the two-dimensional triangular and honeycomb lattices are calculated exactly.

The exact location of the critical temperature was first given in ref. 20. We have followed Onsager's treatment as given by Wannier in the following paper:

30. G. H. Wannier, Revs. Modern Phys., **17,** 50, 1945.

See also

31. C. Domb, Nature, **163,** 775, 1949.
32. C. Domb, Proc. Roy. Soc. (London), **A196,** 36, 1949.
33. J. E. Brooks and C. Domb, Proc. Roy. Soc. (London), **A199,** 199, 1949.

34. C. Domb and R. B. Potts, Proc. Roy. Soc. (London), **A207,** 343, 1951.
35. C. Domb, Proc. Roy. Soc. (London), **A210,** 125, 1951.
36. G. F. Newell, Phys. Rev., **78,** 444, 1950.
37. C. N. Yang, Phys. Rev., **85,** 808, 1952.
38. T. D. Lee and C. N. Yang, Phys. Rev., **87,** 410, 1952.

CHAPTER XIII

STATISTICAL METHODS IN NUCLEAR PHYSICS

§1. The Density of Nuclear Energy Levels. If we are dealing with heavy nuclei—say with atomic weight A larger than 50, that is, corresponding to elements which in the periodic table follow Ti—we may consider the nucleus to be a system consisting of many particles and we can use statistical methods. Our first object in the present chapter will be to derive a formula for the nuclear energy level density in the case of heavy nuclei. Let $\rho(E,Z,N)dE$ be the number of levels with energies between E and $E + dE$ of a nucleus containing Z protons and N neutrons. We must expect ρ to increase rapidly with increasing energy because the number of ways in which the energy can be shared among the constituent nucleons will increase rapidly with energy (compare the rapid increase of $W[\epsilon;\mathfrak{n}_i]$ with increasing energy mentioned on p. 162). We can therefore treat the energy spectrum as being practically continuous.

Let us first sketch the method which we shall use to determine the level density. We can introduce a grand canonical ensemble to represent the nucleus, and knowing $\rho(E,Z,N)$ we can calculate the average energy $\bar{E}$ and the average values of Z and N as functions of the temperature and the thermal potentials. On the other hand, using the elementary method of Part A we can calculate the total energy of the system at a given temperature if we start from a model of the nucleus, for instance, giving the energy spectrum of the single nucleons and treating the constituent nucleons as independent. The two expressions for $\bar{E}$ as a function of temperature should, of course, be the same. Our procedure will now be the following. We shall use the methods of the canonical grand ensembles introduced in Chapters VI and VII to derive a relation between $\rho(E,Z,N)$ and $\bar{E}$, Z, and N. However, instead of considering this relation as giving us $\bar{E}$, once ρ is known, we shall treat it as the equation from which for given $\bar{E}$ we can calculate ρ. We then determine from a suitably chosen model the relation between $\bar{E}$ and the temperature and using that relation determine the energy level density. In the case of very simple models it is possible to determine the energy level density directly from the knowledge of the energy level density $f(\epsilon)$ of the constituent nucleons, provided we may treat those as independent particles. However, this does not give us an easier way of determining ρ and, moreover, it will not be possible for more complicated models so that the statistical method is to be preferred.

Our first object is thus to obtain a relation between the energy level density and the mean energy of the nucleus. Let us consider a canonical grand ensemble with modulus Θ and thermal potentials of the protons and neutrons $\Theta\nu_p$ and $\Theta\nu_n$ respectively. We introduce a quantity μ by the equation

$$\mu = \frac{1}{\Theta} = \frac{1}{kT}. \tag{13.101}$$

From equation (7.403) on page 156 we have for the grand potential q the equation

$$e^q = \sum_Z \sum_N \sum_k \gamma_k e^{\nu_p Z + \nu_n N - \mu E_k}, \tag{13.102}$$

where γ_k is the multiplicity of the nuclear energy level E_k. If the levels are sufficiently dense, we may replace the sum in equation (13.102) by an integral and we have

$$e^q = \sum_Z \sum_N e^{\nu_p Z + \nu_n N} \int \rho(E,Z,N) e^{-\mu E} dE, \tag{13.103}$$

or even

$$e^q = \int dZ \int dN e^{\nu_p Z + \nu_n N} \int \rho(E,Z,N) e^{-\mu E} dE. \tag{13.104}$$

We shall use for the evaluation of this integral the same methods which were used in Chapter V to evaluate the integral on the right-hand side of equation (5.515) on page 115 and which led to equation (5.522). We do not wish to repeat the calculations here and refer to the discussion given in Chapter V.† The final result is

$$e^q \cong \rho(\bar{E},\bar{Z},\bar{N}) e^{\nu_p \bar{Z} + \nu_n \bar{N} - \mu \bar{E}} \left[-\frac{\pi^3}{8} \frac{\partial \bar{Z}}{\partial \nu_p} \frac{\partial \bar{N}}{\partial \nu_n} \frac{\partial \bar{E}}{\partial \mu} \right]^{1/2}. \tag{13.105}$$

Moreover, we have from equation (7.409) on page 157 the following relation for the entropy S,

$$\frac{S}{k} = q - \nu_p \bar{Z} - \nu_n \bar{N} + \mu \bar{E}. \tag{13.106}$$

† The main argument is that the integrand is a function which has a steep maximum for $N = \bar{N}$, $Z = \bar{Z}$ and $E = \bar{E}$ and that, if we write $\rho(E,Z,N) = e^{\phi(E,Z,N)}$, we can expand the exponential in Taylor series and break off after the terms with $(N - \bar{N})^2$, $(Z - \bar{Z})^2$, and $(E - \bar{E})^2$. The integration can then be performed and gives equation (13.105).

Combining equations (13.105) and (13.106) we have

$$\rho(E,Z,N) = e^{\frac{1}{k}S}\left[-\frac{\pi^3}{8}\frac{\partial Z}{\partial \nu_p}\frac{\partial N}{\partial \nu_n}\frac{\partial E}{\partial \mu}\right]^{-1/2}, \tag{13.107}$$

while the entropy is related to the energy by the well-known equation (see, e.g., equations [5.519] and [5.525])

$$\frac{\partial \frac{S}{k}}{\partial E} = \mu, \quad \text{or,} \quad \frac{S}{k} = \int \frac{dE}{d\mu}\,\mu d\mu. \tag{13.108}$$

Having solved our first problem we must now tackle the second one, which consists in obtaining expressions for E, Z, and N as functions of μ (or T), ν_p, and ν_n. We shall consider the following three models.

a) The free particle model.
b) The independent particle model.†
c) The fluid drop model.

a) This model is the simplest one imaginable. We treat the nucleus as consisting of Z protons and N neutrons which can move as free particles inside the nuclear volume V. We shall assume this volume to be proportional to $A(= Z + N)$ and write

$$V = dAr_0^3, \tag{13.109}$$

where d is a numerical factor of the order of magnitude unity and where r_0 is a length of nuclear dimensions, that is, of the order of 10^{-13} cm.

In treating the nucleons as free particles we are dealing with a mixture of two Fermi-Dirac gases in a volume V and we can use the results obtained in §7 of Chapter IV. Let us first of all investigate whether we are dealing with a Fermi-Dirac gas which is nearly classical, or with one which is highly degenerate. Let us use for this purpose equation (4.603) on page 84. The excitation energies with which we will have to deal are of the order of magnitude of 1 to 100 Mev, the mass M is a proton or neutron mass, and the number of particles in the system is the mass number A; for the volume we may use equation (13.109). Inserting numerical values we get

$$\left.\begin{aligned}\left(\frac{2\pi MkT}{h^2}\right)^{3/2}\frac{V}{N} &\approx 10^6, &&\text{for} \quad kT = 1 \text{ Mev},\\ &\approx 10^3, &&\text{for} \quad kT = 100 \text{ Mev}.\end{aligned}\right\} \tag{13.110}$$

† The independent particle model has recently come to the fore through the success of the nuclear shell model. Weisskopf (Science, **113,** 101, 1951) has pointed out that due to the exclusion principle the strong forces between nucleons cannot come into play at low excitation energies of the nucleus. This situation is analogous to the fact that one can treat the gas of conduction electrons in a metal as a system of independent particles. Collisions are impossible since the resulting states after the collision are all occupied.

We see thus that we are in the degenerate region and we can use the formulae at the end of §7 of Chapter IV. We have from equations (4.720), (4.726), and (4.725)

$$Z = \frac{4\pi}{3}\left(\frac{2M}{\mu h^2}\right)^{3/2} V\nu_p^{\,3/2}, \tag{13.111}$$

$$N = \frac{4\pi}{3}\left(\frac{2M}{\mu h^2}\right)^{3/2} V\nu_n^{\,3/2}, \tag{13.112}$$

$$E = E_0 + \frac{\pi^2}{4}(Zg_{0p}^{\;-1} + Ng_{0n}^{\;-1})\mu^{-2}, \tag{13.113}$$

where higher-order terms have been neglected and where g_{0p} and g_{0n} are, respectively, the energies at the top of the Fermi seas of the proton and neutron gas. We shall assume for the sake of simplicity that $N = Z = \frac{1}{2}A$. In that case we have $g_{0p} = g_{0n}$ $(= g_0)$ and also $\nu_p = \nu_n \approx \mu g_0$. We then get finally from equations (13.111–113), (13.107), and (13.108)

$$\rho(E,Z,N) = \frac{2}{3}\sqrt[4]{\frac{2g_0}{AQ^5}}\, e^{\pi\sqrt{\frac{AQ}{g_0}}}, \tag{13.114}$$

where $Q = E - E_0$ is the excitation energy, that is, the amount by which the energy is higher than the ground state level.

The exact form of the factor in front of the exponential is not very important, especially since we have not taken into account the influence of the nuclear angular momentum.† Also we have not taken into account the fact that due to the proton (and neutron) spin each energy level can be occupied by two particles. This would introduce factors 2 everywhere. However, one can show that it will not influence the exponential in equation (13.114), but only the multiplying factor. In general we shall write

$$\rho(E) = \phi_1(E)e^{\pi\sqrt{\frac{AQ}{g_0}}}, \tag{13.115}$$

where $\phi_1(E)$ is a smooth, slowly varying function. The value of g_0 depends on the values adopted for d and r_0 in equation (13.109) (compare equation [4.720]), but it will be of the order of 10 to 100 Mev.

b) A slightly more complicated model results if we assume that we still may treat the protons and neutrons as independent particles, but that the energy spectrum of the nucleus is not that of free particles in a volume V but is given by the equation

$$dZ = f(\epsilon)d\epsilon, \tag{13.116}$$

where dZ is the number of levels with energies between ϵ and $\epsilon + d\epsilon$.

† See, e.g., H. A. Bethe, Revs. Modern Phys., **9**, 83, 1937.

Assuming once more $N = Z = \frac{1}{2}A$ so that $\nu_p = \nu_n$ ($= \mu g, g =$ thermal potential), we have from the general theory of Chapter IV (compare equations [4.215], [4.216], and [4.320])

$$Z = N = \int_0^\infty \frac{f(\epsilon)d\epsilon}{e^{-\nu+\mu\epsilon} + 1}, \tag{13.117}$$

$$E = 2\int_0^\infty \frac{\epsilon f(\epsilon)d\epsilon}{e^{-\nu+\mu\epsilon} + 1}, \tag{13.118}$$

where the factor 2 in the last equation derives from the fact that we are dealing with a mixture of two gases.

Again we are dealing with a nearly completely degenerate gas and we are therefore interested in the deviations from the behavior at the absolute zero. Equations (13.117) and (13.118) reduce to the following two equations at the absolute zero (compare the discussion of equation [4.719]):

$$Z = N = \int_0^{g_0} f(\epsilon)d\epsilon, \tag{13.119}$$

$$E_0 = 2\int_0^{g_0} \epsilon f(\epsilon)d\epsilon. \tag{13.120}$$

At temperatures slightly above the absolute zero we can use Sommerfeld's theorem as in §7 of Chapter IV and we get for E the equation

$$E = E_0 + \frac{\pi^2}{6} f(g_0)\mu^{-2} + \cdots. \tag{13.121}$$

Equation (13.121) is derived as follows.† We write $\mu\epsilon = u$ and $\mu g_0 = u_0$ and introduce a function $\varphi(u)$ by the equation

$$f(\epsilon) = \varphi''(u), \qquad \varphi(0) = \varphi'(0) = 0, \tag{13.122}$$

where primes indicate differentiations with respect to u.

From Sommerfeld's theorem it follows that

$$\mu Z = \varphi'(\nu) + \frac{\pi^2}{6}\varphi'''(\nu) + \cdots, \tag{13.123}$$

$$\mu^2 E = \nu\varphi'(\nu) - \varphi(\nu) + \frac{\pi^2}{6}[\varphi''(\nu) + \nu\varphi'''(\nu)] + \cdots. \tag{13.124}$$

From equation (13.119) we have $\mu Z = \varphi'(u_0)$ and hence, in the first approximation, $\nu = u_0$. Writing

$$\nu = u_0 + v \tag{13.125}$$

and expanding the first terms on the right-hand side of equation (13.123)

† We follow the derivation given by van Lier and Uhlenbeck (Physica, **4**, 531, 1937).

in a Taylor series, we get in the second approximation

$$\mu Z = \varphi'(u_0) + v\varphi''(u_0) + \frac{\pi^2}{6}\varphi'''(u_0),$$

or

$$v = -\frac{\pi^2}{6}\frac{\varphi'''(u_0)}{\varphi''(u_0)}. \tag{13.126}$$

Substituting equations (13.125) and (13.126) into equation (13.124), neglecting terms with v, and using equation (13.122), we get equation (13.121).

Using equations (13.119) and (13.121) we can again derive an expression for the nuclear energy level density from equation (13.107),†

$$\rho(E) = \phi_2(E)e^{\sqrt{\frac{2}{3}f(g_0)E}}. \tag{13.127}$$

where $\phi_2(E)$ is again a slowly varying function of E. We may remark here that equation (13.115) is a special case of equation (13.127). The function $f(\epsilon)$ for model a is given by equation (4.504) and using equation (4.720) and putting $Z = N = \frac{1}{2}A$, we obtain equation (13.115). In the cases of models a and b it is actually possible to calculate $\rho(E)$ directly by remembering that $\rho(E)dE$ should be equal to the number of ways in which E can be realized by adding the contributions from the Z protons and the N neutrons. A special case of this was considered by Bohr and Kalckar and by van Lier and Uhlenbeck, who assumed the existence of equidistant energy levels with a spacing equal to Δ. In that case $\rho(E)$ is proportional to the number of ways in which E/Δ can be written as the sum of A non-negative integers. This problem has been solved by Hardy and Ramanujan‡ and one then gets for $\rho(E)$ the formula

$$\rho(E) = \frac{1}{4E\sqrt{3}}e^{\pi\sqrt{\frac{2E}{3\Delta}}}. \tag{13.128}$$

c) The last model of the nucleus which we wish to consider is the liquid drop model. In view of the fact that the nuclear interactions are strong we can expect only small variations in density; hence a drop of liquid will be a better approximation than a system of independent particles if we are dealing with excited nuclei (compare the footnote on p. 298).

A liquid drop is capable of two kinds of vibrations, namely, capillary surface waves which leave the volume unchanged and volume waves. The change in potential energy for surface waves is due solely to surface tension effects and the energies involved are comparatively small—of the order of a

† From equation (13.119) it follows easily that $\frac{\partial Z}{\partial \nu_p} = \frac{1}{\mu}\frac{\partial Z}{\partial g_0} = \frac{1}{\mu}f(g_0)$.

‡ G. H. Hardy and S. Ramanujan, Proc. London Math. Soc., **42,** 75, 1918.

few hundred kilovolts. Volume waves, however, involve a change in density and hence relatively large energies—of the order of several Mev. At the relatively low excitation energies with which we are dealing we may neglect the volume waves.†

The problem is now somewhat different from the one discussed previously. Instead of dealing with a system of particles, the energies of which together give us the total energy of the nucleus, we are dealing with a system of excited vibrations; and instead of a system of Fermi-Dirac particles we have a system of Bose-Einstein particles. Let $g(\epsilon)d\epsilon$ be the number of surface vibrations with energies between ϵ and $\epsilon + d\epsilon$. From hydrodynamical theory it then follows that‡

$$g(\epsilon) = c \cdot \epsilon^{1/3}, \tag{13.129}$$

where c is a constant depending on the surface tension and on A.

As long as we are not interested in the multiplying factor but only wish to obtain the exponential factor in the energy level density, the calculations are simple, because we only need to calculate E as a function of μ in order to obtain the entropy from equation (13.108). The calculation of the energy is completely analogous to the calculation of the total energy in a radiation field and we can refer to §2 of Chapter III. In that way we get for the total energy

$$E = \int_0^\infty \frac{\epsilon g(\epsilon)d\epsilon}{e^{\mu\epsilon} - 1} = a\mu^{-7/3} \tag{13.130}$$

with

$$a = c\int_0^\infty \frac{x^{4/3}dx}{e^x - 1} = c\Gamma(\tfrac{7}{3})\zeta(\tfrac{7}{3}), \tag{13.131}$$

where $\Gamma(n)$ is the gamma-function§ and $\zeta(n)$ Riemann's ζ-function.||

From equation (13.130) we get for the entropy and for the nuclear energy level density the equations

$$\frac{S}{k} = \tfrac{7}{4}a^{4/7}E^{4/7}, \tag{13.132}$$

$$\rho(E) = \phi_3(E)e^{bE^{4/7}}. \tag{13.133}$$

§2. **The Statistical Theory of Nuclear Reactions.** It would be beyond the scope of this book to give a detailed treatment of nuclear reactions and we shall discuss only nonresonance processes. Furthermore, as far as we go

† Compare the discussion given by Bethe, Revs. Modern Phys., **9,** 88, 1937.
‡ The derivation of equation (13.129) is given, e.g., by Bethe, *loc. cit.*, p. 87.
§ See, e.g., E. Jahnke and F. Emde, Tables of Functions, New York 1945, pp. 9 ff.
|| See p. 53.

into a detailed discussion we shall restrict ourselves to reactions where the incident particle is a neutron.

The basic assumption underlying the statistical theory of nuclear reactions is the following. Due to the strong interaction between the nucleons inside a nucleus each nuclear reaction can be divided into two well-separated stages, as was pointed out by Bohr.† The first stage is the formation of the compound nucleus where the energy of the incident particle—including its binding energy—is shared among all the constituent nucleons. The second stage is the emission from the compound nucleus of a particle. This stage can be treated as being completely independent of the way in which the compound nucleus was formed. If one compares the nucleus with a liquid drop, the second stage is analogous to an evaporation process, as was first emphasized by Frenkel.

We shall especially concentrate on nuclear reactions where heavy nuclei are involved and where the compound nucleus is highly excited so that we are in a region of the energy spectrum where the levels are so dense that we can average over many quantum states.

Let us consider the following reaction,

$$\mathrm{X}(a,b)\mathrm{X}', \tag{13.201}$$

that is, a reaction where the nucleus X is bombarded by a particle a and where the compound nucleus ejects a particle b, and a nucleus X′ is left behind. If we wish to emphasize the two-stage character of the process, we may write reaction (13.201) as

$$\mathrm{X} + a \rightarrow \mathrm{X}^* \rightarrow \mathrm{X}' + b, \tag{13.202}$$

where X* denotes the compound nucleus.

The cross section $\sigma(a,b)$ for the reaction‡ can, according to our basic assumption, be written as the cross section for the formation of a compound nucleus when the bombarding particle a has an energy ϵ_a and the probability $p_b(E)$ for the emission of a particle b by the compound nucleus when it has an energy E

$$\sigma(a,b) = \sigma_a(\epsilon_a)p_b(E). \tag{13.204}$$

The energy E is related to ϵ_a by the relation

$$E = \epsilon_a + E_a, \tag{13.205}$$

† N. Bohr, Nature, **137**, 344, 1936.

‡ The definition of the cross section $\sigma(a,b)$ is the following. Let $p(a,b)$ be the probability that per unit time the reaction (13.201) takes place in a situation where there are inside a volume V one nucleus X and one bombarding particle a. If v be the velocity of a, we have the relation

$$p(a,b) = \frac{\sigma(a,b)v}{V}. \tag{13.203}$$

where E_a is the binding energy of a (see Fig. 47 for the relations between the various energies; E_X, $E_{X'}$, and E_{X^*} are the ground state levels of X, X′, and X*, respectively).

If ϵ_a is sufficiently large—for incident neutrons ϵ_a should be several Mev, which means that we are dealing with fast neutrons—we can easily get an

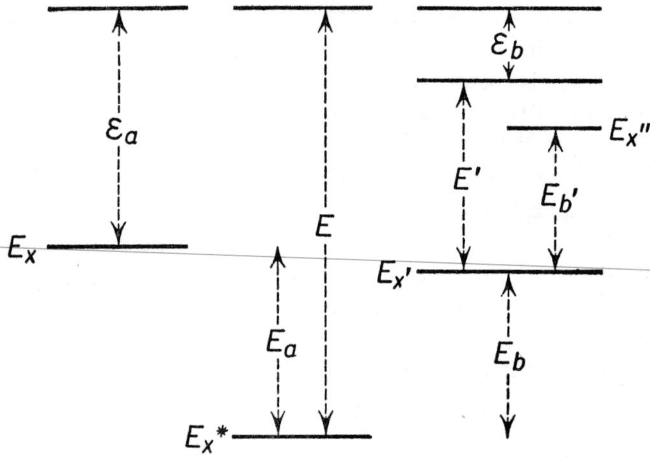

Fig. 47

expression for $\sigma_a(\epsilon_a)$. In that case the De Broglie wavelength λ_a of the particle a is small compared to the nuclear dimensions,† and assuming that all particles hitting the nucleus will lead to a compound nucleus‡ we get for the cross section for the formation of a compound nucleus essentially the geometrical cross section§

$$\sigma_a(\epsilon_a) \cong \pi R^2. \tag{13.206}$$

The compound nucleus X* formed by the bombardment is in such a highly excited state that several processes are possible: the absorbed particle can again be emitted (scattering) or another particle or a photon can be emitted. If the binding energy of the emitted particle is E_b (in

---

† We have as long as $\epsilon_a < 1000$ Mev, $\lambda_a \sim \dfrac{\hbar}{\sqrt{2m\epsilon_a}} = 5 \cdot 10^{-13}\epsilon_a^{-1/2}$ cm if ϵ_a is expressed in Mev. The nuclear radius R is given approximately by the equation $R \sim A^{1/3} r_0$ with r_0 of the order of 10^{-13} cm. Taking $A > 50$ we see that $\lambda_a < R$, if $\epsilon_a \gtrsim 1$ Mev.

‡ This is a reasonable assumption since the energy exchange between the impinging particle and the nucleus will be so fast that elastic scattering is unlikely.

§ Compare a similar situation in optics, when the wavelength is small compared to the dimensions of the scattering object.

the case of a photon $E_b = 0$), the energy ϵ_b with which this particle leaves the compound nucleus may have any value up to $\epsilon_{b,\max}$ which is given by the equation

$$\epsilon_{b,\max} = E - E_b. \tag{13.207}$$

In some cases E may be so large that $\epsilon_{b,\max}$ is still larger than the binding energy $E_{b'}$ of another particle and a second particle may leave the system, if $\epsilon_b + E_{b'} < \epsilon_{b,\max}$ (compare Fig. 47).

In the case of neutron bombardment the following four reactions are the main ones which are possible †: (n,n), (n,2n), (n,p), and (n,γ). The second reaction is possible only if the energy of the impinging neutron is sufficiently high. The fourth reaction, the capture of a fast neutron, has a very small cross section and will not be further considered here. In general we may expect several competing (a,b) reactions and we can write

$$p_b(E) = \frac{p_b'(E)}{\sum_c p_c'(E)}, \tag{13.208}$$

where the p' are probabilities per unit time and where the summation is extended over all possible emissions. In the sum, reactions like the (n,2n) reaction will not enter since such a reaction is supposed to take place in two stages and not in one. The probability p_n' thus is the sum of the two probabilities that the (n,n) and that the (n,2n) reactions take place. In most cases, the sum will be over the two possibilities $c =$ neutron and $c =$ proton with sometimes a small contribution from $c = \gamma$-quantum.

Our next step consists in the evaluation of the p'. We shall once more concentrate on the case where b is a neutron. The formulae for the cases of other emitted particles are analogous. Let $W_n(\epsilon)d\epsilon$ be the probability that per unit time the nucleus X* excited to an energy E emits a neutron with energy between ϵ and $\epsilon + d\epsilon$, thus transforming itself into a nucleus X′ with energy $E'(= E - E_b - \epsilon$; see Figure 47 with $\epsilon_b = \epsilon$). The function $W_n(\epsilon)$ is connected with the cross section $\sigma_n(\epsilon)$ for the inverse process, that is, the process that a neutron with energy impinging on a nucleus X′ with energy E' forms a compound nucleus X* with energy E. The relation is the following one:

$$W_n(\epsilon)d\epsilon = \sigma_n(\epsilon)\frac{8\pi g M}{h^3}\frac{\rho'(E')}{\rho^*(E)}\epsilon d\epsilon, \tag{13.209}$$

where M is the neutron mass, where g is a statistical factor due to the neutron spin (= 2), and where $\rho'(E')$ and $\rho^*(E)$ are the level densities of the X′ and X* nuclei, respectively, at the energies E' and E.

† Other reactions such as (n,α) are extremely improbable.

Equation (13.209) can be derived by using the principle of detailed balancing. Let us suppose that we are considering a system consisting of nuclei X* with energy E, nuclei X′ with energy E', and neutrons with energies between ϵ and $\epsilon + d\epsilon$ in a volume V. At equilibrium the number of processes $X^* \rightarrow X' + n$ must be equal to the number of processes $X' + n \rightarrow X^*$. Let $p(n,X';X^*)$ be the probability that per unit time a neutron with an energy between ϵ and $\epsilon + d\epsilon$ is captured by a nucleus X′ and a nucleus X* with energy between E and $E + d\epsilon$ is formed. We then have (compare equation [13.203])

$$p(\mathrm{n},\mathrm{X}';\mathrm{X}^*) = \sigma_{\mathrm{n}}(\epsilon)\,\frac{v}{V}, \tag{13.210}$$

where v is the velocity of the neutron. We now must take into account the following factors: (a) the capture of the neutron can be in any of the $\rho^*(E)d\epsilon(= N^*)$ states of X* which lie between E and $E + d\epsilon$. (b) During the process $X^* \rightarrow X' + n$, X′ may be produced in any of $\rho'(E')d\epsilon(= N')$ states. (c) The neutron can go into any of the states which correspond to energies between ϵ and $\epsilon + d\epsilon$, the number (N) of which is given by the equation (compare equation [4.504] on p. 82)

$$N = 2\pi g\left(\frac{2M}{h^2}\right)^{3/2} V\epsilon^{1/2}d\epsilon. \tag{13.211}$$

The principle of detailed balancing (compare the discussion in §9 of Appendix I) then gives as the condition for equilibrium the equation

$$N^* \cdot W_{\mathrm{n}}(\epsilon)d\epsilon = N \cdot N' \cdot p(\mathrm{n},\mathrm{X}';\mathrm{X}^*), \tag{13.212}$$

which leads to equation (13.209) if we use for v the nonrelativistic relation $v = \sqrt{2\epsilon/m}$.

As long as ϵ is sufficiently high, we may put $\sigma_{\mathrm{n}}(\epsilon)$ equal to πR^2 in equation (13.209) according to equation (13.206). The energy dependence of $W_{\mathrm{n}}(\epsilon)$ is contained in the factor $\epsilon\rho'(E')$. We can use for $\rho'(E')$ and for $\rho^*(E)$ formula (13.107), which we shall write in the form

$$\rho(E) = \phi(E)e^{\frac{1}{k}S(E)}. \tag{13.213}$$

Furthermore, we shall assume that $\phi(E)$ and $S(E)$ are the same for X′ and X.† We then have from equations (13.209) and (13.213)

$$W_{\mathrm{n}}(\epsilon) = A\epsilon e^{\frac{1}{k}[S(E')-S(E)]}, \tag{13.214}$$

where A does not depend on ϵ. Developing $S(E')$ in a Taylor series and retaining only the first two terms,

$$S(E') = S(E - E_b - \epsilon) = S(E - E_b) - \epsilon\left(\frac{dS}{dE}\right)_{E=E-E_b}, \tag{13.215}$$

† We are dealing with heavy nuclei, and a change in the number of nucleons by one will not make a large difference. We shall neglect these differences for the sake of simplicity.

we get

$$W_n(\epsilon) = B\epsilon e^{-\frac{\epsilon}{k}\frac{dS}{dE}}, \qquad \left(B = Ae^{\frac{1}{k}[S(E-E_b)-S(E)]}\right) \tag{13.216}$$

or

$$W_n(\epsilon) = B\epsilon e^{-\mu\epsilon} \tag{13.217}$$

if we use equation (13.108) for the definition of the temperature.† Equation (13.217) shows that the distribution in energy of the emitted neutrons will practically be a Maxwell distribution corresponding to a temperature defined by equation (13.108).

We saw a short while ago that in the case where the bombarding particle is a neutron, the two most important reactions are the (n,n) and the (n,p) ones. It turns out‡ that p_n' is by far greater than p_p', so that we can write in that case

$$p_n(E) \approx 1, \tag{13.218}$$

$$p_p(E) = \frac{p_p'}{p_p' + p_n'}, \tag{13.219}$$

where p_n' and p_p' must be calculated from equation (13.209) and the analogous equation for the proton case, after the values for ρ' and ρ^* have been inserted, by integrating over ϵ. It will be seen that the final result depends strongly on the spectral densities ρ' and ρ^*. Putting it differently, we see that the distribution in energy of the emitted protons will give us valuable information about the nuclear energy spectra.

Let us finally consider the cross section for the (n,2n) reaction. This reaction is only possible if E', the energy of the residual nucleus X′, is larger than the binding energy $E_{b'}$ of a neutron in X′. The reaction is the two-stage process

$$\mathrm{X} + \mathrm{n} \rightarrow \mathrm{X}^* \rightarrow \mathrm{X}' + b \rightarrow \mathrm{X}'' + b' + b, \tag{13.220}$$

where both b and b' are neutrons.

If $I(\epsilon)d\epsilon$ is the fraction of neutrons which are emitted during the first stage with energies between ϵ and $\epsilon + d\epsilon$, we have for the cross section σ(n,2n) of the (n,2n) reaction the equation

$$\sigma(\mathrm{n,2n}) = \sigma(\mathrm{n,n}) \frac{\int_{E_b'}^{E-E_b} I(\epsilon)d\epsilon}{\int_0^{E-E_b} I(\epsilon)d\epsilon}, \tag{13.221}$$

† This way of introducing a temperature means that $T(= 1/k\mu)$ is the temperature at which $E - E_b$ is the most probable energy of the nucleus X′. Equation (13.217) itself can also be used to see the physical meaning of this temperature T.

‡ See, e.g., V. F. Weisskopf and D. H. Ewing, Phys. Rev., **57**, 472, 1940, especially Fig. 3 on p. 474.

where we have assumed that all (n,n) reactions which leave the nucleus X′ with an excitation energy larger than $E_{b'}$ will lead to a (n,2n) reaction. This means that we exclude the (n,np) and (n,nγ) reactions as being too improbable.

Taking for $I(\epsilon)$ the distribution function (13.217), we have

$$I(\epsilon) = C\epsilon e^{-\mu\epsilon}, \tag{13.222}$$

where C is a normalizing constant which is practically equal to μ^2. Integrating we get from equation (13.221)

$$\sigma(\text{n,2n}) \cong \sigma(\text{n,n}) \int_{E_{b'}}^{E - E_b} I(\epsilon) d\epsilon,$$

or

$$\sigma(\text{n,2n}) \cong \sigma(\text{n,n})[1 - (1 + \mu\Delta E)e^{-\mu\Delta E}], \tag{13.223}$$

where

$$\Delta E = E - E_b - E_{b'}. \tag{13.224}$$

The Purdue cyclotron group has studied the relative yields of (α,n) and (α,2n) reactions in order to verify the equation analogous to equation (13.223) and has found good agreement between the theoretical and observed ratios.

§3. **The Nuclear Partition Function.** In the next chapter we shall consider systems existing at high densities and high temperatures (of the order of 10^{10}°K). In calculating the relative abundances of various nuclear species we need the nuclear partition function $Z_{\text{nucl}}(Z,N)$ corresponding to a nucleus of Z protons and N neutrons. This partition function will be defined by the equation

$$Z_{\text{nucl}}(Z,N) = \sum g_\omega e^{-\mu E_\omega} \cdot \sum g_\nu e^{-\mu E_\nu}, \tag{13.301}$$

where E_ω and E_ν are respectively the rotational and the vibrational energy of the nucleus, while g_ω and g_ν are the corresponding statistical weights. In all cases in which we shall be interested we may replace the sums by integrals.

Let us first consider the vibrational partition function,

$$Z_{\text{vib}} = \sum g_\nu e^{-\mu E_\nu} \cong \int \rho_{\text{vib}}(E) e^{-\mu E} dE. \tag{13.302}$$

We can use for $\rho_{\text{vib}}(E)$ the expressions found in §1 for the nuclear level densities, since in calculating these densities we neglected rotational contributions. Using equation (13.107) we have

$$Z_{\text{vib}} = \int \phi(E) e^{\frac{1}{k}S(E) - \mu E} dE. \tag{13.303}$$

On inspection one finds that the integrand in equation (13.303) is practically constant up to its maximum which occurs for the energy $E_{\max}$ which satisfies the equation

$$\frac{dS}{dE} = k\mu. \tag{13.304}$$

We may therefore write in fair approximation

$$Z_{\text{vib}} \cong E_{\max}\phi(E_{\max})e^{\frac{1}{k}S(E_{\max})-\mu E_{\max}}. \tag{13.305}$$

Due to the strong dependence of S on the atomic weight A, Z_{vib} depends rather strongly on A. Using equation (13.114) for $\rho(E)$, we get

$$Z_{\text{vib}} \approx a(A)e^{0.16A}, \tag{13.306}$$

where $a(A)$ depends only very little on A and is of the order of magnitude of unity.

If we use, on the other hand, equation (13.133) for $\rho(E)$ we have

$$Z_{\text{vib}}' \approx b(A)e^{0.1A^{2/3}}. \tag{13.307}$$

We see that the vibrational partition function depends rather critically on the choice of the model of the nucleus which we are using. The ratio of Z_{vib} to Z_{vib}' ranges from just over 2 for $A = 50$ to a factor 10^{10} for $A = 200$!

The rotational partition function is given by the equation†

$$Z_{\text{rot}} = \sum g_\omega e^{-\mu E_\omega} = \sum_{j=0}^{\infty} (2j+1)^2 e^{-\frac{\mu j(j+1)h^2}{8\pi^2 I}}. \tag{13.308}$$

The moment of inertia I of the nucleus is given by the equation

$$I = \tfrac{2}{5}AMR^2, \tag{13.309}$$

where M is the mass of a nucleon and where R is given by the equation

$$R = A^{1/3}r_0, \tag{13.310}$$

with r_0 of the order of 10^{-13} cm.

Replacing the sum in equation (13.308) by an integral, we have

$$Z_{\text{rot}} \cong \int_0^\infty 4x^2 e^{-\frac{\mu h^2}{8\pi^2 I}x^2}\,dx, \tag{13.311}$$

or, using equations (13.309) and (13.310),

$$Z_{\text{rot}} \cong \sqrt{\pi}\left(\frac{8\pi^2 I}{\mu h^2}\right)^{3/2} = \sqrt{\pi}\left(\frac{16\pi^2 M r_0^2}{5\mu h^2}\right)^{3/2} A^{5/2}. \tag{13.312}$$

† The nucleus is treated as a rigid sphere. Due to the fact that all three moments of inertia of a sphere are equal, the degeneracy is higher than in the case of a rigid rotator discussed in §5 of Chap. III. Compare R. H. Fowler and E. A. Guggenheim, Statistical Thermodynamics, Cambridge 1939, p. 45.

BIBLIOGRAPHICAL NOTES

We refer to the following general references:

1. H. A. Bethe, Revs. Modern Phys., **9**, 69, 1937.
2. H. A. Bethe, Elementary Nuclear Theory, New York 1947.
3. V. F. Weisskopf, Fifth series in Lecture Series in Nuclear Physics (MDDC 1175), Washington 1947.

§1. See reference 1, §53, reference 2, p. 115, reference 3, p. 106, and

4. H. Bethe, Phys. Rev., **50,** 332, 1936.
5. J. Bardeen, Phys. Rev., **51,** 799, 1937.
6. N. Bohr and F. Kalckar, D. Kgl. Danske Videnskab. Selskab, Mat.-fys. Medd., **14,** No. 10, 1937; especially §2 and Addendum I.
7. C. van Lier and G. E. Uhlenbeck, Physica, **4,** 531, 1937.
8. V. Weisskopf, Phys. Rev., **52,** 295, 1937.
9. J. Bardeen and E. Feenberg, Phys. Rev., **54,** 809, 1938.
10. L. Motz and E. Feenberg, Phys. Rev., **54,** 1055, 1938.
11. H. Margenau, Phys. Rev., **59,** 627, 1941.
12. H. Wergeland, Fra Fysikkens Verden, **1945,** 223.
13. S. Devons, Excited States of Nuclei, Cambridge 1949, Chap. 5.

§2. See especially reference 8 and

14. V. F. Weisskopf and D. H. Ewing, Phys. Rev., **57,** 472, 1940.

See also ref. 1, §§54, 56, 65, and 79, refs. 3 and 6, and

15. J. Frenkel, Physik. Z. Sowjetunion, **9,** 533, 1936.
16. L. Landau, Physik. Z. Sowjetunion, **11,** 556, 1937.

We refer to the following references for experimental verification of the theory:

17. K. Lark-Horovitz, J. R. Risser, and R. N. Smith, Phys. Rev., **72,** 1117, 1947.
18. H. L. Bradt and D. J. Tendam, Phys. Rev., **72,** 1117, 1947.
19. S. N. Ghoshal, Phys. Rev., **80,** 939, 1950.
20. E. Bleuler and D. J. Tendam, Phys. Rev., **87,** 216, 1952.

References 17 and 18 investigated the relative yields of (α,n) and (α,2n) reactions, viz., $Rh^{103}(\alpha,n)Ag^{106}$ and $Rh^{103}(\alpha,2n)Ag^{105}$; $Ag^{109}(\alpha,n)In^{112}$ and $Ag^{109}(\alpha,2n)In^{111}$, and checked equation (13.223).

Reference 19 showed, firstly, that the ratios $\sigma(\alpha,n):\sigma(\alpha,2n):\sigma(\alpha,pn)$ for Ni^{60} agreed with the ratios $\sigma(p,n):\sigma(p,2n):\sigma(p,pn)$ for Cu^{63}, thus verifying Bohr's basic assumption about the compound nucleus, namely, that the mode of decay of the compound nucleus should not depend on the way in which it is formed. Secondly, Ghoshal compared these cross sections with the cross sections derived by the statistical theory. He did, however, not arrive at a definite conclusion regarding the validity of the statistical theory due to the uncertainty regarding the energy level densities involved in the calculations of the cross sections.

§3. We refer to the following references:

21. G. Beskow and L. Treffenberg, Arkiv f. Mat., Astron. o. Fys., **34A,** No. 13, 1947.
22. A. Unsöld, Z. Astrophys., **24,** 278, 1948.
23. D. ter Haar, Phys. Rev., **76,** 1525, 1949.

CHAPTER XIV

THE EQUILIBRIUM THEORY OF THE ORIGIN OF THE CHEMICAL ELEMENTS

§1. Basic Theory. As long ago as 1917† it was realized that there existed a relationship between the relative abundances of various nuclear species and their properties, especially their binding energy or mass defect. Recent developments in astrophysics have shown that to a large extent the relative abundances of nuclear species are the same everywhere in the universe. Nuclear physics, on the other hand, is providing us with a wealth of information about nuclear properties. Those two factors together have contributed greatly to the rapid development of theories about the origin of the chemical elements. These theories fall roughly into two groups, the equilibrium theories and the nonequilibrium theories. We must refer to a recent review by Alpher and Herman, who themselves have greatly contributed to the development of nonequilibrium theories, for a detailed discussion of both kinds of theories. In the framework of the present book we can only sketch the main arguments of the equilibrium theories without going into any details.

Since it was found that nuclei with large mass defects were relatively more abundant than those with smaller mass defects, the idea was put forward that all nuclei might have been formed in a situation of statistical equilibrium. As the mass defects are of the order of Mev we must expect temperatures of the order of several thousand million degrees and we shall indeed encounter temperatures of that order of magnitude (see equation [14.116]). The densities involved are also much higher than any densities —apart from the nuclear densities—encountered on the earth.

Let us consider a canonical grand ensemble with modulus Θ and let us again put

$$\mu = \frac{1}{\Theta} = \frac{1}{kT}\cdot \qquad \textbf{(14.101)}$$

The constituent particles of the ensemble will be all kinds of nuclei (denoted

† W. D. Harkins, J. Am. Chem. Soc., **39,** 856, 1917.

by X with Z protons and N neutrons, where Z and N can independently range from zero to infinity), electrons, positrons, neutrinos, and antineutrinos. Their thermal potentials multiplied by μ will be denoted by ν_X (ν_p for a proton and ν_n for a neutron), ν_-, ν_+, ν_ν, and ν_{ν^*}. We have now from equation (6.106) on page 137 the following expression for the relative abundance of systems with N_{X_1} nuclei X_1, N_{X_2} nuclei X_2, $\cdots$, N_- electrons, N_+ positrons, N_ν neutrinos and N_{ν^*} antineutrinos, and energy E,

$$\rho(N_{X_1},N_{X_2},\cdots,N_-,N_+,N_\nu,N_{\nu^*};E) = e^{-q+\sum_i \nu_i N_i - \mu E}. \tag{14.102}$$

We shall assume that we may treat all constituents as independent. In that case E is the sum of the energies of the constituents, the density function on the right-hand side of equation (14.102) can be written as a product of density functions relating to the different constituents, and the grand potential q is the sum of the grand potentials corresponding to the different constituents,

$$E = \sum_i E_i, \tag{14.103}$$

$$q = \sum_i q_i(\nu_i,\mu), \tag{14.104}$$

where the summations extend over all constituents and where q_i depends only on the corresponding ν_i and on μ. Our grand ensemble, representing the system in which the different nuclei were present in about the same relative abundances as are now encountered in the universe, is thus the product of the grand ensembles corresponding to the different constituents.

We can use equation (7.415) on page 158 to get the concentration C_X of nuclei X in the system represented by the grand ensemble and we have

$$C_X = \frac{N_X}{V} = \frac{1}{V}\frac{\partial q}{\partial \nu_X} = \frac{1}{V}\frac{\partial q_X}{\partial \nu_X}. \tag{14.105}$$

The density function of the grand ensemble corresponding to constituent X will be normalized and we have thus

$$\sum_{N_X=0}^{\infty} \sum_{E_X} e^{-q_X+\nu_X N_X - \mu E_X} = 1, \tag{14.106}$$

or

$$e^{q_X} = \sum_{N_X=0}^{\infty} \sum_{E_X} e^{\nu_X N_X - \mu E_X}. \tag{14.107}$$

The energy E_X can be split into four parts,

$$E_X = E_k + E_\nu + E_\omega + E_0, \tag{14.108}$$

where E_k is the kinetic energy of the nucleus, E_ν and E_ω are the vibrational and rotational energies, while E_0 is the binding energy of the nucleus defined by the equation

$$E_0 = (ZM_{\rm p} + NM_{\rm n} - M_{\rm X})c^2, \qquad \textbf{(14.109)}$$

where $M_{\rm p}$ and $M_{\rm n}$ are the proton and neutron mass respectively.

The summation over $N_{\rm X}$ and over E_k can now be performed (compare the derivation of equation [6.403] on p. 144 and that of equation [7.506] on p. 164), and we get†

$$q_{\rm X} = e^{\nu_{\rm X}} V \left(\frac{2\pi M_{\rm X}}{\mu h^2}\right)^{3/2} e^{-\mu E_0} Z_{\rm vib} Z_{\rm rot}, \qquad \textbf{(14.110)}$$

where $Z_{\rm vib}$ and $Z_{\rm rot}$ are the vibrational and rotational partition functions discussed in the last section of the preceding chapter.

From equations (14.105) and (14.110) we now get

$$C_{\rm X} = \left(\frac{2\pi M_{\rm X}}{\mu h^2}\right)^{3/2} e^{\nu_{\rm X} - \mu E_0} Z_{\rm vib} Z_{\rm rot}. \qquad \textbf{(14.111)}$$

In order to be able to compare the concentrations of different nuclei in the equilibrium we must know the relation between the $\nu_{\rm X}$. We make use of the fact that, if the following reactions are possible,

$$\mathrm{X} \rightleftarrows Z \text{ protons} + N \text{ neutrons}, \qquad \textbf{(14.112)}$$

the following relation is an equilibrium condition‡

$$\nu_{\rm X} = Z\nu_{\rm p} + N\nu_{\rm n}. \qquad \textbf{(14.113)}$$

From equations (14.111) and (14.113) we have finally

$$C_{\rm X} = \left(\frac{2\pi M_{\rm X}}{\mu h^2}\right)^{3/2} e^{Z\nu_{\rm p} + N\nu_{\rm n} - \mu E_0} Z_{\rm vib} Z_{\rm rot}. \qquad \textbf{(14.114)}$$

This equation can now be used to discuss the relative abundances of the various chemical elements which would be formed in a statistical equilibrium. Earlier workers in this field did not use grand ensembles. Their conclusions were, however, essentially the same as those which we shall derive from equation (14.114). The advantage of using grand ensembles is twofold. Firstly, it enables one to compare the relative abundances straightaway without first having to solve a great number of simultaneous equations. Secondly, one does not have to worry about complications such as possible degeneracy of the electrons, and so on, since these factors do not enter into the discussion as yet. In the following discussion we

† We must emphasize here that equation (14.110) holds only for nuclei, but not for the protons, neutrons, electrons, positrons, neutrinos, and antineutrinos. For these particles we cannot neglect exclusion effects and relativistic corrections. We return to this point in the next section (compare the discussion leading to equation [14.221]).

‡ See, e.g., O. Klein, Nuovo cimento, **6**, Suppl., 171, 1949, §1.

follow closely the arguments presented by Klein, Beskow, and Treffenberg.

Since the excitation energies of nuclei are relatively high we may put in first approximation Z_{vib} and Z_{rot} equal to one and we then have

$$C_X = \left(\frac{2\pi M_X}{\mu h^2}\right)^{3/2} e^{Z\nu_p + N\nu_n - \mu E_0}. \qquad \textbf{(14.115)}$$

We must use for E_0 either the experimental binding energies or an interpolation formula such as those given, for instance, by Bohr and Wheeler† or van Albada.‡ In equation (14.115) we have three parameters, ν_p, ν_n, and μ, which we can adjust. This adjustment was done as follows by Klein, Beskow, and Treffenberg. First of all they considered those elements for which $N = Z$. By comparing the observed abundances with the abundances given by equation (14.115), μ and $\nu_p + \nu_n$ were determined. After that, comparison of the observed and the calculated abundances of elements with large values of $N - Z$ gave them ν_p and ν_n separately. They found by this method the following values for ν_p, ν_n, and μ:

$$\nu_p = -11.6, \quad \nu_n = -7.6, \quad \mu = 1 \text{ Mev}^{-1} (T = 10^{10}{}^\circ\text{K}). \qquad \textbf{(14.116)}$$

Using these values of ν_p, ν_n, and μ, they were then able to calculate the abundances of all the elements, and they found on the whole satisfactory agreement between observed and calculated abundances up to atomic weights around 60 to 70. The calculated abundances of heavier elements, however, were several orders of magnitude smaller than the observed ones. This constituted the largest problem of equilibrium theories until the developments discussed in the next section pointed to a possible solution. One cannot improve the situation by raising T, since by doing so the agreement for light nuclei is completely spoiled, even though the agreement for heavier nuclei is improved. Some authors suggested that the heavy nuclei and the light nuclei were produced in different epochs. Apart from spoiling the picture of the creation of all nuclei at the same time in *one* system in statistical equilibrium, other difficulties enter and it does not seem to be an acceptable solution.

It is of interest to compute the total density of the system in which the various nuclei are at equilibrium and the parameters of which are given by equation (14.116). We have for this density the equation

$$\rho = \sum M_X C_X = 4 \cdot 10^8 \text{ g cm}^{-3}. \qquad \textbf{(14.117)}$$

At this density, the radius of our earth would be about 10 miles.

§2. Recent Developments. In the preceding section we saw that using equation (14.115) we could obtain agreement between observed and cal-

† N. Bohr and J. A. Wheeler, Phys. Rev., **56**, 426, 1939.
‡ G. B. van Albada, Astrophys. J., **105**, 393, 1947.

culated relative abundances for the light elements, but we could not obtain agreement for the heavy elements. We have, however, neglected a few effects which we must consider now. If these effects are properly taken into account, it turns out that an equilibrium theory may, indeed, possibly account for all the chemical elements in roughly the same relative abundances as those actually observed. The effects which we have neglected are (a) nuclear excited states, (b) electrostatic effects, and (c) gravitational effects.

These three effects will all increase the relative importance of heavy nuclei in the equilibrium, as can be seen from the following qualitative considerations. Excited states can be taken into account by using equation (14.114) instead of equation (14.115). Both Z_{vib} and Z_{rot} increase with increasing atomic weight (see equations [13.306], [13.307], and [13.312]) and the inclusion of the vibrational and rotational partition functions will thus favor heavy nuclei. However, Beskow and Treffenberg showed that this effect is not sufficient. The agreement is extended to atomic weights up to around 100, but not any further.†

Due to the fact that at the high densities and high temperatures with which we are dealing all nuclei will be stripped of all orbital electrons, there will be strong electric fields and we may expect that the electrostatic effects will influence the equilibrium. Van Albada has especially considered these effects. A nucleus consisting of Z protons and N neutrons will give rise to Z electrons, and since we must expect the system to be electrically neutral in each volume element, with dimensions of the order of the average distance between two nuclei—otherwise there will act very strong electric fields which would restore electrical neutrality—we can picture the nucleus and the corresponding Z electrons to be together in a volume of the order of magnitude of $(\Sigma C_{\text{X}})^{-1}$. The nucleus and the Z electrons will give rise to an electrostatic energy. This energy consists of two parts, a negative contribution due to the interaction between the positively charged nucleus and the negatively charged electrons, and a positive contribution due to the interaction between the electrons. The absolute magnitude of the second term is smaller than that of the first one and we get a total electrostatic energy which is negative. Since there are Z electrons and since the charge of the nucleus is Ze (e = charge of a proton), we must expect that we have the equation

$$E_{\text{e.s.}} = -C\frac{Z^2e^2}{r} \cong -C'\frac{Z^2}{A^{1/3}}, \qquad \textbf{(14.201)}$$

† In view of the fact that they probably overestimated the effect by using equation (13.306) instead of equation (13.307)—which is probably more appropriate—it follows that the influence of the excited states is practically negligible.

where r^3 is of the order of the dimensions of the volume available per nucleus, $\bar{A}$ is an average atomic weight, and where C and C' are constants. Since, roughly speaking, Z will be proportional to A, we see that a high atomic weight will decrease $E_{\mathrm{e.s.}}$ and that the electrostatic effects will thus favor heavy nuclei.

The last factor is the influence of gravitational effects. We saw at the end of the preceding section that we are dealing with relatively high densities. It is a well-known fact that at high densities an equilibrium like the one expressed by equation (14.112) will be shifted toward the side with the fewest particles. A large density will thus favor heavy nuclei. A system with a high density will exert gravitational forces on itself and these will tend to increase the density, thus favoring heavier nuclei.

Let us now discuss in slightly more detail how these effects can be taken into account quantitatively. We follow again the investigations of Beskow and Treffenberg. These authors assumed that the chemical elements were formed in the interiors of starlike systems. These stars are supposed to be embedded in a radiation field which ensures that the temperature is kept constant, and for the temperature the value of equation (14.116) was chosen. Inside the star there will be a gravitational potential φ_{gr}, which will be a function of the distance r from the center of the star. This gravitational potential must satisfy the Poisson equation,

$$\nabla^2\varphi_{\mathrm{gr}} = 4\pi G\rho, \tag{14.202}$$

where G is the gravitational constant and ρ the density. There will also be an electrostatic potential φ_{e}. Gibbs† has shown that in equilibrium the thermal potential ν_{X}/μ is related to the gravitational and the electrostatic potentials by the equation

$$\frac{\nu_{\mathrm{X}}}{\mu} + M_{\mathrm{X}}\varphi_{\mathrm{gr}} + Z_{\mathrm{X}}e\varphi_{\mathrm{e}} = \text{independent of } r, \tag{14.203}$$

where $Z_{\mathrm{X}}e$ is the charge of the nucleus X. Using equation (14.113) and writing $M_{\mathrm{X}} = ZM_{\mathrm{p}} + NM_{\mathrm{n}}$, we have from equation (14.203)

$$\frac{1}{\mu}[\nu_{\mathrm{p}}Z + \nu_{\mathrm{n}}N] + [ZM_{\mathrm{p}} + NM_{\mathrm{n}}]\varphi_{\mathrm{gr}} + Ze\varphi_{\mathrm{e}} = \text{constant}. \tag{14.204}$$

This equation is satisfied for any nucleus if it is satisfied for the neutron

† J. W. Gibbs, Trans. Conn. Acad., **3**, 108, 1875; Collected Works, Vol. I, New Haven 1948, p. 144. A generalization of this result, which applies when relativistic effects cannot be neglected, has recently been given by Klein (Revs. Modern Phys., **21**, 531, 1949).

($Z = 0, N = 1$) and for the proton ($Z = 1, N = 0$), or

$$\frac{\nu_{\rm n}}{\mu} + M_{\rm n}\varphi_{\rm gr} = C_1, \tag{14.205}$$

$$\frac{\nu_{\rm p}}{\mu} + M_{\rm p}\varphi_{\rm gr} + e\varphi_{\rm e} = C_2. \tag{14.206}$$

Substituting equation (14.205) into equation (14.202), we get

$$\nabla^2\nu_{\rm n} + 4\pi G\mu M_{\rm n}\rho = 0, \tag{14.207}$$

which gives us a differential equation expressing $\nu_{\rm n}$ in terms of ρ. Writing down the Poisson equation for $\varphi_{\rm e}$ we could similarly obtain an equation for $\nu_{\rm p}$. However, in view of the fact that the matter is practically electrically neutral we can use the equation expressing this neutrality instead.† If we denote the concentrations of the electrons and of the positrons by C_- and C_+, respectively, we have

$$C_- = \sum_{\rm X} C_{\rm X}Z_{\rm X} + C_+. \tag{14.208}$$

At first sight it looks as if we have introduced two new variables, ν_- and ν_+, instead of obtaining an additional relation between $\nu_{\rm p}$ and $\nu_{\rm n}$—both of which enter into the expression for $C_{\rm X}$. However, we must remember that the following reactions can take place:

neutron ⇄ proton + electron + neutrino, (14.209)

proton ⇄ neutron + positron + antineutrino, (14.210)

neutrino + antineutrino ⇄ γ-quanta, (14.211)

electron + positron ⇄ γ-quanta. (14.212)

At equilibrium we then have the following relation between the ν's:

$$\nu_{\rm n} = \nu_{\rm p} + \nu_- + \nu_\nu, \tag{14.213}$$

$$\nu_{\rm p} = \nu_{\rm n} + \nu_+ + \nu_{\nu*}, \tag{14.214}$$

$$\nu_\nu + \nu_{\nu*} = 2\nu_\gamma, \tag{14.215}$$

$$\nu_- + \nu_+ = 2\nu_\gamma. \tag{14.216}$$

From equations (14.213) to (14.216) follows first of all the well-known fact‡ that

$$\nu_\gamma = 0. \tag{14.217}$$

† At the 1953 Astrophysics Colloquium at Liege it was pointed out (see, e.g., the paper by Podolanski and ter Haar in the Proceedings of this Colloquium) that in introducing equation (14.208) instead of using an equation analogous to equation (14.207) one might introduce some inaccuracies.

‡ This is related to the fact that the number of photons in a radiation field is not conserved; compare the remarks on p. 78.

Secondly we see that

$$\nu_\nu = -\nu_{\nu*}, \tag{14.218}$$

$$\nu_- = -\nu_+. \tag{14.219}$$

Klein† has shown that we may assume that by far the most neutrinos are formed in pairs. In that case we have $C_\nu \approx C_{\nu*}$ and thus $\nu_\nu \approx \nu_{\nu*} \cong 0$. From equations (14.219) and (14.213) we then get

$$\nu_- = -\nu_+ = \nu_n - \nu_p. \tag{14.220}$$

Having thus expressed ν_- and ν_+ in terms of ν_p and ν_n we still must express C_- and C_+ in terms of ν_- and ν_+. We can use equations (14.105) and (14.107), but we must now take into account (a) the fact that electrons and positrons are Fermi-Dirac particles, and (b) relativistic effects. We can use the results of Appendix VI and get in that way (see equation [A6.118] on p. 429)

$$C_\pm = \frac{8\pi}{h^3}\int_0^\infty \frac{\mathfrak{p}^2 d\mathfrak{p}}{e^{-\nu_\pm + \mu\epsilon} + 1}, \tag{14.221}$$

where $\mathfrak{p}$ is the absolute magnitude of the momentum which is related to ϵ by the equation

$$\frac{\epsilon^2}{c^2} = \mathfrak{p}^2 + m^2c^2. \tag{14.222}$$

Using equations (14.220) and (14.221), we have C_- and C_+ as functions of ν_p and ν_n, and equation (14.208) thus gives us a relation between these two quantities. Equation (14.207) gives us a relation between ν_n and ρ, while ρ satisfies the equation

$$\rho = \sum_X C_X M_X, \tag{14.223}$$

which gives us the third relation between the three quantities ρ, ν_p, and ν_n. Using these three equations one can determine ν_p and ν_n as functions of the position in the star. Once they have been calculated one can use equation (14.114) to compute the relative abundances as functions of the position in the star. This has been done by Beskow and Treffenberg for various stellar models and they find now rough agreement between the observed and calculated relative abundances.

We do not wish to enter here into a discussion of the many problems which must be considered before a final verdict about the value of the equilibrium theory can be given. We may mention the following. (a) To what extent do the stellar models considered by Beskow and Treffenberg resemble actual stars? (b) In what manner is the equilibrium frozen? (c) At the high densities prevailing in the stars considered by Beskow and Treffenberg the excess of neutrons over protons in the nuclei will be much larger than the excess actually observed. How does the transition from

† O. Klein, Arkiv f. Mat., Astron. o. Fys. **34A,** No. 19, 1947.

neutron-rich to normal nuclei take place and what is the influence of this transition on the final distribution? (d) How does this theory fit in with cosmogonical theories? We refer the reader to the papers mentioned in the bibliographical notes for a discussion of these points.

BIBLIOGRAPHICAL NOTES

Recently, Alpher and Herman have given an elaborate survey of both equilibrium and nonequilibrium theories on the origin of the chemical elements.

1. R. A. Alpher and R. C. Herman, Revs. Modern Phys., **22,** 153, 1950.

We also refer to this review for an extensive bibliography. See also

2. D. ter Haar, Revs. Modern Phys., **22,** 119, 1950, especially §4.
3. J. Podolanski and D. ter Haar, Proc. Liege Astrophys. Colloq. 1953, 19.

In ref. 3 one can find references to papers published after 1950.

§1. We may mention the following references:

4. H. C. Urey and C. A. Bradley, Jr., Phys. Rev., **38,** 718, 1931.
5. T. E. Sterne, Monthly Notices Roy. Astron. Soc., **93,** 736, 1933.
6. C. F. von Weizsäcker, Physik. Z., **38,** 176, 1937.
7. C. F. von Weizsäcker, Physik. Z., **39,** 633, 1938.
8. S. Chandrasekhar and L. Henrich, Astrophys. J., **95,** 288, 1942.
9. O. Klein, G. Beskow, and L. Treffenberg, Arkiv f. Mat., Astron. o. Fys., **33B,** No. 1, 1946.
10. G. Wataghin, Phys. Rev., **70,** 430, 1946.

§2. Apart from refs. 1, 2, and 3 we may also mention

11. F. Hoyle, Monthly Notices Roy. Astron. Soc., **106,** 343, 1946.
12. G. B. van Albada, Bull. Astr. Inst. Netherl., **10,** 161, 1946.
13. G. B. van Albada, Astrophys. J., **105,** 393, 1947.
14. G. Beskow and L. Treffenberg, Arkiv f. Mat., Astron. o. Fys., **34A,** No. 13, 1947.
15. G. Beskow and L. Treffenberg, Arkiv f. Mat., Astron. o. Fys., **34A,** No. 17, 1947.
16. D. ter Haar, Science, **107,** 405, 1948.
17. D. ter Haar, Am. J. Phys., **17,** 282, 1949.
18. O. Klein, Nuovo cimento, **6,** Suppl., 171, 1949.
19. G. Wataghin, Nuovo cimento, **6,** Suppl., 241, 1949.
20. M. G. Mayer and E. Teller, Phys. Rev., **76,** 1226, 1949.
21. C. Hayashi, Prog. Theor. Phys., **5,** 224, 1950.

CHAPTER XV

THE STATISTICAL THEORY OF RUBBER ELASTICITY

§1. The Network Model of Soft Rubber. The last application of statistical methods which we wish to discuss is the statistical theory of rubber elasticity and especially the theory developed by James and Guth. We shall mention only a few aspects of the theory and concentrate on the derivation of the stress-strain relation in this theory.

Let us first of all review a few characteristic properties of rubber. The most striking of its properties is undoubtedly its long-range reversible elasticity. While an elongation of 1 per cent is a large one for an ordinary solid, soft rubber can be stretched to about ten times its original length with relatively small deviations from complete reversibility. Of its thermoelastic properties we mention only that the stress of rubber at given strain varies linearly with temperature.

Rubber resembles a solid in so far as it maintains its original form in the absence of external forces.† However, the great extensibility of rubber shows that the structure of rubber must be different from that of a metal or crystal. In extending a crystal, for instance, one increases the distances between constituent atoms which are linked together by electrostatic or by van der Waals' bonds. Since Young's modulus is so much smaller in the case of rubber we cannot be changing the distances between those atoms which are linked by chemical or other strong bonds by any appreciable amount during extension.

Rubber resembles a liquid in that it has a large volume rigidity, but a small rigidity of shape. We can, indeed, treat rubber as being practically incompressible. Secondly, its coefficient of thermal expansion is of the same order of magnitude as that of liquids. This last point suggests that the interactions between adjacent molecules in bulk rubber are mainly of the same kind as those which maintain the fixed volume of ordinary liquids. The strong bonds mentioned in the preceding paragraph which maintain

† We neglect here the possibility of viscous flow, which is permissible in the present discussion.

the structure of rubber must thus affect only small portions of the very long rubber molecules.

Finally, rubber resembles a gas because of the proportionality of stress with temperature. This proportionality, like the proportionality of the pressure of a perfect gas with temperature, suggests that the tension in stretched rubber does not depend so much on the internal energy as on the change of the number of configurations available to the system for given values of T and the external parameters. We shall return to this point.

In setting up a model for soft rubber we first of all remind ourselves of the structure of one rubber molecule, the chemical formula of which is $(C_5H_8)_n$ with n very large, of the order of 10^2 to 10^4, and which consists of

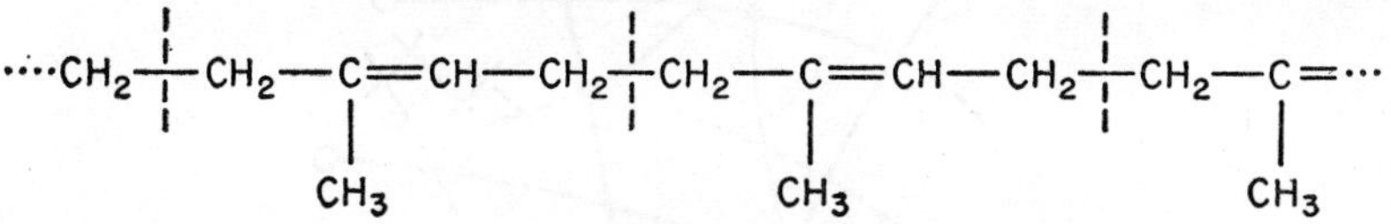

Fig. 48

a long unbranched hydrocarbon chain composed of isoprene groups linked end to end (Fig. 48). It will be seen from Figure 48 that three fourths of the carbon-carbon bonds in the chain are single, only one fourth being double bonds. At any of the single bonds the two parts of the molecule separated by this bond can rotate without appreciably changing the total energy of the molecule.† Since there are hundreds of these bonds in each molecule it follows that the molecule is extremely flexible and can take up a large number of configurations with the same energy. In treating the molecules by statistical methods we shall assume that we may consider a rubber molecule to be a perfectly flexible chain which can take on any configuration without changing its energy.

Let us now consider how soft rubber is manufactured. Raw rubber, whether natural or synthetic, consists of these very long flexible molecules which we just described. It is "milled," during which process any structure it may have possessed is broken down, and the milled rubber is essentially a highly viscous liquid composed of long flexible molecules. It is then "cured." During the curing the structure which differentiates rubber from a liquid is introduced. Strong and definite bonds are formed between the molecules, linking them together into a coherent network. This network determines the form of the material when no external forces are present. The network will be highly irregular, since the bonds are introduced

† The rotation around a single bond is called by James and Guth a "quasi-free" rotation. There are three relative orientations of the molecule with the same minimum potential and with rather low barriers between them.

at random and we may assume that, taken by and large, it will be homogeneous and isotropic. Only a fraction of the molecules will be involved in the network, and there will be many side chains, loose ends, and unattached material (see Fig. 49). In order to get an idea about the relative volumes occupied by the network and by the remainder of the rubber, James and Guth made a rough order of magnitude estimate of about 25 per cent of the molecules being involved in the network. In soft rubbers each molecule which is involved at all will only be involved in a few bonds, so

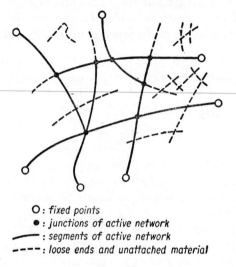

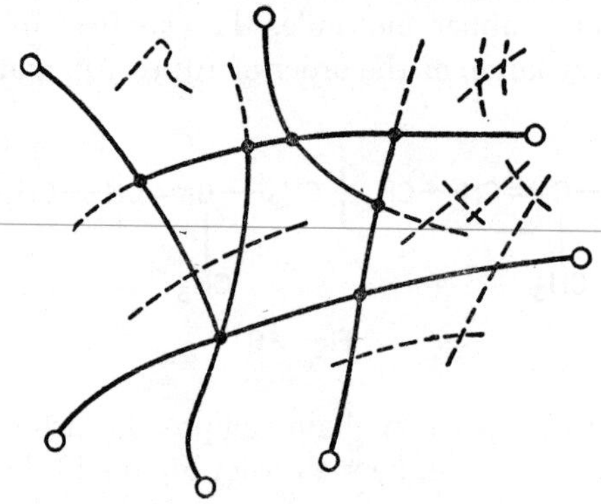

Fig. 49

that large portions of those molecules will be free to take on any configuration which is compatible with the given bonds. Each of the segments, that is, the parts of the rubber between two bonds, can thus again be treated as a long flexible chain. The average length of a segment is estimated by James and Guth to correspond to roughly 100 isoprene groups. Since there are so few bonds the molecules will interact with their surroundings over most of their great length as in the liquidlike milled rubber. In particular, all parts—including the bonds—will show Brownian motion. The only constraints are those imposed by the existence of the relatively few bonds and by the shape of the material.

Summarizing, we can say that a soft rubber may be treated—and will be treated in this chapter—as a liquidlike system of long flexible molecules subject to the permanent constraints imposed on the system by the formation of a network through the introduction of bonds at relatively few points. Rubber differs from an ordinary liquid through these bonds, which give it a definite shape. On the other hand, rubber differs from an ordinary solid by the paucity of these bonds.

We shall now describe in more definite terms the model which we wish to consider (see Fig. 49). First of all we have in the network *fixed points* where the network is immobilized by external constraints. It is at those points that external parameters exert forces on the network. We shall denote the coordinates of these fixed points by $\mathbf{x}_i$. Secondly, we have the *active network*. This consists of that part of the material which stretches between the fixed points and contributes to the forces exerted by the network on the external parameters. Thirdly, there are the *junctions* which are all points of bonding in the active network. The coordinates of the junctions will be denoted by $\boldsymbol{\xi}_i$. A portion of the active network between two adjacent junctions or between a fixed point and the first junction will be called a *segment*. Apart from the active network there are many loose ends, side chains, and unattached molecules which will not contribute to the forces, but which will contribute to the "hydrostatic" pressure in the material (compare the end of §2).

§2. The Derivation of the Stress-Strain Relation. We have defined our model in the preceding section and we can now proceed to evaluate the partition function from which we then can calculate the stress as a function of the strain. We shall assume that the rubber in the absence of external forces has the form of a rectangular parallelepiped of edge lengths L_x^0, L_y^0, and L_z^0, and that, due to forces F_x, F_y, and F_z parallel to the edges, it will be stretched until its form is another rectangular parallelepiped with edges L_x, L_y, and L_z. If the stretching in each direction is uniform, the positions of the fixed points after stretching will be related to the positions in the absence of external forces ($\mathbf{x}_i^0$) as follows:

$$x_i = x_i^0 \frac{L_x}{L_x^0}, \quad y_i = y_i^0 \frac{L_y}{L_y^0}, \quad z_i = z_i^0 \frac{L_z}{L_z^0}. \tag{15.201}$$

We have for the volume V of the system

$$V = L_x L_y L_z. \tag{15.202}$$

The external parameter corresponding to, for instance, the x-component of the stress will be $-L_x$,† and we have from equations (2.701) and (2.713) on pages 40 and 42

$$F_x = -kT \frac{\partial \ln Z}{\partial L_x}, \tag{15.203}$$

where Z is the partition function. In order to obtain the stress-strain

† The minus sign enters since increase of L_x corresponds to work done *on* the system.

relation we must thus compute Z as a function of L_x (and L_y and L_z). From equation (2.701) we have for Z

$$Z = A \int e^{-\frac{\epsilon}{kT}} d\omega, \tag{15.204}$$

where A is a constant and where $d\omega$ is a volume element of phase space. We shall assume that the energy ϵ consists of two parts, the potential energy U, which will be a function of all the coordinates which specify the system, and the kinetic energy $\mathcal{T}$, of which we shall assume that we may neglect its dependence on the coordinates†. In that case, the integration over the momenta will introduce a factor depending only on T, and we can write

$$Z = A \cdot B(T) \int e^{-\frac{U}{kT}} d\omega_q, \tag{15.205}$$

where now the integration is over the coordinates only.

We see here the correspondence with a perfect gas (see, e.g., Chap. II, §8). In the case of a perfect gas, the integration over the momenta also gives a factor which depends only on the temperature while the dependence on the external parameters (V in that case, V, L_x, L_y, and L_z now) enters through the integration over the coordinates.

As the coordinates specifying our system we choose first of all the coordinates of the junctions, $\boldsymbol{\xi}_i$. These will, however, not be sufficient to specify completely the phase of the system. Instead of introducing more coordinates we shall restrict ourselves to the $\boldsymbol{\xi}_i$ and introduce suitable weights to take account of the other degrees of freedom. We do this as follows. We write equation (15.205) in the form

$$Z = A \cdot B(T) \int e^{-\frac{U}{kT}} C(\mathbf{x}_i;\boldsymbol{\xi}_i) \prod_i d\boldsymbol{\xi}_i. \tag{15.206}$$

The functions $C(\mathbf{x}_i;\boldsymbol{\xi}_i)$ introduced in equation (15.206) will be the sum of the relative weights of all situations where the coordinates of the fixed points and the junctions have given values. They will thus be proportional to the number of configurations which the network can take on for given values of the $\mathbf{x}_i$ and $\boldsymbol{\xi}_i$. In the first approximation each function $C(\mathbf{x}_i;\boldsymbol{\xi}_i)$ will be the product of the number of configurations which the various segments can take on—apart from a constant factor. We neglect in making

† In view of the fact that rubber resembles so closely a liquid, it will probably not be too bad an approximation to assume the kinetic energy to be independent of all coordinates. A slightly better approximation would have been to assume $\mathcal{T}$ to depend only on the momenta and on the volume V of the system. In that case, the factor $B(T)$ in equation (15.205) would have been a factor $B(V,T)$.

this approximation the so-called steric hindrances, that is, we neglect the fact that two molecules cannot pass through each other or occupy the same volume in space. It has, however, been shown by James and Guth that the steric hindrances can safely be neglected so long as we are dealing only with not too large extensions. We have thus

$$C(\mathbf{x}_i;\boldsymbol{\xi}_i) = \prod_{i,j} c(\mathbf{r}_i,\mathbf{r}_j), \tag{15.207}$$

where the product extends over all segments in the network and where the $\mathbf{r}_i$ denote both the $\mathbf{x}_i$ and the $\boldsymbol{\xi}_i$.

Since each segment is composed of a large number of links which can take on all possible orientations independently of each other, we should expect for the $c(\mathbf{r}_i,\mathbf{r}_j)$ to find a Gaussian function† and we shall thus assume the following formula to hold,

$$c(\mathbf{r}_i,\mathbf{r}_j) = c_{ij}e^{-\alpha_{ij}(\mathbf{r}_i-\mathbf{r}_j)^2}, \tag{15.208}$$

so that we get from equations (15.206) to (15.208) for Z the expression

$$Z = A \cdot B(T) \cdot C \int e^{-\frac{U}{kT}} e^{-\sum_i\sum_j \alpha_{ij}(\mathbf{r}_i-\mathbf{r}_j)^2} \prod_i d\boldsymbol{\xi}_i, \tag{15.209}$$

where

$$C = \prod_i \prod_j c_{ij}. \tag{15.210}$$

The integration over the $\boldsymbol{\xi}_i$ can be performed as follows. First of all we remind ourselves that if we are dealing with a system with a large number of degrees of freedom, as we are doing here, the probability of finding the system with an energy practically equal to the most probable energy is overwhelmingly larger than the probability of finding the system possessing an appreciably different energy.‡ The most probable energy will be a function of V and T,§ and denoting it by $\bar{U}(V,T)$ we have from equation (15.209)

$$Z \cong A \cdot B(T) \cdot C \cdot e^{-\frac{\bar{U}(V,T)}{kT}} \int e^{-\sum_i\sum_j \alpha_{ij}(\mathbf{r}_i-\mathbf{r}_j)^2} \prod_i d\boldsymbol{\xi}_i. \tag{15.211}$$

The evaluation of the integral in this equation is straightforward and proceeds as follows. The expression in the exponential is a homogeneous quadratic expression in the $\boldsymbol{\xi}_i$ and $\mathbf{x}_i$. By an orthogonal transformation we can write this expression as

$$\sum_i\sum_j \alpha_{ij}(\mathbf{r}_i - \mathbf{r}_j)^2 = \sum_i \beta_i \boldsymbol{\xi}_i'^2 + \sum_i\sum_j \gamma_{ij}\mathbf{x}_i \cdot \mathbf{x}_j, \tag{15.212}$$

† Compare analogous situations in the theory of errors.

‡ Compare a similar situation discussed on p. 117.

§ We assume here that $\bar{U}$ does not depend on L_x, L_y, or L_z. This assumption is based on the fact that rubber resembles so strongly a liquid in that it has a very small rigidity of shape.

where the $\boldsymbol{\xi}_i'$ are linear expressions in the $\boldsymbol{\xi}_i$ and $\mathbf{x}_i$. The integration over the $\boldsymbol{\xi}_i'$ is now elementary† and we get for the partition function the expression

$$Z = e^{-\frac{D(V,T)}{kT}} e^{-\sum_i \sum_j \gamma_{ij} \mathbf{x}_i \mathbf{x}_j}, \tag{15.213}$$

where the first factor embraces all factors apart from the one involving the $\mathbf{x}_i$.

In order to obtain the stress-strain relation by using equation (15.203) we must express Z in terms of the external parameters L_x, L_y, and L_z. Using equation (15.201) we get

$$Z = e^{-\frac{D(V,T)}{kT} - \frac{1}{2}(K_x L_x^2 + K_y L_y^2 + K_z L_z^2)} \tag{15.214}$$

where the constants K_x, K_y, and K_z are given by the equations

$$\left.\begin{aligned} K_x &= \frac{2}{(L_x^{\,0})^2} \sum_{i,j} \gamma_{ij} x_i^{\,0} x_j^{\,0}, \\ K_y &= \frac{2}{(L_y^{\,0})^2} \sum_{i,j} \gamma_{ij} y_i^{\,0} y_j^{\,0}, \\ K_z &= \frac{2}{(L_z^{\,0})^2} \sum_{i,j} \gamma_{ij} z_i^{\,0} z_j^{\,0}. \end{aligned}\right\} \tag{15.215}$$

From equations (15.214), (15.203), and (15.202) we can now derive the stress-strain relations‡ for which we obtain

$$F_x = -kT \frac{\partial \ln Z}{\partial L_x} = \frac{\partial D(V,T)}{\partial L_x} + kTK_x L_x = \frac{\partial D}{\partial V} L_y L_z + kTK_x L_x, \tag{15.216}$$

$$F_y = -kT \frac{\partial \ln Z}{\partial L_y} = \frac{\partial D(V,T)}{\partial L_y} + kTK_y L_y = \frac{\partial D}{\partial V} L_z L_x + kTK_y L_y, \tag{15.217}$$

† The integration is elementary and gives a result which does not depend on the $\mathbf{x}_i$ so long as we integrate from $-\infty$ to $+\infty$. That this is permitted is due to the fact that large extensions of a segment have a vanishingly small probability, as can be seen from equation (15.208).

‡ The relations which we derive are really relations between the total force F and the strains and are thus not a real stress-strain relation, but a load-strain relation, since stress should refer to unit cross section, and the cross section varies during the straining. Some authors refer to F as "stress referred to unstrained section." In order to derive the stress from F one must divide by the cross section. This amounts in the case of unilateral stretch in, say, the x-direction to multiplication by a factor L_x. We shall continue to call the F_x,L_x, F_y,L_y, and F_z,L_z relations stress-strain relations for the sake of simplicity.

$$F_z = -kT\frac{\partial \ln Z}{\partial L_z} = \frac{\partial D(V,T)}{\partial L_z} + kTK_zL_z = \frac{\partial D}{\partial V}L_xL_y + kTK_zL_z. \tag{15.218}$$

For reasons to be discussed presently we put

$$p = -\frac{\partial D}{\partial V}, \tag{15.219}$$

and equations (15.216) to (15.218) then take the form

$$F_x = -pL_yL_z + kTK_xL_x, \tag{15.220}$$

$$F_y = -pL_zL_x + kTK_yL_y, \tag{15.221}$$

$$F_z = -pL_xL_y + kTK_zL_z. \tag{15.222}$$

Let us first discuss the physical meaning of the quantity p introduced by equation (15.219). We shall compare the original uncured material in which there are no junctions or fixed points with the cured rubber. In evaluating the partition function of the uncured material we would have arrived at an expression of the form

$$Z' = C'e^{-\frac{D(V,T)}{kT}}, \tag{15.223}$$

and from the usual equation for the pressure (compare equation [2.715] on p. 42) we would have got

$$p' = kT\frac{\partial \ln Z'}{\partial V} = -\frac{\partial D}{\partial V}. \tag{15.224}$$

We see thus that the total force F consists of two parts, the first one being due to the internal (isotropic) "hydrostatic" pressure p, which gives a negative contribution (tendency to expand), and the second one being due to the network, which gives a positive contribution (tendency to contract).

Let us now consider the case where there are no external forces. We then have $F_x = F_y = F_z = 0$, and using equation (15.202) we get from equations (15.220) to (15.222)

$$\frac{p_0V^0}{kT} = K_x(L_x^0)^2 = K_y(L_y^0)^2 = K_z(L_z^0)^2. \tag{15.225}$$

We see here that the three constants K_x, K_y, and K_z are not independent but must satisfy the equations (15.225).† Putting

$$K_x = \frac{K}{(L_x^0)^2}, \quad K_y = \frac{K}{(L_y^0)^2}, \quad K_z = \frac{K}{(L_z^0)^2}, \tag{15.226}$$

† This could also have been deduced from equations (15.215) and the requirement that the network was isotropic. Note also the resemblance of equation (15.225) and the perfect gas law (compare the remarks on pp. 321 and 324).

and using equation (15.202), we get from equations (15.220) to (15.222)

$$F_x = -\frac{pV}{L_x} + kTK\frac{L_x}{(L_x^{\,0})^2}, \tag{15.227}$$

$$F_y = -\frac{pV}{L_y} + kTK\frac{L_y}{(L_y^{\,0})^2}, \tag{15.228}$$

$$F_z = -\frac{pV}{L_z} + kTK\frac{L_z}{(L_z^{\,0})^2}. \tag{15.229}$$

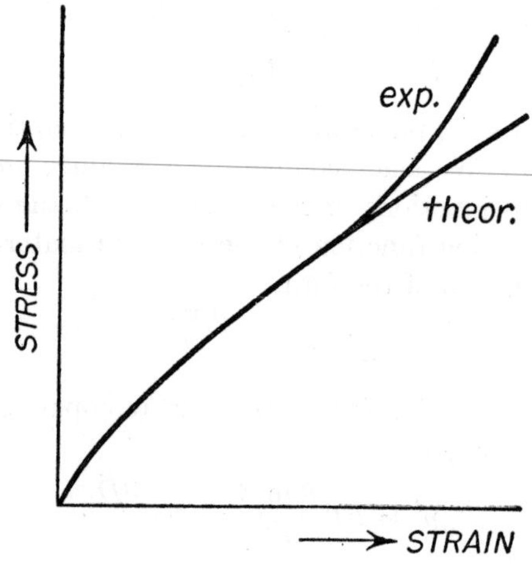

Fig. 50

In the case of unilateral stretch in one direction, say the x-direction, we have $F_y = F_z = 0$ and from equations (15.228) and (15.229) we get

$$p = \frac{KkT}{V}\left(\frac{L_y}{L_y^{\,0}}\right)^2 = \frac{KkT}{V}\left(\frac{L_z}{L_z^{\,0}}\right)^2. \tag{15.230}$$

From this equation we see first of all that the rate of contraction in the y- and z-direction is the same and, second, that the "hydrostatic" pressure is reduced during the stretching.

From equations (15.227) and (15.230) it now follows† that

$$F_x = \frac{KkT}{L_x^{\,0}}\left[\frac{L_x}{L_x^{\,0}} - \frac{V}{V^0}\left(\frac{L_x^{\,0}}{L_x}\right)^2\right]. \tag{15.231}$$

† James and Guth have the equation $F_x = KkT[L_x - V/L_x^2]$ instead of equation (15.231). Since they consider the special case where $L_x^{\,0} = V^0 = 1$, their and our equations are the same. However, if we consider the more general case where $L_x^{\,0}$ and V^0 are not equal to 1, our equation is a generalization of theirs.

In Figure 50 we have drawn both the theoretical curve corresponding to equation (15.231) and an experimental curve for comparison. It is seen that up to a certain value of L_x (actually corresponding to $L_x \approx 3L_x{}^0$) the two curves coincide. The deviations for larger values of L_x can be explained by considering the effect of the approach of some of the segments to their maximum extension. We must refer the reader to James and Guth's papers for detailed discussions.

BIBLIOGRAPHICAL NOTES

This chapter is based mainly on the following reference:

1. H. M. James and E. Guth, J. Polymer Sc., **4,** 153, 1949.

Our representation in §2 is slightly different from the one given in ref. 1 (and also slightly more general; compare the footnote on p. 328), since we have used the approach by means of the partition function instead of using the thermodynamical equation

$$F_x = \frac{\partial U}{\partial L_x} - T\frac{\partial S}{\partial L_x}. \tag{A}$$

James and Guth use equation (A) and then split the entropy into two terms, $S = S_1 + S_2$, where S_1 derives from the kinetic energy (compare the contribution from $\mathcal{T}$ in equation [15.205]) and where S_2 is equal to Boltzmann's constant times the logarithm of the number of configurations accessible to the system for a given value of the energy and the external parameters. The internal pressure p is given by the equation $p = -\frac{\partial U}{\partial V} + T\frac{\partial S_1}{\partial V}$ and the further derivation of the stress-strain relation follows as in the text.

We may also refer to the following references and to others given in refs. 1–3.

2. H. M. James and E. Guth, J. Chem. Phys., **11,** 455, 1943.
3. H. M. James, J. Chem. Phys., **15,** 651, 1947.
4. F. W. Boggs, J. Chem. Phys., **20,** 632, 1952.

§1. The description of the properties of rubber follows §§1 and 2 of ref. 2. The description of the network follows §I of ref. 1.

PART D

APPENDICES

APPENDIX I

THE H-THEOREM AND THE ERGODIC THEOREM

§1. Introduction. In this appendix we are concerned with the various attempts which have been made to justify the use of statistical mechanics in describing physical systems. Although one might argue that there is sufficient justification in the fact that statistical mechanics can predict accurately the behavior of physical systems under equilibrium conditions, there have been several attempts to show that the statistical formalism follows in a straightforward manner from classical or quantum mechanics. These attempts have been only partially successful, but they have played a very important part in the development of statistical mechanics and they have been very helpful in showing the possibilities and limitations of the statistical approach. It was felt, therefore, that they should be fully discussed in a textbook on the subject.

Before embarking upon a description of these various discussions of the fundamental ideas of statistical mechanics, we wish to outline in the present section the contents of the other sections of this appendix. It will be seen that we are steering in the main a historical course.

It must be borne in mind that there are the following two problems which are of fundamental importance to statistical mechanics. It will become clear in the subsequent discussion that they are not independent, but strongly related.

a) Why is it possible to describe the behavior of almost all physical systems by considering only equilibrium situations?

b) Why is it possible to describe the behavior of a physical system by considering a large number of identical systems and identifying the average behavior in this group of systems with the behavior of the physical system in which we are interested?

It is only by considering these problems thoroughly that we see the importance of *statistical* considerations. The first problem can be considered also in kinetic theory, but the second one is of a truly statistical nature.

Boltzmann in his "Gastheorie" was concerned with the first problem and proposed as an answer to it the H-theorem which dates from 1872. We briefly discussed the H-theorem in Chapter I, but now we are entering into a more detailed consideration. The first step in the discussion of the H-theorem is the proof that "equilibrium" can be identified with "the most probable situation." In the special case of a perfect gas we showed this equivalence in Chapter I. From the discussion given there it can be seen that "the most probable situation" must be understood to mean "the most probable situation compatible with a few restricting conditions." These restricting conditions are usually the conditions of given total energy and total number of particles. The second step in the discussion of the H-theorem is the proof that due to interactions in the system (collisions), Boltzmann's H will always decrease, unless it is equal to its minimum value, which is attained only at equilibrium. The unrestricted H-theorem thus proved that any system in which interactions occurred† will tend toward equilibrium if equilibrium did not initially exist. This would thus mean that by waiting a sufficiently long time—which would always be a very short time (of the order of fractions of a second) in practically all cases—our system would be in an equilibrium situation. Problem (a) would thus be solved.

However, it was soon realized that the H-theorem in its original, unrestricted form was not an absolute proof, but was based on the so-called *Stosszahlansatz*, which is the assumption about the number of collisions which a given particle will undergo during a specified time interval. It was realized at the same time that the H-theorem in its unrestricted form could not be true. The two main arguments against the unrestricted H-theorem are the reversibility paradox and the recurrence paradox, which are discussed in §3, after we have illustrated the unrestricted H-theorem in §2 by considering a simplified model of a "gas" due to the Ehrenfests.

Boltzmann realized that the unrestricted H-theorem could not be maintained, and stressed in his later papers the statistical aspects of the H-theorem. The main point is, then, that the Stosszahlansatz should be a statement about the most probable number of collisions. It is possible that fluctuations around this most probable number occur and all statements connected with the H-theorem become probability statements. In §4 we discuss in rather great detail these statistical aspects, firstly, to show the important role they have played in classical statistical mechanics, and, secondly, to show that there are still large gaps in a classical subject which might well be filled by new investigations.

Apart from the attempt to solve (a) by using the H-theorem, there is

† This excludes such clearly hypothetical systems as completely perfect gases within idealized walls.

the attempt to solve the problem by proving that the average behavior of a system will be the same as its equilibrium behavior. This statement is meant as follows. The time average of any phase function, taken over an infinite period, should be equal to the value of this phase function at equilibrium. It is easily seen that this second way of attacking (a) is equivalent to the first one. Firstly, if the H-theorem is correct, it follows that any nonequilibrium situation will develop into an equilibrium situation which will then persist, and in taking a time average of a phase function over an infinite period we obtain the value of this phase function at equilibrium. Secondly, if the time average is equal to the value at equilibrium, it means that the system must be in an equilibrium state during most of the time and hence return to equilibrium from any nonequilibrium state. In order to prove the theorem of the equivalence of average behavior and behavior at equilibrium, one must calculate time averages and one then meets with serious difficulties. Boltzmann tried to surmount these difficulties by assuming that most physical systems are *ergodic*, an ergodic system being one the representative point of which describes an orbit in Γ-space which goes through every point of the energy surface corresponding to the energy of the system. Instead of calculating the time average, Boltzmann could now take the average over the energy surface, which means taking the average over a microcanonical ensemble. The ensemble theory is thus introduced as a mathematical trick to calculate the behavior of one isolated system.

Around the turn of the century, with the development of measure theory, it was realized that ergodic systems would never occur but it was hoped that most physical systems would be quasi-ergodic, that is, that the orbit in Γ-space would cover the energy surface everywhere densely even though not passing through every point of it, and that this would be sufficient to ensure the equality of time averages and averages taken over a suitably chosen ensemble. A great step forward in this direction was the proof of von Neumann and Birkhoff showing that if certain mathematical conditions were fulfilled one could prove the equality of the two averages. The most recent contribution to the problem of the *ergodic theorem*, as it is called, was a paper by Oxtoby and Ulam in which it is proved that the necessary mathematical conditions are satisfied in a very wide group of systems. The whole question of the ergodic theorem and of quasi-ergodic systems is discussed in §5.

The approach via the ergodic theorem is still considered by many authors to be the most satisfactory one and the one providing the best justification of statistical mechanics. It is felt, then, that mechanics can deal only with isolated systems and that the statistical methods are a necessary mathematical device without any further interest. It seems to me that this approach fails to take into account the real reason for statistical methods, even apart from the point that completely isolated systems are of no interest to a physicist since it is impossible to perform experiments with or on them. We mentioned at the very beginning of the book the fact that actual physical systems usually contain so many constituent particles that it is impossible to follow them all along their orbits and that clearly a different method of tackling the problem is needed. We may state it slightly differently by saying that due to the large number of particles we can no longer determine the values of all the integrals of motion, but in general we shall determine only the energy, the total linear momentum, and perhaps one or two more. We now must use this very inadequate knowledge about the system to make predictions about its future behavior. Since our knowledge is insufficient to predict the future of the system with complete certainty, we must have recourse to statistical methods and this is the point where the *representative ensembles* enter (compare also the discussion in Part B). Instead of considering one system, we consider a large collection of systems which all possess the same values of those quantities of which we know the value but which otherwise differ widely. Of course, it is then necessary to make certain assumptions about a priori probabilities in order to give the various systems in the representative ensemble the appropriate weights.† This important point of the a priori probabilities is discussed in §8. Once the need for representative ensembles is recognized, problem (b) is solved in ensemble theory by showing that the great majority of the systems in the ensembles considered behave practically the same and, moreover, give the same values for phase functions as those which one should expect from a system at equilibrium. We refer for this discussion to Chapters V–VII. There remains, however, one point, and that is a proof that one should really use canonical ensembles to represent physical systems. In order to prove this point one introduces a generalized H-theorem and uses the fact that our knowledge about a physical system is always limited so that we can determine from our measurements only the so-called *coarse-grained density* in Γ-space. (See §6 for a definition and a discussion of this density.) It is then shown that this coarse-grained density will change with time in such a way that, if the representative ensemble at a certain moment is not a canonical ensemble, the situation at a later moment will be such that we are then forced to use a representative ensemble which resembles much more closely a canonical ensemble. The whole question of the approach to equilibrium in ensemble theory is discussed in §6.

† We may remark here that this point enters not only in the approach through ensemble theory, but also in the ergodic approach, since it enters, often tacitly, in the construction of the microcanonical ensemble.

The situation does not drastically change if we go over from classical to quantum statistics, and §7 deals with the situation in quantum statistics. The appendix is concluded with a brief discussion of the principle of detailed balancing.

At the end of this introduction we must make a few remarks about some general aspects of the second law of thermodynamics.† From the discussion in §4, it will be clear that the fact that in all practical applications of thermodynamics the entropy always increases is due to two points. First of all, if the entropy is smaller than its equilibrium value, the probability that it will increase is overwhelmingly larger than that it will decrease. Secondly, our observations are always made in such a way that we start from a given situation and then watch the future development, but we are not able to keep the state of a system at a certain time fixed and then watch the preceding time interval. The fact that we can do the one but not the other is related to the fact that we have a memory of the past and we can, therefore, possess knowledge of what happened at an earlier time but not of what will happen at a later moment. To this extent the irreversibility of the second law of thermodynamics is physiological and basic.

A second point is that, as far as we can ascertain, all observations on phenomena in the universe are reconcilable with the idea that the whole universe is developing from some reasonable, though thermodynamically unlikely, state in the distant past. This can be brought into connection with cosmogonical theories involving a more or less singular beginning (about $3 \cdot 10^9$ years ago?). On the other hand, the fact that our world seems to be developing from a less probable to a more probable state is not necessarily in contradiction with the idea that the universe as a whole is in thermodynamical equilibrium. We may quote in that connection some remarks of Boltzmann:‡

"We assume that the whole universe is, and rests for ever, in thermal equilibrium. The probability that one (only one) part of the universe is in a certain state is the smaller the further this state is from thermal equilibrium but this probability is greater, the greater is the universe itself. If we assume the universe great enough, we can make the probability of one relatively small part being in any given state (however far from the state of thermal equilibrium) as great as we please. We can also make the probability great that, though the whole universe is in thermal equilibrium, our world is in its present state. It may be said that the world is so far from thermal equilibrium that we cannot imagine the improbability of such a state. But can we imagine on the other side how small a part of

† I would like to express here my thanks to Professor R. E. Peierls for critical remarks on these points.

‡ L. Boltzmann, Nature, **51,** 413, 1895.

the whole universe this world is? Assuming the universe great enough, the probability that such a small part of it as our world should be in its present state is no longer small.

"If this assumption were correct, one would return more and more to thermal equilibrium; but because the whole universe is so great, it might be probable that at some future time some other world might deviate as far from equilibrium as our world does at present. Then the aforementioned H-curve† would form a representation of what takes place in the universe. The summits of the curve would represent the worlds where visible motion and life exists."

§2. The Kinetical Aspect of the *H*-theorem; Stosszahlansatz. In Chapter I we discussed how the distribution function $f(u,v,w)$ was changed by collisions. It was found that, if we assume no correlation to exist between velocities and positions of different atoms, then the distribution will always change in such a way that it tends to the Maxwell distribution. In order to prove this we introduce a function H by the equation

$$H = \int f \ln f \, d\mathbf{c}, \tag{A1.201}$$

where the integration is extended over the whole of velocity space. In the case of the Maxwell-Boltzmann distribution, we have instead of equation (A1.201) the equation

$$H = \int f \ln f \, d\omega, \tag{A1.202}$$

where $d\omega$ is the volume element in μ-space and where f is now a function of the generalized coordinates and momenta q_k and p_k.

In order to be able critically to examine the various assumptions which are made in arriving at Boltzmann's H-theorem, we shall discuss here a simplified model introduced by the Ehrenfests. In the plane of the paper there may be a large number of point particles, N per unit area, which we shall call the P-molecules. They do not interact with each other, but they collide elastically with another set of entities which we may call the Q-molecules. These Q-molecules are squares with edge length a, distributed at random over the plane. They are fixed in their positions in such a way that their diagonals are exactly parallel to the x- and y-axes. Their average surface density is n, and we shall let their mean distance apart be large compared to a.

Suppose that at a certain moment all the P-molecules have velocities which are of the same absolute magnitude, c, and limited in direction to

† Compare §4.

(1) the positive x-axis, (2) the positive y-axis, (3) the negative x-axis, and (4) the negative y-axis (see Fig. 51). Due to the nature of our system and the interactions allowed in it, the situation at any other time will be similar to the one just described, the only possible difference being in the magnitude of the numbers of P-molecules moving in the four pos-

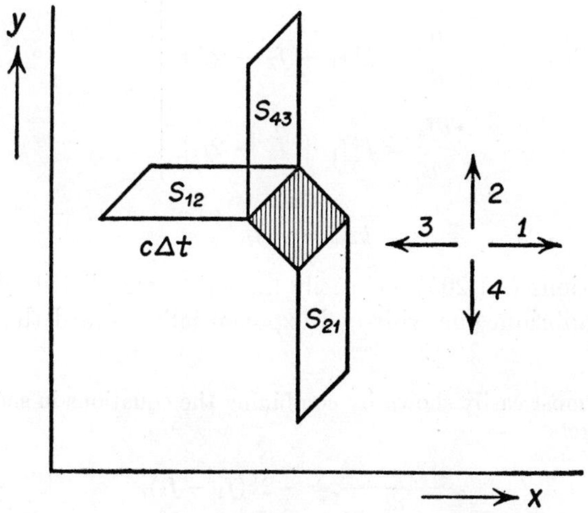

Fig. 51

sible directions. Let f_1, f_2, f_3, and f_4 be the numbers of the P-molecules moving in those four directions. These numbers will be functions of t and together will take the place of the distribution function $f(u,v,w)$ of Chapter I.

The equilibrium distribution will be given by the equation

$$f_1 = f_2 = f_3 = f_4 = \tfrac{1}{4}N, \tag{A1.203}$$

and we shall now show that under certain conditions, corresponding to the Stosszahlansatz in the case of the Maxwell distribution, any distribution different from (A1.203) will tend toward the equilibrium distribution as a consequence of collisions between the P- and the Q-molecules.

Let $N_{ij}\Delta t$ be the number of P-molecules per unit area which during a time interval Δt change from direction i to direction j. This number is given by the equation

$$N_{ij}\Delta t = f_i S_{ij} n, \tag{A1.204}$$

where S_{ij} is the area of a parallelogram of length $c\Delta t$ on that edge of one of the squares which is in the $-i$, j quadrant (see Fig. 51). Since all S_{ij} are equal we get for the change with time of the f_i the equations

$$\left.\begin{aligned} \frac{df_1}{dt} &= k[f_2 + f_4 - 2f_1], \\ \frac{df_2}{dt} &= k[f_3 + f_1 - 2f_2], \\ \frac{df_3}{dt} &= k[f_4 + f_2 - 2f_3], \\ \frac{df_4}{dt} &= k[f_1 + f_3 - 2f_4], \end{aligned}\right\} \tag{A1.205}$$

where

$$k\Delta t = nS_{ij}. \tag{A1.206}$$

From equations (A1.205) one easily finds that any distribution different from the equilibrium one will tend exponentially toward the equilibrium distribution.†

This is most easily shown by combining the equations in such a way that one gets

$$\frac{d(f_1 - f_3)}{dt} = -2k(f_1 - f_3),$$

$$\frac{d(f_2 - f_4)}{dt} = -2k(f_2 - f_4),$$

$$\frac{d[(f_1 + f_3) - (f_2 + f_4)]}{dt} = -4k[(f_1 + f_3) - (f_2 + f_4)],$$

which shows that $f_1 - f_3 \to 0$, $f_2 - f_4 \to 0$, $(f_1 + f_3) - (f_2 + f_4) \to 0$.

In our proof of the approach to equilibrium we have once more introduced a basic assumption about the number of collisions (Stosszahlansatz) without mentioning it explicitly. Equation (A1.204) is based on the assumption that the total number of atoms in the parallelogram S_{ij} is proportional to f_i in the same ratio as S_{ij} to the total area per unit area not occupied by Q-molecules. Once this assumption has been made, the approach to equilibrium follows because all S_{ij} are equal. Occasionally, in order to simplify the discussion, the slightly different but more stringent assumption of *microscopic reversibility* may be introduced. If we do this,

† We must remark here that our model is slightly different from that of the Ehrenfests. In their model the total number of P-molecules is finite. This has the advantage in that there is no need to investigate afterward the influence of spatial fluctuations in N which have tacitly been neglected by choosing our distribution function to be a function of the velocities only. The disadvantage is, however, that k becomes the product of zero (f_i) and an infinite number (the total number of Q-molecules).

we then write, instead of equation (A1.204),

$$N_{ij} = f_i a_{ij}, \tag{A1.207}$$

where the constants a_{ij} can be interpreted as transition probabilities (compare §§7 and 9). The assumption of microscopic reversibility then gives us the equations

$$a_{ij} = a_{ji}, \tag{A1.208}$$

and the approach to equilibrium follows as before.

In Chapter I we limited our discussion of the H-theorem to the case where inverse collisions were possible. However, if we are dealing with polyatomic molecules, this will not always be the case, as can be seen from the following exaggerated example. Consider a collision between two "molecules" of equal mass as pictured in Figure 52. Before the collision "molecule" A may have a velocity **v** in the direction connecting the two centers of gravity. Since the two masses are equal, "molecule" B will possess this velocity after the collision. A moment of reflection reveals that there does not exist an inverse collision such that the velocities of A and B *after* the collision will be **v** and 0. One can, however, still prove in this case the existence of an H-theorem (introducing again a Stosszahlansatz), but instead of considering collisions and their inverse ones, one must consider cycles of collisions. We refer for a discussion of this point to the literature given in the bibliographical notes at the end of this appendix.

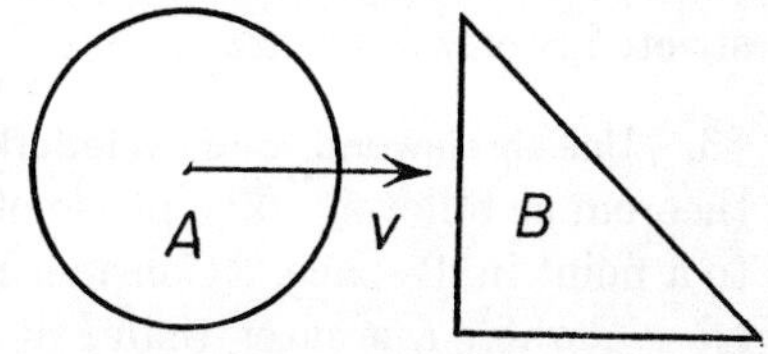

BEFORE THE COLLISION

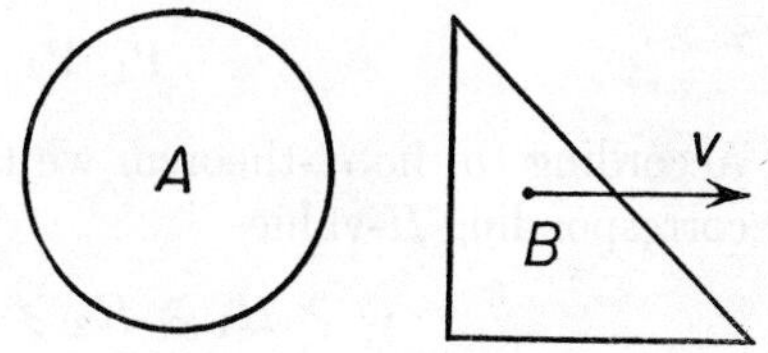

AFTER THE COLLISION

Fig. 52

In the discussion in the present section collisions play the dominant role, and we may therefore call this way of treating the problem the *kinetical* treatment. Once we have made our basic assumption about the number of collisions (Stosszahlansatz), the uniform decrease of H or the uniform approach to the equilibrium distribution follows. If we could justify or prove the Stosszahlansatz, we would have a proof of the statistical results which emerge from calculations involving the equilibrium distribution. In §4 we shall discuss the H-theorem from still another point of view and give the so-called *statistical* treatment where we discuss possible fluctuations. That the statistical treatment must be expected to be more satisfactory than the kinetical one follows from the basic ideas of statistical mechanics. In statistical mechanics we are dealing with systems which are so complicated that it is impossible to obtain complete information about all their details, so that only a few data are known. Hence all our statements must necessarily involve probabilities, so that instead of stating that H will always decrease, we can only state that in a system of which only a few relevant data are known it is exceedingly probable that dH/dt will be negative, especially if H is far different from its equilibrium value.

Before discussing the statistical treatment of the H-theorem we shall see in the next section that the H-theorem as we gave it in Chapter I, which states that H will always decrease until it reaches its equilibrium value, is certainly not true. In other words, we shall see that the unrestricted Stosszahlansatz is never valid.

§3. Umkehreinwand and Wiederkehreinwand.† We can state the H-theorem as follows. The phase of our system will at any time correspond to a point in Γ-space. Consider now a series of instants $\cdots, t_1, t_2, t_3, \cdots, t_n, \cdots$, where t_i is later than t_j if $i > j$. The phase at t_n may correspond to a point P_n in Γ-space so that the representative point of the system passes through the sequence of points

$$\cdots, \mathrm{P}_1, \mathrm{P}_2, \cdots, \mathrm{P}_{n-1}, \mathrm{P}_n, \cdots. \tag{A1.301}$$

According to the H-theorem we then have the following sequence for the corresponding H-values

$$\cdots \geqslant H_1 \geqslant H_2 \geqslant \cdots \geqslant H_{n-1} \geqslant H_n \geqslant \cdots, \tag{A1.302}$$

where the equal sign holds only if the distribution function satisfies the Maxwell-Boltzmann formula.

Consider now two phases P_i and P_i' where all the q_k have the same values, and where all the p_k have the same values but with opposite signs. From the definition (A1.202) of H it follows immediately that

$$H_i = H_i'. \tag{A1.303}$$

Let us now consider the equations of motion

$$\dot{q}_k = \frac{\partial \mathcal{H}}{\partial p_k}, \qquad \dot{p}_k = -\frac{\partial \mathcal{H}}{\partial q_k}, \tag{A1.304}$$

where $\mathcal{H}(p_k, q_k)$ is the Hamiltonian of the system. From equations (A1.304) we can easily verify that a system starting from a point P_n' will

† I have refrained from translating these terms as "the reversibility and recurrence paradoxes" for historical reasons.

pass through the sequence†

$$\cdots, P_n', P_{n-1}', \cdots, P_2', P_1', \cdots, \qquad \textbf{(A1.305)}$$

where the relation between each pair P_i' and P_i is the same as before. During this motion we have as a consequence of (A1.302) and (A1.303) that

$$\cdots \leqslant H_n' \leqslant H_{n-1}' \leqslant \cdots \leqslant H_2' \leqslant H_1' \leqslant \cdots. \qquad \textbf{(A1.306)}$$

We see thus that for each motion where H decreases uniformly from H_1 to H_n there exists a motion where H increases in exactly the same way from H_n to H_1. This is Loschmidt's famous *Umkehreinwand.*

If we apply these considerations to the simplified model of the preceding section, we see immediately the validity of equation (A1.303) and of the Umkehreinwand. Boltzmann's H is now given by the equation

$$H = f_1 \ln f_1 + f_2 \ln f_2 + f_3 \ln f_3 + f_4 \ln f_4, \qquad \textbf{(A1.307)}$$

and the change of sign of the velocities implies the transformation

$$f_1' = f_3, \quad f_2' = f_4, \quad f_3' = f_1, \quad f_4' = f_2, \qquad \textbf{(A1.308)}$$

whence we see immediately that $H' = H$.

From the considerations of the preceding section it also follows that reversing the time direction would mean changing a nearly equal distribution (approaching [A1.203]), to a less equalized distribution (compare the equations in small type on p. 338).

Another difficulty was pointed out by Zermelo, using a theorem of Poincaré's about systems enclosed in a finite volume. Poincaré has shown‡ that if a system passes through the sequence (A1.301) from t_1 to t_n, this sequence will be repeated as accurately as we wish it to be repeated after a finite—be it possibly a very long—time. That is, if we wish to repeat the sequence so closely that the p_k and q_k will be reproduced within margins of Δp_k and Δq_k, respectively, the system will, after a finite time T. pass through a sequence

$$(P_1), (P_2), \cdots (P_{n-1}), (P_n), \cdots \qquad \textbf{(A1.309)}$$

where the distance between P_i and (P_i) is within the specified limits.

We can prove Poincaré's theorem as follows. Let us consider a point P_0 in phase space and let us show that the representative point which has passed through P_0 will return to the neighborhood of P_0 after a finite time. The neighborhood of P_0 is to be understood as being a volume element $\Delta\Omega_0$ in Γ-space which has a *finite* extension. We can follow the trajectories of all systems which have representative points in $\Delta\Omega_0$

† Reversing the sign of the p_k has the same effect as reversing the time direction.

‡ H. Poincaré, Acta Math., **13**, 67, 1890; see also L. Boltzmann, Wien. Ber., **106**, 12, 1897.

at t_0. These trajectories follow from the Hamiltonian equations (A1.304). The volume in phase space occupied at a time t by the representative points which at t_0 are inside $\Delta\Omega_0$ may be denoted by $\Delta\Omega_t$. We now consider all the points in Γ-space which are future representative points of systems which at t have representative points inside $\Delta\Omega_t$. All these points will fill up a domain in Γ-space which contains all $\Delta\Omega_{t'}$ with $t' \geqslant t$. This domain will have a finite extension Ω_t if we are dealing with a system which is enclosed in a finite volume, since in that case the entire accessible region of Γ-space is finite because none of the p_k or q_k can take on infinite values.

From the definition of Ω_t it follows immediately that

$$\Omega_{t_1} \geqslant \Omega_{t_2}, \quad \text{if} \quad t_1 \leqslant t_2. \tag{A1.310}$$

From Liouville's theorem (see equation [5.108] on p. 102) we have that the density in phase space is constant, or

$$\Delta\Omega_t = \text{constant}. \tag{A1.311}$$

Since Ω_t is made up of all future phases of $\Delta\Omega_t$, we have from Liouville's theorem (or from equation [A1.311])

$$\Omega_t = \text{constant}. \tag{A1.312}$$

From equations (A1.310) and (A1.312) it follows that for $t > t_0$ Ω_t and Ω_{t_0} can differ by only at most a set of points of measure zero.† Hence the future phases of $\Delta\Omega_t (t > t_0)$ must include all points (except perhaps a set of measure zero) of $\Delta\Omega_0$. Or the situations represented by the points of $\Delta\Omega_0$ must recur after the lapse of a sufficiently long but finite time.

This time can be extremely long. Boltzmann‡ estimated the time necessary for a return of a situation under the following conditions and within the following limits. All of the 10^{18} atoms of 1 cubic centimeter of gas were to retain their average velocity of $5 \cdot 10^4$ cm sec^{-1} and were to reproduce their positions and velocities within the limits

$$|\Delta x| \leqslant 10^{-7}\ \text{cm}; \qquad |\Delta u| \leqslant 10^2\ \text{cm sec}^{-1};$$
$$|\Delta y| \leqslant 10^{-7}\ \text{cm}; \qquad |\Delta v| \leqslant 10^2\ \text{cm sec}^{-1};$$
$$|\Delta z| \leqslant 10^{-7}\ \text{cm}; \qquad |\Delta w| \leqslant 10^2\ \text{cm sec}^{-1}.$$

The time so calculated would be longer than $10^{10^{19}}$ years!

The H-values corresponding to the sequence (A1.309) will be

$$\cdots (H_1),\ (H_2),\ \cdots,\quad (H_{n-1}),\ (H_n),\ \cdots. \tag{A1.313}$$

If we choose the Δp_k and Δq_k sufficiently small,

$$(H_i) \approx H_i, \tag{A1.314}$$

† We refer the reader who is not acquainted with the idea of "measure" to P. R. Halmos, Measure Theory, New York, 1950; see also the footnote on p. 357.

‡ L. Boltzmann, Ann. Physik, **57**, 773, 1896; see also S. Chandrasekhar, Revs. Modern Phys., **15**, 85, 1943.

and combining equations (A1.302) and (A1.314) we see that

$$(H_1) > H_n, \tag{A1.315}$$

or in going from P_n to (P_1) H must have increased, in contradiction to the H-theorem.

Before discussing in the next section how statistical considerations can clarify these difficulties, we must draw attention to the fact that insofar as Loschmidt's and Zermelo's criticisms invalidate the H-theorem in its unrestricted form, that is, the statement that H can *never* increase, they show that the Stosszahlansatz cannot be correct under *all* circumstances. In order to illustrate this point, we shall once more consider the simplified model of §1.

Consider an arbitrary time interval Δt during the evolution of the system. The distribution function before and after this time interval may be denoted by f_i and $\bar{f}_i$, respectively. The number of collisions which lead to a change from a velocity i to a velocity j during Δt may again be $N_{ij}\Delta t$. In the corresponding evolution in which we suppose all velocities to be reversed we may pick out the corresponding interval and denote the distribution function before the interval by f_i'. We then have (compare equation [A1.308]).

$$f_1' = \bar{f}_3,\ f_2' = \bar{f}_4,\ f_3' = \bar{f}_1,\ f_4' = \bar{f}_2. \tag{A1.316}$$

If $N_{ji}'\Delta t$ is the number of collisions during Δt in the reversed evolution, we have clearly

$$N_{ji}'\Delta t = N_{ij}\Delta t. \tag{A1.317}$$

If the Stosszahlansatz were valid both for the original and for the reversed motion, we should have, from equations (A1.204), (A1.206), and (A1.317),

$$f_j'k\Delta t = f_ik\Delta t, \tag{A1.318}$$

or, using equations (A1.316),

$$\left.\begin{aligned} \bar{f}_4 = f_1,\ \bar{f}_2 = f_1,\ \bar{f}_3 = f_2,\ \bar{f}_1 = f_2, \\ \bar{f}_4 = f_3,\ \bar{f}_2 = f_3,\ \bar{f}_3 = f_4,\ \bar{f}_1 = f_4, \end{aligned}\right\} \tag{A1.319}$$

whence

$$f_1 = f_3 \quad \text{and} \quad f_2 = f_4, \tag{A1.320}$$

which will certainly not be the case at any arbitrarily chosen time. It is thus clearly impossible that the Stosszahlansatz will be valid both for the original and for the reversed motion as long as the distribution is not yet an equilibrium distribution. *For at least one of the two motions the Stosszahlansatz cannot be valid.*

§4. The Statistical Aspect of the *H*-theorem. We mentioned in §§1 and 2 that the nature of the situations studied in statistical mechanics entails that our considerations be truly statistical and that our statements be cast into a statistical language. Once again it was Boltzmann who started this statistical approach and one may, indeed, say that at that moment kinetic theory changed to statistical mechanics, even though another few decades were to elapse before Gibbs coined the expression "statistical mechanics" in his famous monograph. In the main part of this book we have, of course, often used the results of the statistical approach, especially in the discussions in the first seven chapters, but we shall now be concerned with a more critical discussion of the basic assumptions of the method.

Boltzmann tried two different ways of approaching the problem and in doing so he used the following two general definitions of the equilibrium situation.

a) The equilibrium situation is that one which is the *most probable* one for a given energy†—or better—for an energy lying within a given interval δ (see p. 99).

b) The equilibrium situation is the *average* situation in which the system—again with an energy lying within a given interval δ—will find itself during an infinite time interval.

Boltzmann was compelled to introduce a few assumptions in order to prove the occurrence of the Maxwell-Boltzmann distribution starting from either (a) or (b). We shall discuss these assumptions, but before doing so, we shall outline the main arguments.

Consider a system consisting of N independent particles. Each of the particles will be represented by a point $Q^{(k)}$ in μ-space where the superscript numbers the particles ($k = 1,2,\cdots,N$). The phase of the whole system is then determined by the N points $Q^{(1)}, Q^{(2)}, \cdots, Q^{(N)}$. We now divide μ-space into very small *but finite* cells of equal volume ω, which we number, $\omega_1, \omega_2, \cdots$. *This division is one of the fundamental steps in the statistical approach.* Regarding the size of the cells, a compromise must be reached between these two requirements: (a) The cells must be very small compared to the smallest microscopically measurable dimensions, and (b) the cells must be so large that the number of points $Q^{(k)}$ contained in each of them is large. In discussing this division in his thesis, Uhlenbeck adds: "It is as if Boltzmann had here a premonition of the occurrence of discrete quantum states in μ-space."

Let N_i be the number of points $Q^{(k)}$ in cell ω_i. The situation **Z**‡ is

† It must immediately be noted here that this statement is still incomplete as long as one does not define how probability is measured. This point has been strongly emphasized by the Ehrenfests in their discussion of the statistical approach, and we shall return to this point.

‡ We use here the Ehrenfests' notation (**Z** for Zustandsverteilung).

determined by the collective of the numbers N_i. We see then the following points:

a) To each point in Γ-space there corresponds one situation **Z**.

b) For each **Z** there is still a volume in Γ-space of which all points correspond to **Z**. This region in Γ-space shall be called a **Z**-star.

The first statement is self-evident. The second one can be seen as follows. The collective of the numbers N_i remains unchanged during the following two operations.

a) Each of the N points $Q^{(k)}$ moves through the whole of the cell. During this movement of all of the $Q^{(k)}$ a volume Ω in Γ-space is filled out where

$$\Omega = \omega^N. \qquad \textbf{(A1.401)}$$

b) Any permutation of the $Q^{(k)}$ will leave the N_i and hence **Z** unchanged. If we perform all $N!$ permutations the representative point in Γ-space will take up $N!$ different positions which are distributed in the form of a many-dimensional "star".

The volume $W(\mathbf{Z})$ of a **Z**-star is given by the formula for the number of cells of volume Ω in Γ-space, or

$$W(\mathbf{Z}) = \frac{N!}{N_1!N_2!\cdots}\,\omega^N, \qquad \textbf{(A1.402)}$$

which follows from the considerations under (a) and (b) if we remind ourselves that only permutations which permute $Q^{(k)}$ in different cells will bring the point in Γ-space from one cell Ω to another.

In Chapter I we saw that in an equilibrium situation the entropy which, on the one hand, is equal to $-kH$ is, on the other hand, equal to $k \ln W_{\max}$, where $W_{\max}$ is the maximum value of $W(\mathbf{Z})$ which is compatible with the conditions of a given total energy and a given total number of particles.† If we are not in an equilibrium state, it seems reasonable still to assume the relation

$$H = -\ln W(\mathbf{Z}), \qquad \textbf{(A1.403)}$$

and indeed, this relation is the same as relation (A1.202), as we saw in Chapter II, §3. If we use the Stirling formula in its simplest form (MA3.09) for the $N_i!$ and neglect additive constants, equation (A1.403) can be written in the form

$$H(\mathbf{Z}) = \sum_i N_i \ln N_i, \qquad \textbf{(A1.404)}$$

† In choosing as the equilibrium situation that situation for which $\ln W$ is maximum we have made our choice as far as the measuring of the probability of a situation is concerned. We shall discuss this point at the beginning of §8.

where we have used the condition

$$\sum N_i = N = \text{constant}. \tag{A1.405}$$

In discussing the behavior of H as a function of time we must first of all realize that any function of the p_k and q_k considered as a function of the N_i or of the situation $\mathbf{Z}$ is a discontinuous function, since whenever one of the

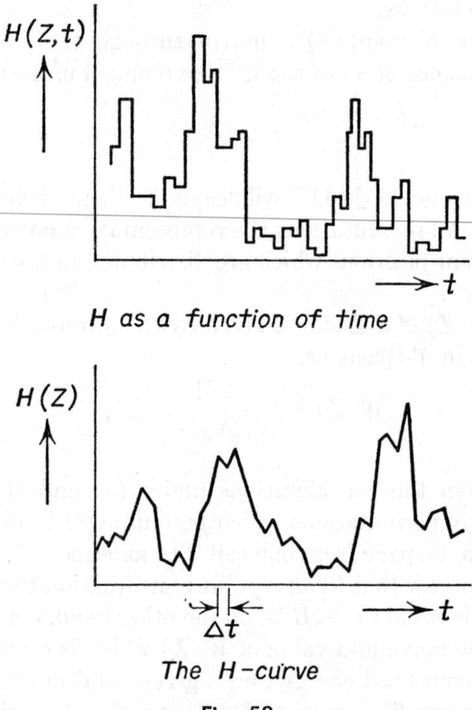

Fig. 53

representative points in μ-space leaves one cell and enters another, the two N_i concerned alter by unity. If we discuss, therefore, the time dependence of $H(\mathbf{Z},t)$ we will get a step function† and its time derivative will be able to take on only three values, 0, $+\infty$, and $-\infty$.

We can now obtain a so-called *H-curve* by picking out of the step function a discrete set of points which are separated by constant time intervals Δt (see Fig. 53).

† It must be noted here that this fact does not depend on the character of the collisions but is a consequence of the fact that we have chosen the cells ω to be finite. It is just as valid when we are considering real atoms whose interaction is governed by smooth potential functions as when we are considering hard spherical atoms.

The time interval Δt must be chosen in such a way that it is small compared to experimental time intervals, but so large that it still contains a large number of collisions.†

In order to see the behavior of the H-curve, the Ehrenfests constructed a curve which showed the same qualitative behavior as an H-curve. Their curve was constructed in the following way. Let N balls numbered from from 1 to N, where N is chosen to be even for the sake of simplicity, be distributed over two urns A and B. There are also N cards numbered from 1 to N. We draw a card and the ball whose number is drawn is removed from the urn in which it was to the other urn. The card is returned to the pack and the process is repeated. Let P_z and Q_z be the number of balls in A and B respectively after z draws, and let

$$\Delta_z = |P_z - Q_z|. \qquad \textbf{(A1.406)}$$

In plotting Δ_z as a function of z we get a curve which is analogous to the H-curve. Part of this curve is drawn in Figure 54, where the actual values of Δ_z are taken from the experimental data of Kohlrausch and Schrödinger.

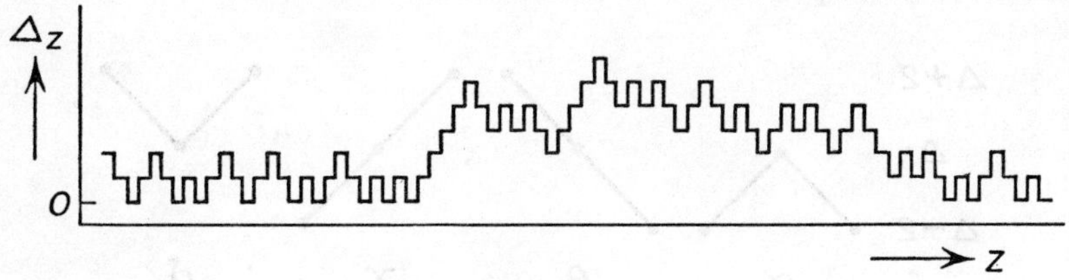

Fig. 54

These authors actually performed the lottery in order to verify certain probability relations, but afterward published their results in such a form that they could be used to illustrate the Ehrenfest curve.

The Δ_z-curve has the following properties. First of all, each point of the curve lies either 2 higher or 2 lower than the preceding or the following point. Secondly, the probabilities p_{up} and p_{down} for going upward or downward from a point with ordinate Δ_z are given by the equations

$$p_{\text{up}} = \frac{N - \Delta_z}{2N}, \qquad p_{\text{down}} = \frac{N + \Delta_z}{2N}, \qquad (\Delta_z \neq 0) \qquad \textbf{(A1.407)}$$

which shows a tendency to go down. This tendency is the stronger, the larger Δ_z is. Thirdly, a point at height Δ_z will most likely be a maximum. In order to see this let us consider such a point. There are four possible behaviors of the curve—unless Δ_z is either 0 or N, which we shall exclude—

† It must be noted that the time scales in the two parts of Fig. 53 are different so that this condition could be realized.

which are illustrated by the following four sequences of ordinates (see Fig. 55):

$$\left.\begin{array}{ll} \alpha) & \Delta_z - 2 \rightarrow \Delta_z \rightarrow \Delta_z - 2 \\ \beta) & \Delta_z - 2 \rightarrow \Delta_z \rightarrow \Delta_z + 2 \\ \gamma) & \Delta_z + 2 \rightarrow \Delta_z \rightarrow \Delta_z - 2 \\ \delta) & \Delta_z + 2 \rightarrow \Delta_z \rightarrow \Delta_z + 2 \end{array}\right\} \quad \text{(A1.408)}$$

The relative probabilities for those four sequences can be found from equations (A1.407), and we have

$$p_\alpha : p_\beta : p_\gamma : p_\delta = \frac{N + \Delta_z}{N - \Delta_z} : 1 : 1 : \frac{N - \Delta_z}{N + \Delta_z}. \quad \text{(A1.409)}$$

We see that the continuous increase (β) and the continuous decrease (γ) are equally probable, and that the maximum (α) and minimum (δ) are respectively the most and the least likely. The higher Δ_z, the more pronounced is the preference for a maximum.

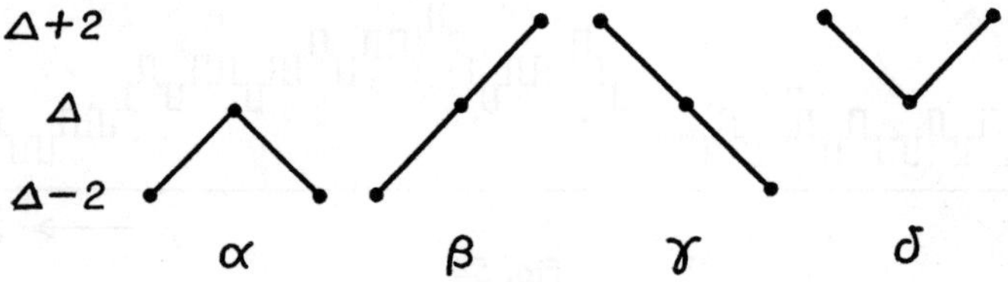

Fig. 55

Finally, let us find the relative probability for the occurrence of an ordinate Δ_z. One can calculate this probability $p(\Delta_z)$ by remarking that a certain situation with given numbers P and Q can be imagined to be obtained by the tossing of a coin where heads entail putting a ball in urn A and tails putting a ball in urn B. Since there are altogether N balls, $p(\Delta_z)$ is equal to the probability of getting P $(=\frac{1}{2}N + \frac{1}{2}\Delta_z)$ heads out of N throws, or

$$p(\Delta_z) = (\tfrac{1}{2})^N \binom{N}{\frac{1}{2}N + \frac{1}{2}\Delta_z}. \quad \text{(A1.410)}$$

If we compare $p(\Delta_z + 2)$ with $p(\Delta_z)$, we get

$$\frac{p(\Delta_z + 2)}{p(\Delta_z)} = \frac{N - \Delta_z}{N + \Delta_z + 2}. \quad \text{(A1.411)}$$

We see both from equation (A1.410) and from equation (A1.411) that the higher the ordinate, the less often it occurs.

Summarizing the results about the Δ_z-curve which we have just obtained, we see the following.

a) The sequence $\Delta_z \rightarrow \Delta_z - 2$ is just as frequent as the sequence $\Delta_z - 2 \rightarrow \Delta_z$.

b) However, both are much more frequent than the sequence $\Delta_z \rightarrow \Delta_z + 2$.

c) As soon as Δ_z reaches an appreciable value, the Δ_z-curve will decrease as a rule.

d) This last statement is true whether we are reading the complete (i.e., infinite) Δ_z-curve from left to right or vice versa.

e) *Every* ordinate occurs and continues to occur. For very large values of N and Δ_z, however, the relative occurrence is small, and given by the Laplace distribution,

$$p(\Delta_z) \backsim \sqrt{\frac{2}{\pi N}}\, e^{-\frac{\Delta_z^2}{2N}}. \qquad \textbf{(A1.412)}$$

From points (a) and (c) we see that although the sequence is reversible, this does not necessarily imply an invalidation of the H-theorem. The situation is different, however, as far as the quasi periodicity (point [e]) is concerned. We shall return to that point presently.

We return now to the H-curves themselves. We wish especially to consider what assumptions must be made in order to arrive at the conclusions of the H-theorem. It must be remarked here that these assumptions were only implicitly made in Boltzmann's own treatment of the statistical approach to the H-theorem and that the Ehrenfests were the first to state them explicitly.

The H-theorem is necessary to prove that the Maxwell-Boltzmann distribution is the equilibrium distribution. As we saw in Chapter II, the Maxwell-Boltzmann distribution is that one where the N_i are given by the equations

$$N_i = Ae^{-\mu\epsilon_i}, \qquad \textbf{(A1.413)}$$

where A and μ are two constants, and where ϵ_i is a representative energy corresponding to the cell ω_i. The first step in proving that the Maxwell-Boltzmann distribution is the equilibrium distribution is the proof of the following statement (compare[a] on p. 344).

I. Consider all situations $\mathbf{Z}$ of a given energy E, where

$$E = E(\mathbf{Z}) = \Sigma N_i\epsilon_i. \qquad \textbf{(A1.414)}$$

Of all the $\mathbf{Z}$-stars, the one corresponding to the Maxwell-Boltzmann distribution will have the largest volume.

Secondly, $W(\mathbf{Z})$ will decrease rapidly as soon as the N_i differ appreciably from the values given by equation (A1.413).

The first part of I was proved in §3 of Chapter II and we refer to the literature for a proof of the second part.†

At this point we must draw attention to the difference between the two equations

$$E(\mathbf{Z}) = E, \tag{A1.415}$$

and

$$E(p,q) = E. \tag{A1.416}$$

The first equation selects from Γ-space a $2sN$-dimensional region consisting of all the **Z**-stars which satisfy equation (A1.414). Equation (A1.416), however, is the equation of a $2sN - 1$ dimensional hypersurface in Γ-space which we shall call henceforth an *energy surface.* If we are considering a completely isolated system, its representative point in Γ-space would always stay on such an energy surface.

If we do not heed the difference between the equations (A1.415) and (A1.416), I leads easily to the following statement, which has, however, never been proved.

> II. On each energy surface the "area" (of $2sN - 1$ dimensions) corresponding to the Maxwell-Boltzmann distribution will be much larger than the areas corresponding to appreciably different distributions.

If we denote by $W_E(\mathbf{Z})$ the area cut out of the energy surface by a **Z**-star, assumption II is often put in the form

$$W_E(\mathbf{Z}) = c_1 W(\mathbf{Z}), \tag{A1.417}$$

where c_1 is a constant. Of course, assumption II follows from equation (A1.417), but is a slightly weaker statement.

The next step consists of assuming that the time $t(\mathbf{Z})$ spent by the representative point on $W_E(\mathbf{Z})$ will be proportional to $W_E(\mathbf{Z})$, or

$$t(\mathbf{Z}) = c_2 W_E(\mathbf{Z}), \tag{A1.418}$$

where c_2 is another constant.

Combining equations (A1.417) and (A1.418) we see that $t(\mathbf{Z})$ is now proportional to $W(\mathbf{Z})$‡ and that the time average $\widetilde{G}$ of a function $G(p,q)$ of the p_k and q_k, which is defined by the equation

$$\widetilde{G} = \lim_{\substack{T_1 \to -\infty \\ T_2 \to +\infty}} \frac{1}{T_2 - T_1} \int_{T_1}^{T_2} G(p,q)\,dt, \tag{A1.419}$$

will now be given by the equation

$$\widetilde{G} = \frac{\sum_{\mathbf{Z}} G(\mathbf{Z}) W(\mathbf{Z})}{\sum_{\mathbf{Z}} W(\mathbf{Z})} \cdot \tag{A1.420}$$ §

From equation (A1.420) the following statement can be proved.

† See, e.g., R. v. Mises, Wahrscheinlichkeitsrechnung, Leipzig-Vienna, 1931, §13.4. The proof for the simplified case of a monatomic gas in a field-free volume is given by Jeans (The Dynamical Theory of Gases, Cambridge 1921, §§43 to 49).

‡ It must be remarked here that Einstein (Ann. Physik, **33**, 1275, 1910) assumed directly the proportionality of $t(\mathbf{Z})$ and $W(\mathbf{Z})$.

§ By combining equations (A1.417) and (A1.420) we obtain equation (5.705). It

III. If the history of a system is followed in time, the Maxwell-Boltzmann distribution will be realized most of the time, and the chance for observing another distribution is so small that the Maxwell-Boltzmann distribution is the same as the average distribution.

The transition from I to III follows—apart from the proof of II—straightforwardly, if we may assume the validity of equation (A1.418), which implies the assumption that any orbit of a representative point in Γ-space will pass in time through *every* point of the energy surface. Systems of which the orbits satisfy this requirement are called *ergodic* systems. However, we shall see in the next section that ergodic systems do not exist, and then there exists definitely a gap between II and III. It is the aim of the H-theorem to fill this gap. If III were valid, the H-theorem follows immediately, since a distribution deviating from the equilibrium distribution at one moment will most probably tend to change toward that distribution which is most often realized, that is, toward the Maxwell-Boltzmann distribution. And the other way round, if the H-theorem is correct, the average distribution will be the Maxwell-Boltzmann distribution, since any other distribution will tend to it, and thus the system will spend most of its time in the Maxwell-Boltzmann distribution.

Instead of III we now have to prove the following:

IV. The step function $H(\mathbf{Z},t)$ will most of the time be in the immediate neighborhood of its minimum value $H_{\min}$ and only relatively seldom will there occur appreciable deviations from $H_{\min}$. Secondly, if H_1 is a value which is appreciably larger than $H_{\min}$ the relative periods during which the step function is above H_1 will decrease very steeply with increasing H_1.

If we consider the H-curve instead of the step function, IV can be stated more stringently, as follows:

V. a) If H_1 is much larger than $H_{\min}$ the H-curve will practically always go downward from H_1.

b) This will be true whether we read the H-curve from $t = -\infty$ to $t = +\infty$ or from $t = +\infty$ to $t = -\infty$.

c) The H-curve is practically always in the immediate neighborhood of $H_{\min}$.

This behavior was exemplified by the Δ_z-curve discussed at the beginning of this section. It would be a valuable step forward if this behavior could be proved for a more physical model.†

As long as we are considering one system with its corresponding H-curve, higher values of H will be reached over and over again in accordance with Poincaré's quasi-periodic movement. However, since only

may be remarked at this moment that the idea of the character of the equilibrium distribution as the *average* distribution is assumed from the start in the Darwin-Fowler method (see Appendix IV).

† Mr. C. D. Green is at present engaged in considering the H-curve of some simplified models. The first model considered was a one-dimensional version of the model considered in §2 (see D. ter Haar and C. D. Green, Proc. Phys. Soc. (London), **A66,** 153, 1953). In two papers in course of publication Green and ter Haar have considered the following three models: (a) the Ehrenfests' two-dimensional wind-wood model (see §2); (b) a one-dimensional model with a velocity distribution; and (c) a two-dimensional model with elastic scattering from circular Q-molecules.

finite time intervals are at our disposal in which measurements can be made, we must conclude that as far as actual observations are concerned only those situations can be considered to behave in a quasi-periodic manner whose period of recurrence is of the same order of magnitude or less than the periods available for our measurements. We may therefore conclude with Smoluchowski—who was especially interested in the case of Brownian motion of colloid particles where the situation is so much more easily treated mathematically—that a process appears irreversible if the initial state is characterized by an average time of recurrence which is large compared to the periods available for experimental observations.

In order to prove that a process starting from a large value of H will appear to be irreversible one must calculate first of all the transition probability $P(H_1,H_2)$ for a transition during a period τ from a value H_1 to a value H_2, and, secondly, the average time elapsed between two occurrences of a value H_1.†

It is shown by the Ehrenfests that one can even go a few steps further, albeit without proofs. Let the situation at the moment t_A be characterized by $\mathbf{Z}_A$ and let $H(\mathbf{Z}_A)$ be appreciably larger than $H_{\min}$. Due to the finite volume of the ω_i-cells there will be a continuum of points in Γ-space—which all belong to the corresponding $\mathbf{Z}_A$-star—all of which give rise to the same $\mathbf{Z}$. However, the ensuing motion in Γ-space will be different, and for each of these motions we can draw in an H,t-plane the corresponding H-curve. All these H-curves will pass through the point H_A, t_A, and one would like to prove the following statements.

VI. a) Let $\mathfrak{H}_n$ be the average of all H-values at $t_A + n\Delta t$ starting from H_A at t_A. The dispersion of the H-values around $\mathfrak{H}_n$ will then be very small.‡

b) The sequence $\mathfrak{H}_1, \mathfrak{H}_2, \cdots, \mathfrak{H}_n \cdots$ may be called the $\mathfrak{H}$-curve. This $\mathfrak{H}$-curve will decrease monotonically from $H(\mathbf{Z}_A)$ until it reaches $H_{\min}$ and will never leave $H_{\min}$ again.

c) By far the most of the H-curves will follow the $\mathfrak{H}$-curve very closely for an appreciable period, but practically none of them will follow the $\mathfrak{H}$-curve at all times.§

† This kind of calculation is at present being considered by Mr. C. D. Green for some simplified models (see ter Haar and Green, *loc. cit.*). The case of Brownian motion has been discussed in detail by Chandrasekhar (Revs. Modern Phys., **15**, 1, 1943). The importance of Brownian motion for our present discussion lies in the fact that it demonstrates *ad oculos* the occurrence of fluctuations as a physical phenomenon.

‡ One should define "average" and "dispersion" at this moment. The average is defined by the equation

$$\mathfrak{H}_n = \frac{1}{W(\mathbf{Z}_A)} \int H d\Omega, \qquad \textbf{(A1.421)}$$

where the integration extends over the whole of the $\mathbf{Z}_A$-star and where H must be taken at $t_A + n\Delta t$. The dispersion is defined in an analogous way. We refer to the Ehrenfests for a more detailed discussion of the reasons for this choice of average (see especially their footnote 170; compare also our footnote on p. 380).

§ The last part of this sentence must here be understood in this sense: "The points of the $\mathbf{Z}_A$ star which correspond to H-curves which follow the $\mathfrak{H}$-curve for all times form at most a set of zero measure."

Let us now discuss in how far there can be a connection between our present discussion and the Stosszahlansatz. A system which satisfies the Stosszahlansatz will, starting from a situation $\mathfrak{H}_A$, after a period Δt have reached a new situation, say $\mathbf{Z}_1$, after $2\Delta t$ $\mathbf{Z}_2$, and so on. The $\mathbf{Z}$-curve, or as the Ehrenfests call it, the *H-theorem curve,* will decrease monotonically from H_A. This follows immediately from our previous considerations, since dH/dt is always nonpositive if the Stosszahlansatz applies. The statistical form of the H-theorem then culminates in the following statement.

VII. The H-theorem curve and the $\mathfrak{H}$-curve are identical.

If one accepts the statistical discussion of the H-theorem to be more to the point than the kinetical discussion, the question arises as to the place of the Stosszahlansatz in this discussion. This point has been examined by Boltzmann, who arrived at the following conclusions without, however, basing them on a rigorous deduction.

a) The Stosszahlansatz gives us for any time interval Δt the most probable number of collisions, and hence leads to the most probable value of dH/dt.

b) The actual number of collisions and the actual value of dH/dt will show fluctuations around these most probable values.†

One might ask why we must return to the Stosszahlansatz and whether the two points (a) and (b) are not implicitly contained in our previous arguments. The answer is that there is still room for a more detailed discussion, since due to the finite size of the cells ω in phase space it is necessary to specify more accurately the coordinates of two molecules if one wishes to ascertain whether or not these two molecules are going to collide in the next time interval Δt. Apart from giving $\mathbf{Z}_A$ one must also indicate the way in which the molecules are grouped in order that the number of collisions between t_A and $t_A + \Delta t$ may be completely determined. In this way the $\mathbf{Z}_A$-star will decompose into several regions, corresponding to the various *groupings* of the molecules. That grouping which corresponds to the largest volume in Γ-space may be called the *Jeans-grouping,* because Jeans has investigated this problem in so much detail. One then hopes that the following situation will be realized.

VIII.‡ Practically the whole volume of the $\mathbf{Z}_A$-star corresponds to the Jeans-grouping or to groupings which are practically identical and only a negligible volume in Γ-space corresponds to appreciably different groupings. Secondly, the Jeans-grouping will lead during Δt exactly to the number of collisions given by the Stosszahlansatz.

Even if conclusion VIII is accepted, there still is a gap between it and

---

† There is a certain amount of mixing of the two terms "Stosszahlansatz" and "assumption of molecular chaos." Jeans keeps these two ideas strictly separated, although even he sometimes uses the second one when referring to the Stosszahlansatz. The Ehrenfests suggest that in Boltzmann's work the "assumption of molecular chaos" (Hypothese der molekularen Unordnung) refers only to the fluctuations in the number of collisions, but not to its most probable value.

‡ Our numbering of the important points in the development of the discussion follows mainly that of the Ehrenfests except that their VIII and IX are our X and XI and vice versa.

the result we wish to obtain, namely, that H will be a uniformly decreasing function. In order to arrive at this last result we must consider more carefully the history of the various points in Γ-space which all belong to the same $\mathbf{Z}_A$-star. During the time interval t_A, $t_A + \Delta t$ we may expect that the probability that the number of collisions is given by the Stosszahlansatz is very nearly equal to 1. However, if we consider at t_B all the points which at t_A make up the $\mathbf{Z}_A$-star, these points will now form part of many stars, say, $\mathbf{Z}_B'$, $\mathbf{Z}_B''$, etc. Furthermore, each of these stars will only partly be made up of points which at t_A belonged to the $\mathbf{Z}_A$-star. In order that not only during the interval t_A, $t_A + \Delta t$, but during any interval the number of collisions will be given with a probability practically equal to unity by the Stosszahlansatz we must make the following additional assumption.

IX. The fraction of points belonging to the different groupings is the same in $\mathbf{Z}_A$ as in each of the point sets of the $\mathbf{Z}_B'$, $\mathbf{Z}_B''$, etc. which at t_A were part of $\mathbf{Z}_A$.

This last assumption has often been questioned. Burbury, for instance, expected to see a certain amount of correlation between velocities of neighboring atoms.

We have now reached the end of the discussion of the statistical H-theorem, but before we start a discussion of the ergodic theorem, it may be good to consider for a moment the relations between the situation as we can in principle define it (e.g., by giving the N_i) and the situation as it is determined by actual observations. As in all physical phenomena, the interpretation of an experiment consists of the identification of the observed change of situation with the calculated change of a particular model. In a statistical theory one must even go one step further and identify the observed change with the most probable change in a group (or ensemble) of models. In other words, one must make, often tacitly, the following assumption.

X. The actually observed evolution of our gaseous system from t_A onward is identical with the evolution shown by practically all the curves discussed on pages 349–353.

However, even so, we still have not really obtained a relation between our models and the actual observations. By an observation we determine the "observable" situation† which consists of a determination—usually rather rough—of a few observables such as pressure, density, temperature, mean velocity, and so on. As discussed in Part B, the fact that the "observable" situation is determined by so many fewer quantities than the completely determined situation enables us to introduce with great success the concept of ensembles (compare also §1). However, if we wish to relate the results discussed in this section with the evolution of an "observable" situation, we must make one more assumption.

XI. Of all the situations $\mathbf{Z}$ corresponding to the same "observable" situation $\mathbf{S}$ there will be one such that it and the $\mathbf{Z}$ which are practically the same take up a very much larger volume in Γ-space than all the other $\mathbf{Z}$ belonging to $\mathbf{S}$ together.

† Called by the Ehrenfests *der "sichtbare" Zustand*, and hence denoted by $\mathbf{S}$.

§5. **The Ergodic and Quasi-Ergodic Theorems.** Instead of following the difficult and complicated path of the H-theorem, it was thought at one time that one might prove in a straightforward way the following theorem.

> The average behavior of a system of independent particles will correspond to the Maxwell-Boltzmann distribution. The average is here the time average taken over an infinite period.

Boltzmann was led to this theorem by the following reasoning. If a closed system starts from a nonequilibrium situation, it will soon reach equilibrium and will henceforth stay in an equilibrium state. Hence the time averages of phase functions, when taken over sufficiently long periods, will correspond to their values in an equilibrium state.

In order to prove the above theorem one calculates the time averages of all functions $\varphi(p,q)$ which together determine the distribution and compares these with their values corresponding to a Maxwell-Boltzmann distribution. Boltzmann calculated the time average $\tilde{\varphi}$, which is defined by the equation (compare equation [A1.419])

$$\tilde{\varphi} = \lim_{T\to\infty} \frac{1}{2T}\int_{t-T}^{t+T} \varphi(p,q)dt, \tag{A1.501}$$

by using the method of introducing microcanonical ensembles (compare Chap. V, §7). A microcanonical ensemble corresponds to the following surface density $\sigma(p,q)$ on the energy surface $\mathfrak{S}$ corresponding to the energy E_0 of the microcanonical ensemble,

$$\sigma(p,q) = \frac{1}{Q(p,q)}, \tag{A1.502}$$

where $Q(p,q)$ is given by the equation

$$Q = \sqrt{\sum_{k=1}^{sN}\left[\left(\frac{\partial\mathcal{H}}{\partial p_k}\right)^2 + \left(\frac{\partial\mathcal{H}}{\partial q_k}\right)^2\right]}, \tag{A1.503}$$

if $\mathcal{H}$ is the Hamiltonian of the system.

According to Liouville's theorem the density in Γ-space is invariant if one follows the representative points along their orbits. Consider now a volume element lying between two neighboring energy surfaces (corresponding to E_0 and $E_0 + \delta E$). This volume element will retain its extension if we follow its points along their orbits. Since the extension is given by the expression $d\mathfrak{S} \cdot \delta N$, where $d\mathfrak{S}$ is a surface element on the energy surface and δN the distance between the two energy surfaces, and since δN will be proportional to $1/Q$, we see that $d\mathfrak{S}$ will vary as Q. In this way the number of points inside a fixed surface element ($= \sigma \cdot d\mathfrak{S}$) will remain constant in time if we choose σ according to equation (A1.502). Hence the surface density given by equation (A1.502) corresponds to a stationary ensemble with a fixed energy, or a microcanonical ensemble.

The average $\overline{\overline{\varphi}}$ of a function $\varphi(p,q)$ taken over the ensemble is now given by the equation

$$\overline{\overline{\varphi(p,q)}} = \frac{\int \varphi\sigma d\mathfrak{S}}{\int \sigma d\mathfrak{S}}, \tag{A1.504}$$

where the integrals are extended over the whole of $\mathfrak{S}$.

In order to prove that $\overline{\overline{\varphi}}$ and $\widetilde{\varphi}$ are the same we put

$$\overline{\overline{\varphi}} = \widetilde{\overline{\overline{\varphi}}} = \overline{\overline{\widetilde{\varphi}}} = \widetilde{\varphi}, \tag{A1.505}$$

where $\widetilde{\overline{\overline{}}}$ and $\overline{\overline{\widetilde{}}}$ stand for the time average of the system average and the system average of the time average, respectively. The first equality follows immediately from the fact that we are dealing with a stationary ensemble. The second equality follows because of the interchangeability of averages. However, the last equality has still to be proved. It follows straightforwardly if we assume that $\widetilde{\varphi}$ is the same for all systems in the ensemble.

This last assumption can be proved if the system is *ergodic.*† A system is ergodic if the orbit of its representative point in Γ-space taken from $t = -\infty$ to $+\infty$ passes through *all* points of the energy surface. One sees immediately the following consequences of ergodicity. Since each orbit passes through all points of $\mathfrak{S}$ and since the orbit passing through a point is uniquely determined by that point, we see that *all* orbits on $\mathfrak{S}$ are the same. The only difference lies in the moment at which a certain point is passed (different values of c_{2sN} in equation [5.104], see p. 100). We get thus for all orbits the same value of $\widetilde{\varphi}$, and equation (A1.505) is proved. Since we know how to calculate $\overline{\overline{\varphi}}$ (see, e.g., Chapter V), we have found a way of obtaining $\widetilde{\varphi}$.

It may be mentioned here that Boltzmann derived a formula which contains more information than equation (A1.504) and from which this equation follows. He wrote down the relative time dt spent by a representative point within a surface element $d\mathfrak{S}$, as follows,

$$\lim_{T\to\infty} \frac{dt}{T} = \frac{\sigma d\mathfrak{S}}{\int \sigma d\mathfrak{S}}, \tag{A1.506}$$

† From ἔργον = work (used here as "energy"; cf. the erg as unit of energy) and ὁδός = path: the orbit passes through every point of the energy surface. This name was introduced by Boltzmann (J. f. Math., **100**, 201, 1887).

from which in principle one can also calculate the frequency of non-equilibrium situations.

Our problem is now reduced to showing that most systems are ergodic. However, one can easily show as follows that it is unlikely that any system is ergodic. We remarked in Chapter V that the equations of motion possess $2sN$ integrals, one of which is the total energy of the system (c_1 in equation [5.104], see p. 100) and one of which fixes the time scale along the orbit (c_{2sN}). By choosing a point on the energy surface, we fix the values of the $2sN - 2$ other integrals. If we now choose the same value for c_1, but different values for $c_2, c_3 \cdots, c_{2sN-1}$ we shall still find a point on the same energy surface, but this second point can never be reached from the first point, since the values of most of the integrals of motion are different. It would appear that this argument shows decisively the impossibility of ergodic systems. However, in order to clinch this matter one still must consider whether or not the values of the $2sN - 2$ integrals $c_2, c_3, \cdots, c_{2sN-1}$ could be constant almost everywhere on the energy surface. One would immediately counter that this would seem to be extremely unlikely, but for a complete proof of the impossibility of ergodic systems this last point must be cleared up. A really watertight proof was given by Plancherel, who showed that the points of an orbit form a set of measure zero on the energy surface the measure of which itself is not zero.†

Once it was realized that ergodic systems did not exist, it was tried to show that most systems are *quasi-ergodic*, that is, that the orbit on $\mathfrak{S}$ will come arbitrarily close to all points of $\mathfrak{S}$. However, for a quasi-ergodic system, equation (A1.505) will not necessarily hold, and one has not really gained anything unless one introduces equation (A1.506) as an additional assumption for which there is no a priori reason.

Even if equation (A1.505) is proved, and we shall see at the end of this section that it can be proved, if we make an assumption about the nature of the systems considered which is probably well justified, there are still reasons to prefer the truly statistical approach of the preceding section to the approach via the ergodic theorem or, at any rate, to discuss the two

† The measure of a point set $\mathfrak{M}$ on $\mathfrak{S}$ is defined as follows (see, e.g., P. R. Halmos, Measure Theory, New York 1950): Let $f(P)$ be a function which is 1, if P belongs to $\mathfrak{M}$ and which is 0 otherwise. The Lebesgue integral $\int f d\mathfrak{S}$, which extends over the whole of $\mathfrak{S}$, is then called the Lebesgue measure of $\mathfrak{M}$ on $\mathfrak{S}$.

It must be remarked here that the Ehrenfests (Enzyklopädie der mathematischen Wissenschaften, Vol. IV, Pt. 32, Leipzig-Berlin 1911, footnote 89) were fully aware of the improbability of ergodic systems and of the fact that the points of an orbit and all the points of the energy surface would have different measures (see also Lord Kelvin, Collected Works, Vol. IV, Cambridge 1891, p. 484). The Ehrenfests (*loc. cit.*, footnotes 90 and 93) also emphasized the fact that quasi-ergodic systems would not provide a solution of this difficulty.

different ways of approach separately. The reasons are, first of all, that while equation (A1.505) gives us information about the time average taken over an infinite period (compare equation [A1.501]), actual measurements are concerned with finite time intervals. Secondly, fluctuations are part of the picture given to us by nature (e.g., Brownian motion) and they should therefore be included in the discussion.†

The remainder of this section is mathematical and given only in order to make it easier for the reader to become acquainted with the development of the ergodic and quasi-ergodic theorems in classical mechanics. We shall sketch Fermi's proof that a large class of systems is quasi-ergodic and, secondly, discuss Birkhoff's proof of the ergodic theorem in its most modern form.

The proof that in general a dynamic system will be quasi-ergodic consists of two parts. We shall assume that the energy surface $\mathfrak{S}$ is simply connected and that $sN > 2$. The first part of the argument consists in proving that the energy surface is the only surface in Γ-space which has the property that any orbit starting from one of its points will always stay on the surface. Stated differently, there is no uniquely valued, time-independent, analytical integral other than the energy if we are dealing with systems called by Fermi "kanonische Normalsysteme." This theorem is a generalization of one formulated by Poincaré,‡ who proved that there did not exist any class of surface other than the energy surface such that an orbit remained on it. The proof of this theorem consists in showing that, if the orbit is completely confined to a surface $\mathcal{F}$, this surface will be the same as the energy surface $\mathfrak{S}$. We refer to Fermi's paper for a discussion of the conditions necessary for this theorem and only remark here that these conditions are satisfied by quite a large class of dynamical systems.

The second part of the proof follows easily. Let σ and σ^* be two arbitrary regions on $\mathfrak{S}$. If we can prove that there are orbits starting from a point of σ which pass through σ^*, we have proved that the system considered is quasi-ergodic, since we can choose both σ and σ^* arbitrarily small.

Let σ' be that part of $\mathfrak{S}$ which is covered by the orbits which start somewhere in σ. If σ' covers all of $\mathfrak{S}$, our point is proved. If σ' does not cover all of $\mathfrak{S}$, let σ'' be that part of $\mathfrak{S}$ which is not covered, and let $\mathcal{B}$ be the boundary surface between σ' and σ''. There can be no orbit which contains points both in σ' and in σ''. This can be seen as follows. Let P′ and P″ be points in σ' and σ'', respectively, and let us assume that there is an orbit passing through both P′ and P″, say at t' and t''. Since the solutions of the equations of motion are analytical functions, we can find small regions η' and η'' around P′ and P″, respectively, and lying completely in σ' and σ'', respectively, such that the orbit passing

† The two methods are more or less equivalent if we base our considerations on equation (A1.506) instead of on equation (A1.505).

‡ H. Poincaré, Les Méthodes nouvelles de la Mécanique céleste, Vol. I, Paris 1892, p. 233.

through an arbitrary point Q′ of η' at t' will pass through η'' at t''. Since, however, η' is part of σ' there will be points Q′ lying on an orbit which passes through σ, and we have arrived at a contradiction.

Let now P be a point on $\mathfrak{B}$ and once again P′ and P″ be points of σ' and σ'', respectively. If we consider orbits passing at t through P, P′, and P″, these orbits will pass at $t_1, t_2 \cdots$ through points P_1, P_1', P_1''; P_2, P_2', P_2''; etc., where P_1', $P_2' \cdots$ are all lying in σ' and P_1'', $P_2'' \cdots$ are all lying in σ''. We can choose P′ and P″ so close to P that P_1' and P_1'' also are close to P_1, P_2' and P_2'' are close to P_2, and so on. It then follows that P, P_1, $P_2 \cdots$ must all lie on $\mathfrak{B}$. However, we saw that there cannot exist a surface on which an orbit stays apart from the energy surface, and the only possible conclusion is that $\mathfrak{B}$ does not exist, or that σ' coincides with $\mathfrak{S}$. In that case, however, σ^* will be part of σ' and there will be orbits starting from σ which pass through σ^*. We have thus proved the existence of quasi-ergodic systems.

The modern development of the ergodic theorem started in 1931 with Birkhoff's investigations. We may remind ourselves that the ergodic theorem, in order to be effective, had to be stated as follows. Practically all orbits on $\mathfrak{S}$ pass through every region of $\mathfrak{S}$ of positive measure and *they remain in these regions for an average time equal to the ratio of this measure to that of* $\mathfrak{S}$ (assumption of equation [A1.506]). In 1922 Birkhoff† conjectured that "practically all" had to be understood in the sense of meaning that the exceptional orbits would form a set of measure zero on $\mathfrak{S}$. The next step forward was von Neumann's proof in 1931 of the so-called mean ergodic theorem.

This theorem states the following. Let P_t be the representative point of a system at t, and let $P_0 = P$. If $Z_{\alpha\beta}(P;\mathfrak{M})$ is the fraction of time spent by P_t in a region $\mathfrak{M}$ of $\mathfrak{S}$ during the time interval $\alpha \leqslant t \leqslant \beta$, then $Z_{\alpha\beta}(P;\mathfrak{M})$ will converge in the mean to a limit $Z(P;\mathfrak{M})$. Furthermore, if the group of transformations $P \rightarrow P_t$ is metrically transitive—which means that $\mathfrak{S}$ cannot be decomposed into two parts $\mathfrak{S}_1$ and $\mathfrak{S}_2$ both of positive measure and both invariant under every transformation of the group—then

$$Z(P;\mathfrak{M}) = \frac{\mathfrak{M}\mathfrak{M}}{\mathfrak{M}\mathfrak{S}} \tag{A1.507}$$

where $\mathfrak{M}\mathfrak{M}$ stands for the measure of $\mathfrak{M}$.

Birkhoff improved on this theorem by showing that for P almost everywhere on $\mathfrak{S}$ we have

$$\lim_{\beta-\alpha\rightarrow\infty} Z_{\alpha\beta}(P;\mathfrak{M}) = Z(P;\mathfrak{M}). \tag{A1.508}$$

As far as statistical mechanics is concerned, von Neumann's proof is sufficient, since one can now show that $\overline{\overline{\varphi}} = \widetilde{\varphi}$ and one can go even one step further, since von Neumann has shown how one can calculate for any $\epsilon > 0$ the lower limit of $\beta - \alpha$ so that

$$\left| \int_\alpha^\beta \varphi(p,q)dt - \int_{-\infty}^{+\infty} \varphi(p,q)dt \right| < \epsilon. \tag{A1.509}$$

† G. D. Birkhoff, Acta Math., **43**, 113, 1922.

Birkhoff's theorem goes further, however, since it proves that equation (A1.506) is true not only on the average, but is true for almost all orbits.

The question still to be decided is whether or not the group of transformations $P \rightarrow P_t$ is metrically transitive. It must be remarked here that this is certainly not true if any of the $2sN - 2$ integrals is single-valued. However, one can always reduce the accessible region of phase space by fixing the values of those integrals if they exist. We saw, moreover, that for the very general class of systems considered by Fermi in his proof of the quasi-ergodicity of these systems such integrals do not exist. Once this difficulty has been removed, the metrical transitivity remains as a final assumption, but we may remark that Oxtoby and Ulam† have made it probable that almost every group of continuous transformations is metrically transitive.

Before we discuss in the next section the situation in ensemble theory, let us briefly summarize the results of the last four sections. We started out to justify our considerations of Chapters I and II, where we identified the Maxwell-Boltzmann distribution as the equilibrium distribution. First of all, we tried to prove the unrestricted H-theorem. This would show that any nonequilibrium situation would always tend to become a Maxwell-Boltzmann distribution and that, on the other hand, once the Maxwell-Boltzmann distribution was attained, it would not change. We saw that the H-theorem in its unrestricted form could not be correct and we were led to consider the problem anew. The problem then split up into two separate problems. First of all, we were forced to consider what we meant when we talked about an equilibrium distribution and, secondly, we wanted to see the place which the H-theorem and the Stosszahlansatz now occupy in thermostatistical considerations. The first problem was considered by Boltzmann, and we saw that either we can consider the equilibrium distribution as being the most probable distribution—as was done in Chapters I and II—provided we give a suitable definition of the "probability" of a distribution, or we can consider it as the average distribution. "Average" can then be understood either in the sense of time average taken over a suitably long time interval, or in the sense of average over an ensemble of systems which all possess the same energy—and possibly the same values of a few other integrals of motion. In the present section (§5) we have seen that von Neumann's and Birkhoff's investigations have proved that these two averages lead to the same results. In this section we have also discussed the historical development of the ergodic and quasi-ergodic theorems. Let us once more stress here that the ergodic theorem makes a statement about the behavior of one isolated system which was, indeed, the situation studied in Part A. As soon as we see the

† I. Oxtoby and S. Ulam, Ann. of Math., **42**, 874, 1941.

terms "average" and "most probable" we realize that we must expect fluctuations. Section 4 dealt with this point and it was shown how one could treat the H-theorem and the Stosszahlansatz as giving statements about the most probable behavior of a system. In that section we followed the Ehrenfests in pointing out how one can on the one hand obtain a relation between observed behavior of physical systems and statistical theory and how on the other hand there still exist many gaps in the arguments establishing this relation.

§6. The *H*-Theorem in Ensemble Theory. In the preceding sections we considered isolated systems and saw that on the average such systems will tend toward an equilibrium situation, although one should still expect fluctuations. We also saw that we could identify the equilibrium situation with the most probable situation. We may remark here that if we prefer to base our statistical considerations on probability arguments as is done in the main part of this book, one can introduce certain assumptions about a priori probabilities and argue that the final justification of the theory lies in its power to explain and predict accurately the outcome of physical experiments. The assumptions made are respectively equal a priori probabilities for equal volumes in phase space (compare §7 of Chapter I, equation [1.713]; equation [2.302]) and equal a priori probabilities for each nondegenerate stationary state (compare §4 of Chapter III, §§1 and 2 of Chapter IV). These assumptions, which we shall further discuss in §8, seem feasible, but the discussion up to this moment was an attempt to give a justification other than that of the practical results obtained.

When we discussed the ensemble theory in Part B we remarked that the behavior of an actual physical system under observation, especially one with its temperature fixed by thermostatic means, corresponds much more closely to the behavior of the average system in a macrocanonical ensemble than to that of an isolated system. We may therefore ask in how far the considerations of the preceding sections are still valid in ensemble theory when we use the ensembles to calculate the time average of a phase function for an isolated system.

Consider an ensemble with density $\rho(p,q)$ and with index of probability η given by the equation (compare equation [5.121]),

$$\eta = \ln \rho. \tag{A1.601}$$

The density will be supposed to be normalized, or

$$\int_{\Gamma} \rho d\Omega = 1, \tag{A1.602}$$

where once again $\int_{\Gamma}$ indicates that the integration extends over the whole of Γ-space.

In this section we shall show that any density in Γ-space will tend to change in such a way that the density between two neighboring energy surfaces, corresponding to E and $E + \delta E$, will be approximately uniform. If we may assume a certain amount of interaction between the various systems in the ensemble, we can go even one step further and show that the density will approximate the density function of a macrocanonical ensemble. In the last case we can treat each of the original systems as a "molecule" of a large gaseous system containing the whole ensemble, and the approach toward a macrocanonical density distribution is the same as the approach to the Maxwell-Boltzmann distribution in an isolated system.†

In order to prove this approach to equilibrium we first of all introduce a function σ through the equation

$$\sigma = \bar{\eta} = \int_\Gamma \rho \ln \rho \, d\Omega. \tag{A1.603}$$

This function has the following properties:

a) If there are no restrictions on ρ, σ will be a minimum when $\rho =$ constant.

b) If ρ is restricted such that

$$\rho = 0, \quad \text{if} \quad \epsilon < E \quad \text{or} \quad \epsilon > E + \delta E, \tag{A1.604}$$

where ϵ is the energy of a system in the ensemble, σ will be a minimum when

$$\rho = \text{ct} \quad \text{for} \quad E \leqslant \epsilon \leqslant E + \delta E. \tag{A1.605}$$

c) If ρ is restricted by the condition

$$\int_\Gamma \epsilon\rho d\Omega = E, \tag{A1.606}$$

σ will be a minimum for the macrocanonical ensemble, that is, when ρ is given by the equation

$$\rho = e^{\frac{\psi - \epsilon}{\Theta}}. \tag{A1.607}$$

In order to prove these propositions we remark that the function $x \cdot e^x + 1 - e^x$ is positive for $x \neq 0$ and zero for $x = 0$. The propositions (a), (b), and (c) are now proved as follows:

a) Compare

$$\rho_1 = c \quad \text{and} \quad \rho_2 = \rho_1 e^{\Delta\eta}, \tag{A1.608}$$

where c is a constant and $\Delta\eta$ a function of the p's and q's. Because of the

† Compare also the considerations in §2 of Chap. V.

normalization of ρ we have

$$\int_\Gamma \rho_1 d\Omega = \int_\Gamma \rho_2 d\Omega. \tag{A1.609}$$

Furthermore, we have

$$\sigma_1 = \int_\Gamma \rho_1 \ln \rho_1 d\Omega, \qquad \sigma_2 = \int_\Gamma \rho_2 \ln \rho_2 d\Omega, \tag{A1.610}$$

and for $\sigma_2 - \sigma_1$ we get

$$\begin{aligned}\sigma_2 - \sigma_1 &= \int_\Gamma (\rho_2 \ln \rho_2 - \rho_1 \ln \rho_1) d\Omega \\ &= \int_\Gamma \rho_1 [\Delta\eta e^{\Delta\eta} + 1 - e^{\Delta\eta}] d\Omega \geqslant 0.\end{aligned} \tag{A1.611}$$

The last integral is obtained by adding to the first integral $\int_\Gamma (1 - \ln \rho_1)(\rho_1 - \rho_2) d\Omega = (1 - \ln \rho_1) \int_\Gamma (\rho_1 - \rho_2) d\Omega = 0.$ The first equality holds since $\rho_1 = c$ and the second one follows in virtue of equation (A1.609).

b) The proof is the same as sub (a), the only difference being that in this case the integration is not over the whole of Γ-space, but only over that part of Γ-space which is confined between the two energy surfaces corresponding to $\epsilon = E$ and $\epsilon = E + \delta E$, respectively.

c) We now must compare two distributions for which, respectively,

$$\eta_1 = \frac{\psi - \epsilon}{\Theta} \quad \text{and} \quad \eta_2 = \frac{\psi - \epsilon}{\Theta} + \Delta\eta = \eta_1 + \Delta\eta. \tag{A1.612}$$

From equations (A1.606) and (A1.609) we now have

$$\int_\Gamma \epsilon e^{\eta_1} d\Omega = \int_\Gamma \epsilon e^{\eta_2} d\Omega = E, \tag{A1.613}$$

and

$$\int_\Gamma e^{\eta_1} d\Omega = \int_\Gamma e^{\eta_2} d\Omega = 1, \tag{A1.614}$$

while σ_1 and σ_2 are given by the equations

$$\sigma_1 = \int_\Gamma \eta_1 e^{\eta_1} d\Omega, \qquad \sigma_2 = \int_\Gamma \eta_2 e^{\eta_2} d\Omega. \tag{A1.615}$$

One easily finds for $\sigma_2 - \sigma_1$ the expression

$$\sigma_2 - \sigma_1 = \int_\Gamma e^{\eta_1} (\Delta\eta e^{\Delta\eta} + 1 - e^{\Delta\eta}) d\Omega \geqslant 0. \tag{A1.616}$$

The right-hand side is obtained by adding to $\int_\Gamma (\eta_2 e^{\eta_2} - \eta_1 e^{\eta_1}) d\Omega$ the integral $\int_\Gamma \left\{ \left(\frac{\psi}{\Theta} + 1 \right) (e^{\eta_1} - e^{\eta_2}) + \frac{\epsilon}{\Theta} (e^{\eta_2} - e^{\eta_1}) \right\} d\Omega$ which, in virtue of equations (A1.613) and (A1.614), is zero. If we use the expressions (A1.612) for η_1 and η_2, equation (A1.616) follows.

We have now proved that σ is a minimum both for a microcanonical ensemble if the energy of each of the systems in the ensemble is the same and fixed, and for a macrocanonical ensemble if only the average energy of the systems in the ensemble is given. Comparing equation (A1.603) for σ with equation (A1.202) for Boltzmann's H, we might hope to be able to prove that $d\sigma/dt$ will always be negative and thus be able to show a tendency toward the establishment of canonical ensembles. We can, however, easily see as follows that σ does not change with time. Compare $\sigma(t'')$ with $\sigma(t')$ and let a representative point with coordinates $p_1', p_2', \cdots, p_{sN}', q_1', \cdots, q_{sN}'$ at $t = t'$ have the coordinates $p_1'', \cdots, p_{sN}'', q_1'', q_1'', \cdots, q_{sN}''$ at $t = t''$. In §1 of Chapter V we saw that the Jacobian J of the transformation from the coordinates at t' to the coordinates at t'' is equal to unity. We saw also that $\rho' = \rho(p_i', q_i'; t') = \rho(p_i'', q_i''; t'') = \rho''$ in virtue of Liouville's theorem (equation [5.122]). Hence we have

$$\sigma(t'') = \int_\Gamma \rho'' \ln \rho'' d\Omega'' = \int_\Gamma \rho' \ln \rho' J d\Omega'$$

$$= \int_\Gamma \rho' \ln \rho' d\Omega' = \sigma(t'). \qquad \textbf{(A1.617)}$$

Although we have just seen that σ is constant, there is still in a certain sense an approach to a stationary state. Let us first illustrate this by an example introduced by Gibbs. Consider a container with a liquid, say water, in which is put some coloring material and let us assume that this coloring material is nondiffusible and consists of colloidal particles. It is a well-known empirical fact that if we start from a state where the coloring material is unevenly distributed, practically any kind of stirring will produce a situation where the color distribution is, as far as our eye can see, uniform. That means that stirring will produce an "equilibrium" state. However, if we look at the system very closely, we will still find that, in microscopic volumes, part of the space is occupied by the water and part occupied by the colloidal particles. Although the coarse distribution is uniform, the finer distribution is still uneven.

From this example it follows that it might be advantageous to introduce apart from the *fine-grained density* ρ a *coarse-grained density* P (read "capital ρ") defined as follows: Divide Γ-space into finite, but small, cells

Ω_i and let P_i be the average of ρ taken over Ω_i, or

$$P_i = \frac{1}{W(\Omega_i)} \int_{\Omega_i} \rho d\Omega, \qquad \textbf{(A1.618)}$$

where $W(\Omega_i)$ is the volume of the cell Ω_i.

From the normalization of ρ (equation [A1.602]) one then gets

$$\sum_i P_i W(\Omega_i) = 1. \qquad \textbf{(A1.619)}$$

We can now introduce the coarse-grained density $P(p,q)$ by putting it constant in each cell Ω_i and equal to P_i. Equation (A1.619) can then be written in the form

$$\int_\Gamma P(p,q) d\Omega = 1. \qquad \textbf{(A1.620)}$$

Instead of σ we can now introduce a function Σ by the equation

$$\Sigma = \overline{H} = \sum_i P_i \ln P_i W(\Omega_i). \qquad \textbf{(A1.621)}\dagger$$

Using the coarse-grained density P, equation (A1.621) takes the form

$$\Sigma = \int_\Gamma P \ln P d\Omega \qquad \textbf{(A1.622)}$$

Since ln P is constant over each cell Ω_i and $\int_{\Omega_i} P d\Omega = P_i W(\Omega_i) = \int_{\Omega_i} \rho d\Omega$, we can also write equation (A1.622) in the form

$$\Sigma = \int_\Gamma \rho \ln P d\Omega, \qquad \textbf{(A1.623)}$$

and we see that

$$\Sigma = \overline{\ln P}. \qquad \textbf{(A1.624)}$$

The conclusions which we reached at the beginning of this section about σ will also hold for Σ, and one can, indeed, easily show, for instance, that in an ensemble of which the constituent systems have all energies within the range E, $E + \delta E$, Σ will be minimum if P is constant in the region between the two corresponding energy surfaces. And when there is a slight interaction between the different members of the ensemble, Σ will be minimum if P corresponds to a coarse-grained macrocanonical distribution.

We can now consider the change of Σ with time. Let us assume that we have made some observations about a physical system at $t = t'$. Since these observations will never give us the maximum possible information, we can construct an ensemble, the average properties of which at t'

† The symbol $\overline{H}$ can be read either as the ensemble average of Boltzmann's H or as the average of a function "capital η".

correspond to the observed properties of the system under observation at t'. Due to experimental limitations we shall at most be able to give $\rho(p,q)$ changing from one cell Ω_i to another, if we have chosen the size of the cells Ω_i in accordance with the experimental limitations, as we shall assume that we have done. In accordance with the principle of equal a priori probabilities for equal volumes in Γ-space, the fine-grained density will be chosen constant in each Ω_i and we have thus at t'

$$\rho' = \mathrm{P}', \tag{A1.625}$$

where the prime indicates values at t'. We have thus for Σ'

$$\Sigma' = \int_\Gamma \mathrm{P}' \ln \mathrm{P}' d\Omega = \int_\Gamma \rho' \ln \rho' d\Omega. \tag{A1.626}$$

If the situation at t' already corresponds to an equilibrium situation—either micro- or macrocanonical, according to whether or not interactions between the members of the ensemble are excluded from our considerations—the situation will be the same at a later time, since it is a stationary distribution (see §2 of Chapter V). Let us therefore assume that ρ' is not a stationary distribution. It can then easily be seen that at a later moment t''† equation (A1.625) will no longer hold and we have

$$\rho'' \neq \mathrm{P}''. \tag{A1.627}$$

This inequality is due to the fact that although ρ will stay constant in extensions in phase of unchanging magnitude Ω_i, the shape of these extensions will change and at a later moment each of the Ω_i will in general be covered by points which at t' belonged to many different cells.

We have now for Σ''

$$\Sigma'' = \int_\Gamma \mathrm{P}'' \ln \mathrm{P}'' d\Omega, \tag{A1.628}$$

and we can no longer replace P'' by ρ''. Comparing Σ' and Σ'' we have after some manipulations

$$\Sigma' - \Sigma'' = \int_\Gamma \mathrm{P}''[\Delta e^\Delta + 1 - e^\Delta] d\Omega > 0, \tag{A1.629}$$

where Δ is defined by the equation

$$\rho'' = \mathrm{P}'' e^\Delta. \tag{A1.630}$$

† It would be more general to say at *another* moment, leaving open the question whether t'' is later or earlier than t'. However, since we have set up our ensemble to represent a system which was observed at t', we shall be interested only in predictions which can actually be verified, that is, in times for which $t'' > t'$.

Equation (A1.629) is derived as follows:

$$\Sigma' - \Sigma'' = \int_\Gamma (\rho' \ln \rho' - \mathrm{P}'' \ln \mathrm{P}'')d\Omega$$
$$= \int_\Gamma (\rho'' \ln \rho'' - \rho'' \ln \mathrm{P}'')d\Omega$$
$$= \int_\Gamma [\rho'' \ln \rho'' - \rho'' \ln \mathrm{P}'' + \mathrm{P}'' - \rho'']d\Omega.$$

The second equality follows from equations (A1.617), (A1.622), and (A1.623), and the last equality from equations (A1.602) and (A1.620).

We see now that Σ'' will be less than Σ' in virtue of the fact that ρ'' and P'' are no longer everywhere equal. Comparing the present situation with the case of the coloring material in a liquid, we may expect that, as time goes on, ρ and P will differ more and more and that Σ will continually decrease until a distribution has been reached for which either

$$\left.\begin{aligned} \mathrm{P} &= \text{ct}, & E \leqslant \epsilon \leqslant E + \delta E, \\ \mathrm{P} &= 0, & \epsilon < E,\ E + \delta E < \epsilon, \end{aligned}\right\} \qquad \textbf{(A1.631)}$$

or

$$\mathrm{P} = Ae^{-\mu\epsilon}, \qquad \textbf{(A1.632)}$$

depending on the situation which we are studying.

Since Σ is minimum when the distributions (A1.631) or (A1.632) are reached, it will no longer decrease. If these distributions are reached we would, on observation, in general come to the conclusion that the state of the physical system would best be represented by a micro- or a macro-canonical ensemble. We have thus found a justification for using these ensembles to describe systems in thermodynamical equilibrium.

We saw that the decrease of Σ resulted from the fact that we came from a state where $\rho = \mathrm{P}$ to a state where ρ was no longer everywhere equal to P. The decrease of Σ thus corresponds to a decrease of the specific information about our physical system which we could obtain. Since Σ can be regarded to be a "coarse-grained" η, and since η was seen to be equal to the negative entropy (apart from a constant factor, see equation [5.309]), we see once more how *increase of lack of knowledge* corresponds to an increase in entropy (compare the discussion on pp. 160–162).

We may end this section by discussing briefly the time needed for approximate attainment of equilibrium. The Ehrenfests suggested that this time would be of the same order of magnitude as the Poincaré periods discussed in §3. It seems to us that they forgot to take account of the fact that as far as observational evidence is concerned we may treat all particles in the system as indistinguishable. If we consider once again the case discussed on page 342, we see that we may divide the period of about $10^{10^{19}}$ sec by 10^{18}! which leads to ordinary time intervals. There is, indeed, no reason for not assuming that the time necessary to reach approximate equilibrium will be of the order of ordinary relaxation times.

§7. The *H*-Theorem and Ergodic Theorem in Quantum Statistics. The situation in quantum statistics is very similar to that in classical statistics although some expressions simplify considerably. Again, one can study either the behavior of one system or that of a representative ensemble. We shall outline the situation in both cases. It will then be clear that the situation, although in many respects much simpler than in the classical case, has many points of similarity and that many of the gaps present in the classical discussion have their counterparts in the quantum mechanical case.

When we discussed the H-theorem in Chapter I we started the discussion by deriving an expression for the number of collisions per unit time which would remove molecules from two volume elements in velocity space ($d\mathbf{c}_1$ and $d\mathbf{c}_2$) and throw them into two other volume elements ($d\mathbf{c}_1{}'$ and $d\mathbf{c}_2{}'$). We must now set up an analogous expression for the number of "collisions" (or better transitions) which remove particles from two groups of states to two other groups of states. Following the discussion of Chapter IV we shall again assume that all energy states of the particles in the system can be put into groups consisting of Z_i states with a representative energy E_i. The number of particles in the group Z_i is denoted by N_i. Let $N_{ij\to i'j'}$ be the average number of transitions per unit time where the groups Z_i and Z_j each lose one particle while at the same time the groups $Z_{i'}$ and $Z_{j'}$ each gain one particle. Because of the energy conservation law $N_{ij\to i'j'}$ will only be appreciably different from zero if

$$E_i + E_j \approx E_{i'} + E_{j'}, \quad \textbf{(A1.701)}$$

where there is not necessarily a complete equality due to the uncertainty in energy because of the finite lifetime of the initial state (compare the discussion on p. 99). It is possible to prove that $N_{ij\to i'j'}$ satisfies the equation†

$$N_{ij\to i'j'} = A_{ij\to i'j'}N_iN_j(Z_{i'} + \alpha N_{i'})(Z_{j'} + \alpha N_{j'}) \quad \textbf{(A1.702)}$$

where α is a quantity distinguishing the three possible statistics—Boltzmann, Bose-Einstein, and Fermi-Dirac—as follows:

$$\left.\begin{aligned} \alpha_{\text{Bo}} &= 0, \\ \alpha_{\text{B.E.}} &= +1, \\ \alpha_{\text{F.D.}} &= -1. \end{aligned}\right\} \quad \textbf{(A1.703)}$$

† See, e.g., R. C. Tolman, The Principles of Statistical Mechanics, Oxford 1938, §100.

The quantity $A_{ij\to i'j'}$, which is a transition probability, satisfies the symmetry relation

$$A_{ij\to i'j'} = A_{i'j'\to ij} \tag{A1.704}$$

because of its relation with the matrix elements of a Hermitean operator.†

Using relation (1.717) on page 25 as a definition of H and using equations (4.305) to (4.307) (see p. 77) for $\ln W$, we see that we get for H the equation‡

$$H = \sum_j \left\{ \alpha Z_j \ln \frac{Z_j}{N_j} - (N_j + \alpha Z_j) \ln \left(\frac{Z_j}{N_j} + \alpha \right) \right\}. \tag{A1.705}$$

We can now easily calculate dH/dt. First of all, we evaluate dN_j/dt using equation (A1.702) and the result is

$$\frac{dN_j}{dt} = \sum_{i,i'j'} A_{ij\to i'j'} \{ N_{i'} N_{j'} (Z_i + \alpha N_i)(Z_j + \alpha N_j) - N_i N_j (Z_{i'} + \alpha N_{i'})(Z_{j'} + \alpha N_{j'}), \tag{A1.706}$$

where the summation is over all groups Z_i and over all possible pairs of groups $Z_{i'}$ and $Z_{j'}$ which for given Z_i and Z_j satisfy condition (A1.701). Also, we have made use of equation (A1.704) in writing down equation (A1.706).

From equation (A1.705) we have§

$$\frac{dH}{dt} = \sum_j \frac{dN_j}{dt} \ln \frac{N_j}{Z_j + \alpha N_j}, \tag{A1.707}$$

and substituting equation (A1.706) into equation (A1.707) we have

$$\frac{dH}{dt} = \sum_{i,j,i'j'} A_{ij\to i'j'} [N_{i'} N_{j'} (Z_i + \alpha N_i)(Z_j + \alpha N_j) - N_i N_j (Z_{i'} + \alpha N_{i'})(Z_{j'} + \alpha N_{j'})] \ln \frac{N_j}{Z_j + \alpha N_j}. \tag{A1.708}$$

Instead of summing separately over i and j we can sum over all pairs of

† See Tolman, *loc. cit.* It must be remarked here that in deriving equation (A1.704) it is necessary to use ensemble theory and to introduce the assumption of equal a priori probability and random a priori phases for the different constituent states in each group Z_i. Therefore, the discussion of the quantum mechanical H-theorem relating to one single system is to a certain extent self-contradictory, unless one does not try to justify equation (A1.704) and accepts it as the quantum mechanical analogy to the Stosszahlansatz, as is done by Pauli.

‡ In the case of Boltzmann statistics, H and $-\ln W$ differ by a term ΣN_j, which, however, is equal to the total number of particles and hence a constant.

§ Note that $\alpha_{\mathrm{B.E.}}{}^2 = \alpha_{\mathrm{F.D.}}{}^2 = 1$, $\alpha_{\mathrm{Bo}}{}^2 = 0$.

groups Z_i and Z_j; then we get instead of equation (A1.708) the result

$$\frac{dH}{dt} = \sum_{ij,i'j'} A_{ij\to i'j'}[N_{i'}N_{j'}(Z_i + \alpha N_i)(Z_j + \alpha N_j)$$

$$-N_iN_j(Z_{i'} + \alpha N_{i'})(Z_{j'} + \alpha N_{j'})] \ln \frac{N_iN_j}{(Z_i + \alpha N_i)(Z_j + \alpha N_j)}. \qquad \textbf{(A1.709)}$$

Interchanging ij with $i'j'$ should leave dH/dt unaltered. Taking the arithmetical mean of expression (A1.709) and the expression obtained by the interchange of ij and $i'j'$ and using once again equation (A1.704), we obtain the expression

$$\frac{dH}{dt} = \frac{1}{2} \sum_{ij,i'j'} A_{ij\to i'j'}[N_{i'}N_{j'}(Z_i + \alpha N_i)(Z_j + \alpha N_j)$$

$$-N_iN_j(Z_{i'} + \alpha N_{i'})(Z_{j'} + \alpha N_{j'})] \ln \frac{N_iN_j(Z_{i'} + \alpha N_{i'})(Z_{j'} + \alpha N_{j'})}{N_{i'}N_{j'}(Z_i + \alpha N_i)(Z_j + \alpha N_j)}, \qquad \textbf{(A1.710)}$$

the right-hand side of which is of the form $\Sigma A(q - p) \ln p/q$ and hence always negative, since $A_{ij\to i'j'}$ is by its very nature of transition probability always positive.†

We thus arrive at the result

$$\frac{dH}{dt} \leqslant 0. \qquad \textbf{(A1.711)}$$

Let us briefly discuss the differences between the result now and in the classical case. The present result is based upon equations (A1.702) and (A1.704) while the classical result was based on the Stosszahlansatz. Since equation (A1.702) gives us an expression involving transition *probabilities*, we see that we are immediately concerned with a *statistical* treatment and not with a kinetical treatment. This in turn means that the discussion here is as satisfactory or as unsatisfactory as that of §4 and that, in fact, the discussion of §4 can practically be translated word for word to apply to the quantum mechanical case. Equation (A1.704) involves the assumptions of equal a priori probabilities and random a priori phases for each nondegenerate state and corresponds to the assumption of equal a priori probabilities for equal volumes in Γ-space which underlies equations (A1.402) and (A1.403).

Let us now consider the case of quantum mechanical ensembles, once again restricting ourselves to petit ensembles. The ensemble is characterized by its *fine-grained* density matrix $\boldsymbol{\rho}$ (see Chapter VII) the matrix

† It must be remembered that $Z_i + \alpha N_i$ can never be negative, since in the Fermi-Dirac case ($\alpha = -1$) $N_i \leqslant Z_i$ because of the exclusion principle.

elements of which are given by the equations

$$\rho_{kl} = \langle a_k{}^* a_l \rangle_{\mathrm{Av}} = \frac{1}{N}\sum_{i=1}^{N} a_k{}^{i*} a_l{}^i, \tag{A1.712}$$

where N is the number of systems in the ensembles, where the quantum states are numbered according to a complete set of orthonormal functions φ_n, and where $a_k{}^i$ is determined by the equation

$$a_k{}^i = \int \varphi_k{}^* \psi^i d\epsilon, \tag{A1.713}$$

where ψ^i is the wave function describing the ith system.

The normalization of the density matrix is given by the equation

$$\mathrm{Tr}\,\boldsymbol{\rho} = \sum_k \rho_{kk} = 1. \tag{A1.714}$$

By analogy with equation (A1.603) for σ we can now introduce a σ given by the equation

$$\sigma = \mathrm{Tr}\,\boldsymbol{\rho} \ln \boldsymbol{\rho}. \tag{A1.715}$$

As in the preceding section we can show the following properties of σ by proofs which are analogous to the proofs given in §6.

a) Comparing the two density matrices

$$\rho_{kl}{}' = c\delta_{kl}, \qquad \rho_{kl}{}'' = ce^{\alpha_{kl}}, \tag{A1.716}$$

σ' will be smaller than σ''.

b) The same holds if equation (A1.716) is valid for only a limited choice of k and l and if for other values of k and l both $\rho_{kl}{}'$ and $\rho_{kl}{}''$ are zero. Taking as the φ_n the characteristic functions of the energy operator, we can choose our k and l, for instance, in such a way that the $\rho_{kl}{}'$ and $\rho_{kl}{}''$ are only different from zero if

$$E \leqslant \epsilon_k,\ \epsilon_l \leqslant E + \delta E, \tag{A1.717}$$

and $\boldsymbol{\rho}'$ will then correspond to a microcanonical ensemble.

c) Choosing again the φ_n to be the characteristic functions of the energy operator and fixing the average value of the energy as follows,

$$E = \mathrm{Tr}\,\boldsymbol{\rho}\mathcal{H} = \sum_{k,l} \rho_{kl} H_{lk} = \sum_k \rho_{kk}\epsilon_k, \tag{A1.718}$$

where $\mathcal{H}$ and H_{kl} are, respectively, the energy operator and its matrix elements, σ will be minimum when $\boldsymbol{\rho}$ is given by the equation

$$\rho_{kl} = \delta_{kl} e^{\frac{\psi - \epsilon_k}{\Theta}}. \tag{A1.719}$$

Once again we can easily see that σ will not change with time. Let one and two primes denote, respectively, the values of various quantities at t'

and t''. We then have

$$\sigma'' = \mathrm{Tr}\,\boldsymbol{\rho}'' \ln \boldsymbol{\rho}'' = \mathrm{Tr}\,\boldsymbol{\rho}' \ln \boldsymbol{\rho}' = \sigma'. \tag{A1.720}$$

We see that $\mathrm{Tr}\,\boldsymbol{\rho}'' \ln \boldsymbol{\rho}''$ equals $\mathrm{Tr}\,\boldsymbol{\rho}' \ln \boldsymbol{\rho}'$ by virtue of the fact that the transformation from $\boldsymbol{\rho}'$ to $\boldsymbol{\rho}''$ is a unitary transformation which leaves the trace invariant.

Since σ does not change with time we must consider as in the case of the classical ensemble theory a *coarse-grained* density **P**. We take as the complete orthonormal set φ_n the characteristic functions corresponding to the different stationary states of the system. Furthermore, we divide the stationary states into groups, as before, where now the grouping is in such a way that it corresponds to the inaccuracy of our observations. By means of our available observational methods we can discern between the different groups, but not within them. Let the groups consist of Z_i levels. We now define the coarse-grained density matrix by its matrix elements as follows:†

$$\mathrm{P}_{kl} = \frac{\delta_{kl}}{Z_i} \sum \rho_{ii}, \tag{A1.721}$$

where k belongs to Z_i and where the summation extends over all the states in the ith group.

From equations (A1.721) and (A1.714) it follows immediately that

$$\mathrm{Tr}\,\mathbf{P} = 1. \tag{A1.722}$$

Using **P** instead of ρ we can again define a quantity Σ by the equation

$$\Sigma = \mathrm{Tr}\,\mathbf{P} \ln \mathbf{P} = \sum_k \mathrm{P}_{kk} \ln \mathrm{P}_{kk}. \tag{A1.723}$$

As a result of equation (A1.721) we can also, if necessary, write equation (A1.723) in the form

$$\Sigma = \sum_k \rho_{kk} \ln \mathrm{P}_{kk}, \tag{A1.724}$$

as long as we are always working in the same representation.

Let us now assume that we have made observations on our system at t' which will give us the coarse-grained density **P**. In accordance with our basic assumption of equal a priori probabilities and random a priori phases we have at t' (compare the discussion in §8)

$$\boldsymbol{\rho}' = \mathbf{P}'. \tag{A1.725}$$

And for Σ' we have

$$\Sigma' = \mathrm{Tr}\,\mathbf{P}' \ln \mathbf{P}' = \mathrm{Tr}\,\boldsymbol{\rho}' \ln \boldsymbol{\rho}'. \tag{A1.726}$$

---

† Equation (A1.721) defines **P** by its matrix elements in the representation which is best suited to our experimental means. Its matrix elements in any other representation follow by the usual transformation rules.

If the situation at t' did not correspond to an equilibrium situation, ρ' would not be stationary and at a later time t'' equation (A1.725) would no longer hold, but we should have

$$\rho'' \neq \mathrm{P}''. \qquad \textbf{(A1.727)}$$

We can then derive the inequality

$$\Sigma'' < \Sigma' \qquad \textbf{(A1.728)}$$

in a way analogous to that leading to equation (A1.629). The discussion of (A1.728) is also completely parallel to the discussion of equation (A1.629) and will not be repeated here.

A different mode of approach to this problem is made by proceeding in a manner analogous to that which led to equation (A1.711). We shall give this discussion here too, since some of its results will be of interest in subsequent discussions.

Let P_i be the probability of finding a system of the ensemble in group Z_i, or

$$P_i = \sum_k \rho_{kk}, \qquad \textbf{(A1.729)}$$

where the summation extends over all states belonging to Z_i and where ρ_{kk} is the probability of finding a system in the kth state (compare equations [7.201] and [7.203]). The P_i are related to the P_{kk} by the relation (see equation [A1.721])

$$P_i = \sum_k \mathrm{P}_{kk} = Z_i \mathrm{P}_{kk}, \qquad \textbf{(A1.730)}$$

where P_{kk} on the right-hand side is one of the Z_i equal diagonal elements corresponding to the ith group.

In terms of the P_i we have for Σ,

$$\Sigma = \sum_i P_i \ln \frac{P_i}{Z_i}, \qquad \textbf{(A1.731)}$$

where now the summation extends over all groups Z_i.

Equation (A1.731) can be derived by introducing equation (A1.730) into equation (A1.723) and writing

$$\Sigma = \sum_i \sum_{k=1}^{Z_i} \frac{P_k}{Z_k} \ln \frac{P_k}{Z_k}.$$

The time derivative of Σ is given by the equation

$$\frac{d\Sigma}{dt} = \sum_i (\ln P_i - \ln Z_i) \frac{dP_i}{dt}. \qquad \textbf{(A1.732)}$$

In deriving equation (A1.732) we have used the fact that from equations (A1.714) and (A1.729) it follows that

$$\sum_i P_i = 1, \quad \text{or} \quad \sum_i dP_i/dt = 0.$$

We now need the expression for the average transition probability $N_{i\to j}$ from a group Z_i to a group Z_j, which is given by the equation†

$$N_{i\to j} = A_{i\to j} Z_j P_i. \tag{A1.733}$$

If we accept the assumptions of equal a priori probabilities and random a priori phases for the various states, it can be shown that

$$A_{i\to j} = A_{j\to i}. \tag{A1.734}$$

Using this equation it follows from equation (A1.733) that

$$\frac{dP_i}{dt} = \sum_j A_{i\to j}[Z_i P_j - Z_j P_i], \tag{A1.735}$$

and we finally get after a few manipulations (substituting equation [A1.735] into equation [A1.732] and taking the arithmetical mean of the ensuing expression and the expression obtained by interchanging i and j)

$$\frac{d\Sigma}{dt} = \tfrac{1}{2}\sum_{i,j} A_{i\to j}[P_j Z_i - P_i Z_j] \ln \frac{P_i Z_j}{P_j Z_i}. \tag{A1.736}$$

The right-hand side of equation (A1.736) is of the same form as the right-hand side of equation (A1.710) and hence is never positive.

Up to the present, we have discussed the quantum mechanical counterpart of the classical H-theorem where one is concerned with the probable behavior of a system and where one thus considers a large number of similar systems and discusses the behavior of the great majority of them. Although the tools used are different, the situation itself is about the same for the discussion of one system or for the discussion of an ensemble of systems. In the classical case we saw that there also existed a different mode of approach by use of the ergodic theorem. In its crudest form one assumed that all systems were ergodic and then proved that the time average of a phase function pertaining to a physical system was equal to the average taken over a representative microcanonical ensemble. The more refined and proper way is Birkhoff's, where one showed the equality of the two averages without having recourse to the assumption of ergodicity—which, as we saw, can never be justified. We can do the same in quantum statistics. An ergodic system is then defined in the following way.‡

† See, e.g., Tolman, *loc. cit.*, §99.

‡ See, e.g., P. Jordan, Statistische Mechanik auf Quantentheoretischer Grundlage, Braunschweig 1933, §2.2; J. E. and M. G. Mayer, Statistical Mechanics, New York 1940, p. 56; H. and B. S. Jeffreys, Methods of Mathematical Physics, Cambridge 1946, p. 152.

Consider all stationary states with energy levels lying in the interval

$$E - \Delta \leqslant \epsilon_k \leqslant E + \Delta. \tag{A1.737}$$

Let the system at $t = t_0$ be in the state k_0. All states which satisfy equation (A1.737) can now be divided into two groups, A and B, where A contains all the states which can be reached from the state k_0—be it sometimes only by devious routes—and where B contains the other states. If w_{kl} is the transition probability for the transition from state k to state l, we have clearly that for any combination of states a, b where a belongs to A and b to B

$$w_{ab} = 0. \tag{A1.738}$$

An ergodic system is now a system where group B is empty. If a system is ergodic, one can easily show that the probability $P(k)$ of finding the system at $t = \infty$ in the state k will be independent of k and given by the equation

$$P(k) = \frac{1}{n}, \tag{A1.739}$$

where n is the number of states in group A. From this it follows that the average time spent in any of the n states is the same as the average taken over group A, or over a representative microcanonical ensemble.

The proof of equation (A1.739) follows from the equation (see Jordan, *loc. cit.*)

$$\frac{dN_l}{dt} = -\sum_k N_l w_{lk} + \sum_k N_k w_{kl} = \sum_k w_{lk}(N_k - N_l),$$

where N_k is the number of systems of the representative ensemble in the kth state and where we have used the fact that $w_{kl} = w_{lk}$.

We have here a situation which is very much akin to that in classical statistics, and one must prove or disprove the existence of ergodic systems. A better approach is that of von Neumann, who gave the quantum mechanical version of Birkhoff's proof.

Von Neumann has shown that for any macroscopically measurable quantity the time average will be equal to the average taken over a suitably chosen microcanonical ensemble (compare equation [A1.505]) and, secondly, that its fluctuations are small.

He starts his discussion by pointing out that, notwithstanding the Heisenberg relations, all macroscopic observables† can be determined

† A macroscopic observable is a quantity which can be measured accurately with macroscopic means. Let A be a continuous variable which can take on any value between $-\infty$ and $+\infty$ and let macroscopic measurement be such that only the intervals $k \leqslant A < k + 1$ $(k = 0, \pm 1, \pm 2, \cdots)$ can be distinguished. In that case we define a function $f(x)$ by the equation

$$f(x) = k, \qquad k \leqslant x < k + 1 (k = 0, \pm 1, \pm 2, \cdots).$$

The macroscopic observable corresponding to the variable A will then be $f(A)$.

simultaneously:† "Bei einer makroskopischen gleichzeitigen Messung von Koordinate und Impuls (oder zwei anderen, quantenmechanisch nicht gleichzeitig messbaren Grössen) werden wirklich zwei physikalische Grössen gleichzeitig und genau gemessen, nur sind diese nicht genau Koordinate und Impuls. Es sind etwa die Stellungen von zwei Zeigern oder die Lagen von zwei Schwärzungen photographischer Platten—nichts hindert uns, diese gleichzeitig und beliebig genau auszumessen, nur ist ihre Kopplung mit den wirklich interessierenden physikalischen Grössen (q_k und p_k) etwas lose, und zwar ist für die naturgesetzlich notwendige Unschärfe dieser Kopplung gerade die Ungenauigkeitsrelation massgebend."

Since these macroscopic observations can be measured simultaneously, the corresponding operators should all commute, and it is possible to find a complete orthonormal set χ_k of which the members are characteristic functions of all the macroscopic observables. Since we are interested in macroscopic measurements we still must take into consideration the fact that we must not in general expect to be able to distinguish, with the observational means at our disposal, between all the different characteristic states but only between groups of them and we shall accordingly renumber the χ_k. We give each function two indices, χ_{ij}, where i is the number of the group and where j runs from 1 to z_i if z_i is the number of states in the ith group. Since the χ_{ij} are the characteristic functions of the observables and since states belonging to the same group cannot be distinguished, all χ_{ij} belonging to the same group (i.e., with the same i) must correspond to the same characteristic value for any of the macroscopic observables.

Let φ_n be the complete set of orthonormal functions given by the characteristic functions of the energy operator $\mathcal{H}$ and let an arbitrary function ψ be expanded in the φ_n as follows:

$$\psi = \sum_n a_n \varphi_n. \tag{A1.740}$$

We now assign to ψ an operator $\mathcal{R}(\psi)$ by the equation‡

$$R_{kl} = a_k a_l^*. \tag{A1.741}$$

From equations (A1.712) and (A1.741) we see that $\mathcal{R}$ is connected with the density matrix by the equation

$$\boldsymbol{\rho} = \frac{1}{N} \sum_i \mathcal{R}(\psi^i), \tag{A1.742}$$

† We do not have the space here to discuss this extremely important point in any detail, and we refer the reader both to von Neumann's paper (Z. Physik, **57**, 30, 1929) and to a discussion in a recent book by C. F. von Weizäcker (Zum Weltbild der Physik, 4th ed., Zürich 1949, pp. 80 ff.).

‡ Our notation is different from von Neumann's, since we have tried to keep our notation in accordance with the rest of the book and to use as far as possible similar symbols for similar quantities. In that way, our $\mathcal{R}$ is connected with $\boldsymbol{\rho}$, $\mathfrak{O}_i$ with the classical Ω_i, $\mathfrak{S}_i$ with the energy surface $\mathfrak{S}$, z_i with Z_i. Von Neumann's and our symbols are connected as follows:

v.N.'s symbols	$\mathbf{P}_\psi$	$\mathbf{E}_p$	$\boldsymbol{\Delta}_a$	s_p	S_a	$\omega_{\lambda,p}$	W_n	$\mathbf{U}$	N_a
our symbols	$\mathcal{R}(\psi)$	$\mathfrak{O}_i$	$\mathfrak{S}_i$	z_i	Z_i	χ_{ij}	ϵ_n	$\boldsymbol{\rho}$	n_i

where the sum is taken over all the members of the ensemble and where ψ^i is the wave function pertaining to the ith system in the ensemble.

Just as we can calculate all averages over the ensemble once $\boldsymbol{\rho}$ is given, so we can also determine all expectation values of the situation described by a wave function ψ once the corresponding operator $\mathcal{R}$ is given and, for instance, the expectation value $\langle G \rangle$ of an operator $\mathcal{G}$ will be given by the equation

$$\langle G \rangle = \operatorname{Tr} \mathcal{R}\mathcal{G}. \tag{A1.743}$$

We introduce now an operator $\mathcal{O}_i$ by the equation

$$\mathcal{O}_i = \sum_{j=1}^{z_i} \mathcal{R}(\chi_{ij}). \tag{A1.744}$$

From equations (A1.743) and (A1.744) and from the fact that all macroscopic observables have the same expectation values for any of the states in the ith group it follows that the operator $\mathcal{O}_i$ singles out the ith alternative group of states which can be discerned by macroscopic means. The relation between $\mathcal{O}_i/z_i$ and the ith group is the same as the relation between $\mathcal{R}(\psi)$ and ψ. Von Neumann calls $\mathcal{O}_i/z_i$, therefore, the quantum mechanical equivalent to the classical cells in Γ-space, Ω_i.

We have for the trace of $\mathcal{O}_i$ the equation

$$\operatorname{Tr} \mathcal{O}_i = \sum_{j=1}^{z_i} \operatorname{Tr} \mathcal{R} = z_i, \tag{A1.745}$$

and this trace gives us, therefore, the number of states in the ith group and hence a measure for the inaccuracy of the macroscopic measurement.

If $\mathcal{G}$ is the operator corresponding to one of the macroscopic observables, we can express $\mathcal{G}$ in terms of the $\mathcal{R}(\chi_{ij})$ and even in terms of the $\mathcal{O}_i$ as

$$\mathcal{G} = \sum_{i,j} G_i \mathcal{R}(\chi_{ij}) = \sum_i G_i \mathcal{O}_i, \tag{A1.746}^\dagger$$

where we have used the fact that all the χ_{ij} belonging to the same group will correspond to the same characteristic value G_i.

If $\mathcal{H}$ is the energy operator of the system with its characteristic functions φ_n and characteristic values ϵ_n, we have

$$\mathcal{H} = \sum_n \epsilon_n \mathcal{R}(\varphi_n), \tag{A1.747}^\dagger$$

but it is now not possible to express $\mathcal{H}$ in terms of the $\mathcal{O}_i$, since $\mathcal{H}$ is not a macroscopic observable, but the exact energy. However, we can divide the energy levels into groups Z_i which can be macroscopically distinguished and we can give each φ_n (and corresponding ϵ_n) two indices instead of one (φ_{ij} and ϵ_{ij}) where i numbers the group and where j runs from 1 to Z_i. Let us now construct a function which shows that the different groups Z_i can be distinguished macroscopically. We introduce

† Compare the discussion in Chapter XII, p. 282, where we also expressed an operator in terms of its characteristic functions and its characteristic values.

thereto a function $f_i(x)$ by the equations

$$\left.\begin{aligned} f_i(x) &= 1, \qquad x = \epsilon_{ij}, \qquad j = 1, 2, \cdots, Z_i \\ f_i(x) &= 0, \qquad \text{otherwise.} \end{aligned}\right\} \tag{A1.748}$$

From equations (A1.747) and (A1.748) it then follows that $\mathfrak{S}_i = f_i(\mathfrak{H})$ is a macroscopic observable for which we have

$$\mathfrak{S}_i = \sum_n f_i(\epsilon_n)\mathfrak{R}(\varphi_n) = \sum_{j=1}^{z_i} \mathfrak{R}(\varphi_{ij}). \tag{A1.749}$$

Von Neumann proves next that $f_i(\mathfrak{H})$ can be written as a sum of $\mathfrak{O}_i$'s. These operators may be renumbered, $\mathfrak{O}_{ij}$, in such a way that all $\mathfrak{O}_{ij}$ with given i correspond to the same $f_i(\mathfrak{H})$. The $\mathfrak{O}_{ij}$ (given i, and $j = 1, 2, \cdots, n_i$) together form Z_i $\mathfrak{O}_i$'s and we have apparently

$$Z_i = \sum_{j=1}^{n_i} z_{ij}. \tag{A1.750}$$

Using the double numbering we have

$$\mathfrak{S}_i = \sum_{j=1}^{Z_i} \mathfrak{R}(\varphi_{ij}) = \sum_{j=1}^{n_i} \mathfrak{O}_{ij}. \tag{A1.751}$$

This equation can also be written in the form

$$\mathfrak{S}_i = \sum_{j=1}^{n_i} z_{ij} \frac{\mathfrak{O}_{ij}}{z_{ij}}, \tag{A1.752}$$

and $\mathfrak{S}_i$ (or rather, $\mathfrak{S}_i/Z_i$) is an operator corresponding to a "Gemisch" of the "Γ-space cell operators" $\mathfrak{O}_{ij}/z_{ij}$, all corresponding to the same macroscopic energy E_i. We may call $\mathfrak{S}_i$, therefore, the quantum mechanical analogy of the energy surface $\mathfrak{S}$. The quantity n_i gives us the number of cells on the energy surface, and for this number we have from equations (A1.745) and (A1.751)

$$n_i = \operatorname{Tr} \mathfrak{S}_i. \tag{A1.753}$$

Let us recapitulate briefly the connection between the various operators and the various possible macroscopic measurements. A macroscopic measurement of the energy can determine which of the energy surfaces $\mathfrak{S}_i$ corresponds to the system under observation. Further macroscopic measurements cannot give us more information about the energy, but they can determine to which of the $\mathfrak{O}_{ij}$ our system corresponds. These further measurements determine quantities which are not commuting with $\mathfrak{H}$ (otherwise they might give further information about the energy) and which thus in classical mechanics correspond to quantities which vary in time.

Let us now assume that the situation of our system corresponds to the wave function ψ. We know that the probability that in that situation an energy of the group Z_i is realized is given by the expression

$$\mathfrak{S}_i(\psi) = \int \psi \mathfrak{S}_i \psi \, d\tau. \tag{A1.754}$$

The density matrix of the microcanonical ensemble corresponding to our knowledge of the situation described by ψ is given by the equation

$$\rho = \sum_i \frac{\mathfrak{S}_i(\psi)}{Z_i} \mathfrak{S}_i. \qquad \textbf{(A1.755)}$$

Von Neumann now shows that if certain conditions regarding the $\mathfrak{O}_{ij}$ and the $\mathfrak{S}_i$ are fulfilled, the following relation between the ensemble average G_{av} and the time average $\widetilde{G}$ of any macroscopically measurable quantity G will hold for practically all ψ,

$$\overline{| G_{av} - \widetilde{G} |^2} \ll (G^2)_{av}. \qquad \textbf{(A1.756)}$$

This proof is the quantum mechanical analogy to Birkhoff's and von Neumann's own proofs of the classical ergodic theorem. We must refer the reader to von Neumann's paper for details of the proof.

§8. The Assumptions of Equal a Priori Probabilities for Equal Volumes in Γ-Space in Classical Statistics and of Equal a Priori Probabilities and Random a Priori Phases for Nondegenerate Stationary States in Quantum Statistics. We have mentioned on various occasions that it is possible to build up statistical mechanics by making certain assumptions about a priori probabilities and afterward justifying these assumptions by their results. In the present section we wish to discuss these assumptions in slightly more detail.

In the classical case our assumption is that of equal a priori probabilities for equal volumes in Γ-space. This meant that we introduced in §4 the volume $W(\mathbf{Z})$ of a $\mathbf{Z}$-star as the measure for the probability of the situation $\mathbf{Z}$. Let us see whether or not this is feasible.

Consider two ensembles in Γ-space. The representative points of the first ensemble may at $t_1, t_2, t_3, \cdots$ occupy the regions $A_1, A_2, A_3, \cdots$ in Γ-space and those of the second ensemble at the same times the regions $B_1, B_2, B_3, \cdots$. Let $w(A_i)$ and $w(B_i)$ be the measures of the relative probabilities for A_i and B_i. We can clearly tolerate only such choices of w that we have

$$\frac{w(A_1)}{w(B_1)} = \frac{w(A_2)}{w(B_2)} = \cdots = \frac{w(A_i)}{w(B_i)} = \cdots. \qquad \textbf{(A1.801)}$$

Let us consider the consequences of this condition. If we choose

$$w(A_i) = W(A_i), \qquad w(B_i) = W(B_i), \qquad \textbf{(A1.802)}$$

where $W(A_i)$ and $W(B_i)$ are, respectively, the volumes of the regions A_i and B_i in Γ-space,

$$W(A_i) = \int_{A_i} d\Omega, \qquad W(B_i) = \int_{B_i} d\Omega, \qquad \textbf{(A1.803)}$$

equation (A1.801) follows immediately by virtue of Liouville's theorem. Should we have chosen a $(q,\dot{q})$-space instead of a (p,q)-space, we could not have taken for the w's the corresponding volumes in this $(q,\dot{q})$-space (compare the remarks on p. 31).

However, we could also have tried

$$w = \int F(E,\varphi_2,\varphi_3,\cdots,\varphi_{2sN-1})d\Omega, \qquad \textbf{(A1.804)}$$

where $F(E,\varphi_2,\varphi_3,\cdots,\varphi_{2sN-1})$ is a once-and-for-all given arbitrary function of the energy and the $2sN - 2$ quantities which are integrals of motion (see p. 100) and where the integration extends over A_i or B_i. Since

$$\rho(p,q) = F(E,\varphi_2,\varphi_3,\cdots,\varphi_{2sN-1}) \qquad \textbf{(A1.805)}$$

are the only stationary density functions in Γ-space (p. 103), we see that equation (A1.804) gives us the most general way of choosing w. We have used expression (A1.802) instead of a more general expression for historical reasons. As long as one expected all systems to be ergodic one restricted oneself to density functions which depended only on the energy; moreover, since Boltzmann was dealing with isolated systems, he could go even one step further and take $F = 1$.†

We must also refer to the discussion in §8 of Chapter V.

We now come to the quantum mechanical case where our assumption is that of equal a priori probabilities and random a priori phases for non-degenerate stationary states. Let us first of all construct an ensemble in such a way that the $a_k{}^i$ in equation (A1.712) are given by the equation

$$a_k{}^i = r_0{}^i e^{\iota\phi_k{}^i}, \qquad (\iota = \sqrt{-1}) \qquad \textbf{(A1.806)}$$

where the real part of $a_k{}^i$, $r_0{}^i$, is independent of k and where the phases $\phi_k{}^i$ for different values of i are randomly distributed. The density of this ensemble is now given by the equation

$$\rho_{kl} = \frac{1}{N}\sum_{i=1}^{N} a_k{}^{i*}a_l{}^i = \langle (r_0{}^i)^2\rangle_{\text{av}}\,\langle e^{\iota(\phi_l{}^i-\phi_k{}^i)}\rangle_{\text{av}}$$

or

$$\rho_{kl} = \rho_0\delta_{kl}. \qquad \textbf{(A1.807)}$$

In keeping with the foregoing discussion of the classical case we must now show that this ensemble is a stationary one and that it is the most general one. The first follows immediately, if our orthonormal system consists of

† We must mention here that the Ehrenfests' remark—that the "ergodic" choice of $F(E)$ instead of $F(E,\varphi_2,\varphi_3,\cdots,\varphi_{2sN-1})$ is often inexpedient—is no longer relevant, since it was based on difficulties encountered by thermostatistics before the introduction of quantum mechanics.

the common characteristic functions of a number of those operators which commute with the Hamiltonian—including possibly the Hamiltonian itself—which take over the role of the integrals of motion in the classical case. This generality of choice of our orthonormal system corresponds to the most general choice (A1.804) of the a priori probability in the classical case. If, as is often done, we take only the characteristic functions of the energy operator as our orthonormal system and do not bother about choosing the subsystems belonging to degenerate energy levels in such a way that they are characteristic functions of other operators which are integrals of the equations of motion, we restrict ourselves to a situation analogous to Boltzmann's choice of $F(E)$.

Just as the choice of $W(\mathbf{Z})$ as the a priori weight of a $\mathbf{Z}$-star was a necessary step in the development of the statistical H-theorem in classical theory, even so is the introduction of equal a priori probabilities and random a priori phases necessary to prove equation (A1.734) which in turn is a necessary step, as we saw, in the proof of the H-theorem in the quantum mechanical ensemble theory.

We finally wish to draw attention to the fact that in the classical limit $(h \rightarrow 0)$ the quantum mechanical assumption goes over into the classical one. This can partly be seen from the considerations on pages 59–61 in Chapter III, where we showed that there are good reasons to let each stationary state correspond to a volume h^s(s = number of degrees of freedom) in phase space (see also Appendix III, §2). Equal volumes in phase space thus contain equal numbers of stationary states and should thus have equal a priori probabilities. This discussion, however, does not demonstrate the necessity of random a priori phases. This second part of the basic assumption comes in when we start from a representation which is not the energy representation. The postulate of equal a priori probability for different states is then not sufficient by itself to ensure equal a priori probability for different energy characteristic states, but the combined postulate of equal a priori probability and random a priori phases will ensure equal a priori probability of different states in any representation and hence the correct correspondence with the classical case.

§9. The Principle of Detailed Balancing. In §4 of Chapter I we saw that in the case of a gas of hard spherical molecules the necessary and sufficient condition for equilibrium was that the number of inverse collisions was equal to the number of original collisions. We called that an example of the principle of detailed balancing. In its simplest form, which can always be applied in quantum mechanical cases, and also in simplified classical cases such as a gas consisting of spherical molecules it states that *in equilibrium* the number of processes which destroy a situation A and produce a situation B will be equal to the number of processes which produce A and destroy B. In the quantum mechanical case this is always realized (in microscopic processes) because the quantum mechanical operators corresponding to observables are Hermitean. In classical statistics one sometimes meets cases where the structure of the molecules under consideration is so complex that one must consider cycles of collisions (compare the discussion on p. 339). We may remark here that Tolman has shown that in that case one can also state a principle of detailed balancing which is then slightly generalized.

Let us briefly discuss a few consequences of the principle and finally point out how it can often be used to simplify calculations of equilibrium rates. In our discussion of the quantum mechanical H-theorem we saw that equilibrium was reached if the following equation held (see equation [A1.710])

$$N_i N_j (Z_{i'} + \alpha N_{i'})(Z_{j'} + \alpha N_{j'}) = N_{i'} N_{j'} (Z_i + \alpha N_i)(Z_j + \alpha N_j), \quad \textbf{(A1.901)}$$

where α is given by equation (A1.703). From equations (A1.901), (A1.704), and (A1.702) we see that the principle of detailed balancing is satisfied. Moreover, from equations (A1.901) and (A1.701) it follows in the same way as equation (1.510) follows from equation (1.507) that for an equilibrium situation N_i must satisfy the equation

$$\frac{N_i}{Z_i + \alpha N_i} = e^{\nu - \mu\epsilon}, \quad \textbf{(A1.902)}$$

or

$$N_i = \frac{Z_i}{e^{-\nu + \mu\epsilon} - \alpha}, \quad \textbf{(A1.903)}$$

which is the same as equations (4.318) to (4.320).

In a similar way we can consider the case of the quantum mechanical ensembles. It then follows from equation (A1.736) that the coarse-grained density must satisfy the equation

$$P_i = Z_i e^{\nu - \mu\epsilon_i}, \quad \textbf{(A1.904)}$$

as we should expect, since for a coarse-grained density the classical result (Maxwell-Boltzmann distribution) should follow.

The main way in which the principle of detailed balancing is applied is in the calculation of rates of processes. If, for instance, we wish to calculate the number of collisions in a gas which lead to excited states of a molecule (a chemically active state), we can calculate the number of collisions leading to deactivation and then use detailed balancing to give us the first number. Since the second number is more easily computed than the first, we have a clear gain.

BIBLIOGRAPHICAL NOTES

General references to this appendix are†

1. P. and T. Ehrenfest, Encyklopädie der mathematischen Wissenschaften, Vol. IV, Pt. 32, Leipzig-Berlin 1911.
2. A. Smekal, Encyklopädie der mathematischen Wissenschaften, Vol. V, Pt. 28, Leipzig-Berlin 1926.
3. G. E. Uhlenbeck, Over Statistische Methoden in de Theorie der Quanta, Thesis, Leiden 1927.
4. R. C. Tolman, The Principles of Statistical Mechanics, Oxford 1938, especially Chaps. VI and XII.

Reference 1 especially should be consulted. In their survey the Ehrenfests discuss critically and in great detail the fundamental ideas of classical statistics. Our §§2–5 are to a large extent based on their discussion. We also refer to them for further references.

§2. See ref. 1, §§5, 6; ref. 3, Chap. I, §2; ref. 4, Chap. VI. For a discussion of the principle of microscopic reversibility see

5. R. C. Tolman, Proc. Nat. Acad., **11**, 436, 1925.

The fact that inverse collisions will not always exist was first stressed by Lorentz in 1887 in

6. H. A. Lorentz, Wien. Ber., **95**, 115, 1887.

See also ref. 4, §§42 and 48, and

7. L. Boltzmann, Wien. Ber., **95**, 153, 1887.

§3. See ref. 1, §§7, 8. The criticisms of Loschmidt and Zermelo were voiced in 1876, 1877, and 1896, in

8. J. Loschmidt, Wien. Ber., **73**, 139, 1876.
9. J. Loschmidt, Wien. Ber., **75**, 67, 1877.
10. E. Zermelo, Ann. Physik, **57**, 485, 1896.

Compare also

11. J. W. Gibbs, Elementary Principles in Statistical Mechanics (Vol. II of his Collected Works), New Haven 1948, Chap. XII.

§4. See ref. 1, §§12, 14, 16, 17, 18; ref. 3, Chap. I, §§3, 4; ref. 4, Chap. VI, and also

12. L. Boltzmann, Wien. Ber., **76**, 373, 1877.
13. S. Chandrasekhar, Revs. Modern Phys., **15**, 1, 1943, especially Chap. III.
14. M. v. Smoluchowski, Physik. Z., **13**, 1069, 1912.
15. J. H. Jeans, The Dynamical Theory of Gases, Cambridge 1921, Chap. IV.

For simple *H*-curves, see

16. L. Boltzmann, Nature, **51**, 413, 1895.
17. P. and T. Ehrenfest, Physik. Z., **8**, 311, 1907.
18. K. W. F. Kohlrausch and E. Schrödinger, Physik. Z., **27**, 306, 1926.

Boltzmann's *H*-curve appeared in a long series of letters in Nature (Vol. **51**)

† This appendix was finished in the summer of 1951 and covers therefore the literature up to 1951. In a forthcoming review article in the Reviews of Modern Physics more recent developments will be discussed. That paper discusses the basic ideas of thermostatistics from the point of view of the present situation rather than from a historical point of view and supplements thus to a large extent this appendix.

by Bryan, Culverwell, Burbury, Boltzmann, and others. Our discussion of the Δ_z-curve is based on refs. 17 and 18.

19. D. ter Haar and C. D. Green, Proc. Phys. Soc. (London), **A66,** 153, 1953.

§5. A rigorous proof of the impossibility of ergodic systems was given independently by Rosenthal and Plancherel:

20. A. Rosenthal, Ann. Physik, **42,** 796, 1913.
21. M. Plancherel, Ann. Physik, **42,** 1061, 1913.

The argument which we gave is due to Tolman (ref. 4, p. 67) but it is not completely rigorous.

The fact that a very general class of mechanical systems is quasi-ergodic was proved by Fermi. We followed the main argument of his proof but must refer to his paper for details:

22. E. Fermi, Physik. Z., **24,** 261, 1923.

See also ref. 1, §§9, 10, 11 and ref. 2.

The ergodic theorem in its modern version is due to Birkhoff and von Neumann:

23. G. D. Birkhoff, Proc. Nat. Acad., **17,** 650, 656, 1931.
24. G. D. Birkhoff and B. O. Koopman, Proc. Nat. Acad., **18,** 279, 1932.
25. J. von Neumann, Proc. Nat. Acad., **18,** 70, 263, 1932.

See also

26. E. Hopf, Ergodentheorie, Berlin 1937 (Ergeb. Math., **5,** No. 2).
27. A. I. Khinchin, Mathematical Foundations of Statistical Mechanics, New York, 1949, Chaps. II and III.

In refs. 23 to 27 further literature is quoted. The discussion in the last part of this section is based on refs. 24 and 27.

§6. See ref. 11, Chaps. XI and XII; ref. 1, §§22, 23, 24, 27; ref. 4, §51. Gibbs uses $\bar{\eta}$ both for σ and Σ, and in his discussion the fine-grained and coarse-grained densities are never clearly distinguished. The Ehrenfests pointed out the necessity for this distinction. While the Ehrenfests discuss the change of Σ in a very critical way, Tolman stresses more the connection between the change of Σ, for which he uses throughout the symbol H, and the change in an actually observed physical system.

We refer to Tolman for a discussion of the relation between the H-theorem dealing with one system and the H-theorem dealing with an ensemble (ref. 4, §51d).

§7. See ref. 4, Chap. XII and also

28. W. Pauli, Probleme der modernen Physik (Sommerfeld Festschrift; P. Debye, ed.), Leipzig 1928, p. 30.
29. P. Jordan, Statistische Mechanik auf Quantentheoretischer Grundlage, Braunschweig 1933, §2.2.
30. J. von Neumann, Z. Physik, **57,** 30, 1929.
31. R. von Mises, Wahrscheinlichkeitsrechnung, Leipzig-Vienna 1931, §16.
32. O. Klein, Z. Physik, **72,** 767, 1931.
33. W. Pauli and M. Fierz, Z. Physik, **106,** 572, 1937.
34. E. C. Kemble, Phys. Rev., **56,** 1013, 1939.
35. E. C. Kemble, Phys. Rev., **56,** 1146, 1939.
36. M. Born and H. S. Green, Proc. Roy. Soc. (London), **A192,** 166, 1948.
37. M. J. Klein, Phys. Rev., **87,** 111, 1952.

38. E. C. G. Stueckelberg, Helv. Phys. Acta, **23,** 239, 1952.

In refs. 4, 28, and 30 the quantum mechanical H-theorem is discussed while von Neumann discusses both the H-theorem and the ergodic theorem. The first part of this section follows closely refs. 4 and 28 and the last part is based on refs. 29–31. Our treatment of the H-theorem in quantum mechanical ensemble theory and also our nomenclature is slightly different from that of Tolman. We have introduced the fine-grained and coarse-grained densities and also σ and Σ in complete analogy with the classical case, while the quantities discussed by Tolman in his equation (104.10) are not the quantum mechanical analogies of the quantities discussed in the classical case. The differences are minor ones and mainly of aesthetic interest.

Neither Klein nor Born and Green pay sufficient attention to the fact that actual physical systems should be *represented* by ensembles the coarse-grained density of which is given. It is interesting to note that although Born and Green in an earlier paper (Proc. Roy. Soc. (London), **A191,** 168, 1947) use an equation similar to equation (A1.715) for the entropy, their discussion of the H-theorem fails to arrive at equation (A1.720).

§8. See ref. 1, footnote 170; ref. 4, §§23, 84, 85; ref. 28.

§9. See ref. 4, §§50, 116; ref. 28 and

39. R. H. Fowler, Statistical Mechanics, Cambridge 1936, Chap. XVII.

APPENDIX II

IRREVERSIBLE PROCESSES

§1. The Return to Equilibrium. Equilibrium situations have been treated satisfactorily for a very long time, both in thermodynamics and in statistical mechanics. The situation is, however, very different as far as nonequilibrium situations are concerned. The second law of thermodynamics deals with such nonequilibrium situations, but only with the direction in which the situation will develop and not with any quantitative aspects. The previous appendix dealt with the second law from a statistical point of view, but in the present appendix we wish to consider some other aspects of nonequilibrium processes. More quantitative results have mainly been obtained by using Boltzmann's transport equation (see §5 of Chapter II), which has been used to treat effects such as heat conduction, electrical conduction, thermoelectricity, and so on.† Recently, Onsager has studied these processes from a different point of view, and his approach has led to a large number of papers in this new field, the *thermodynamics of irreversible processes.* The original theory was based on a discussion of fluctuations and their regression, but we shall use ensemble theory, as was also done in a recent paper by Cox. In the first section of this appendix we shall consider the return to equilibrium and in the second section we shall derive the so-called Onsager relations, applications of which will be discussed in the last section.

Let us consider a system containing a number of different constituents. In Part B we have showed how such a system can be described by a canonical grand ensemble and how the equilibrium situation is completely determined once we know the grand potential q as a function of the temperature T (or the modulus Θ), the thermal potentials g_i $(=\nu_i\Theta)$, and the external parameters a_i. We shall again introduce a quantity μ by the equation

$$\mu = \frac{1}{\Theta} = \frac{1}{kT}, \tag{A2.101}$$

† See, e.g., E. H. Kennard, Kinetic Theory of Gases, New York 1938. We refer to S. Chapman and T. G. Cowling, The Mathematical Theory of Non-Uniform Gases, Cambridge 1939, for a more advanced treatment. Compare also §2 of Chap. X.

and we then have

$$q = q(\mu, \nu_i, a_i). \tag{A2.102}$$

Once μ, the ν_i, and the a_i are fixed, the relative occurrence of a situation where the number of particles of the ith kind is $\mathfrak{n}_i$ while the total energy of the system is E_k is given by the following expression (compare equations [7.401] and [7.403] on p. 156),

$$\rho(\mathfrak{n}_i, E_k) = e^{-q + \sum_i \mathfrak{n}_i \nu_i - \mu E_k}. \tag{A2.103}$$

From equation (7.408) on page 157 we have

$$\delta q = \sum_i \hat{\mathfrak{n}}_i \delta \nu_i - \hat{\epsilon} \delta \mu + \mu \sum_j \hat{A}_j \delta a_j, \tag{A2.104}$$

where the $\wedge$ signs indicate averages taken over the ensemble and where the $\hat{A}_j$ are the generalized forces defined by the equations

$$\hat{A}_j = -\sum_{\mathfrak{n}_i} \sum_k \rho(\mathfrak{n}_i, E_k) \frac{\partial E_k}{\partial a_j}. \tag{A2.105}$$

From equation (A2.104) it follows that the average energy, the average numbers of particles, and the average generalized forces can be derived from q by differentiation (see equations [7.415] to [7.417]),

$$-\hat{\epsilon} = \frac{\partial q}{\partial \mu}, \tag{A2.106}$$

$$\hat{\mathfrak{n}}_i = \frac{\partial q}{\partial \nu_i}, \tag{A2.107}$$

$$\hat{A}_j = \frac{1}{\mu} \frac{\partial q}{\partial a_j}. \tag{A2.108}$$

We shall for the sake of simplicity denote by b_i any of the variables μ, ν_i, or a_j; the corresponding "forces" we shall denote by B_i so that equations (A2.106) to (A2.108) can be written as

$$\hat{B}_i = \frac{\partial q}{\partial b_i}. \tag{A2.109}$$

Let us now suppose that the values of the b_i are changed so fast that they have taken on their new values, $b_i + \Delta b_i$, before the density function $\rho(\mathfrak{n}_i, E_k)$ can change. If we wait long enough, the density function $\tilde{\rho}$ of the new ensemble which represents the system under the changed conditions will again be of the canonical form and we have

$$\tilde{\rho}(\mathfrak{n}_i, E_k) = \rho(\mathfrak{n}_i, E_k) + \Delta\rho, \tag{A2.110}$$

where

$$\Delta\rho = \sum_i \Delta b_i \frac{\partial \rho}{\partial b_i} = \sum_i \Delta b_i \frac{\partial \tilde{\rho}}{\partial b_i}, \tag{A2.111}$$

provided the Δb_i are sufficiently small. Using equations (A2.103) and (A2.109), we find

$$\Delta\rho = \tilde{\rho} \sum_i (B_i - \hat{B}_i)\Delta b_i, \tag{A2.112}$$

where the $\hat{B}_i$ and B_i stand, respectively, for the values of the "forces" corresponding to the equilibrium situation and to the situation where the number of particles of the ith kind is $\mathfrak{n}_i$ and where the energy is E_k, while those values are not necessarily the equilibrium values.

Immediately after the disturbance the density function differs from the equilibrium density function by $\Delta\rho$. Let us now consider the rate of change of the density function, $d\rho/dt$. We have for this rate of change the equation†

$$\frac{d\rho_m}{dt} = \sum_n [\rho_n e^{-\sum \mathfrak{n}_i'\nu_i + \mu E_l} - \rho_m e^{-\sum \mathfrak{n}_i\nu_i + \mu E_k}] d_{mn}, \tag{A2.113}$$

where ρ_m stands for $\rho(\mathfrak{n}_i, E_k)$ and ρ_n for $\rho(\mathfrak{n}_i', E_l)$, where the summation extends over all possible values of all the $\mathfrak{n}_i'$ and of E_l, and where $d_{mn}\,(=d_{nm})$ is related to the probability per unit time $a_{m\to n}$ that a transition takes place from m to n,

$$d_{mn} = a_{m\to n} e^{\sum \mathfrak{n}_i\nu_i - \mu E_k}. \tag{A2.114}$$

This equation can be derived as follows.‡ Our system is in contact with a heat bath and a particle bath which fix the values of the temperature and of the thermal potentials. The density function of the system which forms the heat and the particle bath will be given by the equation

$$\bar{\rho}(\bar{\mathfrak{n}}_i, \bar{E}_k) = e^{-\bar{q} + \sum \bar{\mathfrak{n}}_i\nu_i - \mu \bar{E}_k}, \tag{A2.115}$$

and this function will not depend on the situation of the original system.

Let us consider a transition from a state where the situation of the original system is characterized by $\mathfrak{n}_i$ and E_k and the situation of the bath system by $\bar{\mathfrak{n}}_i$ and $\bar{E}_k$ to a state where we have $\mathfrak{n}_i'$, E_l and $\bar{\mathfrak{n}}_i'$, $\bar{E}_l$. We shall denote the corresponding density functions by ρ_m, $\bar{\rho}_m$, ρ_n and $\bar{\rho}_n$, and indicate the transition by $m\bar{m} \to n\bar{n}$. The probability per unit time for the transition $m\bar{m} \to n\bar{n}$ may be denoted by $a_{m\bar{m}\to n\bar{n}}$. We know that $a_{m\bar{m}\to n\bar{n}}$ will be equal to zero, unless the following conditions are fulfilled:

$$E_k + \bar{E}_k = E_l + \bar{E}_l, \tag{A2.116}$$

$$\mathfrak{n}_i + \bar{\mathfrak{n}}_i = \mathfrak{n}_i' + \bar{\mathfrak{n}}_i'. \tag{A2.117}$$

---

† This equation does not hold when a magnetic field is present, a case which we shall exclude from our considerations.

‡ Compare R. T. Cox, Revs. Modern Phys., **22**, 238, 1950, §2, and also the discussion in §7 of Appendix I.

Furthermore, from the principle of microscopic reversibility it follows that (compare the discussion on pp. 339, 369, and 374)

$$a_{m\bar{m}\to n\bar{n}} = a_{n\bar{n}\to m\bar{m}}. \tag{A2.118}$$

We are interested in a transition where the original system goes from a state specified by ρ_m to a state specified by ρ_n, irrespective of the states of the bath system. Let $a_{m\to n}$ be the probability per unit time that such a transition takes place. It can be shown that

$$a_{m\to n} = \sum_{\bar{m}} \sum_{\bar{n}} \bar{\rho}_m a_{m\bar{m}\to n\bar{n}}, \tag{A2.119}$$

or, using equation (A2.115),

$$a_{m\to n} = \sum_{\bar{m}} \sum_{\bar{n}} a_{m\bar{m}\to n\bar{n}} e^{-\bar{q}+\sum \bar{n}_i\nu_i - \mu \bar{E}_k}. \tag{A2.120}$$

Similarly, we have for $a_{n\to m}$ the equation

$$a_{n\to m} = \sum_{\bar{m}} \sum_{\bar{n}} a_{m\bar{m}\to n\bar{n}} e^{-\bar{q}+\sum \bar{n}_i'\nu_i - \mu \bar{E}_l}, \tag{A2.121}$$

where equation (A2.118) has been used.

From equations (A2.120), (A2.121), and the fact that $a_{m\bar{m}\to n\bar{n}}$ is zero unless conditions (A2.116) and (A2.117) are fulfilled it follows that the quantity d_{mn} given by equation (A2.114) is symmetrical in its two indices,

$$d_{mn} = d_{nm}. \tag{A2.122}$$

We have for the rate of change of ρ_m the equation

$$\frac{d\rho_m}{dt} = \sum_n (\rho_n a_{n\to m} - \rho_m a_{m\to n}), \tag{A2.123}$$

and using equations (A2.114) and (A2.122), equation (A2.113) follows.

It may be remarked here that it follows from equation (A2.113) that a nonequilibrium situation will change until ρ satisfies equation (A2.103).

From equations (A2.113), (A2.110), and (A2.112) we get

$$\frac{d\rho_m}{dt} = e^{-q} \sum_n \sum_i (B_i^{(n)} - B_i^{(m)}) \Delta b_i d_{mn}, \tag{A2.124}$$

where the superscripts (n) and (m) are self-explanatory.

From this equation we can calculate the rate of change of the B_i, and we have

$$\frac{dB_i}{dt} = \frac{d}{dt} \sum_m \rho_m B_i^{(m)} = \sum_m B_i^{(m)} \frac{d\rho_m}{dt} \tag{A2.125}$$

$$= \frac{\partial T}{\partial \Delta b_i}, \tag{A2.126}$$

where

$$T = \tfrac{1}{4} e^{-q} \sum_i \sum_m \sum_n (B_i^{(m)} - B_i^{(n)})^2 \Delta b_i^2 d_{mn}. \tag{A2.127}$$

One obtains equation (A2.126) by substituting equation (A2.124) for $d\rho_m/dt$ into equation (A2.125) and taking the arithmetic mean of that equation and the equation obtained by exchanging m and n and using equation (A2.122).

One can use equations (A2.112), (A2.124), (A2.114), and (A2.103) to obtain an order of magnitude estimate of relaxation times. The relaxation time τ will be of the order of magnitude of the ratio of $\Delta\rho_m$ to $-d\rho_m/dt$ and we get from the afore-mentioned equations

$$\tau = \frac{\hat{B}_i - B_i^{(m)}}{\sum_n a_{m\to n}(B_i^{(n)} - B_i^{(m)})}, \tag{A2.128}$$

which means that τ will be of the order of magnitude of $a_{m\to n}^{-1}$ (with $m \approx n$), which might have been expected. The actual value of $a_{m\to n}$ will vary from example to example, but in the case of a perfect gas we can make a rough estimate by assuming $a_{m\to n}$ to be of the order of $n \cdot a_{12\to 1'2'}$ where $a_{12\to 1'2'}$ is the quantity encountered in §4 of Chapter I and where n is the number of particles per cm³. We then get

$$\tau \sim \frac{\lambda}{\bar{c}}, \tag{A2.129}$$

where λ is the mean free path and $\bar{c}$ the average velocity of a particle in the gas. Equation (A2.129) might also have been derived from simple dimensional considerations.

Taking as an example helium gas under normal conditions we get

$$\tau \sim 10^{-7} \text{ sec.} \tag{A2.130}$$

§2. The Onsager Relations. In many instances when we are interested in irreversible processes these will be described by phenomenological laws, for instance, Ohm's law giving a proportionality between electric current and potential gradient, or Fourier's law giving a proportionality between heat flow and temperature gradient. In such cases the phenomenological law is of the kind

$$J_i = L_{ii}X_i, \tag{A2.201}$$

where J_i is the *flux* (electric current and heat flow in the two examples given above), X_i the affinity† (potential gradient and temperature gradient in our examples), and L_{ii} the coefficients of proportionality (coefficients of electric and thermal conductivity).

Sometimes two or more affinities are present and cross phenomena may occur, such as the well-known thermoelectric effects, the Peltier effect which is the production of heat as the result of the existence of an electric current and the thermoelectric force, that is, a potential drop as the result of the existence of a temperature difference (see §3). In such cases equation

† We do not wish to use the term "force" since we have used it already in another sense.

(A2.201) must be generalized to read

$$J_i = \sum_j L_{ij} X_j. \tag{A2.202}$$

It can be shown that if a proper choice is made for the affinities and the fluxes, the L_{ij} satisfy the equation

$$L_{ij} = L_{ji} \tag{A2.203}$$

which was first derived by Onsager as a general principle. We shall see presently how one can choose the J_i and the X_i in a proper way so that equation (A2.203) holds.

Let $\alpha_i (i = 1,2,\cdots)$ be a number of macroscopic variables which together describe the macroscopic state of the system, and let $\alpha_i^{(m)}$ be the values of these variables in a situation where the number of particles of the ith kind is $\mathfrak{n}_i$ and the energy of the system E_k. If the state of the system can be represented by an ensemble with a density function $\rho(\mathfrak{n}_i,E_k)$, we have the equation

$$\alpha_i = \sum_m \alpha_i^{(m)} \rho^{(m)}. \tag{A2.204}$$

Consider now a situation where the values of the α_i are not those corresponding to equilibrium, but are slightly different. The system will then try to regain equilibrium and we shall assume that a state of steady flow has set in. In that case we may expect that at any time the situation present, though not in equilibrium, will correspond to a state where the entropy has the largest value consistent with the momentary values of the α_i. The entropy in a nonequilibrium state is defined by the equation

$$S = -k \widehat{\ln \rho} = -k \sum_m \rho^{(m)} \ln \rho^{(m)}. \tag{A2.205}$$

The condition that S should be maximum for given values of the α_i leads to the following expression for $\rho^{(m)}$ (by a reasoning completely similar to the one which in §5 of Chapter I led to equation [1.510]),

$$\rho^{(m)} = \frac{e^{-\frac{1}{k}\sum X_i \alpha_i^{(m)}}}{\sum_m e^{-\frac{1}{k}\sum X_i \alpha_i^{(m}}}, \tag{A2.206}$$

and substituting equation (A2.206) into equation (A2.205) and expressing δS in terms of the $\delta \alpha_i$, we have

$$X_i = \frac{\partial S}{\partial \alpha_i}. \tag{A2.207}$$

From equation (A2.206) it follows that

$$\frac{\partial \rho^{(m)}}{\partial X_i} = \frac{1}{k}(\alpha_i - \alpha_i^{(m)})\rho^{(m)}, \tag{A2.208}$$

a result which we shall need presently.

Let us now consider the rate of change of the α_i. We have from equations (A2.204) and (A2.113)

$$\begin{aligned}\frac{d\alpha_i}{dt} &= \sum_m \alpha_i^{(m)} \frac{d\rho^{(m)}}{dt} = \sum_m \sum_n \alpha_i^{(m)} \left[\rho^{(n)} e^{-\sum \mathfrak{n}_i'\nu_i + \mu E_l} - \rho^{(m)} e^{-\sum \mathfrak{n}_i \nu_i + \mu E_k}\right] d_{mn} \\ &= \sum_m \sum_n (\alpha_i^{(n)} - \alpha_i^{(m)})\rho^{(m)} e^{-\sum \mathfrak{n}_i \nu_i + \mu E_k} d_{mn}.\end{aligned} \tag{A2.209}$$

In order to find out how this expression depends on the X_j we take the derivative with respect to X_j, and using equation (A2.208) we have

$$\frac{\partial}{\partial X_j}\frac{d\alpha_i}{dt} = \frac{1}{k}\sum_m \sum_n (\alpha_i^{(n)} - \alpha_i^{(m)})(\alpha_j - \alpha_j^{(m)})\rho^{(m)} e^{-\sum \mathfrak{n}_i \nu_i + \mu E_k} d_{mn}. \tag{A2.210}$$

In the first approximation we may use for $\rho^{(m)}$ the equilibrium expression given by equation (A2.103) and we get—after interchanging m and n in the summation, taking the arithmetical mean of the two expressions, and using equation (A2.122)—

$$\frac{\partial}{\partial X_j}\frac{d\alpha_i}{dt} = \frac{e^{-q}}{2k}\sum_m \sum_n (\alpha_i^{(n)} - \alpha_i^{(m)})(\alpha_j^{(n)} - \alpha_j^{(m)}) d_{mn}, \tag{A2.211}$$

or

$$\frac{d\alpha_i}{dt} = \sum_j X_j L_{ij}, \tag{A2.212}$$

where

$$L_{ij} = \frac{e^{-q}}{2k}\sum_m \sum_n (\alpha_i^{(n)} - \alpha_i^{(m)})(\alpha_j^{(n)} - \alpha_j^{(m)}) d_{mn}. \tag{A2.213}$$

In deriving equation (A2.212) we have used the fact that at equilibrium we have $\partial S/\partial \alpha_i = X_i = 0$ and also $d\alpha_i/dt = 0$.

Identifying the X_i with the affinities and the $d\alpha_i/dt$ with the fluxes J_i, we see from equation (A2.213) that equation (A2.203) holds.

In order to choose in a given situation the proper fluxes and affinities, one usually considers the *entropy source strength*, which is the time derivative of the entropy and given by the equation

$$\frac{dS}{dt} = \sum_i X_i \frac{d\alpha_i}{dt} = \sum_i X_i J_i. \tag{A2.214}$$

We may remark here that although our derivation of the Onsager relations was based on the use of grand canonical ensembles, which implies that we are considering systems which can exchange energy and particles with their surroundings, this restriction can easily be removed. If we are interested in a system which, although still able to exchange energy with its surroundings, cannot exchange particles, we must use macrocanonical ensembles and this results only in some changes in equations (A2.113) and (A2.209), but not in equation (A2.213). Finally, when we are dealing with an adiabatically insulated system, again slight changes must be made in some equations, but not in the final results.

The changes to be made are that instead of letting the situation n range over all possible values of all the $\mathfrak{n}_i$ and of the energy, we must restrict these situations to those with fixed numbers of particles and with fixed energy.

§3. Applications. We shall consider the following two cases: (a) a perfect gas enclosed in a reservoir consisting of two connected vessels, and (b) thermoelectric processes.

a) If we maintain a temperature difference between the two vessels which together form the reservoir in which our perfect gas finds itself, there will result a flow of matter leading to a pressure difference. The ratio of this pressure difference to the temperature difference is the so-called *thermomolecular pressure difference.* Similarly, a pressure difference at constant temperature will result in a heat flow, the so-called thermomechanical effect.†

We shall assume that the volumes of the two vessels are the same and that the gas contains only one constituent. Let N_1 and N_2 be the number of particles in the two vessels and T_1 and T_2 the respective temperatures. At equilibrium we have

$$N_1 = N_2(= N), \qquad T_1 = T_2(= T). \tag{A2.301}$$

We shall assume that the system is adiabatically insulated so that the total energy, which in the case of a perfect gas is the total kinetic energy, and that the total number of particles are constant, or

$$N_1T_1 + N_2T_2 = 2NT, \tag{A2.302}$$

$$N_1 + N_2 = 2N. \tag{A2.303}$$

We choose for our α_i the two quantities

$$\alpha_1 = N_1T_1 - NT(= NT - N_2T_2), \tag{A2.304}$$

$$\alpha_2 = N_1 - N(= N - N_2). \tag{A2.305}$$

† Although we restrict our discussion to the case of a perfect gas, it is of interest to note that the same effects also occur in helium II. The thermomolecular pressure difference is then called the *fountain effect* (J. F. Allen and H. Jones, Nature, **141,** 243, 1938).

We have for the entropy the following equation (compare equation [2.810] on p. 44),

$$S = S_1 + S_2 = k\left[\frac{3}{2}(N_1 \ln T_1 + N_2 \ln T_2) - \frac{5}{2}(N_1 \ln N_1 + N_2 \ln N_2)\right.$$

$$\left. - 2N \ln \frac{k}{V} + 2N\mathfrak{C} + 3N \ln M + 5N\right]$$

$$= S_{eq} - \frac{3k}{2N}\frac{\alpha_1{}^2}{T^2} + \frac{3k\alpha_1\alpha_2}{NT} - \frac{5k\alpha_2{}^2}{2N}, \tag{A2.306}$$

where only terms up to the second degree in the α_i are included.

From equation (A2.306) we have

$$\dot{S} = \left(-\frac{3k}{NT^2}\alpha_1 + \frac{3k}{NT}\alpha_2\right)\dot{\alpha}_1 + \left(\frac{3k}{NT}\alpha_1 - \frac{5k}{N}\alpha_2\right)\dot{\alpha}_2, \tag{A2.307}$$

and thus

$$X_1 = -\frac{3k}{NT^2}\alpha_1 + \frac{3k}{NT}\alpha_2, \tag{A2.308}$$

$$X_2 = \frac{3k}{NT}\alpha_1 - \frac{5k}{N}\alpha_2. \tag{A2.309}$$

These equations could also have been obtained from equation (A2.306) by using equation (A2.207).

We can express the affinities in terms of the pressure difference Δp and the temperature difference ΔT between the two vessels, where

$$\Delta p = \frac{k}{V}(N_1 T_1 - N_2 T_2) = \frac{2k\alpha_1}{V}, \tag{A2.310}$$

$$\Delta T = T_1 - T_2 \cong \frac{2\alpha_1}{N} - \frac{2\alpha_2 T}{N}, \tag{A2.311}$$

and where V is the volume of one vessel.

From equations (A2.308) to (A2.311) we get

$$X_1 = -\frac{3}{2}k\frac{\Delta T}{T^2}, \tag{A2.312}$$

$$X_2 = -\frac{V\Delta p}{NT} + \frac{5}{2}k\frac{\Delta T}{T}. \tag{A2.313}$$

Taking $J_i = d\alpha_i/dt$, we see that J_1 is proportional to the energy flow and that J_2 is the flow of particles. From equations (A2.212), (A2.312), and (A2.313) we have

$$J_1 = \left[-\frac{3k}{2T} L_{11} + \frac{5k}{2} L_{12} \right] \frac{\Delta T}{T} - L_{12} \frac{V \Delta p}{NT}, \tag{A2.314}$$

$$J_2 = \left[-\frac{3k}{2T} L_{21} + \frac{5k}{2} L_{22} \right] \frac{\Delta T}{T} - L_{22} \frac{V \Delta p}{NT}. \tag{A2.315}$$

Let us first consider the case where $\Delta T = 0$. We then have from equations (A2.314) and (A2.315)

$$J_1 = \frac{L_{12}}{L_{22}} J_2 = \frac{2\mathfrak{E}}{3k} J_2, \tag{A2.316}$$

and on inspection it is seen that $\mathfrak{E}$ is the average energy transferred per particle. Equation (A2.316) describes the thermomechanical effect, transfer of energy, although $\Delta T = 0$.

We can consider two limiting cases, the Knudsen case and the ordinary case. The difference between these two cases lies in the geometry of the communicating opening between the two vessels. Whereas in the Knudsen case we are dealing with an opening the width of which is small compared to the mean free path of the particles in the gas, in the ordinary case the width of the opening is large compared to the mean free path.

In the second case, $\mathfrak{E}$ is equal to the average kinetic energy per particle plus the average work done against the pressure, or

$$\mathfrak{E} = \frac{3}{2} kT + \frac{pV}{N} = \frac{5}{2} kT. \tag{A2.317}$$

In the Knudsen case we must calculate the average energy per particle, averaged over all the particles arriving at the hole, since these particles will pass freely through it. The average energy is then calculated in the usual manner from the velocity distribution function $f(u,v,w)$,

$$\mathfrak{E} = \frac{\int_{-\infty}^{+\infty} du \int_{-\infty}^{+\infty} dv \int_0^{\infty} dw f(u,v,w) \frac{1}{2} mc^2}{\int_{-\infty}^{+\infty} du \int_{-\infty}^{+\infty} dv \int_0^{\infty} dw f(u,v,w)}, \tag{A2.318}$$

where $c^2 = u^2 + v^2 + w^2$ and where we have supposed the z-coordinate to be perpendicular to the hole. Using for $f(u,v,w)$ the Maxwell distribution (see equation [1.104] on p. 3), we get

$$\mathfrak{E} = 2kT. \tag{A2.319}$$

We can now study the so-called stationary state, which occurs when we wait until there is no net flow of particles from one vessel to the other, so that $J_2 = 0$. From equation (A2.315) we then have

$$\frac{\Delta p}{\Delta T} = \frac{N}{V}\left[\frac{5k}{2} - \frac{\mathcal{E}}{T}\right], \tag{A2.320}$$

which gives us the thermomolecular pressure difference. In deriving equation (A2.320) we have used the fact that, according to the Onsager relations, $L_{12} = L_{21}$.

In the Knudsen case, equations (A2.319) and (A2.320) lead to

$$\frac{\Delta p}{\Delta T} = \frac{1}{2}\frac{kN}{V} = \frac{1}{2}\frac{p}{T}, \tag{A2.321}$$

or

$$\frac{p_1}{\sqrt{T_1}} = \frac{p_2}{\sqrt{T_2}}. \tag{A2.322}$$

In the ordinary case we have

$$\frac{\Delta p}{\Delta T} = 0, \qquad \text{or} \qquad p_1 = p_2. \tag{A2.323}$$

b) We consider now the case of a thermocouple made of two metals A and B. The two junctions are at temperatures T and $T + \Delta T$ and in the wire made of metal A there is a condenser over which there exists a

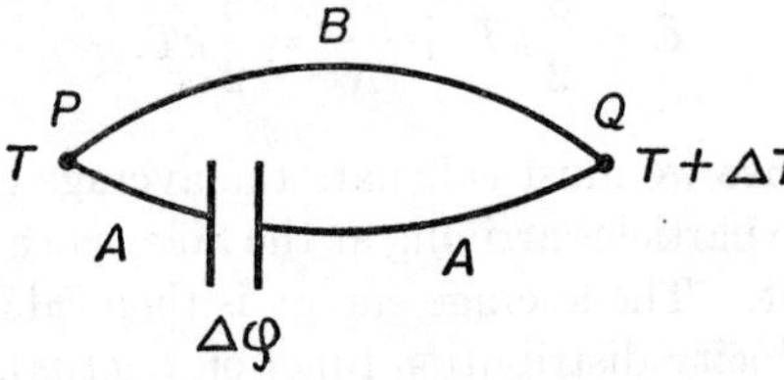

Fig. 56

potential drop $\Delta\varphi$ (see Fig. 56). In order to treat this case we must once more find an expression for the entropy production. We can use the equation

$$\delta S = \frac{1}{T}\,\delta U + \frac{1}{T}\,\Sigma A_i \delta a_i. \tag{A2.324}$$

In our case energy will be transported from P to Q and the only external parameter is the charge e on the condenser, so that A_i will be $-\Delta\varphi$. The change in the entropy of the total system, when δU is transported from P to Q and a charge δe is brought on the condenser, will be given by the equation

$$\delta S = -\frac{\delta U}{T} + \frac{\delta U}{T + \Delta T} - \frac{\Delta\varphi}{T}\,\delta e, \tag{A2.325}$$

or

$$\frac{dS}{dt} = -\frac{dU}{dt}\frac{\Delta T}{T^2} - \frac{de}{dt}\frac{\Delta\varphi}{T}. \tag{A2.326}$$

From equations (A2.326) and (A2.214) it follows that we can choose

$$J_1 = \frac{dU}{dt}, \qquad J_2 = \frac{de}{dt}, \tag{A2.327}$$

$$X_1 = -\frac{\Delta T}{T^2}, \qquad X_2 = -\frac{\Delta\varphi}{T}. \tag{A2.328}$$

Equation (A2.212) now reads

$$J_1 = -L_{11}\frac{\Delta T}{T^2} - L_{12}\frac{\Delta\varphi}{T}, \tag{A2.329}$$

$$J_2 = -L_{21}\frac{\Delta T}{T^2} - L_{22}\frac{\Delta\varphi}{T}. \tag{A2.330}$$

Let us first consider the stationary case, where $J_2 = 0$. We then get from equation (A2.330)

$$\frac{\Delta\varphi}{\Delta T} = -\frac{L_{21}}{L_{22}}\frac{1}{T}, \tag{A2.331}$$

giving the thermoelectric power of the thermocouple (Seebeck effect), that is, the potential difference per unit temperature difference when there is no electric current.

A second case is that where $\Delta\varphi$ is fixed and $\Delta T = 0$. We then get the so-called *Peltier effect*. The Peltier heat Π is defined as the flow of energy per unit electric current, and we get from equations (A2.329) and (A2.330), putting $\Delta T = 0$,

$$\frac{J_1}{J_2} = \Pi = \frac{L_{12}}{L_{22}}. \tag{A2.332}$$

From equations (A2.331) and (A2.332) and the Onsager relations (A2.203) we then get the following relation between the thermoelectric power and the Peltier heat:

$$\frac{\Delta\varphi}{\Delta T} = -\frac{\Pi}{T}. \tag{A2.333}$$

This relation goes back to Thomson, who derived it in 1854 by a different method.†

BIBLIOGRAPHICAL NOTES

The following general reference may be noted to which we may also refer for an extensive bibliography:

1. S. R. de Groot, Thermodynamics of Irreversible Processes, Amsterdam 1951.

§1. Compare ref. 1, §22. See also

2. R. T. Cox, Revs. Modern Phys., **22,** 238, 1950, especially §§2 and 5. Cox's treatment is based on petit ensembles while we have used the theory of the grand ensembles.

§2. Equation (A2.203) was derived by Onsager in 1931:

3. L. Onsager, Phys. Rev., **37,** 405, 1931.
4. L. Onsager, Phys. Rev., **38,** 2265, 1931.

See also ref. 1, Chap. II; ref. 2, §6; and

5. H. B. G. Casimir, Revs. Modern Phys., **17,** 343, 1945.
6. H. B. Callen, Phys. Rev., **73,** 1349, 1948.

§3. See ref. 1, §§9, 14, 57; ref. 5, §3; and ref. 6. We refer especially to ref. 1 for a discussion of more applications.

† W. Thomson, Proc. Roy. Soc. (Edinburgh), **3,** 255, 1854.

APPENDIX III

THE THIRD LAW OF THERMODYNAMICS

§1. Nernst's Heat Theorem. "The greatest advance in thermodynamics since van der Waals' time is the enunciation of a new general law of thermodynamics in 1905 by Nernst, the Third Law." This is the opening sentence of a paper by Simon on Nernst's heat theorem. A textbook on statistical mechanics is not the place to enter into a detailed discussion of Nernst's heat theorem and we must refer the reader to the literature given in the bibliographical notes at the end of this appendix for such a discussion. We shall be concerned only with those aspects of this theorem which are most closely connected with statistical considerations.

First of all, let us state the third law in the now generally accepted form given by Simon: *The contribution to the entropy of a system due to each component which is in internal equilibrium disappears at absolute zero.* A slightly different though equivalent way of stating the third law is the following one, given by Fowler and Guggenheim: *For any isothermal process involving only phases in internal equilibrium or, alternatively, if any phase is in frozen equilibrium, provided the process does not disturb this frozen equilibrium,*

$$\lim_{T\to 0} \Delta S = 0. \qquad \textbf{(A3.101)}$$

As Simon has emphasized in his discussion of the third law, it should not be surprising that there are some restricting clauses in the formulation of the third law but these clauses do not mean that the third law is not a general thermodynamical law. Indeed, one sees immediately that the restrictions are equivalent to the statement that the third law is valid as long as we are dealing with systems to which thermodynamics applies at all.

It can be shown that the two formulations of the third law which we have just given are equivalent to the following one: *It is impossible by any procedure, no matter how idealized, to reduce any system to the absolute zero in a finite number of operations.* This means that the third law of thermodynamics is equivalent to the principle of the unattainability of the absolute zero.†

We may briefly sketch the proof of the equivalence of the two principles.‡ Consider a process where a transition from a situation 1 to a situation 2 takes place. This process may be the result of a change in one of the external parameters. Denoting by $S_i(T)$ the entropy per unit mass in situation i at a temperature T we have from the thermodynamical formula

$$dS = \frac{CdT}{T} \tag{A3.102}$$

the equations

$$S_1(T) = S_1(0) + \int_0^T \frac{C_1}{T}\,dT, \tag{A3.103}$$

$$S_2(T) = S_2(0) + \int_0^T \frac{C_2}{T}\,dT, \tag{A3.104}$$

where C_i is the specific heat per unit mass in situation i. It follows from general quantum mechanical principles that the integrals in equations (A3.103) and (A3.104) converge since the specific heats go sufficiently rapidly to zero for $T \rightarrow 0$.§

I. Let us assume that equation (A3.101) holds. If the transition $1 \rightarrow 2$ takes place adiabatically (no change of entropy during the transition) and reversibly,‖ and if the initial temperature is T_1 and the final temperature T_2, we have from equations (A3.101), (A3.103), and (A3.104)

$$\int_0^{T_1} \frac{C_1}{T}\,dT = \int_0^{T_2} \frac{C_2}{T}\,dT. \tag{A3.105}$$

If the process could be used to reach the absolute zero ($T_2 = 0$), we should have

$$\int_0^{T_1} \frac{C_1}{T}\,dT = 0, \tag{A3.106}$$

but this is clearly impossible, since C_1 is always larger than zero. It is also clear that the inverse transition ($2 \rightarrow 1$) cannot be used to reach the absolute zero.

II. Let us now start from the principle of the unattainability of the absolute zero and prove that $S_1(0)$ and $S_2(0)$ are equal. Consider again an adiabatic, reversible process. We then have

$$S_2(0) - S_1(0) = \int_0^{T_1} \frac{C_1}{T}\,dT - \int_0^{T_2} \frac{C_2}{T}\,dT. \tag{A3.107}$$

† It should be mentioned that in classical physics the unattainability of the absolute zero is a triviality and becomes meaningful only if we remind ourselves that according to quantum mechanics all specific heats must vanish at the absolute zero.

‡ F. E. Simon, Science Museum Handbook, **3**, 61, 1937.

§ Compare, e.g., equation (3.419) on p. 61.

‖ If the process is not reversible, our conclusions hold a fortiori (see Simon, *loc. cit.*).

Let us assume first that $S_2(0) > S_1(0)$. We can then choose T_1 in such a way that

$$\int_0^{T_1} \frac{C_1}{T}\, dT = S_2(0) - S_1(0). \qquad \textbf{(A3.108)}$$

From equations (A3.107) and (A3.108) we see that it is now possible to reach the absolute zero by an adiabatic, reversible process. Since this is in contradiction to the principle of the unattainability of the absolute zero, we must have the condition

$$S_2(0) \leqslant S_1(0). \qquad \textbf{(A3.109)}$$

Similarly, we can prove that

$$S_2(0) \geqslant S_1(0), \qquad \textbf{(A3.110)}$$

from which equation (A3.101) follows.

Fowler and Guggenheim's formulation of the third law deals only with entropy differences, but Simon's formulation opens the door to the introduction of an *absolute entropy*. We can introduce an absolute entropy only when we have a means to determine the entropy at the absolute zero (or at any other temperature) absolutely, corresponding to the fixing of the value of the constant $S_1(0)$ in equation (A3.103). This can be done by using the statistical definition of the entropy (see equation [4.301] on p. 76 and equation [7.426] on p. 160 with the subsequent discussion),

$$S = k \ln W, \qquad \textbf{(A3.111)}$$

where W is the number of ways (microsituations) in which a given thermodynamical situation (macrosituation) can be realized. It is generally believed—though it has never actually been proven—that the ground state of any system will be nondegenerate.† From this it follows that at the absolute zero, where the system will be in the ground state, W will be equal to one and thus we would have

$$\lim_{T \to 0} S = 0, \qquad \textbf{(A3.112)}$$

from which equation (A3.101) follows as a consequence.

In our discussion up to this moment we have tacitly assumed that we are always dealing with situations which are in stable equilibria. Often, however, one is dealing with a state of metastable equilibrium, and equation (A3.112) will no longer hold, but the third law as formulated at the beginning of the present section still holds. Indeed, the existence of

† It must be remembered that even if the degree of degeneracy of the ground state is larger than one, then if that degree of degeneracy is independent of the total number of particles in the system, N, the entropy at the absolute zero would only be of the order of k, which would be negligibly small compared to the usual values of entropies at finite temperatures which are of the order kN.

glasses and other metastable equilibria was the reason why many scientists doubted the general validity of Nernst's heat theorem, until Simon discussed in great detail the domain of applicability of the third law and gave the formulation which we quoted. The problem of metastability really lies outside the normal thermodynamical or statistical discussion and we must therefore refer the reader to Simon's papers on this subject. The only case where we met with an example of metastable equilibrium was in the discussion of the specific heat of hydrogen (pp. 64–66); otherwise we have disregarded the existence of frozen equilibria.

§2. The Chemical Constants. In Chapter II we introduced a constant $\mathfrak{C}$ by the equation

$$\mathfrak{C} = \ln \left(\frac{2\pi m_{\mathrm{H}} k}{h^2}\right)^{3/2} k, \qquad \textbf{(A3.201)}$$

where m_{H} is the molecular weight unit. We mentioned then that $\mathfrak{C}$ is connected with the so-called chemical constants. This relationship will now be discussed.

Let us consider the equilibrium between a vapor and its condensed state, especially at low temperatures. At low temperatures the vapor pressure will be so low that we may treat it as a perfect Boltzmann gas. We have then from equation (2.810) on page 44 for the entropy per particle of the vapor, S_v, the equation

$$S_v = k[\tfrac{5}{2} \ln T - \ln p + \mathfrak{C} + \tfrac{3}{2} \ln M + \tfrac{5}{2}], \qquad \textbf{(A3.202)}$$

where p is the vapor pressure and M the molecular weight of the vapor. Let S_c be the entropy per particle of the condensed state. Since the condensation takes place at constant temperature we have from the second law of thermodynamics

$$S_v - S_c = \frac{\chi}{T}, \qquad \textbf{(A3.203)}$$

where χ is the sublimation heat per particle at the temperature T.

We can use equations (A3.202) and (A3.203) to write down an equation for the vapor pressure, and the result is

$$\ln p = -\frac{\chi}{kT} + \tfrac{5}{2} \ln T + \mathfrak{C} + \tfrac{3}{2} \ln M + \tfrac{5}{2} - S_c. \qquad \textbf{(A3.204)}$$

From equation (A3.204) or from an integration of the Clausius-Clapeyron equation, and assuming S_c at $T = 0$ to be equal to zero, we have the vapor pressure equation

$$\ln p = -\frac{\chi_0}{kT} + \frac{5}{2} \ln T + \frac{1}{k} \int_0^T \frac{dT'}{T'^2} \int_0^{T'} c_c dT'' + i, \qquad \textbf{(A3.205)}$$

where c_c is the specific heat per particle of the condensed state, where χ_0 is the value of χ at the absolute zero, and where the quantity i, which is called the *chemical constant* of the substance under consideration, is given by the equation (m = mass of one particle)†

$$i = \ln \left(\frac{2\pi m}{h^2}\right)^{3/2} k^{5/2}. \tag{A3.206}$$

One can now compare the theoretical value of i given by equation (A3.206) with the value following from equation (A3.205) by inserting experimental values. If this is done, it is found that there exists excellent agreement. This can be interpreted as meaning either that Nernst's heat theorem is satisfied in this case, or that the fundamental assumptions, which were introduced in deriving equation (A3.201) (which is the same as equation [2.808] on p. 44) for $\mathfrak{C}$, are sound.

Nowadays one usually accepts equation (A3.205) as correct, and when Abraham, Osborne, and Weinstock found that in the case of liquid He_3—where one may neglect the term involving c_c in equation (A3.205) —the value of i determined experimentally was different from the value given by equation (A3.206), they immediately concluded that liquid He_3 should show a transition involving either a latent heat or a hump in the specific heat, similar to the λ-transition of liquid He_4. The effect is not as pronounced as in the case of He_4, but probably sufficiently large to be established beyond reasonable doubt.‡

Tetrode used equation (A3.205) to derive from the experimental data the size of the cells in Γ-space. It must be noted that he introduced the factor $1/N!$—corresponding to the factor e/N in equation (2.717) on page 43. His reason for the introduction of this factor was that otherwise the entropy would not be an extensive quantity, and he stated explicitly that one should use generic and not specific phases in calculating the entropy (compare the discussion on p. 146). He then put the elementary cell in Γ-space equal to σ and on dimensional grounds wrote

$$\sigma = (zh)^n, \tag{A3.207}$$

where n is the number of degrees of freedom, z a numerical factor, and h Planck's constant. From the experimental data about mercury, Tetrode

† We do not wish to discuss here the influence of the statistical weights of the atoms on the chemical constants, but refer the reader to the literature given in the bibliographical notes at the end of this appendix.

‡ Probably the easiest way of showing this is by plotting the data of Abraham, Osborne, and Weinstock in a $\ln p - \frac{5}{2} \ln T$ against $1/T$ diagram (See D. ter Haar, Phys. Rev., **91**, 1018, 1953). It is then seen that the vapor pressure curve in this diagram is indeed a straight line, but does not cut the ordinate axis in the point corresponding to the value of i given by equation (A3.206).

determined z, and the result was

$$z = 1.0_5, \qquad \textbf{(A3.208)}$$

from which he arrived at the conclusion: "Es erscheint plausibel, dasz z genau 1 zu setzen ist, was schon von O. Sackur angenommen wurde." In this way Tetrode found an experimental justification for the choice of h^n as the size of the elementary cell in Γ-space.

We wish to conclude this section with a brief discussion of the importance of the chemical constants and of equation (A3.205). In the derivation of equation (A3.205) use was made of Nernst's heat theorem by putting S_c equal to zero at the absolute zero. From equation (A3.205) it follows that we can determine i and thus the entropy constant S_{v0} of the gas, which is defined by the equation

$$S_v = k \ln \frac{T^{5/2}}{p} + S_{v0}, \qquad \textbf{(A3.209)}$$

from a measurement of the vapor pressure. Once S_{v0} is determined, all thermodynamic properties of the gas can be calculated. Since these properties play an important role in the computation of chemical equilibria, Nernst gave i the name of chemical constant. We must refer to the literature and especially to numerous papers of Giauque and collaborators for a discussion of the calculation of chemical constants and their importance in the discussion of chemical reactions and equilibria.

§3. Special Cases. In this last section we want to verify that in three special cases considered in the preceding chapters of this book, the third law in its most stringent form is actually valid. These three cases are the case of a substitutional solution (Chapter XII) and the cases of the perfect Bose-Einstein and Fermi-Dirac gases (Chapters IV and VII). After that we shall consider as a last example of the applicability of the third law the melting line of helium.

In Chapter XII we found the following expression for the entropy of a substitutional solution (equation [12.224] on p. 259):

$$S = kN[\ln 2 - \tfrac{1}{2}(1 + R) \ln (1 + R) - \tfrac{1}{2}(1 - R) \ln (1 - R)], \qquad \textbf{(A3.301)}$$

where N is the number of atoms in the lattice and where R is the long-range order parameter. Since always $R \rightarrow 1$ for $T \rightarrow 0$, we see that equation (A3.112) is indeed satisfied.†

† We have here actually a case where one might argue that at the absolute zero there would be two equivalent, completely ordered situations which can be obtained from each other by the interchange of A and B atoms. This would lead to $S = k \ln 2$ at the absolute zero. One might argue that due to external fields (gravitational or otherwise) one or the other of the two ordered states would probably have a slightly smaller energy

Let us now consider the case of a perfect gas. Since at the absolute zero all particles of a Bose-Einstein gas will be in the lowest energy level (compare equation [9.229] on p. 215), it follows from the considerations of Chapter IV that the entropy will be equal to zero at the absolute zero, since there is clearly only one way of distributing all particles over one level. It also follows from the formulae which were derived in §6 of Chapter IV. We found there that the so-called q-potential—or the grand potential (compare the discussion in Chapter VII)—is related to the entropy on the one hand and to the pressure on the other hand by the equations

$$q = \frac{pV}{kT} = \frac{S}{k} + \nu N - \frac{E}{kT}, \tag{A3.302}$$

where V is the volume occupied by the gas, E its total energy, and ν the thermal potential divided by kT. In the case of a perfect Bose-Einstein gas this potential is given by equation (4.609) on page 85, or

$$\frac{pV}{kT} = \left(\frac{2\pi mk}{h^2}\right)^{3/2} T^{3/2} V \sum_{n=1}^{\infty} \frac{e^{n\nu}}{n^{5/2}}. \tag{A3.303}$$

Since we are interested in the value of S at $T = 0$, we are in the condensation region (see Chapter IX) where $\nu = 0$, and we have thus from equations (A3.302) and (A3.303)

$$S = \frac{pV}{T} + \frac{E}{T} = \frac{5}{2}\frac{pV}{T} = \left(\frac{2\pi mk}{h^2}\right)^{3/2} kVT^{3/2}\zeta\left(\frac{5}{2}\right), \tag{A3.304}$$

where we have used the equation

$$pV = \tfrac{2}{3}E, \tag{A3.305}$$

and where $\zeta\ (\frac{5}{2})$ is Riemann's $\zeta =$ function. From equation (A3.304) it is seen immediately that equation (A3.112) is satisfied.

In the case of a perfect Fermi-Dirac gas we could again argue that since there is only one way in which N particles can be distributed over the lowest N levels, the entropy at the absolute zero should be equal to zero. We can also prove this by using equation (4.307) on page 77 for the entropy and using the fact that we have shown in Chapter VII that this equation remains valid, if we put all Z_i equal to 1, so that the N_i reduce to the number of particles in the ith energy level, n_i. We have thus for the

---

in any practical case. However, from this example it can be seen that it must be considered to be highly improbable that it will ever be possible to prove generally that the ground estate of *any* system will be nondegenerate. This does not exclude the possibility mentioned in the footnote on p. 401 that at the absolute zero one will always at most have an entropy of the order of magnitude k. (Compare the discussion of such a situation by Stern (Ann. Physik., **49,** 823, 1916, especially p. 837.)

entropy

$$S = -k\sum_i[(1 - n_i) \ln (1 - n_i) + n_i \ln n_i], \tag{A3.306}$$

and since for $T \to 0$, all n_i corresponding to the lowest N levels go to 1 and all other n_i go to zero, we see that equation (A3.112) holds ($x \ln x \to 0$ for $x \to 0$).

Let us finally consider the melting curve of helium. According to the Clausius-Clapeyron equation we have

$$\frac{dp}{dT} = \frac{\Delta S}{\Delta V}, \tag{A3.307}$$

where ΔS and ΔV are, respectively, the change of entropy and the change of volume during melting, while the left-hand side of this equation gives us the slope of the melting curve in a p-T-diagram. Recent measurements by Simon and Swenson show that indeed the slope of the melting curve becomes zero for $T \to 0$, as should follow from equations (A3.101) and (A3.307). Below 1.4°K dp/dT vanishes as T^7, a most striking example of the third law.

In this connection there is also another point of interest. If ρ be the heat of melting, one has on the one hand the equation

$$\rho = T\Delta S, \tag{A3.308}$$

and on the other hand the equation

$$\rho = \Delta E + p\Delta V, \tag{A3.309}$$

where ΔE is the difference in energy content between the liquid and the solid state. From equations (A3.308) and (A3.101) it follows that $\rho \to 0$ for $T \to 0$. Since ΔV does not vanish at the absolute zero and remains positive, it follows that at sufficiently low temperatures the energy of the liquid is lower than that of the solid, a most unusual situation.

BIBLIOGRAPHICAL NOTES

It would be outside the scope of the present book to enter into a detailed discussion of Nernst's heat theorem, its applications, and its foundations. We refer the interested reader to the extensive discussion given by Simon in 1930. In his survey one can also find an extensive bibliography:

1. F. Simon, Ergeb. exakt. Naturwiss., **9**, 222, 1930.

We may also refer to the following papers:

2. F. Simon, Physica, **4**, 1089, 1937.
3. G. O. Jones and F. E. Simon, Endeavour, **8**, 175, 1949.
4. F. E. Simon, Z. Naturf., **6a**, 397, 1951.

§1. See ref. 1 and

5. P. Jordan, Statistische Mechanik auf Quantentheoretischer Grundlage, Braunschweig 1933, §3.7.

6. R. H. Fowler and E. A. Guggenheim, Statistical Thermodynamics, Cambridge 1939, p. 219.
7. E. Schrödinger, Statistical Thermodynamics, Cambridge 1948, Chap. III.

§2. See refs. 1, 6, and
8. O. Sackur, Ann. Physik, **36,** 958, 1911.
9. H. Tetrode, Ann. Physik, **38,** 434, 1912 (corrections to this paper in Ann. Physik, **39,** 255, 1912).
10. O. Sackur, Ann. Physik, **40,** 67, 1912.
11. H. Tetrode, Proc. Kon. Ned. Akad. Wet. (Amsterdam), **17,** 1167, 1915.
12. P. Ehrenfest and V. Trkal, Proc. Kon. Ned. Akad. Wet. (Amsterdam), **23,** 162, 1920.
13. P. Ehrenfest and V. Trkal, Ann. Physik, **65,** 609, 1921.
14. B. M. Abraham, D. W. Osborne, and B. Weinstock, Phys. Rev., **80,** 366, 1950.

§3. See refs. 1, 5, and
15. F. E. Simon and C. A. Swenson, Nature, **165,** 829, 1950.

APPENDIX IV

THE DARWIN-FOWLER METHOD

§1. **Basic Theory.** In Chapter IV we discussed the elementary method of obtaining the equilibrium values of the various thermodynamical quantities of a system consisting of independent particles, once the energy spectrum of one particle is given. It was found necessary to lump together a large number of energy levels with approximately the same value of the energy. One of the reasons for this procedure—which was not mentioned at that time—was that the elementary method, which consists in identifying the equilibrium situation with the most probable situation, breaks down if we consider the separate levels instead of groups of levels. This can be seen most easily by considering a system of Fermi-Dirac particles (or of Bose-Einstein particles). The relative probability for *any* (permissible) distribution of the particles of the system over the different energy levels will always be the same (see equations [4.211] and [4.214] on p. 73.)† On the other hand, there are cases where it is essential to consider the separate levels as, for instance, in the discussion of the Einstein condensation (see pp. 88 and 212). All these difficulties are removed when we consider canonical grand ensembles, as we saw in Part B. However, there is also another method, devised by Darwin and Fowler, and no book on statistical mechanics would be complete without a discussion of this powerful method. As we mentioned before (see, e.g., p. 129), it is possible to consider both the Darwin-Fowler method and the method of the ensemble theory as mathematical tricks. If one does that there is, of course, nothing to choose between the two methods from a physical point of view, and it is a matter of taste or expediency which of the two methods is chosen. However, we have discussed in Part B why we think that there are strong physical arguments for using the grand ensembles since they can represent a system about which our knowledge is incomplete—as it will practically always be in the case of real systems.

† Compare also the discussion given by Schrödinger, Berliner Ber., **1925**, 434.

In Chapter IV we were concerned with finding the most probable distribution of N particles over given energy levels ϵ_i for a given value of the total energy E. Instead of looking for the most probable distribution we could also have asked for the average distribution. In Appendix I we discussed how Boltzmann emphasized that there were these two ways of defining the equilibrium situation, namely, either by identifying it with the most probable situation, or by identifying it with the average situation. As long as we are dealing with systems consisting of large numbers of particles, the most probable situation will be so much more probable that it is also the average situation. Moreover, by taking the energy levels in groups as is done in Chapter IV, which is necessary in order that one may use Stirling's formula for the factorial, one calculates in fact the average situation and not the most probable situation.†

Our problem is now to calculate the average situation and we shall restrict ourselves to the case of a system in which there is only one kind of independent particle. We can state the problem as follows. Let the weight of a situation where n_1 particles occupy level ϵ_1, n_2 particles occupy level $\epsilon_2, \cdots, n_i$ particles occupy level $\epsilon_i, \cdots$ be $W(n_k)$. It can easily be verified that $W(n_k)$ can always be written in the form

$$W(n_k) = \prod_i \gamma(n_i). \qquad \textbf{(A4.101)}$$

(See equations [4.209], [4.211], and [4.214] on pp. 72–73.) The actual form of the $\gamma(n_i)$ depends on the nature of the particles and is different for the three cases of Boltzmann, Bose-Einstein, or Fermi-Dirac statistics.

We now wish to calculate the average values of the n_i under the supplementary conditions of given total number of particles and given total energy,

$$N = \sum n_i, \qquad \textbf{(A4.102)}$$

$$E = \sum n_i\epsilon_i. \qquad \textbf{(A4.103)}$$

† See Schrödinger, *loc. cit.* One sees this as follows. Let $W(n_k)$ be the probability for a situation where n_i is the number of particles occupying the ith energy level. The most probable situation is found by writing for the entropy, $S = k \ln W_{\text{max}} \cdots (1)$. The average situation, however, corresponds to the equation $S = k \ln \sum W \cdots (2)$. In the elementary method used in Chapter IV we lumped all levels into groups where all levels in one group had about the same energy E_i, and again using equation (1), but now with W being the probability for a situation where N_i particles are in the ith group, we calculated the entropy. We now must take into account the following two facts. (a) The maximum of $W(N_i)$ is so steep that, apart from a negligible constant, we may in equation (2) substitute $W_{\text{max}}(N_i)$ for the sum. (b) $W_{\text{max}}(N_i)$ itself is, however, a sum of several $W(n_k)$ (see equation [4.217] on p. 74). We see thus that by using the $W(N_i)$ instead of the $W(n_k)$ we can reduce equation (2) to equation (1).

We have clearly for the average values n_i the equation

$$\overline{n_i} = \frac{1}{G}\sum{}'' n_i W(n_k), \tag{A4.104}$$

where

$$G = \sum{}'' W(n_k). \tag{A4.105}$$

The summations extend over all possible combinations of the n_k compatible with the conditions (A4.102) and (A4.103); this is indicated by the two primes on the summation signs.

In order to be able to consider fluctuations and correlations we are also interested in expressions of the type

$$\overline{n_i{}^p n_j{}^q} = \frac{1}{G}\sum{}'' n_i{}^p n_j{}^q W(n_k). \tag{A4.106}$$

The first problem is the evaluation of G. This is done by introducing a generating function† $F(x,y;\epsilon_i)$ by the equation

$$F(x,y;\epsilon_i) = \sum W(n_k) x^{n_1+n_2+\cdots} y^{n_1\epsilon_1+n_2\epsilon_2+\cdots}, \tag{A4.107}$$

where the summation is over all values of the n_k without any restrictions. In order to obtain G from $F(x,y;\epsilon_i)$ we must pick out of the sum those terms of which the exponent of x is equal to N and the exponent of y is equal to E. This is done by using the theory of complex functions and one has

$$G = \left(\frac{1}{2\pi i}\right)^2 \oint dx \oint dy\, x^{-N-1} y^{-E-1} F(x,y;\epsilon_i), \tag{A4.108}$$

where both integrations are counterclockwise along a closed contour around the origin in the complex planes of x and y respectively,‡

In a similar way one can show that

$$\overline{n_i{}^p n_j{}^q} = \frac{1}{G}\left(\frac{1}{2\pi i}\right)^2 \oint dx \oint dy\, x^{-N-1} y^{-E-1} \left(\frac{1}{\ln y}\frac{\partial}{\partial \epsilon_i}\right)^p \left(\frac{1}{\ln y}\frac{\partial}{\partial \epsilon_j}\right)^q F(x,y;\epsilon_i). \tag{A4.109}$$

We may remark here that if we use equation (A4.101) for $W(n_k)$, $F(x,y;\epsilon_i)$ can be written as

$$F(x,y;\epsilon_i) = \prod_i f(xy^{\epsilon_i}), \tag{A4.110}$$

† This method goes back to Laplace, who introduced it in his Théorie analytique des Probabilités.

‡ The contours are supposed to lie within the circles of convergence of F. It must be noted that x and y are both complex variables and not the real and imaginary parts of a complex variable.

where

$$f(z) = \sum_{n=0}^{\infty} \gamma(n) z^n. \qquad \textbf{(A4.111)}$$

Equations (A4.108) and (A4.109) are exact. In some cases one can evaluate the integrals and thus obtain exact expressions for the n_i and for the fluctuations (see [a] in the next section). However, in most cases these integrals cannot be evaluated and we must have recourse to approximation methods. One uses the method of the steepest descents described in §2 of the Mathematical Appendix. It can be shown that the integrands of the integrals under consideration possess a steep minimum on the real axis which lies inside the circle of convergence. The path of integration can then be taken through this minimum and the results obtained in the Mathematical Appendix can be used. In order to have our integrals in the form discussed there we write

$$F(x,y;\epsilon_i)x^{-N-1} = e^{Ng(x)}. \qquad \textbf{(A4.112)}$$

Concentrating on the integration over x we are concerned with the integral

$$I(x) = \frac{1}{2\pi i} \oint e^{Ng(x)}, \qquad \textbf{(A4.113)}$$

which, according to equation (MA2.19) on page 443, is approximately given by the equation†

$$I(x) = e^{Ng(x_0)} \sqrt{\frac{1}{2\pi N g''(x_0)}}, \qquad g''(x) = \frac{\partial^2 g}{\partial x^2} \qquad \textbf{(A4.114)}$$

where x_0 satisfies the equation

$$\frac{\partial g}{\partial x} = 0, \qquad \text{or} \qquad x\frac{\partial F}{\partial x} - (N+1)F = 0. \qquad \textbf{(A4.115)}$$

The last factor in the expression for $I(x)$ is only of the order $N^{1/2}$, while the first factor contains a factor N in the exponent. We may therefore to a first approximation neglect the second factor‡ and write

$$I(x) = e^{Ng(x_0)} = F(x_0,y;\epsilon_i){x_0}^{-N-1}. \qquad \textbf{(A4.116)}$$

In a similar way the integration over y can be performed, and we finally get

$$G \cong {x_0}^{-N-1}{y_0}^{-E-1}F(x_0,y_0;\epsilon_i), \qquad \textbf{(A4.117)}$$

† The path is along a circle around the origin so that $\alpha = \frac{1}{2}\pi$.

‡ Since in averages like the ones in equation (A4.109) we are concerned with the ratio of two integrals, the neglect of this factor is completely negligible.

where x_0 and y_0 are the roots of equation (A4.115) and the equation

$$y\frac{\partial F}{\partial y} - (E+1)F = 0. \tag{A4.118}$$

Since the method of the steepest descents provides only a reasonable approximation, if N and E are large, we may neglect the 1 in equations (A4.115) and (A4.118) and have thus

$$N = \frac{x}{F}\frac{\partial F}{\partial x}. \tag{A4.119}$$

$$E = \frac{y}{F}\frac{\partial F}{\partial y}. \tag{A4.120}$$

By the same method we get for $\overline{n_i{}^p n_j{}^q}$,

$$\begin{aligned}\overline{n_i{}^p n_j{}^q} &= \frac{1}{G} x_0{}^{-N-1} y_0{}^{-E-1} \left(\frac{1}{\ln y_0}\frac{\partial}{\partial \epsilon_i}\right)^p \left(\frac{1}{\ln y_0}\frac{\partial}{\partial \epsilon_j}\right)^q F(x_0, y_0; \epsilon_i) \\ &= \frac{1}{F}(\ln y_0)^{-p-q}\left(\frac{\partial}{\partial \epsilon_i}\right)^p \left(\frac{\partial}{\partial \epsilon_j}\right)^q F,\end{aligned} \tag{A4.121}$$

where we used equation (A4.117) for G.

If we use for F equation (A4.110), we see immediately that $\overline{n_i{}^p n_j{}^q}$ is zero unless either p or q is equal to zero, and we then have

$$\overline{n_i{}^p} = (\ln y_0)^{-p}\frac{1}{f_i}\frac{\partial^p f_i}{\partial \epsilon_i{}^p}, \qquad f_i = f(x_0 y_0{}^{\epsilon_i}), \tag{A4.122}$$

where f is given by equation (A4.111).

Equations (A4.117), (A4.122), (A4.119), and (A4.120) together give us all the necessary information and we shall use these equations in the next section when discussing various applications.

§2. Applications. We shall consider the following examples:

a) A perfect gas in a volume V without an external field of force. (In this case we are not concerned with condition [A4.103].)

b) A system of independent particles, obeying either Boltzmann, Bose-Einstein, or Fermi-Dirac statistics.

a) Let the volume V be divided into m equal cells and let $n_1, n_2, \cdots, n_m$ be the number of particles in cells $1, 2, \cdots, m$. The probability $W(n_k)$ for a distribution $n_1, n_2, \cdots$ is clearly given by the equation

$$W(n_k) = N! \prod_{i=1}^{m} (n_i!)^{-1}. \tag{A4.201}$$

There is only one supplementary condition to be satisfied by the n_i, namely,

$$\Sigma n_i = N. \tag{A4.202}$$

In order to calculate G we must find the coefficient of x^N in the following generating function,

$$F(x) = \Sigma W(n_k)x^{n_1+n_2+\cdots}. \tag{A4.203}$$

The sum on the right-hand side of equation (A4.203) can be calculated and we have

$$F(x) = N! \prod_{i=1}^{m} \sum_{n_i=0}^{\infty} \frac{x^{n_i}}{n_i!} = N!e^{mx}, \tag{A4.204}$$

and thus

$$G = m^N. \tag{A4.205}$$

In order to find $\overline{n_i}$ we must find the coefficient of x^N in the generating function $F_i(x)$ given by the equation

$$\begin{aligned} F_i(x) &= \frac{1}{G}\Sigma W(n_k)n_i x^{n_1+n_2+\cdots} \\ &= \frac{N!}{G}\Sigma \frac{n_i x^{n_1+n_2+\cdots}}{n_1!n_2!\cdots} = \frac{N!xe^{mx}}{G}, \end{aligned} \tag{A4.206}$$

and hence

$$\overline{n_i} = \frac{N!\dfrac{m^{N-1}}{(N-1)!}}{G} = \frac{N}{m}, \tag{A4.207}$$

which expresses the uniform distribution of the gas over the volume.

The fluctuations can also easily be calculated. We must find the coefficient of x^N in the generating function $F_{ii}(x)$ given by the equation

$$\begin{aligned} F_{ii}(x) &= \frac{1}{G}\Sigma W(n_k)n_i^2 x^{n_1+n_2+\cdots} \\ &= \frac{N!}{G}x(x+1)e^{mx}. \end{aligned} \tag{A4.208}$$

We thus get

$$\begin{aligned} \overline{n_i^2} &= \frac{N!}{m^N}\left[\frac{m^{N-2}}{(N-2)!} + \frac{m^{N-1}}{(N-1)!}\right] \\ &= \frac{N(N-1)}{m^2} + \frac{N}{m}, \end{aligned} \tag{A4.209}$$

and for the fluctuations we get

$$\overline{(n_i - \overline{n_i})^2} = \overline{n_i^2} - \bar{n}_i^2 = \overline{n_i}\left(1 - \frac{\overline{n_i}}{N}\right), \tag{A4.210}$$

showing that the distribution is practically normal.†

The generating functions could be evaluated exactly in this example. That is, however, an exception and in most cases the method of the steepest descents must be used.

b) We now have the two conditions (A4.102) and (A4.103) and can use immediately formulae (A4.122). The difference between the various statistics lies in the expressions for the $\gamma(n_i)$. We have (see equations [4.209], [4.211], and [4.214] on pp. 72–73, and equation [A4.101])

$$\text{Boltzmann:} \quad \gamma(n_i) = \frac{1}{n_i!}; \tag{A4.211}$$

$$\text{Bose-Einstein:} \quad \gamma(n_i) = 1; \tag{A4.212}$$

$$\text{Fermi-Dirac:} \quad \left.\begin{aligned} \gamma(n_i) &= 1, \quad n_i = 0 \quad \text{or} \quad 1, \\ &= 0, \quad n_i > 1. \end{aligned}\right\} \tag{A4.213}$$

And we get from equation (A4.111) for the functions f,

$$f_{\text{Bo}} = \sum_{n=0}^{\infty} \frac{z^n}{n!} = e^z, \tag{A4.214}$$

$$f_{\text{B.E.}} = \sum_{n=0}^{\infty} z^n = \frac{1}{1-z}, \tag{A4.215}$$

$$f_{\text{F.D.}} = \sum_{n=0}^{1} z^n = 1 + z. \tag{A4.216}$$

We then get from equation (A4.110) for F

$$F_{\text{Bo}} = e^{x\sum_i y^{\epsilon_i}}, \tag{A4.217}$$

$$F_{\text{B.E.}} = \prod_i \frac{1}{1 - xy^{\epsilon_i}}, \tag{A4.218}$$

$$F_{\text{F.D.}} = \prod_i (1 + xy^{\epsilon_i}). \tag{A4.219}$$

† A normal distribution is one for which $\overline{(n_i - \overline{n_i})^2} = \overline{n_i}$. Equation (A4.210) shows that, strictly speaking, the n_i-distribution is infranormal.

The x_0 and y_0 follow from equations (A4.119) and (A4.120), or

$$N = \sum_i \frac{\partial \ln f_i}{\partial \ln x_0}, \tag{A4.220}$$

$$E = \sum_i \frac{\partial \ln f_i}{\partial \ln y_0}. \tag{A4.221}$$

Using equations (A4.122) with $p = 1$ we see that equations (A4.220) and (A4.221) can be written in the following translucent form:

$$N = \sum_i \overline{n_i}, \tag{A4.222}$$

$$E = \sum_i \overline{n_i}\epsilon_i. \tag{A4.223}$$

From equation (A4.122) we have

$$\overline{n_i} = \frac{x_0}{f_i}\frac{\partial f_i}{\partial x_0}, \tag{A4.224}$$

or, using equations (A4.214) to (A4.216),

$$(\overline{n_i})_{\text{Bo}} = x_0 y_0^{\epsilon_i}, \tag{A4.225}$$

$$(\overline{n_i})_{\text{B.E.}} = \frac{x_0 y_0^{\epsilon_i}}{1 - x_0 y_0^{\epsilon_i}}, \tag{A4.226}$$

$$(\overline{n_i})_{\text{F.D.}} = \frac{x_0 y_0^{\epsilon_i}}{1 + x_0 y_0^{\epsilon_i}}. \tag{A4.227}$$

If we compare expressions (A4.225) to (A4.227) with equations (7.511), (7.606), and (7.705) on pages 165, 167, and 168, we see that we have the same equations, provided

$$y_0 = e^{-\frac{1}{kT}}, \tag{A4.228}$$

$$x_0 = e^{\nu}. \tag{A4.229}$$

These equations give us the physical meaning of x_0 and y_0. They can be derived directly, as was done by Darwin and Fowleı in their original papers.

We can also calculate the fluctuations in the n_i and find by a straightforward calculation, using equation (A4.122) with $p = 2$,

$$[\overline{(n_i - \overline{n_i})^2}]_{\text{Bo}} = \overline{n_i}, \tag{A4.230}$$

$$[\overline{(n_i - \overline{n_i})^2}]_{\text{B.E.}} = \overline{n_i} + \overline{n_i}^2, \tag{A4.231}$$

$$[\overline{(n_i - \overline{n_i})^2}]_{\text{F.D.}} = \overline{n_i} - \overline{n_i}^2, \tag{A4.232}$$

which are the same as equations (7.513), (7.607), and (7.706).

We see that we can derive by using the Darwin-Fowler method the same formulae which in Chapter VII were derived by the method of the grand ensembles. If we wish to calculate the fluctuations in the energy of a system in temperature equilibrium, the Darwin-Fowler method can also be used, but must then be applied to an ensemble, the total energy of which is constant. The introduction of an ensemble is also necessary in order to apply the method to imperfect gases. The results are the same as those we derived by using the method of the grand ensembles, as would be expected.

BIBLIOGRAPHICAL NOTES

The Darwin-Fowler method was first developed in the following papers:

1. C. G. Darwin and R. H. Fowler, Phil. Mag., **44,** 450, 1922.
2. C. G. Darwin and R. H. Fowler, Phil. Mag., **44,** 823, 1922.
3. C. G. Darwin and R. H. Fowler, Proc. Cambridge Phil. Soc., **21,** 262, 1922.
4. R. H. Fowler, Phil. Mag., **45,** 1, 1923.
5. R. H. Fowler, Phil. Mag., **45,** 497, 1923.
6. C. G. Darwin and R. H. Fowler, Proc. Cambridge Phil. Soc., **21,** 391, 1923.
7. C. G. Darwin and R. H. Fowler, Proc. Cambridge Phil. Soc., **21,** 730, 1923.
8. R. H. Fowler, Proc. Cambridge Phil. Soc., **22,** 861, 1925.
9. R. H. Fowler, Phil. Mag., **1,** 845, 1926.
10. R. H. Fowler, Proc. Roy. Soc. (London), **A113,** 432, 1926.

See also

11. R. H. Fowler, Statistical Mechanics, Cambridge 1936.
12. G. E. Uhlenbeck, Over Statistische Methoden in de Theorie der Quanta, Thesis, Leiden 1927, Chap. II.
13. E. Schrödinger, Statistical Thermodynamics, Cambridge 1948, Chap. VI.

APPENDIX V

INTERMOLECULAR FORCES

§1. General Discussion. From the discussion in Parts A, B, and C it is clear that one of the most important functions which enter into the discussion of particular physical systems is the intermolecular potential energy $\varphi(r)$. Especially in the discussion of the equation of state (Chapter VIII) and of condensation phenomena (Chapter IX) did we encounter this function, but in disguised form it also entered other chapters of Part C. The interaction energies entering into the order-disorder theories and the scattering laws for electrons in a metal, for instance, are quantities which are directly related to the forces between the various particles.

In Chapter VIII we discussed briefly the method of Keesom, later extended by De Boer and Michels to include quantum effects, by which intermolecular forces could be derived from the experimental data regarding the second virial coefficient. This method consisted essentially in choosing a particular form of the interaction potential—usually a Lennard-Jones potential—which contained a few undetermined parameters. The values of these parameters were then determined by seeking a reasonable fit between computed and measured values of the second virial coefficient. An additional incentive for using a potential of this type was that it led—as we saw in Chapter VIII—to a law of corresponding states, known to be approximately correct for various classes of substances.†

There is, however, another way of approaching the question of intermolecular forces, namely, by deriving them from first principles. This is a more fundamental method of approach, but the calculations which are necessary in order to compute the potential energy function are so cumbersome that it can be used completely only in the cases of the simplest molecules, such as H, He, and H_2. On the other hand, semifundamental methods can also be used, as we shall see at the end of this appendix. These consist in computing the forces from first principles, but determining

† The fact that a law of corresponding states exists points to the existence of relations between the parameters entering into the potential energy. For instance, in the case of a potential energy of the form (A5.108) one should expect $B\alpha^6/A$ to be approximately constant for all substances belonging to the class for which the law of corresponding states holds (compare D. ter Haar, Physica, **19**, 375, 1953).

from experimental data the parameters which enter the expression for the potential energy.

Before we describe in somewhat more detail some of the methods by which it is possible to determine intermolecular forces, we shall briefly consider the various possibilities of intermolecular forces. One might argue that all these forces will be of electromagnetic character as they derive from the interaction between the orbital electrons of the two molecules, with possibly a slight contribution from the electrostatic fields of the nuclei. However, for the sake of simplicity we shall call only those forces electrostatic which are due to charges, dipoles, or higher multipole moments of the molecules. We shall restrict ourselves to forces between like particles. The extension to unlike particles can easily be made.

The intermolecular forces fall, roughly speaking, into four categories, although it must be borne in mind that such a division is artificial and that in actual fact several kinds of forces will be present at the same time and that they will interact and influence each other, although one can usually neglect this mutual interaction. The four categories of intermolecular forces are as follows:

a) Electrostatic forces between ions

b) Electrostatic forces between atoms possessing permanent dipole, quadrupole or higher multipole moments

c) Van der Waals' forces

d) Repulsive forces

a) *Forces between ions.* If $\varphi_1(r)$ be the potential energy of two ions at a distance r apart, we have from electromagnetic theory

$$\varphi_1(r) = \frac{Z^2e^2}{r}, \qquad \textbf{(A5.101)}$$

where Ze is the charge per ion. The forces are repulsive long-range Coulomb forces.

b) *Forces between multipoles.* If φ_2 be the potential energy in this case, we have from electromagnetic theory

$$\varphi_2 = f\frac{\mu^2}{r^3}, \qquad \textbf{(A5.102)}$$

in the case of two permanent dipoles moments μ, or

$$\varphi_2 = g\frac{Q^2}{r^5}, \qquad \textbf{(A5.103)}$$

in the case of two permanent quadrupole moments Q, and so on. The functions f and g depend on the relative orientations of the two moments, that is, we are dealing in these cases with forces which do not depend only on the distance apart.

If one is interested in computing, for instance, the equation of state of a dipole gas, one must average the potential energy φ_2 over all possible orientations. If these orientations all had the same weight, the average would be zero, but attractive relative orientations will have a smaller potential energy and hence greater weight. The net result in a gas is thus an attractive force due to the preponderance of attractive alignments (Keesom's Richteffekt). The average interaction energy turns out to be of the form

$$\overline{\varphi_2} = -\frac{\mu^4}{r^6}. \tag{A5.104}$$

c) *Van der Waals' forces.* The term "van der Waals' forces" is not very well defined. Margenau defines it as those forces which give rise to the term a in van der Waals' equation of state (equation [1.303] on p. 7). In that case Keesom's alignment forces are included among the van der Waals' forces.

It is immediately clear that Keesom's alignment effect cannot be used to explain all attractive forces, as most molecules do not possess dipole moments, or even quadrupole moments.† However, even if these moments were present, the alignment would decrease with increasing temperature, as the statistical weight factors for the different orientations would tend to become equal. It was, however, known that the attractive forces persisted up to relatively high temperatures and Debye therefore suggested a different explanation for the attractive forces. He pointed out that molecules are not rigid structures, but deformable distributions of charge. Hence, if the molecules possess dipole or quadrupole moments, they can polarize other molecules and thus produce an attractive force which is independent of temperature. The average interaction energy between two polarizable quadrupole moments Q is given by the equation

$$\overline{\varphi_2} = -k\alpha\frac{Q^2}{r^8}, \tag{A5.105}$$

where α is the polarizability of the molecule and where k is a numerical factor.

The polarizability α is defined by the equation

$$\Delta\epsilon = -\tfrac{1}{2}\alpha E^2, \tag{A5.106}$$

† Keesom attempted to account for the attractive forces by postulating quadrupole moments, but the numerical values of the quadrupole moments he had to assume in order to explain the observed equation of state are far larger than the values following from our present knowledge of atomic structure.

where $\Delta\epsilon$ is the change of energy when the molecule is placed in an electric field of strength E.

Even Debye's induction effect is, however, insufficient to account for the attractive forces between molecules, unless we use values of the quadrupole or dipole moments which are much higher than the values following from modern atomic theory.

A general effect which could account satisfactorily for the observed attractive forces was discussed in 1930 by London. This effect is related to the process of optical dispersion, as we shall see in §2, and was thus named by London the *dispersion effect,* whence the attractive van der Waals' forces are called *dispersion forces.* The effect is roughly the following one. Consider two atoms, say, for the sake of simplicity, two hydrogen atoms. The wave functions of their electrons have spherical symmetry about the nucleus and hence would not influence each other if the charge distribution corresponding to these wave functions were static. However, the current density corresponding even to the ground state of the hydrogen atom is not zero and therefore each atom can act as a temporary dipole which can polarize and thus attract the other atom. One obtains in this way a rough qualitative picture of the electrons in the two hydrogen atoms "moving in phase" and thus producing an attractive force of the same character as the force described by equation (A5.104). The main part of the dispersion forces varies, indeed, as $1/r^6$.

d) *Repulsive forces.* When two atoms approach each other closely they will repel each other. This is due partly to the repulsive forces between the nuclei and partly to the impenetrability of the electron clouds. This latter effect is a typical quantum effect like the dispersion forces and, indeed, in principle by solving the Schrödinger equation one should be able to derive the potential energy as a function of the distance apart of the two nuclei. This has been done in the case of the interaction between two hydrogen atoms and also in the case of two helium atoms, and the potential energy is, indeed, found to behave in the way we expected from our rough qualitative arguments. It turns out that in the case of the inert gases (He, Ne, A, Xe) the repulsive potential energy is of the form

$$\varphi_4 = P(r)e^{-\alpha r}, \tag{A5.107}$$

where $P(r)$ is a polynomial in r. To a fair approximation $P(r)$ may be taken to be constant and we obtain, then, to a first approximation for the total potential energy an equation of the form

$$\varphi(r) = Ae^{-\alpha r} - \frac{B}{r^6}\cdot \tag{A5.108}$$

Buckingham† has, indeed, found that a potential energy of this form can satisfactorily describe the behavior of He, Ne, and A.

In the next section we shall describe in some more detail how one can in general obtain from first principles the potential energy corresponding to the forces between nonpolar molecules. We shall mainly be concerned with the van der Waals' forces and we refer to the literature mentioned in the bibliographical notes at the end of this appendix for a discussion of the forces between polar molecules, the repulsive forces, and for a discussion of special cases.

§2. Derivation of Intermolecular Forces by Perturbation Theory. We shall assume, for the sake of simplicity, that we are considering two atoms. Let the distance apart of their two nuclei be denoted by r. Our problem is to find the energy of the system consisting of the two atoms. This energy will contain r as a parameter so that we shall obtain an expression of the energy as a function of r.

Let us formulate our problem quantitatively. Our problem is to find the lowest characteristic value of the Schrödinger equation

$$\mathcal{H}\Psi = E\Psi, \tag{A5.201}$$

where the Hamiltonian $\mathcal{H}$ contains three parts,

$$\mathcal{H} = \mathcal{H}' + \mathcal{H}'' + \mathcal{H}_{\text{int}}. \tag{A5.202}$$

In equation (A5.202) $\mathcal{H}'$ is the Hamiltonian of the first atom, $\mathcal{H}''$ that of the second atom, and $\mathcal{H}_{\text{int}}$ the interaction Hamiltonian.

As it will not be possible to solve equation (A5.201) exactly we must use approximate methods. The first method which suggests itself is a perturbation method. Let us for the moment suppose that we know the solutions of the Schrödinger equations

$$\mathcal{H}'\psi' = E'\psi' \quad \text{and} \quad \mathcal{H}''\psi'' = E''\psi''. \tag{A5.203}$$

We now assume that to a first approximation equation (A5.201) is solved by

$$\Psi = \psi' \cdot \psi'', \qquad E = E' + E'', \tag{A5.204}$$

that is, we assume that $\mathcal{H}_{\text{int}}$ may be neglected with respect to $\mathcal{H}' + \mathcal{H}''$. Considering $\mathcal{H}_{\text{int}}$ as a small perturbation we can then use the normal method of perturbation theory to find the change in energy ΔE. The result is

$$\Delta E = \frac{3e^4\hbar^4}{2m^2r^6} \sum_{k,l} \frac{f_{0k}'f_{0l}''}{(E_k' - E_0')(E_l'' - E_0'')(E_0' + E_0'' - E_k' - E_l'')} \tag{A5.205}$$

† R. A. Buckingham, Proc. Roy. Soc., (London), **A168**, 264, 1938.

In equation (A5.205) m is the electron mass; f_{0k}' and f_{0l}'' are the oscillator strengths corresponding to the transitions from E_0' to E_k' and from E_0'' to E_l'', respectively; and E_0', E_0'', E_k' and E_l'' are, respectively, the ground state energies of the two atoms and the energies of the kth and lth excited states; the summation is over all states which do not lead to vanishing denominators. The oscillator strengths are defined by the equation

$$f_{0k} = \frac{2m}{\hbar^2}(E_k - E_0) \mid X_{0k} \mid^2, \tag{A5.206}$$

where X_{0k} is the matrix element corresponding to the transition from E_0 to E_k of the operator

$$X = \sum_i x_i \tag{A5.207}$$

where the x_i are the x-coordinates of the positions of the electrons in the atom and where the summation is over all electrons in the atom. In deriving equation (A5.205) we have assumed both atoms to be in the ground state. From equations (A5.205) and (A5.206) and the fact that $E_k' > E_0'$, $E_l'' > E_0''$ it follows that ΔE is negative for atoms in their ground state. We see thus that *molecules in their ground states attract each other.*

We cannot give here a derivation of equation (A5.205). It follows directly from applying the usual methods of perturbation theory† and using the fact that the first order ΔE is equal to zero. The perturbation energy $\mathcal{H}_{\text{int}}$ is given by the equation

$$\mathcal{H}_{\text{int}} = \sum_i e_i \Phi(\mathbf{r} + \mathbf{r}_i), \tag{A5.208}$$

where the summation extends over all electrons of the second atom, where $\Phi(\mathbf{r} + \mathbf{r}_i)$ is the potential due to the electrons of the first atom at the position of the electrons of the second atom, where $\mathbf{r}$ is the vector from the first to the second nucleus, and where the $\mathbf{r}_i$ are the position vectors of the electrons in the second atom taken from the second nucleus as origin. The potential Φ is the sum of the electrostatic potentials of the electrons of the first atom,

$$\Phi(\mathbf{R}) = \sum_j \frac{e_j}{\mid \mathbf{R} - \mathbf{r}_j \mid}, \tag{A5.209}$$

where now the $\mathbf{r}_j$ are taken from the first nucleus as origin and the summation extends over all electrons in the first atom. From equations (A5.208) and (A5.209) it follows‡ that we have

$$\mathcal{H}_{\text{int}} = -\frac{1}{r^3}\sum_{i,j} e_i e_j (2z_i z_j - x_i x_j - y_i y_j), \tag{A5.210}$$

$$= \frac{e^2}{r^3}[X'X'' + Y'Y'' - 2Z'Z''], \tag{A5.211}$$

† See, for instance, H. A. Kramers, Hand- u. Jahrb. d. Chem. Phys., Vol. I, Leipzig 1938, §48.

‡ See, for instance, H. Margenau, Phys. Rev., **38**, 747, 1931.

where the summation in equation (A5.210) extends over the electrons of both atoms, i pertaining to the one atom and j to the other atom, where we have neglected higher powers of $1/r$, where we have taken the z-axis along $\mathbf{r}$, and where we have used equation (A5.207) and similar equations for Y and Z to get equation (A5.211).

The fact that the oscillator strengths f_{0k}, which also occur in the formula for the optical dispersion of the atom, enter into equation (A5.205) is the reason why the attractive London-van der Waals' forces are called dispersion forces.

In order to evaluate ΔE one must know the f_{0k}. These are known only for hydrogen, but it is often possible to use the following semi-empirical method for evaluating the right-hand side of equation (A5.205). The polarizability α of the atom in its ground state is related on the one hand to the f_{0k} by the equation

$$\alpha = \frac{e^2\hbar^2}{m} \sum_k \frac{f_{0k}}{(E_k - E_0)^2 - (h\nu)^2}, \tag{A5.212}$$

and on the other hand to the index of refraction r by the equation

$$\frac{\mathsf{r}^2 + 1}{\mathsf{r}^2 + 2} = \frac{4\pi n}{3}\alpha, \tag{A5.213}$$

where n is the number of atoms per unit volume. From the measurements of r one can determine α, and it turns out that often to a fair approximation only one term of the sum in equation (A5.212) contributes appreciably. In that case we have approximately

$$f_{0k} = 0 \text{ for all } k \neq l, \quad f_{0l} = \alpha_{\nu=0} \frac{m}{e^2\hbar^2} \Delta^2, \quad \Delta = E_l - E_0. \tag{A5.214}$$

From equation (A5.205) we then get

$$\Delta E = -\frac{3\Delta}{r^6} (\alpha_{\nu=0})^2. \tag{A5.215}$$

In many cases Δ turns out to be approximately equal to the ionization energy. Equation (A5.215) has been used to evaluate the attractive van der Waals' forces for many substances.

If one takes into account higher-order terms which are neglected in equation (A5.211), one obtains higher-order terms of the van der Waals' forces. The discussion of these terms is, however, outside the scope of this appendix.

A different method for obtaining ΔE is to use variational methods. These are especially important if one wants to obtain both the repulsive and the attractive forces. We refer to the literature mentioned in the bibliographical notes for a discussion of this method.

BIBLIOGRAPHICAL NOTES†

We may mention the following general references:

1. H. Hellmann, Einführung in die Quantenchemie, Leipzig-Vienna 1937, Chap. V.
2. E. H. Kennard, Kinetic Theory of Gases, New York 1938, 130.
3. H. Margenau, Revs. Modern Phys., **11**, 1, 1939.
4. R. H. Fowler, Statistical Mechanics, Cambridge 1936, Chap. X.

In refs. 1 and 3 it is shown how intermolecular forces can be derived from first principles and both give elaborate lists of further references. Reference 2 gives a general discussion of the various component parts of intermolecular forces, while in ref. 4 it is shown how one can derive information about intermolecular forces from experimental data, such as the equation of state, viscosity, or properties of crystals.

§1. See refs. 2 and 3. Keesom's Richteffekt is discussed in

5. W. H. Keesom, Physik. Z., **22**, 129, 1921.

See also the following paper discussing Debye's induction effect:

6. P. Debye, Physik. Z., **21**, 178, 1920.

The dispersion effect was discussed by London in

7. F. London, Z. Physik, **63**, 245, 1930.

The repulsive forces, sometimes called *Heitler-London forces*, are discussed in

8. W. Heitler and F. London, Z. Physik, **44**, 455, 1927.

An extensive discussion can be found in Hellmann's book:

9. H. Hellmann, Einführung in die Quantenchemie, Leipzig-Vienna 1937, Chap. IV.

See also

10. J. C. Slater, Phys. Rev., **32**, 349, 1928.
11. N. Rosen, Phys. Rev., **38**, 255, 1931.
12. H. M. James, A. S. Coolidge, and R. D. Present, J. Chem. Phys., **4**, 187, 1936.
13. H. Margenau, Phys. Rev., **56**, 1000, 1939.
14. P. Rosen, J. Chem. Phys., **18**, 1182, 1950.

§2. See references 1, 3, 7, and

15. R. Eisenschitz and F. London, Z. Physik, **60**, 491, 1930.
16. J. E. Lennard-Jones, Proc. Phys. Soc. (London), **43**, 461, 1931.
17. J. C. Slater and J. G. Kirkwood, Phys. Rev., **37**, 682, 1931.
18. H. Margenau, Phys. Rev., **38**, 747, 1931.
19. R. A. Buckingham, Proc. Roy. Soc. (London), **A160**, 113, 1937.
20. H. Margenau, J. Chem. Phys., **6**, 896, 1938.
21. F. G. Brooks, Phys. Rev., **86**, 92, 1952.
22. J. F. Hornig and J. O. Hirschfelder, J. Chem. Phys., **20**, 1812, 1952.

Our treatment follows mainly ref. 3.

At the end of these bibliographical notes is a list of some references dealing with more specific cases. The case of the interaction between two helium atoms has probably been discussed in the greatest detail. See refs. 10, 11, 13, 14, 17, 18, and

23. H. Margenau, Phys. Rev., **37**, 1425, 1931.

† I am greatly indebted to Dr. H. Margenau for putting an extensive bibliography on van der Waals' forces at my disposal.

24. W. H. Keesom, Helium, Amsterdam-New York 1942, Chap. VIII.
25. J. de Boer and A. Michels, Physica, **5**, 945, 1938.
26. J. de Boer, Contribution to the Theory of Compressed Gases, Thesis, Amsterdam 1940.
27. J. O. Hirschfelder, R. B. Ewell, and J. R. Roebuck, J. Chem. Phys., **6**, 205, 1938.
In the last three references the form of the intermolecular potential energy is derived from experimental data about the equation of state and the Joule-Thomson coefficient (compare also §8 of Chapter VIII).
The interaction between a hydrogen molecule and a hydrogen atom is discussed by Margenau in
28. H. Margenau, Phys. Rev., **66**, 303, 1944,
and that between two hydrogen molecules by De Boer and Margenau:
29. J. de Boer, Physica, **9**, 363, 1942.
30. H. Margenau, Phys. Rev., **63**, 385, 1943.
Other references to specific cases are
31. H. Margenau, Philosophy of Science, **8**, 603, 1941 (forces between ions and neutral molecules).
32. H. Margenau and W. G. Pollard, Phys. Rev., **60**, 128, 1941 (forces between a metal surface and neutral molecules).
33. R. Meyerott, Phys. Rev., **66**, 242, 1944 (He-Li^+).
34. H. Margenau and V. Myers, Phys. Rev., **66**, 307, 1944 (water).
35. V. Myers, J. Chem. Phys., **18**, 1442, 1950 (benzene and ammonia).
36. V. Myers, J. Chem. Phys., **20**, 1806, 1952 (acetone, methyl alcohol).
Finally we may draw attention to a paper by Casimir and Polder in which they show that due to retardation effects the asymptotic expression for the London-van der Waals' forces is not proportional to r^{-6} but to r^{-7}:
37. H. B. G. Casimir and D. Polder, Phys. Rev., **73**, 360, 1948.
See also
38. H. B. G. Casimir, Proc. Kon. Ned. Akad. Wet. (Amsterdam), **51**, 793, 1948.

APPENDIX VI

RELATIVISTIC STATISTICS

§1. The Electron Gas; General Formulae. Although in all applications in Parts A, B, and C except in Chapter XIV we have used only nonrelativistic formulae, it can easily be shown that most formulae in Parts A and B can immediately be adapted to the case of relativistic statistics. We wish to discuss in this appendix how such an adaptation can be made and we have chosen as the case to be discussed in some detail the case of a gas of free electrons, since this is the case which has been of most interest in the application of relativistic statistics. These applications have been in the field of astrophysics and especially in the discussion of the theory of white dwarfs by Fowler, Chandrasekhar, and other authors† (see also Chapter XIV). We are thus confining ourselves to the case of a system of independent Fermi-Dirac particles. On inspection it will be seen that we can use most of the results of Chapter VII and we have, for instance, for the grand potential q from equation (7.703) on page 168

$$q = \sum_s \ln\,(1 + e^{\nu - \mu\epsilon_s}), \tag{A6.101}$$

where the summation is over all energy levels of one particle and where we have put

$$\mu = \frac{1}{\Theta} = \frac{1}{kT}\cdot \tag{A6.102}$$

In the derivation of equation (A6.101) no use was made of the fact that in Chapter VII we were interested only in the nonrelativistic case, but only of the fact that we are dealing with a system of independent particles, since the ϵ_s are the energy levels of one particle.

If the energy levels are lying sufficiently densely, the sum in equation (A6.101) may be replaced by an integral and we have

$$q = \int \ln\,(1 + e^{\nu - \mu\epsilon})dZ, \tag{A6.103}$$

† We refer for an account of the application of relativistic statistics to the theory of white dwarfs to S. Chandrasekhar, An Introduction to the Study of Stellar Structure, Chicago 1939, Chapters X and XI. The reader will also find extensive bibliographies there.

where dZ is once again the number of energy levels between ϵ and $\epsilon + d\epsilon$.

It is at this juncture that the relativistic case differs from the nonrelativistic one. We can no longer use for dZ (equation [4.504] on p. 82), but we must derive its relativistic counterpart. We shall again assume the gas to be enclosed in a cube of edge length L and volume $V = L^3$. The wave functions of a free particle which satisfy the Dirac equations can be written as

$$\psi_\lambda = a_\lambda e^{\frac{i}{\hbar}(\mathfrak{p}\cdot\mathbf{x} - \epsilon t)}, \tag{A6.104}$$

where λ runs from 1 to 4, where the ψ_λ are the four components of the Dirac wave function, and where the momentum $\mathfrak{p}$† and the energy ϵ are related to each other as follows:

$$\frac{\epsilon^2}{c^2} = \mathfrak{p}^2 + m^2c^2. \tag{A6.105}$$

Moreover, for a given $\mathfrak{p}$ there are two linearly independent solutions of the Dirac equations, which means that each energy level is twofold degenerate. This degeneracy is the usual spin degeneracy ($g_s = 2s + 1$, $s = \frac{1}{2}$).

The fact that the particle is enclosed in a cube of edge length L entails that not all values of $\mathfrak{p}_x$, $\mathfrak{p}_y$, and $\mathfrak{p}_z$ are permissible, but only those which satisfy the equations

$$\mathfrak{p}_x = \frac{k_1 h}{L}, \qquad \mathfrak{p}_y = \frac{k_2 h}{L}, \qquad \mathfrak{p}_z = \frac{k_3 h}{L}, \tag{A6.106}$$

where the k_i can take on the values $\pm 1, \pm 2, \cdots$.‡

Substituting expressions (A6.106) into equation (A6.105), we have

$$\frac{\epsilon^2}{c^2} = \frac{h^2k^2}{L^2} + m^2c^2, \tag{A6.107}$$

where

$$k^2 = k_1{}^2 + k_2{}^2 + k_3{}^2. \tag{A6.108}$$

In terms of k we have for dZ (compare equation [4.503] and the second footnote on this page)

$$dZ = 8\pi k^2\, dk. \tag{A6.109}$$

From equations (A6.107) and (A6.109) we now get

$$dZ = \frac{8\pi}{h^3} V \left(\frac{\epsilon^2}{c^2} - m^2c^2\right)^{1/2} \frac{\epsilon d\epsilon}{c^2}. \tag{A6.110}$$

† We use the symbol $\mathfrak{p}$ for the momentum in order to distinguish it from the pressure p.

‡ The situation is slightly different here from the case discussed in §5 of Chapter IV. In the nonrelativistic case the wave functions with negative values of the k_i are not linearly independent of those with only positive values of the k_i, but in the relativistic case they are.

If the energy ϵ is only just larger than the rest energy mc^2, we can write $\epsilon = mc^2 + \epsilon'$, where ϵ' is now the usual nonrelativistic energy. Substituting this expression into equation (A6.110) and neglecting all terms but the most important one, we get

$$dZ = 4\pi \left(\frac{2m}{h^2}\right)^{3/2} V\sqrt{\epsilon'}d\epsilon', \tag{A6.111}$$

which is equation (4.504) apart from a factor 2 due to the spin.

If we introduce as variable instead of ϵ the absolute magnitude $\mathfrak{p}$ of the momentum, we can write equation (A6.110) by using equation (A6.110) in the form†

$$dZ = 2 \cdot \frac{V \cdot 4\pi\mathfrak{p}^2 d\mathfrak{p}}{h^3} \cdot \tag{A6.112}$$

Since $4\mathfrak{p}^2 d\mathfrak{p} \cdot V$ is the volume in phase space corresponding to momenta of absolute magnitude between $\mathfrak{p}$ and $\mathfrak{p} + d\mathfrak{p}$, equation (A6.112) expresses the fact that to each volume h^3 in μ-space there correspond two stationary states, the factor 2 arising from spin degeneracy.

From equations (A6.103) and (A6.110) we now have for the grand potential

$$q = \frac{8\pi}{h^3c^3} V \int \epsilon(\epsilon^2 - m^2c^4)^{1/2} \ln(1 + e^{\nu - \mu\epsilon}) d\epsilon, \tag{A6.113}$$

where the integration extends from mc^2 to ∞.

We remarked that the energy ϵ contains the rest energy. As a consequence, the ν in the equations of this appendix differs from the ν encountered, for instance, in Chapter VII by a term μmc^2. If we denote the ν of Chapter VII by ν', we have $\nu - \mu\epsilon = \nu' - \mu\epsilon'$, or

$$\nu = \nu' + \mu mc^2. \tag{A6.114}$$

From equations (7.415), (7.416), and (7.414) on pages 157–158, we have now for the total number of particles, N, the total energy (including the rest energy Nmc^2), E, and the pressure p the following equations:

$$N = \frac{\partial q}{\partial \nu} = \frac{8\pi}{h^3c^3} V \int_{mc^2}^{\infty} \frac{\epsilon(\epsilon^2 - m^2c^4)^{1/2}}{e^{-\nu+\mu\epsilon} + 1} d\epsilon, \tag{A6.115}$$

$$E = -\frac{\partial q}{\partial \mu} = \frac{8\pi}{h^3c^3} V \int_{mc^2}^{\infty} \frac{\epsilon^2(\epsilon^2 - m^2c^4)^{1/2}}{e^{-\nu+\mu\epsilon} + 1} d\epsilon, \tag{A6.116}$$

$$p = \frac{kT}{V} q = \frac{8\pi}{h^3c^3} kT \int_{mc^2}^{\infty} \epsilon(\epsilon^2 - m^2c^4)^{1/2} \ln(1 + e^{\nu-\mu\epsilon}) d\epsilon. \tag{A6.117}$$

† It can easily be verified by using the nonrelativistic relation $\epsilon' = \mathfrak{p}^2/2m$ that equation (A6.112) is valid both in the nonrelativistic and in the relativistic case. That such should be the case follows also from the discussion of equation (A6.112).

These equations can be simplified by introducing $\mathfrak{p}$ instead of ϵ as the integration variable and we get

$$N = \frac{8\pi}{h^3} V \int_0^\infty \frac{\mathfrak{p}^2 d\mathfrak{p}}{e^{-\nu+\mu\epsilon}+1}, \tag{A6.118}$$

$$E = \frac{8\pi}{h^3} V \int_0^\infty \frac{\epsilon\mathfrak{p}^2 d\mathfrak{p}}{e^{-\nu+\mu\epsilon}+1}, \tag{A6.119}$$

$$p = \frac{8\pi}{h^3} kT \int_0^\infty \ln\,(1+e^{\nu-\mu\epsilon})\mathfrak{p}^2 d\mathfrak{p}, \tag{A6.120}$$

where ϵ is a function of $\mathfrak{p}$ given by equation (A6.105).

It is more convenient for the further discussion to introduce with Jüttner a variable θ defined by the equation

$$\theta = \text{arc sinh}\,\frac{\mathfrak{p}}{mc}\cdot \tag{A6.121}$$

From equations (A6.105) and (A6.121) we get

$$\epsilon = mc^2 \cosh\theta, \tag{A6.122}$$

and equations (A6.118) to (A6.120) can be written in the form

$$N = 8\pi \frac{m^3c^3}{h^3} V \int_0^\infty \frac{\sinh^2\theta \cosh\theta\, d\theta}{e^{-\nu+\mu mc^2\cosh\theta}+1}, \tag{A6.123}$$

$$E = 8\pi \frac{m^4c^5}{h^3} V \int_0^\infty \frac{\sinh^2\theta \cosh^2\theta\, d\theta}{e^{-\nu+\mu mc^2\cosh\theta}+1}, \tag{A6.124}$$

$$p = 8\pi \frac{m^3c^3kT}{h^3} \int_0^\infty \sinh^2\theta \cosh\theta \ln(1+e^{\nu-\mu mc^2\cosh\theta})\, d\theta. \tag{A6.125}$$

Integrating by parts we can write equation (A6.125) in the form

$$p = \frac{8\pi}{3}\frac{m^4c^5}{h^3} \int_0^\infty \frac{\sinh^4\theta\, d\theta}{e^{-\nu+\mu mc^2\cosh\theta}+1}\cdot \tag{A6.126}$$

§2. **The Degenerate Electron Gas.** As was remarked in Chapter IV (p. 90) a Fermi-Dirac gas is degenerate if $e^\nu \gg 1$. Let us now consider the case where $e^\nu \to \infty$. We can split the integrals in equations (A6.123), (A6.124), and (A6.126) in two parts. We have in that way, for instance, for N

$$N = 8\pi \frac{m^3c^3}{h^3} V \left\{ \int_0^{\theta_0} \frac{\sinh^2\theta\cosh\theta\, d\theta}{e^{-\nu\left[1-\frac{\mu}{\nu}mc^2\cosh\theta\right]}+1} + \int_{\theta_0}^\infty \frac{\sinh^2\theta\cosh\theta\, d\theta}{e^{\nu\left[\frac{\mu}{\nu}mc^2\cosh\theta-1\right]}+1} \right\}, \tag{A6.201}$$

where θ_0 is given by the equation

$$\nu = \mu mc^2 \cosh \theta_0. \tag{A6.202}$$

In the limit $\nu \to \infty$ the second integral will be equal to zero, and in the first integral the denominator reduces to 1 (compare the discussion of equation [4.719] on p. 91). In a first approximation we get thus for large ν the following equations for N, E, and p:

$$N = 8\pi \frac{m^3c^3}{h^3} V \int_0^{\theta_0} \sinh^2 \theta \cosh \theta \, d\theta, \tag{A6.203}$$

$$E = 8\pi \frac{m^4c^5}{h^3} V \int_0^{\theta_0} \sinh^2 \theta \cosh^2 \theta \, d\theta, \tag{A6.204}$$

$$p = \frac{8\pi}{3} \frac{m^4c^5}{h^3} \int_0^{\theta_0} \sinh^4 \theta \, d\theta. \tag{A6.205}$$

These equations are exact for a completely degenerate relativistic Fermi-Dirac gas. We shall discuss presently under what circumstances they represent a reasonable approximation for a not completely degenerate gas. Before doing this, however, we shall evaluate the integrals in equations (A6.203) to (A6.205). Introducing a quantity x by the equation

$$x = \sinh \theta_0, \tag{A6.206}$$

we have easily

$$N = \frac{8\pi}{3} \frac{m^3c^3}{h^3} V x^3, \tag{A6.207}$$

$$E = \frac{\pi}{3} \frac{m^4c^5}{h^3} V g(x), \tag{A6.208}$$

$$p = \frac{\pi}{3} \frac{m^4c^5}{h^3} f(x), \tag{A6.209}$$

where $f(x)$ and $g(x)$ are given by the equations†

$$f(x) = (2x^3 - 3x)(x^2 + 1)^{1/2} + 3 \operatorname{arc\,sinh} x, \tag{A6.210}$$

$$g(x) = 8x^3(x^2 + 1)^{1/2} - f(x). \tag{A6.211}$$

The physical meaning of the variable x can most easily be seen as follows. From equations (A6.121) and (A6.206) it follows that we can also write

$$x = \frac{\mathfrak{p}_0}{mc}, \tag{A6.212}$$

† It must be noted that our $g(x)$ differs from the function $g(x)$ introduced by Chandrasekhar (*loc. cit.*), $g_{\text{here}} = g_{\text{Chand}} + 8x^3$. This difference is due to the fact that Chandrasekhar's U does not include the rest mass energy while our E does.

and that by using equation (A6.112) we can write equation (A6.207) in the form

$$N = \frac{8\pi}{3}\frac{V}{h^3}\mathfrak{p}_0{}^3 = \int_0^{\mathfrak{p}_0} dZ. \qquad \textbf{(A6.213)}$$

This equation is exact in the case of complete degeneracy. It expresses the fact that all the lowest energy levels up to a limiting energy are fully occupied, as should be expected at the absolute zero, which is the temperature at which complete degeneracy exists (compare the considerations on p. 92 and also formula [A6.217]). The limiting energy corresponds to a threshold momentum $\mathfrak{p}_0$.

Equations (A6.207), (A6.209), and (A6.210) give us together the equation of state of a completely degenerate (relativistic) electron gas in parameter form.

It has been shown by Chandrasekhar (*loc. cit.*) that equations (A6.203) to (A6.205) are a fair approximation as long as

$$4\pi^2 \frac{x(x^2+1)^{1/2}}{f(x)} \ll (\mu mc^2)^2. \qquad \textbf{(A6.214)}$$

The left-hand side of this inequality depends only on the mean density $n(= N/V)$ of the electron gas, since we have from equation (A6.207)

$$x = \frac{h}{mc}\left(\frac{3n}{8\pi}\right)^{1/3}. \qquad \textbf{(A6.215)}$$

Since h/mc, the Compton wavelength of the electron, is only $2 \cdot 10^{-10}$ cm, we see that unless n becomes of the order of 10^{30} cm^{-3} (corresponding to densities of at least 10^6 g cm^{-3}), x will always be small compared to one. The function $f(x)$ behaves for small x as $\frac{8}{5}x^5$, and inequality (A6.214) can thus nearly always be written in the form

$$c\frac{h^2}{mk}\frac{n^{2/3}}{T} \gg 1, \qquad \textbf{(A6.216)}$$

where c is a numerical constant ($c = 10.2$). Expressing T in °K and n in cm^{-3}, we have from inequality (A6.216)

$$3.6 \cdot 10^{-9}\frac{n^{2/3}}{T} \gg 1 \qquad \textbf{(A6.217)}$$

as the condition for the validity of equations (A6.207) to (A6.209).†

† It can easily be verified that this condition is equivalent to the condition $e^{\nu} \gg 1$ (compare equation [4.603] on p. 84) or to the condition $\beta \ll 1$ which we met on p. 92 as the condition for the applicability of the formulae for complete degeneracy in the nonrelativistic case

We remarked a moment ago that x is practically always small compared to one and we can in that case simplify equations (A6.208) and (A6.209) by using the asymptotic expressions for $f(x)$ and $g(x)$,

$$f(x) \approx \tfrac{8}{5}x^5, \qquad g(x) \approx 8x^3 + \tfrac{12}{5}x^5. \tag{A6.218}$$

We get in that way for E and p the expressions

$$E = Nmc^2 + \frac{4\pi}{5}\frac{m^4c^5}{h^3}Vx^5, \qquad (x \ll 1), \tag{A6.219}$$

$$p = \frac{8\pi}{15}\frac{m^4c^5}{h^3}x^5, \qquad (x \ll 1). \tag{A6.220}$$

Denoting the kinetic energy $E - Nmc^2$ by $\mathcal{T}$ and using equation (A6.215) for x, we get the equations

$$\mathcal{T} = \frac{3}{40}\left(\frac{3}{\pi}\right)^{2/3}\frac{h^2}{m}Vn^{5/3}, \qquad (x \ll 1), \tag{A6.221}$$

$$pV = \tfrac{2}{3}\mathcal{T}, \qquad (x \ll 1). \tag{A6.222}$$

Equation (A6.222) is the same as equation (4.615) on page 86. The derivation of equation (4.615) is now no longer always applicable since the energy ϵ of one electron now includes the rest energy so that it is not always true that ϵ' is proportional to $V^{-2/3}$. Indeed, we shall see presently a case where equation (A6.222) is not valid.

In some astrophysical applications we may encounter cases where $x \gg 1$ (see, e.g., Chapter XIV). In that case we have for $f(x)$ and $g(x)$ the asymptotic expressions

$$f(x) \approx 2x^4, \qquad g(x) \approx 6x^4. \tag{A6.223}$$

Inequality (A6.214) reduces also in this case to an inequality of the form (A6.216) or (A6.217), the only difference being a factor $\frac{1}{2}\sqrt{5}$ in the numerical constant.

We get easily for E, which is now in a first approximation equal to $\mathcal{T}$, and for p the expressions

$$\mathcal{T} \simeq E = 2\pi\frac{m^4c^5}{h^3}Vx^4, \qquad (x \gg 1) \tag{A6.224}$$

$$p = \frac{2\pi}{3}\frac{m^4c^5}{h^3}x^4, \qquad (x \gg 1) \tag{A6.225}$$

or

$$\mathcal{T} = \frac{3}{8}\left(\frac{3}{\pi}\right)^{1/3}hcVn^{4/3}, \qquad (x \gg 1) \tag{A6.226}$$

$$pV = \tfrac{1}{3}\mathcal{T}, \qquad (x \gg 1) \tag{A6.227}$$

and we see that now, indeed, equation (4.615) is no longer valid. The reason is that while in the case $x \ll 1$ the kinetic energy is small compared to the rest energy so that the nonrelativistic case is a good approximation, in the case $x \gg 1$ the rest energy is small compared to the kinetic energy and the nonrelativistic approximation breaks down.†

§3. The Nondegenerate Electron Gas. In this last section we shall consider the case where the temperature is so high or the density is so low that $e^\nu \ll 1$. In that case the term 1 in the denominator of the integrands in equations (A6.123) and (A6.124) can be neglected and the logarithm in the integrand in equation (A6.125) can be expanded. We then get

$$N = 8\pi \frac{m^3c^3}{h^3} Ve^\nu \int_0^\infty e^{-\mu mc^2 \cosh\theta} \sinh^2\theta \cosh\theta \, d\theta, \qquad \textbf{(A6.301)}$$

$$E = 8\pi \frac{m^4c^5}{h^3} Ve^\nu \int_0^\infty e^{-\mu mc^2 \cosh\theta} \sinh^2\theta \cosh^2\theta \, d\theta, \qquad \textbf{(A6.302)}$$

$$p = 8\pi \frac{m^3c^3}{h^3} kTe^\nu \int_0^\infty e^{-\mu mc^2 \cosh\theta} \sinh^2\theta \cosh\theta \, d\theta. \qquad \textbf{(A6.303)}$$

First of all we note that the perfect gas law is identically true, since from equations (A6.301) and (A6.303) it follows that

$$pV = NkT. \qquad \textbf{(A6.304)}$$

We see that, irrespective of the inclusion or exclusion of relativistic effects, the Boyle–Gay-Lussac formula applies in the nondegenerate case.

The integrals in equations (A6.301) and (A6.302) can be expressed in Bessel functions (see Chandrasekhar, *loc. cit.*), but it would be beyond the scope of this appendix to enter into a detailed discussion. However, we shall discuss briefly the two limiting cases, $\mu mc^2 \ll 1$ and $\mu mc^2 \gg 1$.

Putting

$$\mu mc^2 = a \qquad \textbf{(A6.305)}$$

and introducing as a new integration variable the quantity u defined by the equation

$$u = a \cosh\theta, \qquad \textbf{(A6.306)}$$

† It must, however, be mentioned that one can derive equations (A6.222) and (A6.227) in an elementary way completely similar to the derivation of equation (4.615). The energy levels ϵ_k now satisfy the equation (A6.107). If the kinetic energy is small compared to the rest mass energy we have approximately $\epsilon_k = mc^2 + \epsilon_k'$ where ϵ_k' is proportional to $V^{-2/3}$ and hence p will be equal to $\frac{2}{3}\mathcal{T}/V$. If the rest mass, on the other hand, is small compared to the kinetic energy, ϵ_k is proportional to $V^{-1/3}$ and p will be equal to $\frac{1}{3}E/V$, or $\frac{1}{3}\mathcal{T}/V$. The question whether or not the gas is degenerate does not enter into these considerations and we can thus expect to find a similar situation in the next section (see equations [A6.313] and [A6.320]).

we have from equations (A6.301) to (A6.303)

$$N = \frac{pV}{kT} = A\int_a^\infty e^{-u}\sqrt{u^2 - a^2}udu, \quad \textbf{(A6.307)}$$

$$E = AkT\int_a^\infty e^{-u}\sqrt{u^2 - a^2}u^2du, \quad \textbf{(A6.308)}$$

where

$$A = 8\pi\frac{m^3c^3}{h^3a^3}Ve^{\nu}. \quad \textbf{(A6.309)}$$

We now consider the two limiting cases $a \to 0$ and $a \to \infty$.

a) In the limit $a \to 0$ we have from equations (A6.307) and (A6.308)

$$N = \frac{pV}{kT} \cong A\int_0^\infty e^{-u}u^2du = 2A, \quad \textbf{(A6.310)}$$

$$E \cong AkT\int_0^\infty e^{-u}u^3du = 6AkT. \quad \textbf{(A6.311)}$$

Since it follows from equations (A6.304) and (A6.305) that

$$\frac{Nmc^2}{pV} = a, \quad \textbf{(A6.312)}$$

we see that for $a \ll 1$, $Nmc^2 \ll pV = 2AkT = \frac{1}{3}E$. This means that the rest energy is small compared to E. We get thus for the relation between the kinetic energy $\mathcal{T}$ and pV

$$pV = \tfrac{1}{3}E \cong \tfrac{1}{3}\mathcal{T}. \quad \textbf{(A6.313)}$$

We could have expected a deviation from the nonrelativistic relation, since we are now in the region of the very high temperatures and energies where relativistic effects make equation (A6.222) inapplicable.

b) In the limit $a \to \infty$ it is more advantageous to introduce a new variable v by the equation

$$v = u - a, \quad \textbf{(A6.314)}$$

and we get from equations (A6.307) and (A6.308)

$$N = \frac{pV}{kT} = B\int_0^\infty e^{-v}\sqrt{(v^2 + 2av)}(v + a)dv, \quad \textbf{(A6.315)}$$

$$E = BkT\int_0^\infty e^{-v}\sqrt{(v^2 + 2av)}(v + a)^2\,dv, \quad \textbf{(A6.316)}$$

where

$$B = Ae^{-a}. \quad \textbf{(A6.317)}$$

For large values of a we may expand the integrands in powers of v/a and we get in that way†

$$N = \frac{pV}{kT} = Ba\sqrt{2a}\int_0^\infty e^{-v}v^{1/2}dv = Ba\sqrt{2\pi a}. \quad \textbf{(A6.318)}$$

$$E = BkT\left[a^2\sqrt{2a}\int_0^\infty e^{-v}v^{1/2}dv + a\sqrt{2a}\int_0^\infty e^{-v}v^{3/2}dv\right]$$

$$= Nmc^2 + \tfrac{3}{2}BkTa\sqrt{2\pi a}, \quad \textbf{(A6.319)}$$

and we get for the relation between $\mathcal{T}$ and pV

$$E - Nmc^2 = \mathcal{T} = \tfrac{3}{2}pV, \quad \textbf{(A6.320)}$$

as we should expect, since now $\mathcal{T} \ll Nmc^2$.

BIBLIOGRAPHICAL NOTES

The treatment in this appendix is mainly based on the following reference to which we also refer for a more extensive bibliography:

1. S. Chandrasekhar, An Introduction to the Study of Stellar Structure, Chicago 1939, Chap. X.

See also

2. R. H. Fowler, Statistical Mechanics, Cambridge 1936, §§16.3–16.5.

§1. Formula (A6.110) appears for the first time in

3. P. A. M. Dirac, Proc. Roy. Soc. (London), **A112,** 671, 1926.

See also

4. P. Jordan, Statistische Mechanik auf Quantentheoretischer Grundlage, Braunschweig 1933, p. 20.
5. C. Møller and S. Chandrasekhar, Monthly Notices Roy. Astron. Soc., **95,** 673, 1935.
6. R. Peierls, Monthly Notices Roy. Astron. Soc., **96,** 780, 1936.
7. E. K. Broch, Phys. Rev., **51,** 586, 1937,
and ref. 1, §2.

The general formulae for the case of an electron gas can be found in §5 of ref. 1. Our representation differs slightly from Chandrasekhar's since we have throughout used ϵ and not ϵ' as variable. This entails that ν includes a term μmc^2 and that our E differs from Chandrasekhar's U by a term Nmc^2.

Formulae (A6.123) to (A6.125) are due to Jüttner:

8. F. Jüttner, Z. Physik, **47,** 542, 1928.

§2. See ref. 1, §6.

§3. See ref. 1, §7, and also

9. F. Jüttner, Ann. Physik, **34,** 856, 1911.
10. R. C. Tolman, Phil. Mag., **28,** 583, 1914.

† The integrals in equations (A6.318) and (A6.319) reduce to the integrals I_{2n} of §1 of the Mathematical Appendix by putting $t^2 = v$.

This last reference also contains other applications of relativistic statistics. General remarks on relativistic statistics can also be found in Pauli's article on the theory of relativity in the Enzyklopädie der mathematischen Wissenschaften:

11. W. Pauli, Enzyklopädie der mathematischen Wissenschaften, Vol. V, Pt. 19, Leipzig-Berlin 1921, §§48 and 49.

APPENDIX VII

TABLES OF PHYSICAL AND MATHEMATICAL CONSTANTS

In the first table we give the values of a number of physical constants taken from a recently published table (J. A. Bearden and H. M. Watts, Phys. Rev., **81,** 73, 1951).†‡ We have included a few constants which are not used in the text in order to increase the usefulness of the table. The second table lists some mathematical constants.

Physical constants

Symbol	Constant	Value
R	absolute gas constant	$8.314 \cdot 10^{7}$ g cm^2 sec^{-2} mol^{-1} deg^{-1}
m_{H}	atomic weight unit	$1.660 \cdot 10^{-24}$ g
$\mathfrak{A}$	Avogadro's number§	$6.026 \cdot 10^{23}$ mol^{-1}
μ_{B}	Bohr magneton‖	$9.271 \cdot 10^{-21}$ g cm^2 sec^{-2} gauss^{-1}
a_{B}	Bohr radius	$5.291 \cdot 10^{-9}$ cm
k	Boltzmann's constant	$1.380 \cdot 10^{-16}$ g cm^2 sec^{-2} deg^{-1}
a	constant in the Stefan-Boltzmann law	$7.564 \cdot 10^{-15}$ g cm^{-1} sec^{-2} deg^{-4}
$\hbar$	Dirac's constant	$1.054\,2 \cdot 10^{-27}$ g cm^2 sec^{-1}
m	electron mass	$9.107 \cdot 10^{-28}$ g
e	electronic charge	$4.802 \cdot 10^{-10}$ esu
$\alpha\left(=\frac{e^2}{\hbar c}\right)$	fine structure constant	137.04^{-1}
h	Planck's constant	$6.623\,6 \cdot 10^{-27}$ g cm^2 sec^{-1}
μ_p	proton magnetic moment	$1.410 \cdot 10^{-23}$ g cm^2 sec^{-2} gauss^{-1}
m_p/m	ratio of proton to electron mass	1 836.09
R_∞	Rydberg constant for infinite mass	109 737.3 cm^{-1}
c	velocity of light	$2.997\,90 \cdot 10^{10}$ cm sec^{-1}

† I would like to express my thanks to Dr. J. A. Bearden and to the American Institute of Physics for their kind permission to quote from this table.

‡ A slightly different list was published by J. W. M. DuMond and E. R. Cohen, Phys. Rev., **82,** 555, 1951.

§ We use the physical scale of atomic weights.

‖ There is a misprint in the exponent of 10 in the case of μ_{B} in Bearden and Watts' paper (see Phys. Rev., **83,** 457, 1951).

Mathematical constants

π	$= 3.141\ 59$	e	$= 2.718\ 28$
$\ln 10$	$= 2.302\ 585$	$\log_{10} e$	$= 0.434\ 294\ 5$
$\zeta(\frac{3}{2})$	$= 2.612$	$\zeta(\frac{5}{2})$	$= 1.341$†

$$\gamma = \text{Euler's constant} = 1.781\ 07$$

† The function $\zeta(s)$ is Riemann's ζ-function, $\zeta(s) = \sum_{n=1}^{\infty} n^{-s}$.

MATHEMATICAL APPENDIX

§1. Some Definite Integrals. The following integrals occur frequently in statistical calculations:

$$I_m(a) = \int_0^\infty t^m e^{-at^2} dt, \tag{MA1.01}$$

where m is a positive integral or zero. These integrals can immediately be reduced to the form

$$I_m = I_m(1) = \int_0^\infty t^m e^{-t^2} dt, \tag{MA1.02}$$

and the relation between $I_m(a)$ and I_m is

$$I_m = a^{\frac{m+1}{2}} I_m(a). \tag{MA1.03}$$

We can thus restrict ourselves to the I_m.

Integrating by parts, one finds the recurrence relation

$$I_{m+2} = \frac{m+1}{2} I_m. \qquad m \geqslant 0 \tag{MA1.04}$$

The problem is thus finally reduced to finding I_0 and I_1. The second one of these integrals is elementary:

$$I_1 = \int_0^\infty t e^{-t^2} dt = \tfrac{1}{2}, \tag{MA1.05}$$

and for odd m we have thus

$$I_{2n+1} = \frac{n!}{2}. \tag{MA1.06}$$

It will be shown that

$$I_0 = \frac{\sqrt{\pi}}{2}; \tag{MA1.07}$$

whence follows for even m, if we use equation (MA1.04),

$$I_{2n} = \frac{(2n-1)!}{2^{2n}(n-1)!}\sqrt{\pi}. \qquad \textbf{(MA1.08)}$$

If the integral taken from $-\infty$ to $+\infty$ is denoted by I_m', we have

$$I_m' = 0, \quad m = 2n+1; \qquad I_m' = 2I_m, \quad m = 2n. \qquad \textbf{(MA1.09)}$$

The easiest, though not necessarily the most rigorous, way of proving equation (MA1.07) is by considering I_0^2:†

$$I_0^2 = \int_0^\infty e^{-t^2}dt \int_0^\infty e^{-u^2}du. \qquad \textbf{(MA1.10)}$$

Introducing two new variables α and β instead of t and u through the equations

$$t = \alpha \cos \beta, \qquad u = \alpha \sin \beta, \qquad \textbf{(MA1.11)}$$

equation (MA1.10) can be written in the form

$$I_0^2 = \int_0^\infty \alpha d\alpha \int_0^{\pi/2} d\beta e^{-\alpha^2},$$

or

$$I_0^2 = \frac{\pi}{2} I_1, \qquad \textbf{(MA1.12)}$$

and equation (MA1.07) follows immediately.

§2. The Method of the Steepest Descents.‡ This method is used to obtain an approximate evaluation of integrals of the kind

$$I = \int_A^B \chi(z)e^{tf(z)}dz, \qquad \textbf{(MA2.01)}$$

where t is large, real, and positive, and $f(z)$ is an analytic function of the complex variable z $(= x + iy)$. The real and imaginary parts of $f(z)$ will be called ϕ and ψ

$$f = \phi + i\psi, \qquad \textbf{(MA2.02)}$$

and since $f(z)$ is an analytic function, ϕ and ψ both have to satisfy Laplace's equation

$$\frac{\partial^2\phi}{\partial x^2} + \frac{\partial^2\phi}{\partial y^2} = \frac{\partial^2\psi}{\partial x^2} + \frac{\partial^2\psi}{\partial y^2} = 0. \qquad \textbf{(MA2.03)}$$

† See, e.g., H. and B. S. Jeffreys, Methods of Mathematical Physics, Cambridge 1946, p. 161.

‡ We follow here more or less closely H. and B. S. Jeffreys (*loc. cit.*, §§17.03 and 17.04); see also E. Schrödinger, Statistical Thermodynamics, Cambridge 1948, p. 29. The method is due to P. Debye (Math. Ann., **67**, 535, 1909).

In the integral on the right-hand side of equation (MA2.01) the largest contribution will come from regions where ϕ is large. From the theory of complex functions it follows that ϕ has nowhere an absolute maximum, but that there are points where

$$\frac{\partial\phi}{\partial x} = \frac{\partial\phi}{\partial y} = 0. \tag{MA2.04}$$

Since

$$\frac{\partial\phi}{\partial x} = \frac{\partial\psi}{\partial y} \quad \text{and} \quad \frac{\partial\phi}{\partial y} = -\frac{\partial\psi}{\partial x}, \tag{MA2.05}$$

it then follows that

$$\frac{\partial\psi}{\partial x} = \frac{\partial\psi}{\partial y} = 0 \quad \text{and} \quad f'(z) = 0, \tag{MA2.06}$$

where f' stands for df/dz. These points are called *saddle-points*. It is possible to draw through such a saddle-point at least two curves along which ϕ is constant. Between those curves, ϕ will alternately be larger and smaller than at the saddle-point, in other words, there are at least two hills and two valleys.

Let us now consider a path in the complex plane. The line element of such a path will be denoted by ds and the angle between ds and the positive x-axis by θ. We then have

$$\frac{\partial\phi}{\partial s} = \cos\theta\,\frac{\partial\phi}{\partial x} + \sin\theta\,\frac{\partial\phi}{\partial y}\cdot \tag{MA2.07}$$

If we are looking for paths along which $\left|\frac{\partial\phi}{\partial s}\right|$ is maximum, θ has to be solved from the equation

$$0 = -\sin\theta\,\frac{\partial\phi}{\partial x} + \cos\theta\,\frac{\partial\phi}{\partial y}\cdot \tag{MA2.08}$$

From equation (MA2.05) it then follows that on these paths $\partial\psi/\partial s = 0$ or ψ is constant. Such a path will be called a *line of steepest descent.* In each valley there will be such a line. The path over which we shall now integrate from A to B will be the following one. From A along a line of constant ϕ to the line of steepest descent, then via this line over the saddle-point to the valley in which B is situated and finally again along a line of constant ϕ to B.†

Let z_0 be the coordinate of the saddle-point. In the neighborhood of z_0, $f(z)$ can be expanded in the form (compare equation [MA2.06])

$$f(z) = f(z_0) + \tfrac{1}{2}(z - z_0)^2 f''(z_0) + \cdots. \tag{MA2.09}$$

† We do not consider here the case where A and B are in the same valley.

We take the path in the direction of the valley such that $(z - z_0)^2 f''(z_0)$ is real and negative, because we *descend* along a line of constant ψ. Introducing a new variable ζ by putting

$$f(z) - f(z_0) = -\tfrac{1}{2}\zeta^2, \tag{MA2.10}$$

equation (MA2.01) takes the form

$$I = e^{tf(z_0)} \int_A^B \chi(z) e^{-\frac{1}{2}t\zeta^2} \frac{dz}{d\zeta}\, d\zeta. \tag{MA2.11}$$

Introducing

$$z - z_0 = re^{i\alpha}, \tag{MA2.12}$$

we have

$$\frac{dz}{d\zeta} = e^{i\alpha} \,|\, f''(z_0) \,|^{-\frac{1}{2}}, \tag{MA2.13}$$

where we have made use of the fact that $(z - z_0)^2 f''(z_0)$ is real and negative.

Before introducing expression (MA2.13) into equation (MA2.11) we will consider the integral

$$J = \int_{-\infty}^{+\infty} g(z) e^{-\frac{1}{2}a^2 z^2} dz, \tag{MA2.14}$$

where $g(z)$ is analytic and bounded on the real axis, and a is real and large.

The function $g(z)$ can be expanded as follows:

$$g(z) = a_0 + a_1 z + a_2 z^2 + \cdots = \sum_{n=0}^{\infty} a_n z^n. \tag{MA2.15}$$

Introducing this expansion into J, we get

$$J = \sum_{n=0}^{\infty} \int_{-\infty}^{+\infty} a_n z^n e^{-\frac{1}{2}a^2 z^2} dz, \tag{MA2.16}$$

and using the results of the preceding section (equations [MA1.03], [MA1.08], and [MA1.09]), we get†

$$J = \sqrt{2\pi} \sum_{n=0}^{\infty} \frac{(2n-1)!a_{2n}}{(n-1)!2^n a^{2n+1}}. \tag{MA2.17}$$

Since a is supposed to be large, we break off after only a few terms. Taking the first term only and remembering the meaning of a_0, we have, asymptotically,

$$J \approx \sqrt{2\pi}\, \frac{g(0)}{a}. \tag{MA2.18}$$

† For a rigorous proof we refer to the Jeffreys' treatment.

Now introducing expression (MA2.13) into equation (MA2.11) and using equation (MA2.18), we get

$$I \approx e^{tf(z_0)}\chi(z_0)e^{i\alpha}\left|\frac{2\pi}{tf''(z_0)}\right|^{1/2} \tag{MA2.19}$$

The other terms in the expansion are difficult to obtain and are very often not needed.

§3. The Stirling Formula for the Factorial.† We can use the method of the steepest descents to obtain an asymptotic formula for the factorial. If the real part of z is larger than -1, the factorial is defined as

$$z! = \int_0^\infty e^{-t}t^z dt, \tag{MA3.01}$$

which for integral values of z leads to the well-known formula $z! = \prod_{i=1}^{z} i$.

We are now interested in the asymptotic expression for $z!$ when z is large. Let us first introduce a new variable u by means of the equation

$$t = z(1 + u). \tag{MA3.02}$$

We then have from equation (MA3.01)

$$z! = z^{z+1}e^{-z}\int_{-1}^\infty e^{-uz}(1 + u)^z du. \tag{MA3.03}$$

If we now introduce v such that

$$(1 + u)e^{-u} = e^{-\frac{1}{2}v^2}, \tag{MA3.04}$$

we get

$$z! = z^{z+1}e^{-z}\int_{-\infty}^{+\infty} e^{-\frac{1}{2}zv^2}\frac{du}{dv}\,dv. \tag{MA3.05}$$

We thus have an integral of the form (MA2.14) and the result is

$$z! \approx \sqrt{2\pi}z^{z+\frac{1}{2}}e^{-z}\left(\frac{du}{dv}\right)_{v=0}. \tag{MA3.06}$$

We must now calculate $(du/dv)_{v=0}$. Since $v = 0$ corresponds to $u = 0$, we can expand both sides of equation (MA3.04) and after solving for u, we find ultimately that

$$\left(\frac{du}{dv}\right)_{v=0} = 1; \tag{MA3.07}$$

† See, e.g., H and B. S. Jeffreys, *loc. cit.*, §17.06.

whence we find Stirling's asymptotic formula for the factorial

$$z! \approx \sqrt{2\pi z}\left(\frac{z}{e}\right)^z. \qquad \textbf{(MA3.08)}$$

The ratio of the neglected terms to the term which is retained is of the order of $1/z$.

In many cases we can use an even rougher approximation, which is obtained as follows:†

Since $\ln x$ is a monotonously increasing function of x, we have

$$\sum_{k=1}^{N} \ln k < \int_0^N \ln x\, dx < \sum_{k=1}^{N} \ln (k+1),$$

or

$$\int_0^{N-1} \ln x\, dx < \sum_{k=1}^{N} \ln k < \int_0^N \ln x\, dx,$$

and hence

$$(N-1)[\ln (N-1) - 1] < \ln N! < N(\ln N - 1).$$

Since $(N-1)[\ln (N-1) - 1]$ and $N(\ln N - 1)$ differ relatively less the larger N is, we have asymptotically for large N

$$\ln N! \approx N \ln N - N. \qquad \textbf{(MA3.09)}$$

We have mostly used the simplified Stirling formula (MA3.09) for the factorial.

§4. Lagrange's Method of Undetermined Multipliers. Consider a function $f(x_1, x_2, \cdots, x_n)$ of n variables. Let us ask for which values of the x_i this function reaches an extremum under the following p restraining conditions:

$$g_j(x_1, x_2, \cdots, x_n) = 0, \qquad j = 1, 2, \cdots, p. \qquad \textbf{(MA4.01)}$$

The extremum of f can be found by requiring that the variation of f will be zero for any possible variation of the x_i from their values corresponding to the extremum, or

$$\delta f = \sum_i \frac{\partial f}{\partial x_i} \delta x_i = 0. \qquad \textbf{(MA4.02)}$$

If there were no restraining conditions, the x_i could be varied independently and equation (MA4.02) would lead to the well-known conditions for an extremum:

$$\frac{\partial f}{\partial x_i} = 0, \qquad i = 1, \cdots, n. \qquad \textbf{(MA4.03)}$$

† See P. Jordan, Statistische Mechanik auf Quantentheoretischer Grundlage, Braunschweig 1933; J. Satterly, Nature, **111**, 220, 1923.

However, if equations (MA4.01) must be satisfied, the δx_i cannot be chosen arbitrarily, but must satisfy the p equations,

$$\delta g_j = 0 = \sum_i \frac{\partial g_j}{\partial x_i}\,\delta x_i, \qquad j = 1, \cdots, p. \tag{MA4.04}$$

From equations (MA4.04) we can solve p of the δx_i in terms of the other $n - p$ variations and substitute for these p variations into equation (MA4.02). The remaining $n - p$ variations are then arbitrary and their coefficients must vanish identically in the x_i. We can also eliminate p of the δx_i, say, δx_i, δx_2, $\cdots$, δx_p by multiplying the p equations (MA4.04) with constants $\lambda_1, \lambda_2, \cdots, \lambda_p$ and adding them to equation (MA4.02). The result will be

$$\sum_i \left[\frac{\partial f}{\partial x_i} + \lambda_1 \frac{\partial g_1}{\partial x_i} + \lambda_2 \frac{\partial g_2}{\partial x_i} + \cdots + \lambda_p \frac{\partial g_p}{\partial x_i}\right] \delta x_i = 0. \tag{MA4.05}$$

We eliminate δx_1 to δx_p by determining the λ_j in such a way that

$$\frac{\partial f}{\partial x_i} + \lambda_1 \frac{\partial g_1}{\partial x_i} + \cdots + \lambda_p \frac{\partial g_p}{\partial x_i} = 0, \qquad i = 1, \cdots, p. \tag{MA4.06}$$

Once δx_1 to δx_p are eliminated, the remaining δx_i can be chosen arbitrarily, and equation (MA4.05) can only be satisfied for all choices if their coefficients vanish, or

$$\frac{\partial f}{\partial x_i} + \lambda_1 \frac{\partial g_1}{\partial x_i} + \cdots + \lambda_p \frac{\partial g_p}{\partial x_i} = 0, \qquad i = p + 1, \cdots, n. \tag{MA4.07}$$

We see here that the values of the x_i for which f is extremum while equations (MA4.01) are satisfied can be determined from the equations

$$\frac{\partial f}{\partial x_i} + \sum_{j=1}^{p} \lambda_j \frac{\partial g_j}{\partial x_i} = 0, \qquad i = 1, \cdots, n. \tag{MA4.08}$$

The x_i are now functions of the λ_j, but these quantities, which are called the undetermined multipliers or the Lagrangian multipliers, can be eliminated by substituting for the x_i into equations (MA4.01) and solving for the λ_j.

In classical statistics one meets the case where f depends on a continuous set of variables. In that case one can still use the method of the undetermined multipliers. Its justification is more difficult to prove. The easiest, though not necessarily the most rigorous, manner is to use the argument as we have given it here: to group the variables in finite intervals and afterward to make the transition to the continuous case.

GLOSSARY of SYMBOLS

This glossary contains a list of the more important symbols occurring in the text. The page number indicates where these symbols are introduced.

$a_{12\to1'2'}$, $a_{1'2'\to12}$, transition probabilities	12, 14
a, constant in Stefan-Boltzmann's law	53
a_i, external parameters	39, 105
a_n, in Chapter VIII, defined by equation (8.123)	175
a_{ij}, transition probabilities	339
A, work done by system	79
A_i, generalized forces	40, 107
A_{kl}, Einstein transition probability	54
$\mathfrak{A}_i$, generalized force operators	153
$\mathfrak{A}$, Avogadro's number	5
b_n, in Chapters VIII and IX, defined by equation (8.115)	174
B, second virial coefficient	8, 176
B_i, time averages of the A_i	113
B_i, in Appendix II, generalized forces	387
B_{kl}, Einstein transition probability	54
c, absolute value of velocity	3
c, velocity of light	51
c_0, in Chapters X and XI, velocity of light	231
c_v, specific heat at constant volume	22, 58
$\mathbf{c}$, velocity vector	5
$\mathbf{c}_1$, $\mathbf{c}_2$, velocity vectors before collision	11
$\mathbf{c}_1'$, $\mathbf{c}_2'$, velocity vectors after collision	11
C, third virial coefficient	8, 176
C_v, specific heat at constant volume per mole	35, 87
C_p, specific heat at constant pressure per mole	87
$\mathfrak{C}$, constant related to the chemical constants and given by equation (2.807)	44

d, length of dumbbell molecule	30
D, atomic diameter	10
D, in Chapter V, density in phase	101
E, total energy of the system	20
E_F, Fermi level	229
E_j, energy corresponding to jth group of levels	74
f, distribution function	2, 29, 90
$f(\epsilon)$, energy level density	246, 299
F, free energy of system	41, 57, 80, 109
F, function 0 inside and ∞ outside the volume containing the system	43, 111
F, in Chapters X and XI, normalized Fermi distribution	237
g_n, degree of degeneracy	56
g, g_i, partial free energy, or partial thermal potential	81, 139
$g(\nu)$, function defined by equation (4.610)	85
G, thermal potential	81, 139
h, Planck's constant	43
$\hbar$, Dirac's constant	63
$h(\nu)$, function defined by equation (4.705)	89
H, Boltzmann's H-function	18, 33, 336
$\mathcal{H}$, Hamiltonian	31, 100
$\boldsymbol{\mathcal{H}}$, Hamiltonian operator	148
i, chemical constant	402
I, phase integral	47
I_n, in Chapter VIII, defined by equation (8.114)	174
I_n, in the Mathematical Appendix, defined by equation (MA1.01)	439
j, current	235
J, Jacobian	15
J, in Chapter XII, interaction energy	255
J_i, flux	390
J_k, phase integral	59
k, Boltzmann's constant	3
K, in Chapter XII, defined by equation (12.211)	257
L_{ij}, coefficients of proportionality	391

m, mass of one particle 3
M, molecular weight 21

n, number of particles per unit volume 2
n_s, number of particles in energy state 71
N, number of particles in system 1
N, in Chapters XIII and XIV, number of neutrons in a nucleus 296, 312
N_j, number of particles in jth group of energy levels 74
$\mathfrak{n}_i$, number of particles of ith kind in system 136
$\mathfrak{n}_i$, number operators 156

p, pressure 5
p^*, reduced pressure 181
p_i, generalized momenta 31, 100
P, permutations 71
P, coarse-grained density 364
P, total momentum of system 19

q, heat content per unit mass 21
q, in Part A, q-potential 81
q, grand potential 137, 156
q_i, generalized coordinates 30, 100
Q, heat content of system 21
Q_m, heat content per mole 21
Q, in Chapter XII, number of nearest neighbor pairs 266

r^*, reduced distance 178
R, gas constant 5
R, in Chapters X and XI, Hall constant 239
R, in Chapter XII, long-range order 257

s, number of degrees of freedom 30
s, in Chapter X, defined by equation (10.222) 234
S, entropy of system 41, 80, 109, 258
S, in Chapter III, spin 64
S_m, entropy per mole 21
S_v, entropy per unit volume 21

T, absolute temperature 3
T^*, reduced temperature 178
T_c, critical temperature 207, 253
$\mathcal{T}$, kinetic energy 3, 100

U, potential energy 7, 29, 100
U, internal energy of system 21
U_m, internal energy per mole 21
U_n, in Chapter VIII, defined by equation (8.110) 173

v, volume of 1 gr 21
v, in Chapter IX, specific volume 208
v_c, critical value of specific volume 210
v_0, defined by equation (8.107) 172
V, volume 1
V^*, reduced volume 181
V_m, molar volume 5

W, probability 23, 71, 74
W, work done by system 41
W, in Appendix I, volume of **Z**-star 345
W_{BO}, weight of distribution in Boltzmann case 72, 75
$W_{B.E.}$, weight of distribution in Bose-Einstein case 73, 75
$W_{F.D.}$, weight of distribution in Fermi-Dirac case 73, 75
W_{max}, maximum or equilibrium value of W 76
W_n, in Chapter VIII, defined by equation (8.109), 173; or by equation (8.405) 183

x, in Chapter XII, defined by equation (12.231) 260
x_c, in Chapter XII, critical value of x 260
x, in Appendix VI, defined by equation (A6.206) 430
X_i, affinity 390

y, activity 210

Z, in Chapters XIII and XIV, number of protons in a nucleus 296, 312
Z_j, number of energy levels in jth group 72
Z_μ, $Z_\mu^{(qu)}$, Z_Γ, partition functions 40, 49, 111

α, quantity defined by equation (4.618) 87
α, in Appendix V, polarizability 419

β, quantity defined by equation (4.725) 92

γ, multiplicity 163
Γ-space 100

δ, Dirac's delta function	106
δ_{mn}, Kronecker's delta	151
Δ_N, defined by equations (8.408) to (8.410)	184
ϵ, energy of one particle	23, 29
ϵ, energy of system	100
ϵ_i, energy levels of one particle	48, 70
ϵ_0, lowest energy level	82
ϵ_P, $+1$ or -1 according to permutation P	73
$\epsilon_{\min}$, smallest possible value of energy for given values of the a_i	113
η, index of probability	104
θ, in Appendix VI, defined by equation (A6.121)	429
Θ, in Chapter III, rotational temperature	63
Θ, modulus of ensemble	105
κ, in Chapter IV, ratio of specific heats	87
κ, in Chapter VIII, depth of potential hole	178
κ, in Chapter X, thermal conductivity	236
λ_{DBr}, De Broglie wavelength	85
λ, mean free path	233
λ_i, absolute activities	139
Λ^*, measure for quantum mechanical effects	181
$\mu = 1/kT$	80, 172
μ^*, reduced μ	181
μ, μ_i, in Chapter XII, spin parameters	254
$\boldsymbol{\mu}$, magnetic moment of dumbbell molecule with absolute value μ	36
μ-space	30
ν, in Chapter III, frequency of harmonic oscillator	50
$\nu = g/kT$	81
$\nu_i = g_i/\Theta$	137
ν_{kl}, frequency of light quantum emitted or absorbed at transition from state k to state l	53
Π, Peltier heat	397
ρ, in Chapter II, density of system	28
$\rho(\nu)$, density of radiation field	52

ρ, coefficient of probability or density of ensemble 103
ρ_{spec}, specific density 137
ρ_{gen}, generic density 137
ρ, in Chapter XIII, density of nuclear energy levels 296
$\boldsymbol{\rho}$, density matrix 149
P, coarse-grained density 364

σ, in Chapter VIII, diameter of atom 178
σ, in Chapters X and XI, electrical conductivity 236
σ, in Chapter XII, short-range order 267
σ, in Appendix I, defined by equation (A1.603); or by equation (A1.715) 362, 371
Σ, in Appendix I, defined by equation (A1.621); or by equation (A1.723) 365, 372

τ, relaxation time 390

ϕ, in Chapter V, entropy, defined by equation (5.504) 114
ϕ, in Chapter VIII and Appendix V, potential energy function 171, 417

χ, sublimation heat or internal energy of liquid per atom 200, 217

ψ, free energy of system 105
Ψ, wave function of system 70
$\Psi_{\text{B.E.}}$, wave function of system of Bose-Einstein particles 73
$\Psi_{\text{F.D.}}$, wave function of system of Fermi-Dirac particles 73

ω_i, cells in μ-space 344
$\boldsymbol{\omega}$, unit vector in direction of line of centers 12
$\boldsymbol{\omega}'$, unit vector in direction of line of centers of inverse collision 14
Ω, extension in phase 113

—, indicates average values, over a Maxwell distribution 3
over a Maxwell-Boltzmann distribution 32
over a classical canonical ensemble 104
over a quantum mechanical canonical ensemble 150
═, indicates average values over a microcanonical ensemble 126
ˆ, indicates average values over a grand canonical ensemble 137, 156
~, indicates a time average 125, 355
$đ$, δ, indicate differentials or variations which are not total 21
$d\mathbf{c} = du\,dv\,dw$, volume element in velocity space 18

$d\mathbf{r} = dxdydz$, volume element in configuration space 29
$d\boldsymbol{\omega} = \sin\theta d\theta d\varphi$, surface element on unit sphere, or unit solid angle 12
$d\omega$, volume element in μ-space 31
$d\Omega$, extension in phase, or volume element in Γ-space 101
$\boldsymbol{\nabla}$, vector with components $\partial/\partial x$, $\partial/\partial y$, $\partial/\partial z$. 38
$\boldsymbol{\nabla}_c$, vector with components $\partial/\partial u$, $\partial/\partial v$, $\partial/\partial w$. 38
$\binom{a}{b}$, binomial coefficient 23

NAME INDEX

SUBJECT INDEX